DATA BOOK 4: PERIPHERAL CHIPS

compiled by P. Hogenboom

Elektor Electronics

Elektor Electronics (Publishing)
Down House
Broomhill Road
LONDON SW18 4JQ
England

First printed 1990

Printed in the Netherlands

ISBN 0 905705 32 7

Foreword

Last in the series of databooks on peripheral integrated circuits, this second microprocessor peripheral databook presents a number of ICs that do not form part of any of the well-known families of microprocessors and/or microcontrollers. The ICs included in this book are grouped according to their function, and form a selection from a much larger and much more diversified body of ICs. The selection criterion applied during the compilation of the datasheets has been whether or not a particular chip is widely applicable, i.e., whether or not it is commonly used in many types of PC and other computers.

This book presents a wide variety of peripheral integrated circuits. In particular, a great deal of attention is given to ICs that are typically used in the currently popular XT and AT class of personal computer. The Type CS8221 chip set, for instance, is included because it is used on virtually any AT-type motherboard. A part of the datasheet covering the CS8221 provides useful details on the operation of the EMS (Extended Memory System), and way in which the available registers are programmed—a subject on which there appears to be little information.

Mathematical co-processors have become affordable over the past few years and the most widely used types are given due attention. Another group of peripheral ICs included in this book has been made popular by the widespread use of serial data communications between PCs. This group includes serial drivers, receivers, UARTs and associated bit-rate generators.

The general lay-out of this book follows that of Part 1. Part 2 however is marked by a much larger number of components, with a corresponding increase in the lengths of the overview of manufacturer logos and the list of manufacturer [and distributor] addresses.

The kind co-operation of the following IC manufacturers is gratefully acknowledged:

AMD
Chips & Technologies
Cybernetic
Cyrix
Dallas Semiconductor
Exar
Fujitsu
Headland Technology
IIT
Intel
Harris Semiconductor
Linear Technology
Maxim
Micro Electronic Marin
Microchip
Motorola
National Semiconductor
Newport Components
OAK Technology
OKI
Opti
Philips
Samsung
Seiko-Epson
Silicon General
SMC
ST SGS-Thomson
Statek
Teledyne Semiconductor
Texas Instruments
UMC
VTI
Weitek
Zymos

Overview of logos

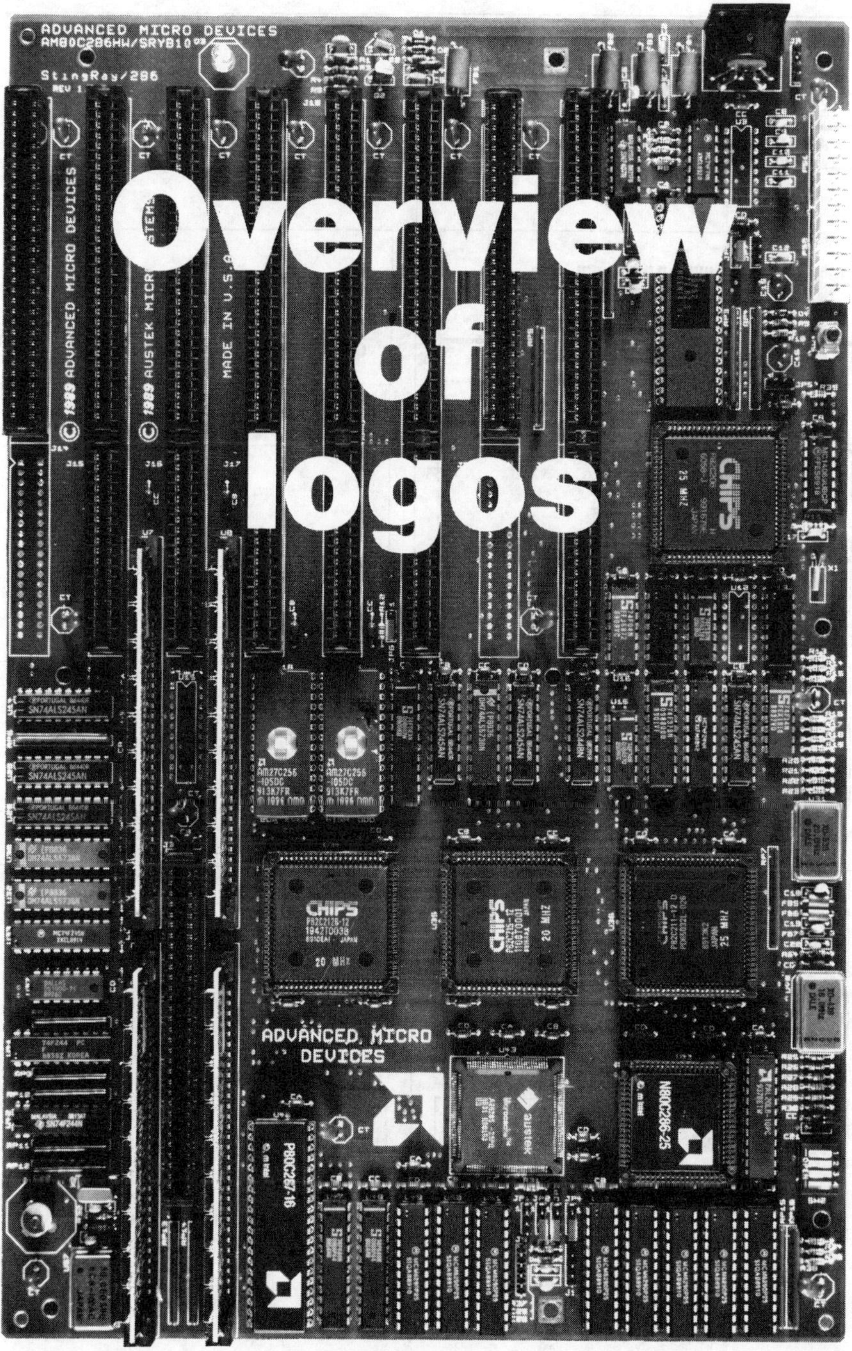

AMD (Advanced Micro Devices)	**Coprocessors** **Serial Datacommunications**
Chips & Technologies	**Chip Sets**
Cybernetic	**UARTS**
Cyrix	**Coprocessors**
Dallas Semiconductor	**Real Time Clocks** **Serial Datacommunication**
Exar	**Serial Datacommunications**

Fujitsu

Headland
Technology Inc

Headland Technology

INTEGRATED
INFORMATION
TECHNOLOGY • INC

IIT (Integrated Information Technology)

Intel

Intersil (Harris Semiconductor)

Linear Technology

UARTS

Chip Sets

Coprocessors

Coprocessors

Real Time Clocks

Serial Datacommunications

Manufacturer	Products
Maxim	Serial Datacommunications
μEM (Microelectronic Marin)	Real Time Clocks
Microchip	UARTS Bit Rate Generators
Motorola	Serial Datacommunications Bit Rate Generators
National Semiconductor	Real Time Clocks Serial Datacommunications
Newport Components	Serial Datacommunications

Oak Technology

OKI

OKI

OPTi

Opti

PHILIPS

Philips

Samsung

Seiko-Epson

Chip Sets

Real Time Clocks

Chip Sets

Serial Datacommunications

Serial Datacommunications

Real Time Clocks

Silicon General	**Serial Datacommunications**
SMC	**UARTS** **Bit Rate Generators**
ST (SGS-Thomson)	**Serial Datacommunications**
Statek	**Real Time Clocks** **Bit Rate Generators**
Teledyne Semiconductor	**Serial Datacommunications**
Texas Instruments	**Serial Datacommunications**

UMC (United Mircrocircuits Corporation) | Chip Sets

VTI (VLSI Technology) | Chip Sets

= WEITEK =

Weitek | Coprocessors

ZyMOS

Zymos | Chip Sets

Overview of datasheets

This part of the book provides a selection of datasheets on a number of peripheral chips. The information found on the originals is reproduced in whole. For a number of components, datasheets of different manufacturers are available. In most cases however the compilation is based on the information supplied by the so-called prime source (first manufacturer) of a particular device. The other chapters in this book provide a ready guide to the so-called second sources, i.e., the manufacturers that produce a licensed version of a chip. In many cases, the relevant distributor may be able to provide you with more information on a particular device. In particular, consult the chapter that lists the various documentation sources used.

- **High Performance Numeric Data Coprocessor**
- **Adds Arithmetic, Trigonometric, Exponential, and Logarithmic Instructions to the Standard 8086/8088 and 80186/80188 Instruction Set for All Data Types**
- **CPU/8087 Supports 7 Data Types: 16-, 32-, 64-Bit Integers, 32-, 64-, 80-Bit Floating Point, and 18-Digit BCD Operands**
- **Compatible with IEEE Floating Point Standard 754**
- **Available in 5 MHz (8087), 8 MHz (8087-2) and 10 MHz (8087-1): 8 MHz 80186/80188 System Operation Su;pported with the 8087-1.**
- **Adds 8 x 80-Bit Individually Addressable Register Stack to the 8086/8088 and 80186/80188 Architecture.**
- **7 Built-in Exception Handling Functions**
- **MULTIBUS® System Compatible Interface**

The 8087 Numeric Data Coprocessor provies the instructions and data types needed for high performance numeric numeric applications, providing up to 100 times the performance of a CPU alone. The 8087 is implemented in N-channel, depletion load, silicon gate technology (HMOS III), housed in a 40-pin package. Sixty-eight numeric processing instructions are added to the 8086/8088, 80186/80188 instruction sets and eight 80-bit registers are added to the register set. The 8087 is compatible with the IEEE Floating Point Standard 754.

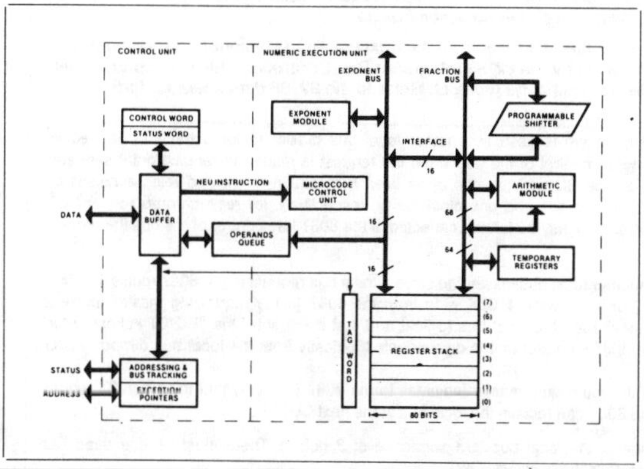

Figure 1. 8087 Block Diagram

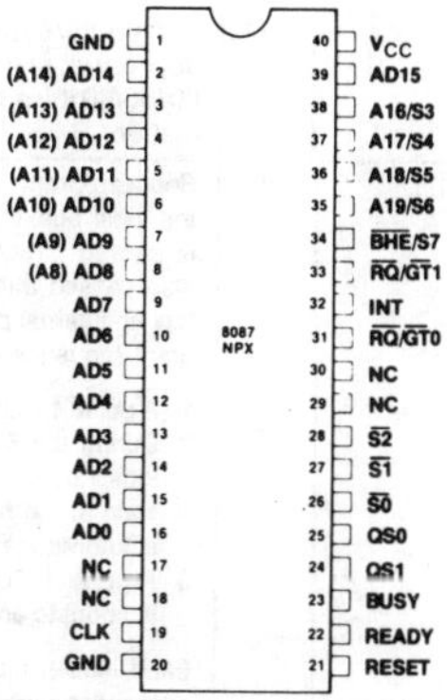

Figure 2. 8087 Pin Configuration

Table 1. 8087 Pin Description

Symbol	Type	Name and Function
AD15-AD0	I/O	**Address Data:** These lines constitute the time multiplexed memory address (T_1) and data (T_2, T_3, T_W, T_4) bus. A0 is analogous to $\overline{BHE}$ for the lower byte of the data bus, pins D7-D0. It is LOW during T_1 when a byte is to be transferred on the lower portion of the bus in memory operations. Eight-bit oriented devices tied to the lower half of the bus would normally use A0 to condition chip select functions. These lines are active HIGH. They are input/output lines for 8087-driven bus cycles and are inputs which the 8087 monitors when the CPU is in control of the bus. A15–A8 do not require an address latch in an 8088/8087 or 80188/8087. The 8087 will supply an address for the T_1-T_4 period.
A19/S6, A18/S5, A17/S4, A16/S3	I/O	**Address Memory:** During T_1 these are the four most significant address lines for memory operations. During memory operations, status information is available on these lines during T_2, T_3, T_W, and T_4. For 8087-controlled bus cycles, S6, S4, and S3 are reserved and currently one (HIGH), while S5 is always LOW. These lines are inputs which the 8087 monitors when the CPU is in control of the bus.
BHE/S7	I/O	**Bus High Enable:** During T_1 the bus high enable signal ($\overline{BHE}$) should be used to enable data onto the most significant half of the data bus, pins D15-D8. Eight-bit-oriented devices tied to the upper half of the bus would normally use $\overline{BHE}$ to condition chip select functions. $\overline{BHE}$ is LOW during T_1 for read and write cycles when a byte is to be transferred on the high portion of the bus. The S7 status information is available during T_2, T_3, T_W, and T_4. The signal is active LOW. S7 is an input which the 8087 monitors during the CPU-controlled bus cycles.

Table 1. 8087 Pin Description (Continued)

Symbol	Type	Name and Function
$\overline{S2}$, $\overline{S1}$, $\overline{S0}$	I/O	**Status:** For 8087-driven bus cycles, these status lines are encoded as follows: $\overline{S2}$ — $\overline{S1}$ — $\overline{S0}$ 0 (LOW) X X Unused 1 (HIGH) 0 0 Unused 1 0 1 Read Memory 1 1 0 Write Memory 1 1 1 Passive Status is driven active during T_4, remains valid during T_1 and T_2, and is returned to the passive state (1, 1, 1) during T_3 or during T_w when READY is HIGH. This status is used by the 8288 Bus Controller (or the 82188 Integrated Bus Controller with an 80186/80188 CPU) to generate all memory access control signals. Any change in $\overline{S2}$, $\overline{S1}$, or $\overline{S0}$ during T_4 is used to indicate the beginning of a bus cycle, and the return to the passive state in T_3 or T_w is used to indicate the end of a bus cycle. These signals are monitored by the 8087 when the CPU is in control of the bus.
$\overline{RQ}/\overline{GT}0$	I/O	**Request/Grant:** This request/grant pin is used by the 8087 to gain control of the local bus from the CPU for operand transfers or on behalf of another bus master. It must be connected to one of the two processor request/grant pins. The request grant sequence on this pin is as follows: 1. A pulse one clock wide is passed to the CPU to indicate a local bus request by either the 8087 or the master connected to the 8087 $\overline{RQ}/\overline{GT}1$ pin. 2. The 8087 waits for the grant pulse and when it is received will either initiate bus transfer activity in the clock cycle following the grant or pass the grant out on the $\overline{RQ}/\overline{GT}1$ pin in this clock if the initial request was for another bus master. 3. The 8087 will generate a release pulse to the CPU one clock cycle after the completion of the last 8087 bus cycle or on receipt of the release pulse from the bus master on $\overline{RQ}/\overline{GT}1$. For 80186/80188 systems the same sequence applies except $\overline{RQ}/\overline{GT}$ signals are converted to appropriate HOLD, HLDA signals by the 82188 Integrated Bus Controller. This is to conform with 80186/80188's HOLD, HLDA bus exchange protocol. Refer to the 82188 data sheet for further information.
$\overline{RQ}/\overline{GT}1$	I/O	**Request/Grant:** This request/grant pin is used by another local bus master to force the 8087 to request the local bus. If the 8087 is not in control of the bus when the request is made the request/grant sequence is passed through the 8087 on the $\overline{RQ}/\overline{GT}0$ pin one cycle later. Subsequent grant and release pulses are also passed through the 8087 with a two and one clock delay, respectively, for resynchronization. $\overline{RQ}/\overline{GT}1$ has an internal pullup resistor, and so may be left unconnected. If the 8087 has control of the bus the request/grant sequence is as follows: 1. A pulse 1 CLK wide from another local bus master indicates a local bus request to the 8087 (pulse 1). 2. During the 8087's next T_4 or T_1 a pulse 1 CLK wide from the 8087 to the requesting master (pulse 2) indicates that the 8087 has allowed the local bus to float and that it will enter the "RQ/GT acknowledge" state at the next CLK. The 8087's control unit is disconnected logically from the local bus during "RQ/GT acknowledge." 3. A pulse 1 CLK wide from the requesting master indicates to the 8087 (pulse 3) that the "RQ/GT" request is about to end and that the 8087 can reclaim the local bus at the next CLK. Each master-master exchange of the local bus is a sequence of 3 pulses. There must be one dead CLK cycle after each bus exchange. Pulses are active LOW. For 80186/80188 system, the $\overline{RQ}/\overline{GT}1$ line may be connected to the 82188 Integrated Bus Controller. In this case, a third processor with a HOLD, HLDA bus exchange system may acquire the bus from the 8087. For this configuration, $\overline{RQ}/\overline{GT}1$ will only be used if the 8087 is the bus master. Refer to 82188 data sheet for further information.
QS1, QS0	I	**QS1, QS0:** QS1 and QS0 provide the 8087 with status to allow tracking of the CPU instruction queue. **QS1** — **QS0** 0 (LOW) 0 No Operation 0 1 First Byte of Op Code from Queue 1 (HIGH) 0 Empty the Queue 1 1 Subsequent Byte from Queue
INT	O	**Interrupt:** This line is used to indicate that an unmasked exception has occurred during numeric instruction execution when 8087 interrupts are enabled. This signal is typically routed to an 8259A for 8086/8088 systems and to INTO for 80186/80188 systems. INT is active HIGH.
BUSY	O	**Busy:** This signal indicates that the 8087 NEU is executing a numeric instruction. It is connected to the CPU's $\overline{TEST}$ pin to provide synchronization. In the case of an unmasked exception BUSY remains active until the exception is cleared. BUSY is active HIGH.
READY	I	**Ready:** READY is the acknowledgement from the addressed memory device that it will complete the data transfer. The RDY signal from memory is synchronized by the 8284A Clock Generator to form READY for 8086 systems. For 80186/80188 systems, RDY is synchronized by the 82188 Integrated Bus Controller to form READY. This signal is active HIGH.
RESET	I	**Reset:** RESET causes the processor to immediately terminate its present activity. The signal must be active HIGH for at least four clock cycles. RESET is internally synchronized.
CLK	I	**Clock:** The clock provides the basic timing for the processor and bus controller. It is asymmetric with a 33% duty cycle to provide optimized internal timing.

V_{CC}		**Power:** V_{CC} is the +5V power supply pin.
GND		**Ground:** GND are the ground pins.

NOTE:
For the pin descriptions of the 8086, 8088, 80186 and 80188 CPUs, reference the respective data sheets (8086, 8088, 80186, 80188).

APPLICATION AREAS

The 8087 provides functions meant specifically for high performance numeric processing requirements. Trigonometric, logarithmic, and exponential functions are built into the coprocessor hardware. These functions are essential in scientific, engineering, navigational, or military applications.

The 8087 also has capabilities meant for business or commercial computing. An 8087 can process Binary Coded Decimal (BCD) numbers up to 18 digits without roundoff errors. It can also perform arithmetic on integers as large as 64 bits $\pm 10^{18}$).

PROGRAMMING LANGUAGE SUPPORT

Programs for the 8087 can be written in Intel's high-level languages for 8086/8088 and 80186/80188 Systems; ASM-86 (the 8086, 8088 assembly language), PL/M-86, FORTRAN-86, and PASCAL-86.

RELATED INFORMATION

For 8086, 8088, 80186 or 80188 details, refer to the respective data sheets, For 80186 or 80188 systems, also refer to the 82188 Integrated Bus Controller data sheet.

FUNCTIONAL DESCRIPTION

The 8087 Numeric Data Processor's architecture is designed for high performance numeric computing in conjunction with general purpose processing.

The 8087 is a numeric processor extension that provides arithmetic and logical instruction support for a variety of numeric data types. It also executes numerous built-in transcendental functions (e.g., tangent and log functions). The 8087 executes instructions as a coprocessor to a maximum mode CPU. It effectively extends the register and instruction set of the system and adds several new data types as well. Figure 3 presents the registers of the CPU+8087. Table 2 shows the range of data types supported by the 8087. The 8087 is treated as an extension to the CPU, providing register, data types, control, and instruction capabilities at the hardware level. At the programmers level the CPU and the 8087 are viewed as a single unified processor.

System Configuration

As a coprocessor to an 8086 or 8088, the 8087 is wired in parallel with the CPU as shown in Figure 4. Figure 5 shows the 80186/80188 system configuration. The CPU's status (S0–S2) and queue status lines (QS0–QS1) enable the 8087 to monitor and decode instructions in synchronization with the CPU and without any CPU overhead. For 80186/80188 systems, the queue status signals of the 80186/80188 are synchronized to 8087 requirements by the 8288 Integrated Bus Controller. Once started, the 8087 can process in parallel with, and independent of, the host CPU. For resynchronization, the 8087's BUSY signal informs the CPU that the 8087 is executing an instruction and the CPU WAIT instruction tests this signal to insure that the 8087 is ready to execute subsequent instructions. The 8087 can interrupt the CPU when it detects an error or exception. The 8087's interrupt request line is typically routed to the CPU through an 8259A Programmable Interrupt Controller for 8086, 8088 systems and INT0 for 80186/80188.

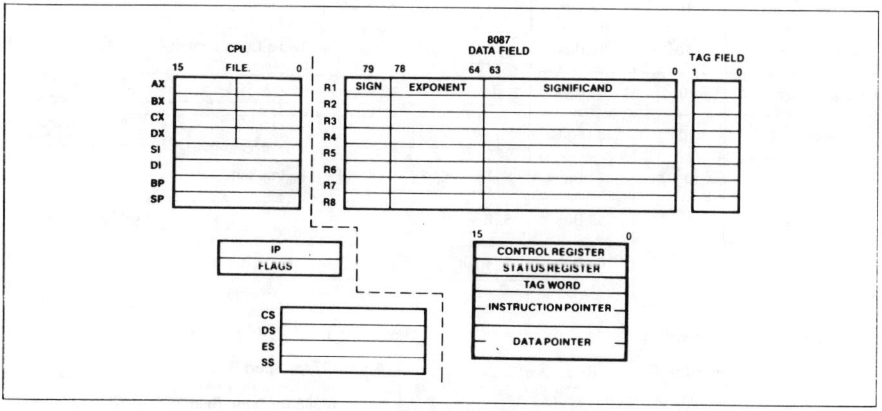

Figure 3. CPU+8087 Architecture

The 8087 uses one of the request/grant lines of the 8086/8088 architecture (typically $\overline{RQ}/\overline{GT}0$) to obtain control of the local bus for data transfers. The other request/grant line is available for general system use (for instance by an I/O processor in LOCAL mode). A bus master can also be connected to the 8087's $\overline{RQ}/\overline{GT}1$ line. In this configuration the 8087 will pass the request/grant handshake signals between the CPU and the attached master when the 8087 is not in control of the bus and will relinquish the bus to the master directly when the 8087 is in control. In this way two additional masters can be configured in an 8086/8088 system; one will share the 8086/8088 bus with the 8087 on a first-come first-served basis, and the second will be guaranteed to be higher in priority than the 8087.

For 80186/80188 systems, $\overline{RQ}/\overline{GT}0$ and $\overline{RQ}/\overline{GT}1$ are connected to the corresponding inputs of the 82188 Integrated Bus Controller. Because the 80186/80188 has a HOLD, HLDA bus exchange protocol, an interface is needed which will translate $\overline{RQ}/\overline{GT}$ signals to corresponding HOLD, HDLA signals and vice versa. One of the functions of the 82188 IBC is to provide this translation. $\overline{RQ}/\overline{GT}0$ is translated to HOLD, HLDA signals which are then directly connected to the 80186/80188. The $\overline{RQ}/\overline{GT}1$ line is also translated into HOLD, HLDA signals (referred to as SYSHOLD, SYSHLDA signals) by the 82188 IBC. This allows a third processor (using a HOLD, HLDA bus exchange protocol) to gain control of the bus.

Unlike an 8086/8087 system, $\overline{RQ}/\overline{GT}$ is only used when the 8087 has bus control. If the third processor requests the bus when the current bus master is the 80186/80188, the 82188 IBC will directly pass the request onto the 80186/80188 without going through the 8087. The third processor has the highest bus priority in the system. If the 8087 requests the bus while the third processor has bus control, the grant pulse will not be issued until the third processor releases the bus (using SYSHOLD). In this configuration, the third processor has the highest priority, the 8087 has the next highest, and the 80186/80188 has the lowest bus priority.

Bus Operation

The 8087 bus structure, operation and timing are identical to all other processors in the 8086/8088 series (maximum mode configuration). The address is time multiplexed with the data on the first 16/8 lines of the address/data bus. A16 through A19 are time multiplexed with four status lines S3-S6. S3, S4 and S6 are always one (HIGH) for 8087-driven bus cycles while S5 is always zero (LOW). When the 8087 is monitoring CPU bus cycles (passive mode) S6 is also monitored by the 8087 to differentiate 8086/8088 activity from that of a local I/O processor or any other local bus master. (The 8086/8088 must be the only processor on the local bus to drive S6 LOW). S7 is multiplexed with and has the same value as $\overline{BHE}$ for all 8087 bus cycles.

The first three status lines, $\overline{S0}$-$\overline{S2}$, are used with an 8288 bus controller or 82188 Integrated Bus Controller to determine the type of bus cycle being run:

$\overline{S2}$	$\overline{S1}$	$\overline{S0}$	
0	X	X	Unused
1	0	0	Unused
1	0	1	Memory Data Read
1	1	0	Memory Data Write
1	1	1	Passive (no bus cycle)

Programming Interface

The 8087 includes the standard 8086, 8088 instruction set for general data manipulation and program control.

Table 2. 8087 Data Types

Data Formats	Range	Precision	Most Significant Byte (7 0 7 0 7 0 7 0 7 0 7 0 7 0 7 0 7 0 7 0)
Word Integer	10^4	16 Bits	I_{15} … I_0 Two's Complement
Short Integer	10^9	32 Bits	I_{31} … I_0 Two's Complement
Long Integer	10^{18}	64 Bits	I_{63} … I_0 Two's Complement
Packed BCD	10^{18}	18 Digits	S — $D_{17}D_{16}$ … D_1 D_0
Short Real	$10^{\pm 38}$	24 Bits	S E_7 … E_0 F_1 … F_{23} F_0 Implicit
Long Real	$10^{\pm 308}$	53 Bits	S E_{10} … E_0 F_1 … F_{52} F_0 Implicit
Temporary Real	$10^{\pm 4932}$	64 Bits	S E_{14} … E_0 F_0 … F_{63}

Integer: I

Packed BCD: $(-1)^S(D_{17} \ldots D_0)$

Real: $(-1)^S(2^{E-BIAS})(F_0 \cdot F_1 \ldots)$

Bias = 127 for Short Real
1023 for Long Real
16383 for Temp Real

It also includes 68 numeric instructions for extended precision integer, floating point, trigonometric, logarithmic, and exponential functions. Sample execution times for several 8087 functions are shown in Table 3. Overall performance is up to 100 times that of an 8086 processor for numeric instructions.

Any instruction executed by the 8087 is the combined result of the CPU and 8087 activity. The CPU and the 8087 have specialized functions and registers providing fast concurrent operation. The CPU controls overall program execution while the 8087 uses the coprocessor interface to recognize and perform numeric operations.

Table 2 lists the seven data types the 8087 supports and presents the format for each type. Internally, the 8087 holds all numbers in the temporary real format. Load and store instructions automatically convert operands represented in memory as 16-, 32-, or 64-bit integers, 32- or 64-bit floating point numbers or 18-digit packed BCD numbers into temporary real format and vice versa. The 8087 also provides the capability to control round off, underflow, and overflow errors in each calculation.

Computations in the 8087 use the processor's register stack. These eight 80-bit registers provide the equivalent capacity of 20 32-bit registers. The 8087 register set can be accessed as a stack, with instructions operating on the top one or two stack elements, or as a fixed register set, with instructions operating on explicitly designated registers.

Table 5 lists the 8087's instructions by class. All appear as ESCAPE instructions to the host. Assembly language programs are written in ASM-86, the 8086, 8088 assembly language.

Table 3. Execution Times for Selected 8086/8087 Numeric Instructions and Corresponding 8086 Emulation

Floating Point Instruction	Approximate Execution Time (µs)	
	8086/8087 (8 MHz Clock)	8086 Emulation
Add/Subtract	10.6	1000
Multiply (single precision)	11.9	1000
Multiply (extended precision)	16.9	1312
Divide	24.4	2000
Compare	5.6	812
Load (double precision)	6.3	1062
Store (double precision)	13.1	750
Square Root	22.5	12250
Tangent	56.3	8125
Exponentiation	62.5	10687

NUMERIC PROCESSOR EXTENSION ARCHITECTURE

As Shown in Figure 1, the 8087 is internally divided into two processing elements, the control unit (CU) and the numeric execution unit (NEU). The NEU executes all numeric instructions, while the CU receives and decodes instructions, reads and writes memory operands and executes 8087 control instructions. The two elements are able to operate independently of one another, allowing the CU to maintain synchronization with the CPU while the NEU is busy processing a numeric instruction.

Figure 4. 8086/8087, 8088/8087 System Configuration

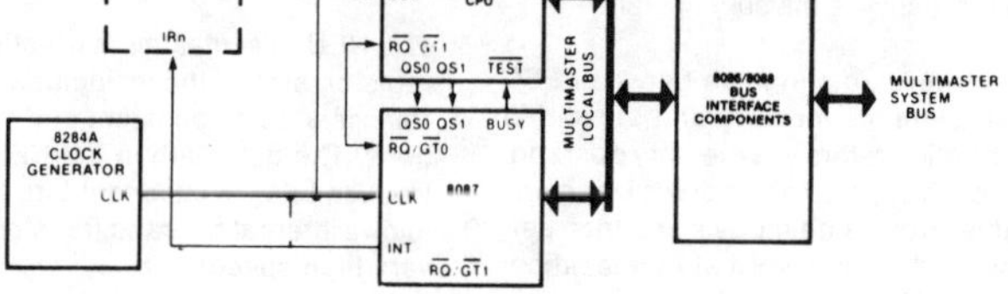

Figure 5. 80186/8087, 80188/8087 System Configuration

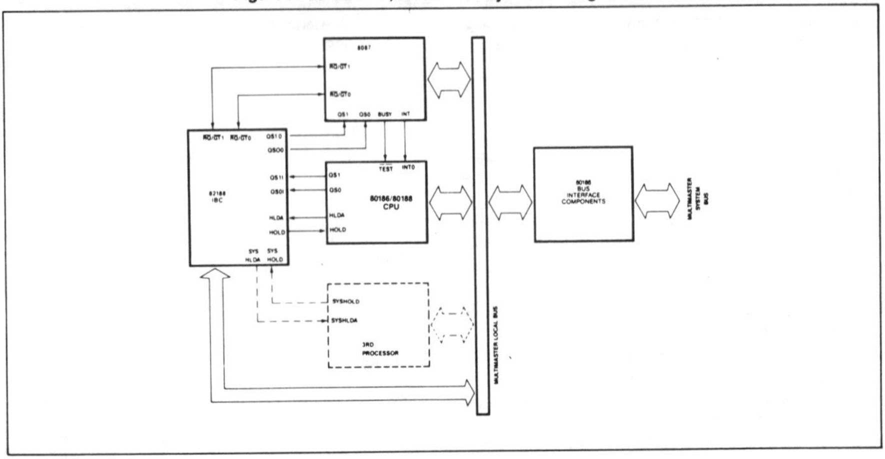

Control Unit

The CU keeps the 8087 operating in synchronization with its host CPU. 8087 instructions are intermixed with CPU instructions in a single instruction stream. The CPU fetches all instructions from memory; by monitoring the status (S0-S2, S6) emitted by the CPU, the control unit determines when an instruction is being fetched. The CU monitors the data bus in parallel with the CPU to obtain instructions that pertain to the 8087.

The CU maintains an instruction queue that is identical to the queue in the host CPU. The CU automatically determines if the CPU is an 8086/80186 or an 8088/80188 immediately after reset (by monitoring the BHE/S7 line) and matches its queue length accordingly. By monitoring the CPU's queue status lines (QS0, QS1), the CU obtains and decodes instructions from the queue in synchronization with the CPU.

A numeric instruction appears as an ESCAPE instruction to the CPU. Both the CPU and 8087 decode and execute the ESCAPE instruction together. The 8087 only recognizes the numeric instructions shown in Table 5. The start of a numeric operation is acomplished when the CPU executes the ESCAPE instruction. The instruction may or may not identify a memory operand.

The CPU does, however, distinguish between ESC instructions that reference memory and those that do not. If the instruction refers to a memory operand, the CPU calculates the operand's address using any one of its available addressing modes, and then performs a "dummy read" of the word at that location. (Any location within the 1M byte address space is allowed.) This is a normal read cycle except that the CPU ignores the data it receives. If the ESC instruction does not contain a memory reference (e.g. an 8087 stack operation), the CPU simply proceeds to the next instruction.

An 8087 instruction can have one of three memory reference options; (1) not reference memory; (2) load an operand word from memory into the 8087; or (3) store an operand word from the 8087 into memory. If no memory reference is required, the 8087 simply executes its instruction. If a memory reference is required, the CU uses a "dummy read" cycle initiated by the CPU to capture and save the address that the CPU places on the bus. If the instruction is a load, the CU additionally captures the data word when it becomes available on the local data bus. If data required is longer than one word, the CU immediately obtains the bus from the CPU using the request/grant protocol and reads the rest of the information in consecutive bus cycles. In a store operation, the CU captures and saves the store address as in a load, and ignores the data word that follows in the "dummy read" cycle. When the 8087 is ready to perform the store, the CU obtains the bus from the CPU and writes the operand starting at the specified address.

Numeric Execution Unit

The NEU executes all instructions that involve the register stack; these include arithmetic, logical, transcendental, constant and data transfer instructions. The data path in the NEU is 84 bits wide (68 fraction bits, 15 exponent bits and a sign bit) which allows internal operand transfers to be performed at very high speeds.

When the NEU begins executing an instruction, it activates the 8087 BUSY signal. This signal can be used in conjunction with the CPU WAIT instruction to resynchronize both processors when the NEU has completed its current instruction.

Register Set

The CPU+8087 register set is shown in Figure 3. Each of the eight data registers in the 8087's register stack is 80 bits and is divided into "fields" corresponding to the 8087's temporary real data type.

At a given point in time the TOP field in the control word identifies the current top-of-stack register. A "push" operation decrements TOP by 1 and loads a value into the new top register. A "pop" operation stores the value from the current top register and then increments TOP by 1. Like CPU stacks in memory, the 8087 register stack grows "down" toward lower-addressed registers.

Instructions may address the data registers either implicitly or explicitly. Many instructions operate on the register at the top of the stack. These instructions implicitly address the register pointed to by the TOP. Other instructions allow the programmer to explicitly specify the register which is to be used. Explicit register addressing is "top-relative."

Status Word

The status word shown in Figure 6 reflects the overall state of the 8087; it may be stored in memory and then inspected by CPU code. The status word is a 16-bit register divided into fields as shown in Figure 6. The busy bit (bit 15) indicates whether the NEU is either executing an instruction or has an interrupt request pending (B = 1), or is idle (B = 0). Several instructions which store and manipulate the status word are executed exclusively by the CU, and these do not set the busy bit themselves.

The four numeric condition code bits (C_0-C_3) are similar to flags in a CPU: various instructions update these bits to reflect the outcome of 8087 operations. The effect of these instructions on the condition code bits is summarized in Table 4.

Bits 14–12 of the status word point to the 8087 register that is the current top-of-stack (TOP) as described above.

Bit 7 is the interrupt request bit. This bit is set if any unmasked exception bit is set and cleared otherwise.

Bits 5–0 are set to indicate that the NEU has detected an exception while executing an instruction.

Tag Word

The tag word marks the content of each register as shown in Figure 7. The principal function of the tag word is to optimize the 8087's performance. The tag word can be used, however, to interpret the contents of 8087 registers.

Instruction and Data Pointers

The instruction and data pointers (see Figure 8) are provided for user-written error handlers. Whenever the 8087 executes a math instruction, the CU saves the instruction address, the operand address (if present) and the instruction opcode. 8087 instructions can store this data into memory.

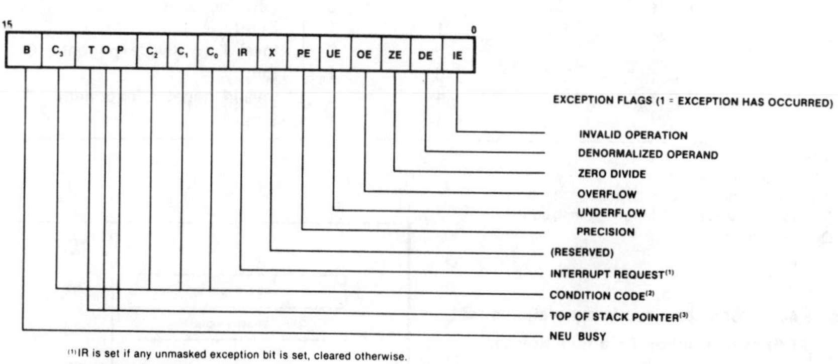

(1) IR is set if any unmasked exception bit is set, cleared otherwise.
(2) See Table 3 for condition code interpretation.
(3) Top Values:
000 = Register 0 is Top of Stack.
001 = Register 1 is Top of Stack.
•
•
•
111 = Register 7 is Top of Stack.

Figure 6. 8087 Status Word

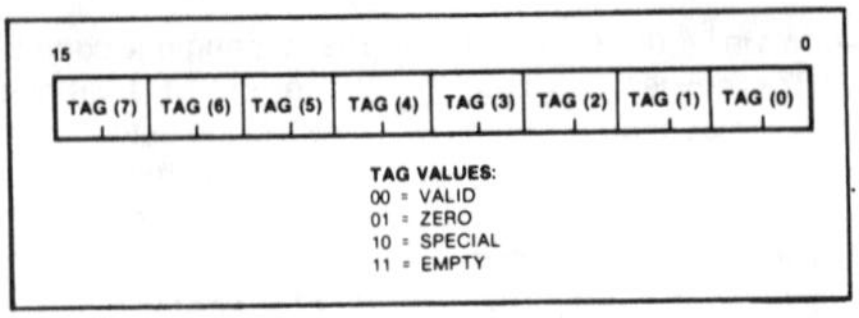

Figure 7. 8087 Tag Word

Table 4a. Condition Code Interpretation

Instruction Type	C_3	C_2	C_1	C_0	Interpretation
Compare, Test	0	0	X	0	ST > Source or 0 (FTST)
	0	0	X	1	ST < Source or 0 (FTST)
	1	0	X	0	ST = Source or 0 (FTST)
	1	1	X	1	ST is not comparable
Remainder	Q_1	0	Q_0	Q_2	Complete reduction with three low bits of quotient (See Table 4b)
	U	1	U	U	Incomplete Reduction
Examine	0	0	0	0	Valid, positive unnormalized
	0	0	0	1	Invalid, positive, exponent =0
	0	0	1	0	Valid, negative, unnormalized
	0	0	1	1	Invalid, negative, exponent =0
	0	1	0	0	Valid, positive, normalized
	0	1	0	1	Infinity, positive
	0	1	1	0	Valid, negative, normalized
	0	1	1	1	Infinity, negative
	1	0	0	0	Zero, positive
	1	0	0	1	Empty
	1	0	1	0	Zero, negative
	1	0	1	1	Empty
	1	1	0	0	Invalid, positive, exponent = 0
	1	1	0	1	Empty
	1	1	1	0	Invalid, negative, exponent = 0
	1	1	1	1	Empty

NOTES:
1. ST = Top of stack
2. X = value is not affected by instruction
3. U = value is undefined following instruction
4. Q_n = Quotient bit n

Table 4b. Condition Code Interpretation after FPREM Instruction As a Function of Dividend Value

Dividend Range	Q_2	Q_1	Q_0
Dividend < 2 * Modulus	C_3[1]	C_1[1]	Q_0
Dividend < 4 * Modulus	C_3[1]	Q_1	Q_0
Dividend ≥ 4 * Modulus	Q_2	Q_1	Q_0

NOTE:
1. Previous value of indicated bit, not affected by FPREM instruction execution.

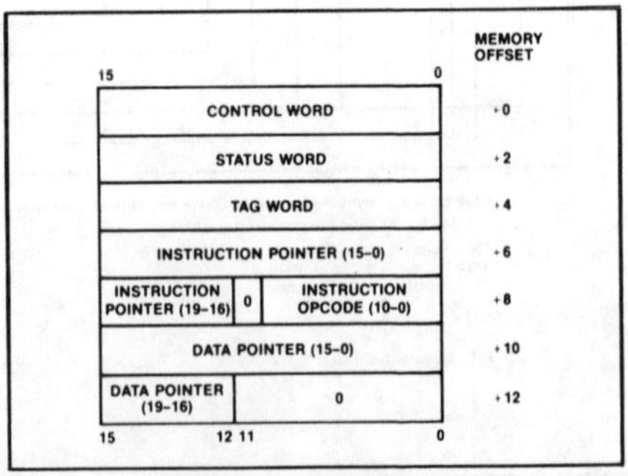

Figure 8. 8087 Instruction and Data Pointer Image in Memory

Control Word

The 8087 provides several processing options which are selected by loading a word from memory into the control word. Figure 9 shows the format and encoding of the fields in the control word.

The low order byte of this control word configures 8087 interrupts and exception masking. Bits 5–0 of the control word contain individual masks for each of the six exceptions that the 8087 recognizes and bit 7 contains a general mask bit for all 8087 interrupts. The high order byte of the control word configures the 8087 operating mode including precision, rounding, and infinity controls. The precision control bits (bits 9–8) can be used to set the 8087 internal operating precision at less than the default of temporary real precision. This can be useful in providing compatibility with earlier generation arithmetic processors of smaller precision than the 8087. The rounding control bits (bits 11–10) provide for directed rounding and true chop as well as the unbiased round to nearest mode specified in the proposed IEEE standard. Control over closure of the number space at infinity is also provided (either affine closure, $\pm\infty$, or projective closure, ∞, is treated as unsigned, may be specified).

Exception Handling

The 8087 detects six different exception conditions that can occur during instruction execution. Any or all exceptions will cause an interrupt if unmasked and interrupts are enabled.

If interrupts are disabled the 8087 will simply continue execution regardless of whether the host clears the exception. If a specific exception class is masked and that exception occurs, however, the 8087 will post the exception in the status register and perform an on-chip default exception handling procedure, thereby allowing processing to continue. The exceptions that the 8087 detects are the following:

1. INVALID OPERATION: Stack overflow, stack underflow, indeterminate form (0/0, $\infty - \infty$, etc.) or the use of a Non-Number (NAN) as an operand. An exponent value is reserved and any bit pattern with this value in the exponent field is termed a Non-Number and causes this exception. If this exception is masked, the 8087's default response is to generate a specific NAN called INDEFINITE, or to propagate already existing NANs as the calculation result.

2. OVERFLOW: The result is too large in magnitude to fit the specified format. The 8087 will generate an encoding for infinity if this exception is masked.

3. ZERO DIVISOR: The divisor is zero while the dividend is a non-infinite, non-zero number. Again, the 8087 will generate an encoding for infinity if this exception is masked.

4. UNDERFLOW: The result is non-zero but too small in magnitude to fit in the specified format. If this exception is masked the 8087 will denormalize (shift right) the fraction until the exponent is in range. This process is called gradual underflow.

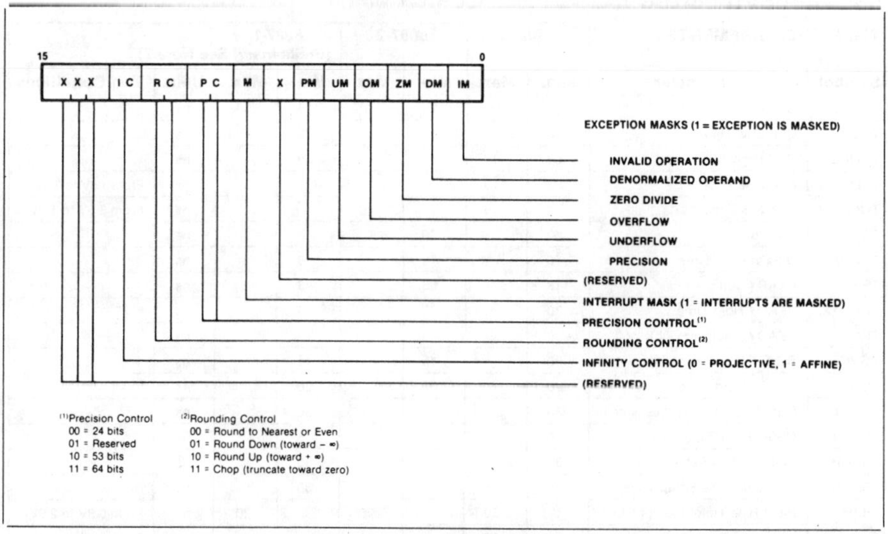

Figure 9. 8087 Control Word

5. DENORMALIZED OPERAND: At least one of the operands or the result is denormalized; it has the smallest exponent but a non-zero significand. Normal processing continues if this exception is masked off.

6. INEXACT RESULT: If the true result is not exactly representable in the specified format, the result is rounded according to the rounding mode, and this flag is set. If this exception is masked, processing will simply continue.

ABSOLUTE MAXIMUM RATINGS*

Ambient Temperature Under Bias .... 0°C to 70°C
Storage Temperature .... −65°C to +150°C
Voltage on Any Pin with
Respect to Ground .... −1.0V to +7V
Power Dissipation .... 3.0 Watt

**NOTICE: Stresses above those listed under Absolute Maximum Ratings may cause permanent damage to the device. This is a stress rating only and functional operation of the device at these or any other conditions above those indicated in the operational sections of this specification is not implied. Exposure to absolute maximum rating conditions for extended periods may affect device reliability.*

D.C. CHARACTERISTICS (T_A = 0°C to 70°C, V_{CC} = +5V ±5%)

Symbol	Parameter	Min.	Max.	Units	Test Conditions
V_{IL}	Input Low Voltage	−0.5	+0.8	V	
V_{IH}	Input High Voltage	2.0	V_{CC} +0.5	V	
V_{OL}	Output Low Voltage (See Note 8)		0.45	V	I_{OL} = 2.5 mA
V_{OH}	Output High Voltage	2.4		V	I_{OH} = −400 μA
I_{CC}	Power Supply Current		475	mA	T_A = 25°C
I_{LI}	Input Leakage Current		±10	μA	0V ≤ V_{IN} ≤ V_{CC}
I_{LO}	Output Leakage Current		±10	μA	0.45V ≤ V_{OUT} ≤ V_{CC}
V_{CL}	Clock Input Low Voltage	−0.5	+0.6	V	
V_{CH}	Clock Input High Voltage	3.9	V_{CC} + 1.0	V	
C_{IN}	Capacitance of Inputs		10	pF	fc = 1 MHz
C_{IO}	Capacitance of I/O Buffer (AD0-15, A_{16}–A_{19}, BHE, S2-S0, RQ/GT) and CLK		15	pF	fc = 1 MHz
C_{OUT}	Capacitance of Outputs BUSY, INT		10	pF	fc = 1 MHz

A.C. CHARACTERISTICS (T_A = 0°C to 70°C, V_{CC} = +5V ±5%)

TIMING REQUIREMENTS		8087		8087-2		8087-1 (Preliminary: See Note 7)			
Symbol	Parameter	Min.	Max.	Min.	Max.	Min.	Max.	Units	Test Conditions
TCLCL	CLK Cycle Period	200	500	125	500	100	500	ns	
TCLCH	CLK Low Time	118		68		53		ns	
TCHCL	CLK High Time	69		44		39		ns	
TCH1CH2	CLK Rise Time		10		10		15	ns	From 1.0V to 3.5V
TCL2CL2	CLK Fall Time		10		10		15	ns	From 3.5V to 1.0V
TDVCL	Data in Setup Time	30		20		15		ns	
TCLDX	Data in Hold Time	10		10		10		ns	
TRYHCH	READY Setup Time	118		68		53		ns	
TCHRYX	READY Hold Time	30		20		5		ns	
TRYLCL	READY Inactive to CLK**	- 8		- 8		-10		ns	
TGVCH	RQ/GT Setup Time(See Note 8)	30		15		15		ns	
TCHGX	RQ/GT Hold Time	40		30		20		ns	
TQVCL	QS0-1 Setup Time (See Note 8)	30		30		30		ns	
TCLQX	QS0-1 Hold Time	10		10		5		ns	
TSACH	Status Active Setup Time	30		30		30		ns	
TSNCL	Status Inactive Setup Time	30		30		30		ns	
TILIH	Input Rise Time (Except CLK)		20		20		20	ns	From 0.8V to 2.0V
TIHIL	Input Fall Time (Except CLK)		12		12		15	ns	From 2.0V to 0.8V

**See Note 6

TIMING RESPONSES

Symbol	Parameter	8087 Min.	8087 Max.	8087-2 Min.	8087-2 Max.	8087-1 (Preliminary: See Note 7) Min.	8087-1 (Preliminary: See Note 7) Max.	Units	Test Conditions
TCLML	Command Active Delay (See Notes 1,2)	10/0	35/70	10/0	35/70	10/0	35/70	ns	C_L = 20 - 100pF for all 8087 Outputs (in addition to 8087 self-load)
TCLMH	Command Inactive Delay (See Notes 1,2)	10/0	35/55	10/0	35/55	10/0	35/70	ns	
TRYHSH	Ready Active to Status Passive (See Note 5)		110		65		45	ns	
TCHSV	Status Active Delay	10	110	10	60	10	45	ns	
TCLSH	Status Inactive Delay	10	130	10	70	10	55	ns	
TCLAV	Address Valid Delay	10	110	10	60	10	55	ns	
TCLAX	Address Hold Time	10		10		10		ns	
TCLAZ	Address Float Delay	TCLAX	80	TCLAX	50	TCLAX	45	ns	
TSVLH	Status Valid to ALE High (See Notes 1,2)		15/30		15/30		15/30	ns	
TCLLH	CLK Low to ALE Valid (See Notes 1,2)		15/30		15/30		15/30	ns	
TCHLL	ALE Inactive Delay (See Notes 1,2)		15/30		15/30		15/30	ns	
TCLDV	Data Valid Delay	10	110	10	60	10	50	ns	
TCHDX	Status Hold Time	10		10		10	45	ns	
TCLDOX	Data Hold Time	10		10		10		ns	
TCVNV	Control Active Delay (See Notes 1,3)	5	45	5	45	5	45	ns	
TCVNX	Control Inactive Delay (See Notes 1,3)	10	45	10	45	10	45	ns	
TCHBV	BUSY and INT Valid Delay	10	150	10	85	10	65	ns	
TCHDTL	Direction Control Active Delay (See Notes 1,3)		50		50		50	ns	
TCHDTH	Direction Control Inactive Delay (See Notes 1,3)		30		30		30	ns	
TSVDTV	STATUS to DT/$\overline{R}$ Delay (See Notes 1,4)	0	30	0	30	0	30	ns	
TCLDTV	DT/$\overline{R}$ Active Delay (See Notes 1,4)	0	55	0	55	0	55	ns	
TCHDNV	$\overline{DEN}$ Active Delay (See Notes 1,4)	0	55	0	55	0	55	ns	
TCHDNX	DEN Inactive Delay (See Notes 1,4)	5	55	5	55	5	55	ns	
TCLGL	RQ/GT Active Delay (See Note 8)	0	85	0	50	0	38	ns	C_L = 40pF (in addition to 8087 self-load)
TCLGH	RQ/GT Inactive Delay	0	85	0	50	0	45	ns	
TOLOH	Output Rise Time		20		20		15	ns	From 0.8V to 2.0V
TOHOL	Output Fall Time		12		12		12	ns	From 2.0V to 0.8V

NOTES:
1. Signal at 8284A, 8288, or 82188 shown for reference only.
2. 8288 timing/82188 timing
3. 8288 timing
4. 82188 timing
5. Applies only to T_3 and wait states
6. Applies only to T_2 state (8ns into T_3)
7. IMPORTANT SYSTEM CONSIDERATION: Some 8087-1 timing parameters are constrained relative to the corresponding 8086-1 specifications. Therefore, 8086-1 systems incorporating the 8087-1 should be designed with the 8087-1 specifications.
8. Changes since last revision.

A.C. TESTING INPUT, OUTPUT WAVEFORM

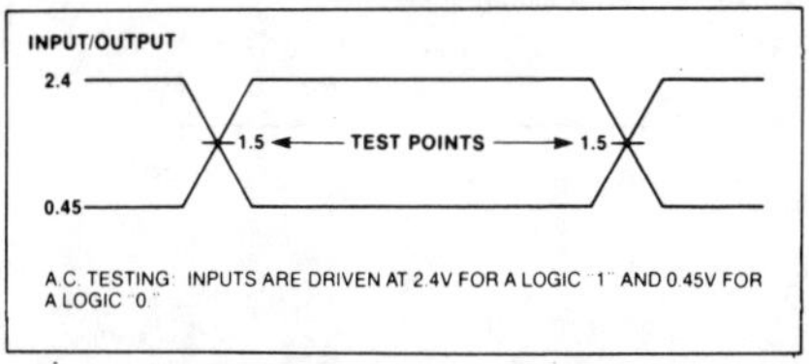

A.C. TESTING LOAD CIRCUIT

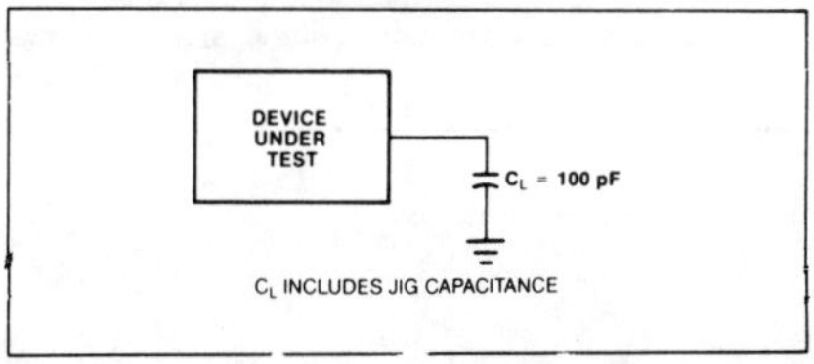

WAVEFORMS

MASTER MODE (with 8288 references)

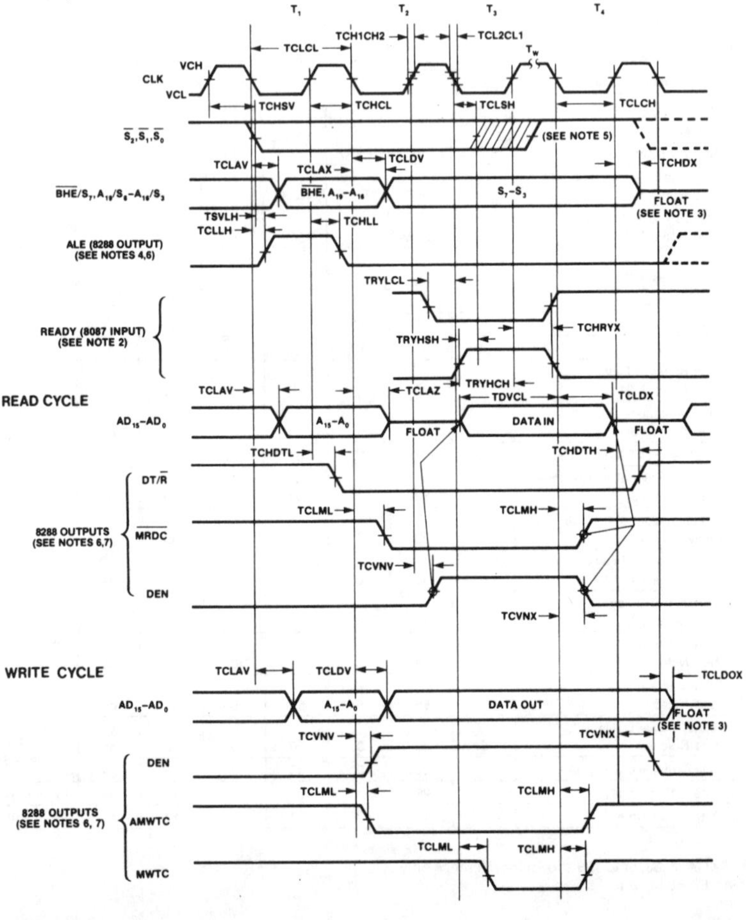

NOTES:

1. ALL SIGNALS SWITCH BETWEEN V_{OL} AND V_{OH} UNLESS OTHERWISE SPECIFIED.
2. READY IS SAMPLED NEAR THE END OF T_2, T_3 AND T_W TO DETERMINE IF T_W MACHINE STATES ARE TO BE INSERTED.
3. THE LOCAL BUS FLOATS ONLY IF THE 8087 IS RETURNING CONTROL TO THE 8086/8088.
4. ALE RISES AT LATER OF (TSVLH, TCLLH).
5. STATUS INACTIVE IN STATE JUST PRIOR TO T_4.
6. SIGNALS AT 8284A OR 8288 ARE SHOWN FOR REFERENCE ONLY.
7. THE ISSUANCE OF 8288 COMMAND AND CONTROL SIGNALS (MRDC, MWTC, AMWC AND DEN) LAGS THE ACTIVE HIGH 8288 CEN.
8. ALL TIMING MEASUREMENTS ARE MADE AT 1.5V UNLESS OTHERWISE NOTED.

MASTER MODE (with 82188 references)

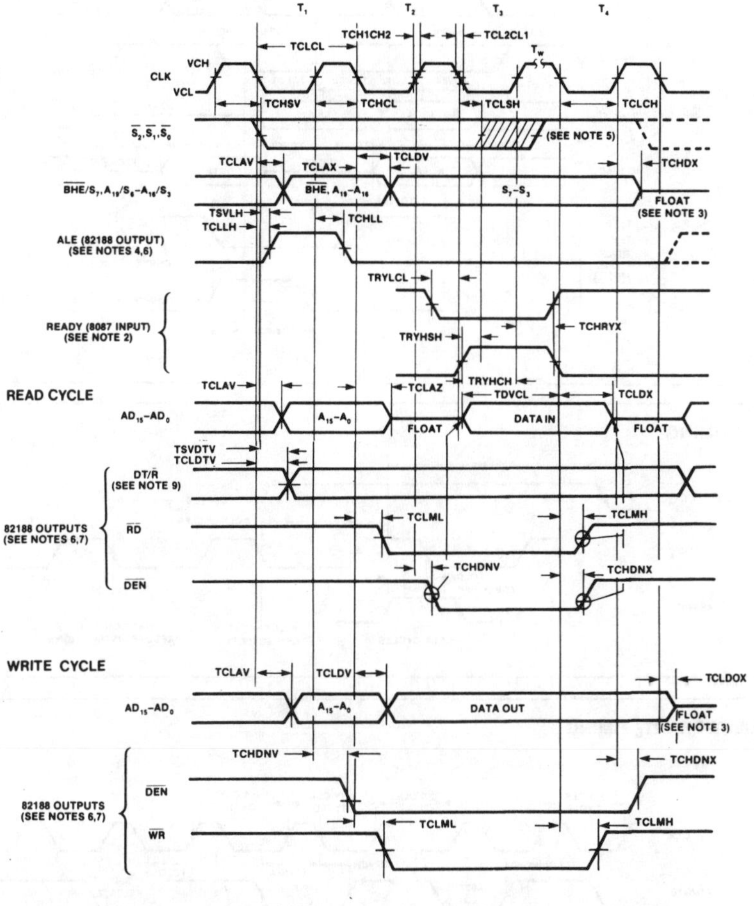

NOTES:

1. ALL SIGNALS SWITCH BETWEEN V_{OL} AND V_{OH} UNLESS OTHERWISE SPECIFIED.
2. READY IS SAMPLED NEAR THE END OF T_2, T_3 AND T_W TO DETERMINE IF T_W MACHINE STATES ARE TO BE INSERTED.
3. THE LOCAL BUS FLOATS ONLY IF THE 8087 IS RETURNING CONTROL TO THE 80186/80188
4. ALE RISES AT LATER OF (TSVLH, TCLLH).
5. STATUS INACTIVE IN STATE JUST PRIOR TO T_4.
6. SIGNALS AT 8284A OR 82188 ARE SHOWN FOR REFERENCE ONLY.
7. THE ISSUANCE OF 8288 COMMAND AND CONTROL SIGNALS ($\overline{MRDC}$, $\overline{MWTC}$, $\overline{AMWC}$, AND DEN) LAGS THE ACTIVE HIGH 8288 CEN.
8. ALL TIMING MEASUREMENTS ARE MADE AT 1.5V UNLESS OTHERWISE NOTED.
9. DT/$\overline{R}$ BECOMES VALID AT THE LATER OF (TSVDTV, TCLDTV).

PASSIVE MODE

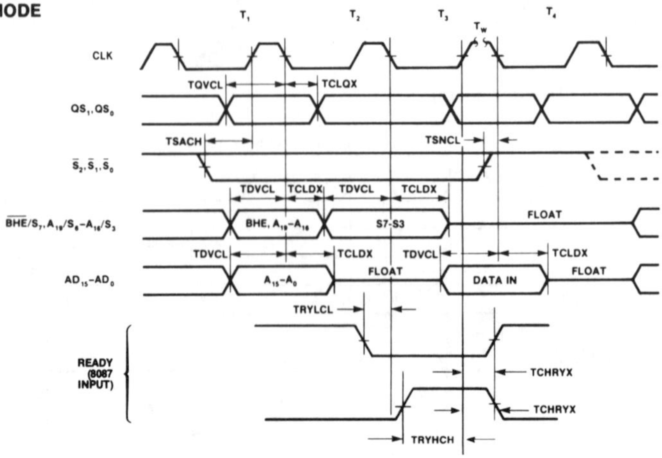

RESET TIMING

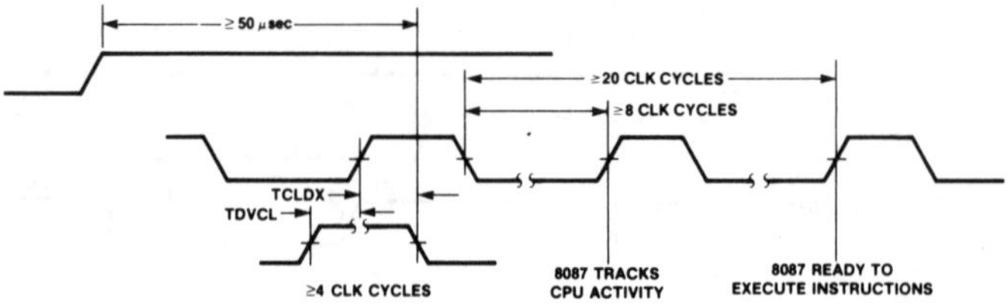

REQUEST/GRANT$_0$ TIMING

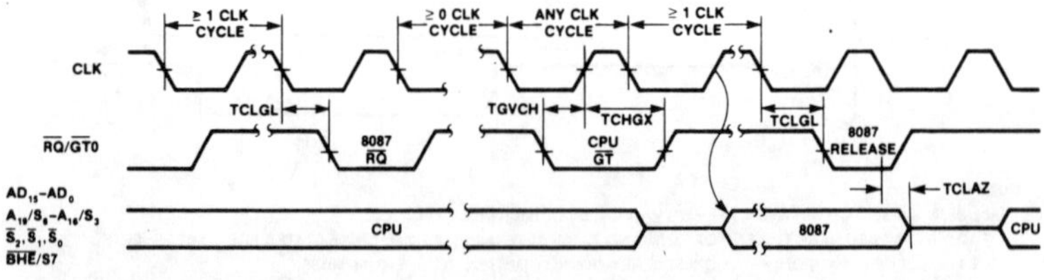

NOTE: THE CPU PROVIDES ACTIVE PULLUP OF RQ/GT0, SEE TCLGH SPEC.

BUSY AND INTERRUPT TIMING

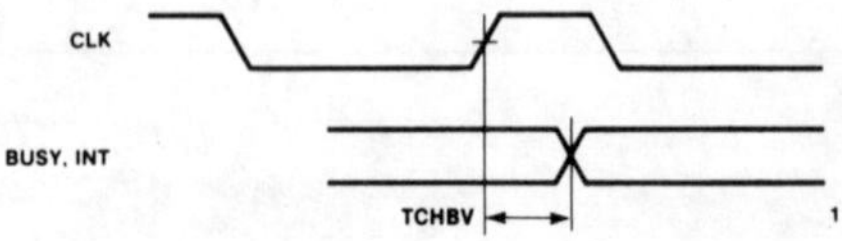

REQUEST/GRANT$_1$ TIMING

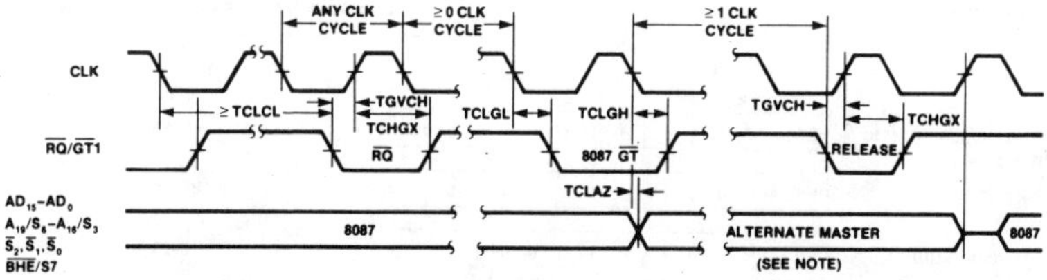

NOTE: ALTERNATE MASTER MAY NOT DRIVE THE BUSES OUTSIDE OF THE REGION SHOWN WITHOUT RISKING BUS CONTENTION.

Table 5. 8087 Extensions to the 86/186 Instructions Sets

Data Transfer			Optional 8,16 Bit Displacement	Clock Count Range: 32 Bit Real	32 Bit Integer	64 Bit Real	16 Bit Integer
FLD = LOAD	MF	=		00	01	10	11
Integer/Real Memory to ST(0)	ESCAPE MF 1	MOD 0 0 0 R/M	DISP	38–56 + EA	52–60 + EA	40–60 + EA	46–54 + EA
Long Integer Memory to ST(0)	ESCAPE 1 1 1	MOD 1 0 1 R/M	DISP	60–68 + EA			
Temporary Real Memory to ST(0)	ESCAPE 0 1 1	MOD 1 0 1 R/M	DISP	53–65 + EA			
BCD Memory to ST(0)	ESCAPE 1 1 1	MOD 1 0 0 R/M	DISP	290–310 + EA			
ST(i) to ST(0)	ESCAPE 0 0 1	1 1 0 0 0 ST(i)		17–22			
FST = STORE							
ST(0) to Integer/Real Memory	ESCAPE MF 1	MOD 0 1 0 R/M	DISP	84–90 + EA	82–92 + EA	96–104 + EA	80–90 + EA
ST(0) to ST(i)	ESCAPE 1 0 1	1 1 0 1 0 ST(i)		15–22			
FSTP = STORE AND POP							
ST(0) to Integer/Real Memory	ESCAPE MF 1	MOD 0 1 1 R/M	DISP	86–92 + EA	84–94 + EA	98–106 + EA	82–92 + EA
ST(0) to Long Integer Memory	ESCAPE 1 1 1	MOD 1 1 1 R/M	DISP	94–105 + EA			
ST(0) to Temporary Real Memory	ESCAPE 0 1 1	MOD 1 1 1 R/M	DISP	52–58 + EA			
ST(0) to BCD Memory	ESCAPE 1 1 1	MOD 1 1 0 R/M	DISP	520–540 + EA			
ST(0) to ST(i)	ESCAPE 1 0 1	1 1 0 1 1 ST(i)		17–24			
FXCH = Exchange ST(i) and ST(0)	ESCAPE 0 0 1	1 1 0 0 1 ST(i)		10–15			
Comparison							
FCOM = Compare							
Integer/Real Memory to ST(0)	ESCAPE MF 0	MOD 0 1 0 R/M	DISP	60–70 + EA	78–91 + EA	65–75 + EA	72–86 + EA
ST(i) to ST (0)	ESCAPE 0 0 0	1 1 0 1 0 ST(i)		40–50			
FCOMP = Compare and Pop							
Integer/Real Memory to ST(0)	ESCAPE MF 0	MOD 0 1 1 R/M	DISP	63–73 + EA	80–93 + EA	67–77 + EA	74–88 + EA
ST(i) to ST(0)	ESCAPE 0 0 0	1 1 0 1 1 ST(i)		45–52			

Table 5. 8087 Extensions to the 86/186 Instruction Sets (cont.)

Constants			Optional 8,16 Bit Displacement	Clock Count Range: 32 Bit Real	32 Bit Integer	64 Bit Real	16 Bit Integer
	MF	=		00	01	10	11
FCOMPP = Compare ST(1) to ST(0) and Pop Twice	ESCAPE 1 1 0	1 1 0 1 1 0 0 1		45–55			
FTST = Test ST(0)	ESCAPE 0 0 1	1 1 1 0 0 1 0 0		38–48			
FXAM = Examine ST(0)	ESCAPE 0 0 1	1 1 1 0 0 1 0 1		12–23			
FLDZ = LOAD + 0.0 into ST(0)	ESCAPE 0 0 1	1 1 1 0 1 1 1 0		11–17			
FLD1 = LOAD + 1.0 into ST(0)	ESCAPE 0 0 1	1 1 1 0 1 0 0 0		15–21			
FLDPI = LOAD π into ST(0)	ESCAPE 0 0 1	1 1 1 0 1 0 1 1		16–22			
FLDL2T = LOAD $\log_2 10$ into ST(0)	ESCAPE 0 0 1	1 1 1 0 1 0 0 1		16–22			
FLDL2E = LOAD $\log_2 e$ into ST(0)	ESCAPE 0 0 1	1 1 1 0 1 0 1 0		15–21			
FLDLG2 = LOAD $\log_{10} 2$ into ST(0)	ESCAPE 0 0 1	1 1 1 0 1 1 0 0		18–24			
FLDLN2 = LOAD $\log_e 2$ into ST(0)	ESCAPE 0 0 1	1 1 1 0 1 1 0 1		17–23			
Arithmetic							
FADD = Addition							
Integer/Real Memory with ST(0)	ESCAPE MF 0	MOD 0 0 0 R/M	DISP	90–120 + EA	108–143 + EA	95–125 + EA	102–137 + EA
ST(i) and ST(0)	ESCAPE d P 0	1 1 0 0 0 ST(i)		70–100 (Note 1)			
FSUB = Subtraction							
Integer/Real Memory with ST(0)	ESCAPE MF 0	MOD 1 0 R R/M	DISP	90–120 + EA	108–143 + EA	95–125 + EA	102–137 + EA
ST(i) and ST(0)	ESCAPE d P 0	1 1 1 0 R R/M		70–100 (Note 1)			
FMUL = Multiplication							
Integer/Real Memory with ST(0)	ESCAPE MF 0	MOD 0 0 1 R/M	DISP	110–125 + EA	130–144 + EA	112–168 + EA	124–138 + EA
ST(i) and ST(0)	ESCAPE d P 0	1 1 0 0 1 R/M		90–145 (Note 1)			
FDIV = Division							
Integer/Real Memory with ST(0)	ESCAPE MF 0	MOD 1 1 R R/M	DISP	215–225 + EA	230–243 + EA	220–230 + EA	224–238 + EA
ST(i) and ST(0)	ESCAPE d P 0	1 1 1 1 R R/M		193–203 (Note 1)			
FSQRT = Square Root of ST(0)	ESCAPE 0 0 1	1 1 1 1 1 0 1 0		180–186			
FSCALE = Scale ST(0) by ST(1)	ESCAPE 0 0 1	1 1 1 1 1 1 0 1		32–38			
FPREM = Partial Remainder of ST(0) ÷ ST(1)	ESCAPE 0 0 1	1 1 1 1 1 0 0 0		15–190			
FRNDINT = Round ST(0) to Integer	ESCAPE 0 0 1	1 1 1 1 1 1 0 0		16–50			

NOTE:
1. If P=1 then add 5 clocks.

Table 5. 8087 Extensions to the 86/186 Instructions Sets (cont.)

			Optional 8,16 Bit Displacement	Clock Count Range
FXTRACT = Extract Components of St(0)	ESCAPE 0 0 1	1 1 1 1 0 1 0 0		27–55
FABS = Absolute Value of ST(0)	ESCAPE 0 0 1	1 1 1 0 0 0 0 1		10–17
FCHS = Change Sign of ST(0)	ESCAPE 0 0 1	1 1 1 0 0 0 0 0		10–17
Transcendental				
FPTAN = Partial Tangent of ST(0)	ESCAPE 0 0 1	1 1 1 1 0 0 1 0		30–540
FPATAN = Partial Arctangent of ST(0) ÷ ST(1)	ESCAPE 0 0 1	1 1 1 1 0 0 1 1		250–800
F2XM1 = $2^{ST(0)} - 1$	ESCAPE 0 0 1	1 1 1 1 0 0 0 0		310–630
FYL2X = ST(1) • Log_2 |ST(0)|	ESCAPE 0 0 1	1 1 1 1 0 0 0 1		900–1100
FYL2XP1 = ST(1) • Log_2 [ST(0) + 1]	ESCAPE 0 0 1	1 1 1 1 1 0 0 1		700–1000
Processor Control				
FINIT = Initialized 8087	ESCAPE 0 1 1	1 1 1 0 0 0 1 1		2–8
FENI = Enable Interrupts	ESCAPE 0 1 1	1 1 1 0 0 0 0 0		2–8
FDISI = Disable Interrupts	ESCAPE 0 1 1	1 1 1 0 0 0 0 1		2–8
FLDCW = Load Control Word	ESCAPE 0 0 1	MOD 1 0 1 R/M	DISP	7–14 + EA
FSTCW = Store Control Word	ESCAPE 0 0 1	MOD 1 1 1 R/M	DISP	12–18 + EA
FSTSW = Store Status Word	ESCAPE 1 0 1	MOD 1 1 1 R/M	DISP	12–18 + EA
FCLEX = Clear Exceptions	ESCAPE 0 1 1	1 1 1 0 0 0 1 0		2–8
FSTENV = Store Environment	ESCAPE 0 0 1	MOD 1 1 0 R/M	DISP	40–50 + EA
FLDENV = Load Environment	ESCAPE 0 0 1	MOD 1 0 0 R/M	DISP	35–45 + EA
FSAVE = Save State	ESCAPE 1 0 1	MOD 1 1 0 R/M	DISP	197 – 207 + EA
FRSTOR = Restore State	ESCAPE 1 0 1	MOD 1 0 0 R/M	DISP	197 – 207 + EA
FINCSTP = Increment Stack Pointer	ESCAPE 0 0 1	1 1 1 1 0 1 1 1		6–12
FDECSTP = Decrement Stack Pointer	ESCAPE 0 0 1	1 1 1 1 0 1 1 0		6–12
				Clock Count Range
FFREE = Free ST(i)	ESCAPE 1 0 1	1 1 0 0 0 ST(i)		9–16
FNOP = No Operation	ESCAPE 0 0 1	1 1 0 1 0 0 0 0		10–10
FWAIT = CPU Wait for 8087	1 0 0 1 1 0 1 1			3 + 5n*

*n = number of times CPU examines TEST line before 8087 lowers BUSY.

NOTES:

1. if mod=00 then DISP=0*, disp-low and disp-high are absent
   if mod=01 then DISP=disp-low sign-extended to 16-bits, disp-high is absent
   if mod=10 then DISP=disp-high; disp-low
   if mod=11 then r/m is treated as an ST(i) field
2. if r/m=000 then EA=(BX) + (SI) +DISP
   if r/m=001 then EA=(BX) + (DI) +DISP
   if r/m=010 then EA=(BP) + (SI) +DISP
   if r/m=011 then EA=(BP) + (DI) +DISP
   if r/m=100 then EA=(SI) + DISP
   if r/m=101 then EA=(DI) + DISP
   if r/m=110 then EA=(BP) + DISP
   if r/m=111 then EA=(BX) + DISP

   *except if mod=000 and r/m=110 then EA =disp-high; disp-low.
3. MF= Memory Format
   00—32-bit Real
   01—32-bit Integer
   10—64-bit Real
   11—16-bit Integer
4. ST(0)= Current stack top
   ST(i) i^{th} register below stack top
5. d= Destination
   0—Destination is ST(0)
   1—Destination is ST(i)
6. P= Pop
   0—No pop
   1—Pop ST(0)
7. R= Reverse: When d=1 reverse the sense of R
   0—Destination (op) Source
   1—Source (op) Destination
8. For **FSQRT:** $-0 \leq ST(0) \leq +\infty$
   For **FSCALE:** $-2^{15} \leq ST(1) < +2^{15}$ and ST(1) integer
   For **F2XM1:** $0 \leq ST(0) \leq 2^{-1}$
   For **FYL2X:** $0 < ST(0) < \infty$
   $-\infty < ST(1) < +\infty$
   For **FYL2XP1:** $0 \leq |ST(0)| < (2 - \sqrt{2})/2$
   $-\infty < ST(1) < \infty$
   For **FPTAN:** $0 \leq ST(0) \leq \pi/4$
   For **FPATAN:** $0 \leq ST(0) < ST(1) < +\infty$

DISTINCTIVE CHARACTERISTICS

- **Pin compatible and functionally equivalent to the Intel 80287**
- **High-performance CMOS process yields 10-MHz, 12-MHz, and 16-MHz speed grades**
- **Enhanced sleep feature automatically shuts off the internal clock when no instruction is executing, reducing power consumption. This feature is transparent to the user**
- **Available in space-saving 44-pin PLCC as well as 40-pin DIP**
- **80-bit numeric accelerator for 80C286 and 80286-based systems**
- **Compatible with IEEE floating-point standard 754**
- **Static CMOS design does not require a minimum clock rate, resulting in significantly lower power dissipation**
- **Performs single-, double-, and extended-precision floating-point, as well as word, short, and long integer and 18-digit BCD conversions**
- **Adds trigonometric, logarithmic, exponential, and arithmetic instructions to the 80C286 instruction set**

GENERAL DESCRIPTION

The 80EC287 is implemented in AMD's advanced static CMOS process that allows for significantly higher speeds at a much lower power dissipation than traditional NMOS versions or standard CMOS. The 80EC287 is a high-performance arithmetic processor that expands the 80C286 instruction set with floating-point instructions including transcendentals, and integer and BCD conversions. The 80EC287 is functionally equivalent to the Intel 80287 and AMD 80C287 plus adds a low power sleep feature for battery powered applications. This enhanced 80EC287 can be a direct replacement for an AMD 80C287. The sleep feature is an automatic inherent feature of the device and thus requires no external entry. The floating-point operations comply with the IEEE Standard 754. The device is available in 12- and 16-MHz speed grades and is provided in 44-pin PLCC and 40-pin DIP packages. When coupled with the 80C286, the 80EC287 provides a complete solution for high-performance numeric processing applications.

BLOCK DIAGRAM

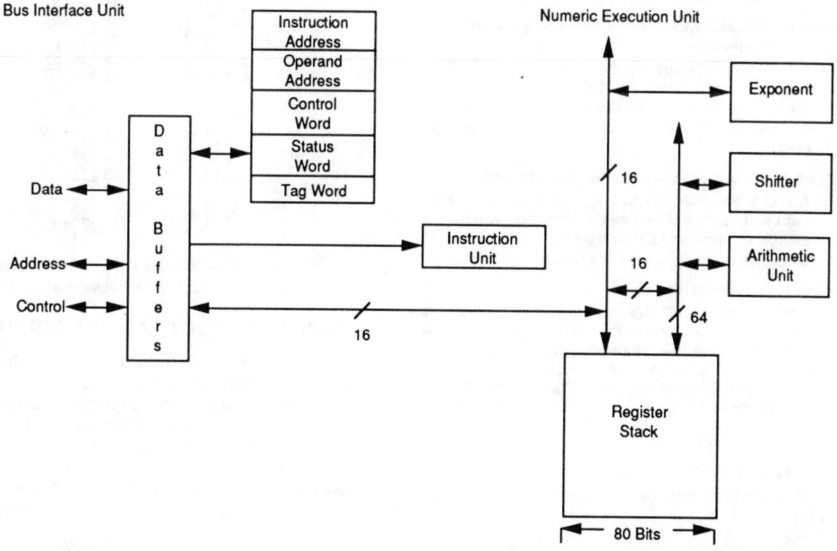

PIN DESCRIPTION

BUSY Busy Status (Output; Active Low)

A LOW level indicates that the 80EC287 is currently executing a command.

CKM Clock Mode Signal (Input)

When CKM is HIGH, the CLK is used directly. When CKM is LOW, CLK is divided by three. This input must be either HIGH or LOW 20 CLK cycles before RESET goes LOW.

CLK Clock (Input)

Provides timing for 80EC287 operations.

CMD$_1$, CMD$_0$ Command Lines (Input)

CMD$_1$ and CMD$_0$, along with select inputs, allow the CPU to direct the 80EC287 operations. These inputs are timed relative to the read and write strobes.

D$_{15}$–D$_0$ Data (Input/Output)

Bidirectional data bus. These inputs are timed relative to the read and write strobes.

ERROR Error Status (Output; Active Low)

Reflects the error summary status bit of the status word. A LOW level indicates that an unmasked exception condition exists.

NPRD Numeric Processor Read (Input; Active Low)

A LOW level enables transfer of data from the 80EC287. This input may be asynchronous to the 80EC287 clock.

NPS$_1$, NPS$_2$ Numeric Processor Selects (Input)

Indicates the CPU is transferring data to and from the 80EC287. Asserting both signals (NPS$_1$ LOW and NPS$_2$ HIGH) enables the 80EC287 to transfer floating-point data or instructions. No data transfers involving the 80EC287 will occur unless the 80EC287 is selected via NPS$_1$ and NPS$_2$. These inputs are timed relative to the read and write strobes.

NPWR Numeric Processor Write (Input; Active Low)

A LOW level enables transfer of data from the 80EC287. This input may be asynchronous to the 80EC287 clock.

PEACK Processor Extension Acknowledge (Input; Active Low)

A LOW level indicates that the request signal (PEREQ) has been recognized. PEACK causes the request (PEREQ) to be withdrawn when no more transfers are required. PEACK may be asynchronous to the 80EC287 clock.

PEREQ Processor Extension Request (Output)

A HIGH level indicates that the 80EC287 is ready to transfer data. PEREQ will be disabled upon assertion of PEACK or upon actual data transfer, whichever occurs first, when no more transfers are required.

RESET System Reset (Input)

Reset causes the 80EC287 to immediately terminate its present activity and enter a dormant state. Reset must be HIGH for more than four CLK cycles. For proper initialization the HIGH-LOW transition must occur no sooner than 50 µs after V_{CC} and CLK meet their DC and AC specifications.

V_{CC} +5 V Supply (Input)

V_{SS} System Ground (Input)

Both pins must be connected to ground.

CONNECTION DIAGRAM

PLCC

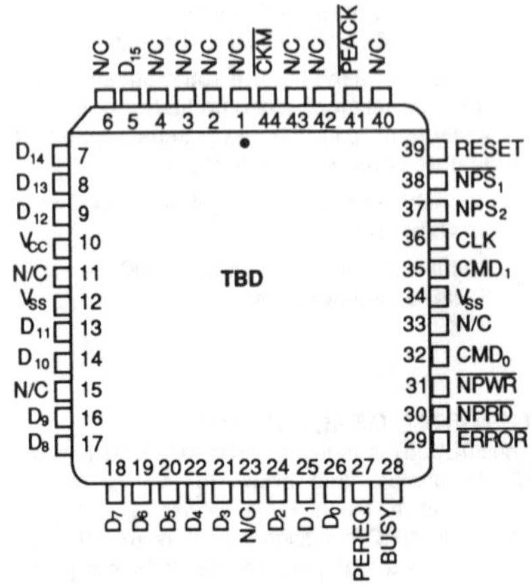

DIP

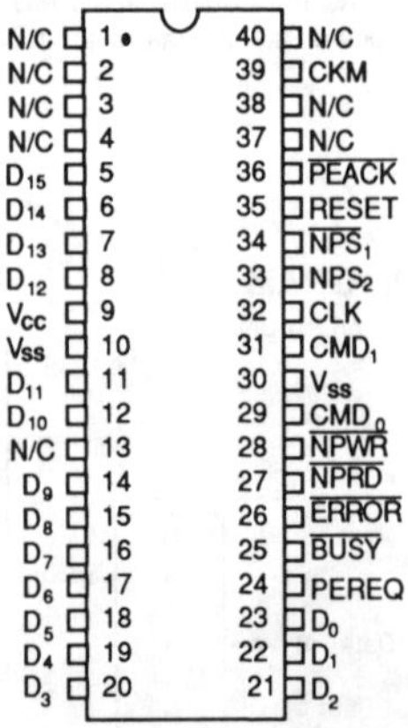

Note: N/C pins should not be connected.
Pin 1 is marked for orientation.

SIMPLIFIED FUNCTIONAL DESCRIPTION

The 80EC287 is internally divided into two basic processing units; the numeric execution unit, and the bus interface unit as shown in the block diagram. The numeric execution unit performs numeric instructions. The bus interface unit receives and decodes instructions, executes processor control instructions, and requests operands transfers to and from memory. The

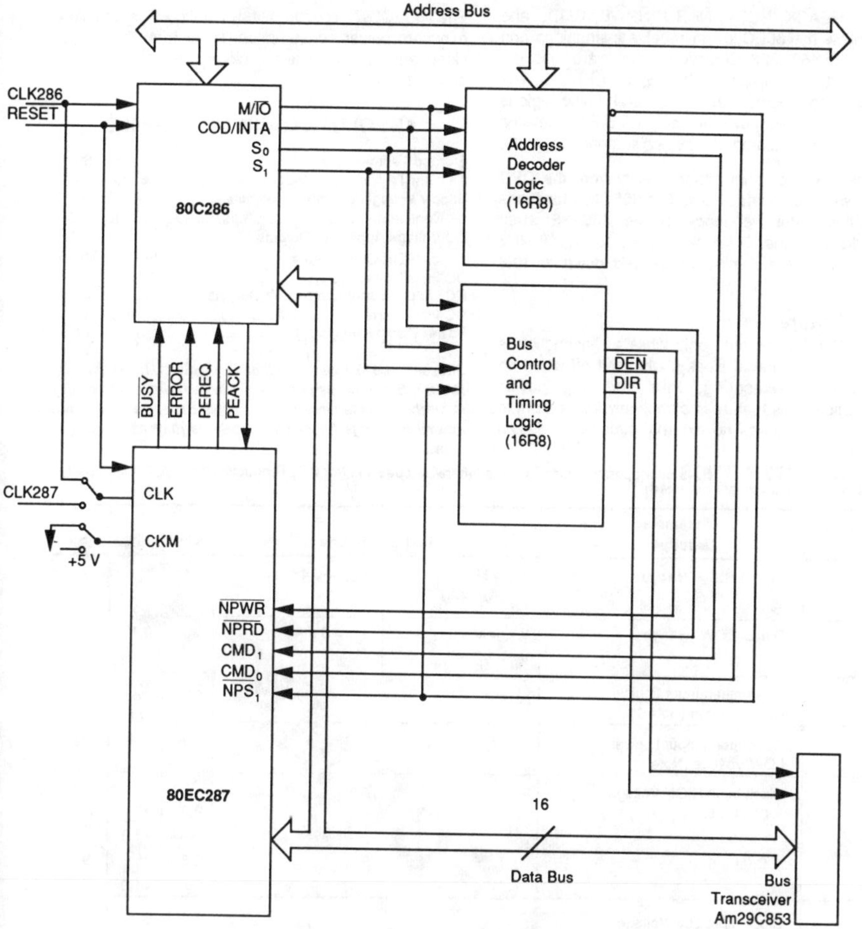

Figure 1. 80C286/80EC287 Simplified System Configuration

80C286 may execute non-numeric instruction concurrently with numeric instruction executed on the 80EC287. Synchronization and error recognition occurs when the next numeric instruction is decoded by the 80C286.

The Numeric Execution Unit

The numeric execution data path is 80 bits wide. All operands are converted to the internal 80-bit format before use. These instructions include arithmetic, transcendental, constant, and data transfer instructions.

The Bus Interface Unit

The bus interface unit decodes the ESC instruction executed by the 80C286. The signal BUSY is activated for 80C286/80EC287 synchronization and the signal ERROR is activated for error detection. BUSY is activated when an instruction is transferred and deactivated when the instruction completes. ERROR will be asserted if an error has occurred when BUSY is deactivated.

The signals PEREQ, PEACK, NPRD, NPWR, NPS_1, CMD_0, CMD_1, and NPS_2 control data transfers between the 80EC287 and the 80C286. The 80C286 performs the actual data transfer with memory.

The Register Stack

The register stack contains eight 80-bit data registers, organized as a push down stack. Operations are performed on the stack top, between the stack top and another register, or between the stack top and memory.

System Configuration with 80C286

A simplified block diagram of the 80EC287 interface to a 80C286 CPU is shown in Figure 1. The 80EC287 can operate concurrently with the host CPU. The signals

PEREQ, $\overline{PEACK}$, $\overline{BUSY}$, $\overline{NPRD}$, $\overline{NPWR}$, CMD_0, and CMD_1 allow the 80EC287 to receive instructions and data from the 80C286. Detection of errors are indicated to the CPU by asserting the signal $\overline{ERROR}$. The address decode logic, bus control and timing logic is shown in this implementation using AMD PAL® devices but may also be accomplished using standard chip sets.

The 80EC287 operates either directly from the CPU clock or with a dedicated clock. The 80EC287 functions at two-thirds the frequency of the 80C286 when operating with the CPU clock (i.e., for a 16-MHz 80C286, the 32-MHz clock is divided down to 10.6 MHz).

Sleep Feature

The 80EC287 clock runs only while an instruction is executing. The internal clock shuts itself off when no instruction is executing, thus reducing power consumption. This feature is completely transparent to the user and requires no external circuitry or design interface.

The 80EC287 is completely static. For absolute minimum power consumption, lower than that of the sleep feature, the external clock can be stopped in phase 2.

ABSOLUTE MAXIMUM RATINGS

Storage Temperature .... –65 to +150° C
Ambient Temperature Under Bias .... –55 to +125° C
Supply Voltage to Ground Potential
Continuous .... –1.0 to +7.0 V
DC Voltage Applied to Outputs
for HIGH Output State .... –0.3 V to + V_{CC} +0.3 V
DC Input Voltage .... –0.3 to V_{CC} +0.3 V
DC Output Current, into LOW Outputs .... 30 mA
DC Input Current .... –10 to +10 mA
Power Dissipation (max.) .... 1.5 W

Stresses above those listed under ABSOLUTE MAXIMUM RATINGS may cause permanent device failure. Functionality at or above these limits is not implied. Exposure to absolute maximum ratings for extended periods may affect devices reliability.

DC CHARACTERISTICS over operating range unless otherwise specified (for APL Products, Group A, Subgroups 1, 2, 3 are tested unless otherwise noted)

Parameter Symbol	Parameter Description	Test Conditions		Min.	Max.	Unit
V_{OH}	Output HIGH Voltage	V_{CC} = Min. V_{IN} = V_{IL} or V_{IH}	I_{OH} = -0.4 mA	2.4		V
V_{OL}	Output LOW Voltage	V_{CC} = Min. V_{IN} = V_{IL} or V_{IH}	I_{OL} = 3 mA		0.45	
V_{IH}	Guaranteed Input Logical HIGH Voltage (Note 1)			2.0	V_{CC} +0.5	V
V_{IL}	Guaranteed Input Logical LOW Voltage (Note 1)			–0.5	0.8	V
V_{IHC}	Clock Input HIGH Voltage CKM = 1 CKM = 0			 2.0 3.8	 V_{CC} +1.0 V_{CC} +1.0	 V V
V_{ILC}	Clock Input Low Voltage CKM = 1 CKM = 0			 –0.5 –0.5	 0.8 0.6	 V V
I_{LI}	Input Leakage Current	$0 V \le V_{IN} \le V_{CC}$			±10	µA
I_{OZH}	Off-State (HIGH Impedance) Output Current	V_{CC} = Max., V_O = 2.4 V			10	µA
I_{OZL}	Off-State (HIGH Impedance) Output Current	V_{CC} = Max., V_O = 0.45 V			–10	µA
I_{CCS}	Power Supply Current, Static	V_{CC} = Max., V_{IN}-V_{CC} or GND, I_O=0 µA		5 mA		
I_{CC}	Supply Current, operating	V_{CC}=Max. Outputs Unloaded		10 mA/MHz (Note 2)		
I_{CCSM}	Power Supply Current, Sleep Mode	V_{CC} = Max. Outputs Unloaded		1 mA/MHz		

Notes: 1. These input levels provide zero-noise immunity and should only be statically tested in a noise-free environment (not functionally tested).
2. This reduces to I_{CCSM} when no instruction is executing, reducing overall power consumption.

SWITCHING CHARACTERISTICS over COMMERCIAL operating range

No.	Parameter Description	Test Conditions	80EC287-12 Min.	80EC287-12 Max.	80EC287-16 Min.	80EC287-16 Max.	Unit
1	Clock Period						
	CLM = 1		80	00	62.5	00	ns
	CLM = 0		35		30		ns
2	Clock LOW Time						
	CLM = 1		50		37		ns
	CLM = 0		9		8		ns
3	Clock HIGH Time						
	CLM = 1		22		17		ns
	CLM = 0		13		12		ns
4	Clock Rise Time			8		4	ns
5	Clock Fall Time			8		4	ns
6	Data Setup to NPWR Inactive		75		60		ns
7	Data Hold from NPWR Inactive		10		10		ns
8	NPWR, NPRD Active Time		70		50		ns
9	Command Valid Setup Time		0		0		ns
10	PEREQ Active to NPRD Active		80		62		ns
11	PEACK Active Time		50		36		ns
12	PEACK Inactive Time		160		125		ns
13	PEACK Inactive to NPRD, NPWR Inactive		32		25		ns
14	NPRD, NPWR Inactive to PEACK Active		–30		–30		ns
15	Command Valid Hold Time		18		15		ns
16	PEACK Active Setup to NPRD, NPWR		30		30		ns
17	NPRD, NPWR to CLK Setup		40		30		ns
18	NPRD, NPWR CLK Hold		29		22		ns
19	RESET to CLK Setup		20		20		ns
20	RESET from CLK Hold		20		20		ns
21	NPRD Inactive to Data Float			17		13	ns
22	NPRD Active to Data Valid			50		40	ns
23	ERROR Active to BUSY Inactive		100		100		ns
24	NPWR, Active to BUSY Active			80		60	ns
25	PEACK Active to PEREQ Inactive			80		60	ns
26	NPRD, NPWR Active to PEREQ Inactive			80		60	ns
27	Command Inactive Time						
	Write to Write		60		50		ns
	Read to Read		60		50		ns
	Write to Read		60		50		ns
	Read to Write		60		50		ns
28	Data Hold from Time NPRD Inactive		1		1		ns

SWITCHING WAVEFORMS

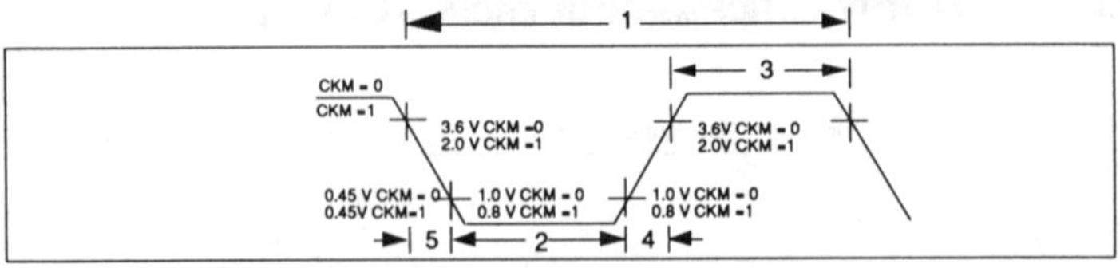

AC Drive and Measurement Points—CLK Input

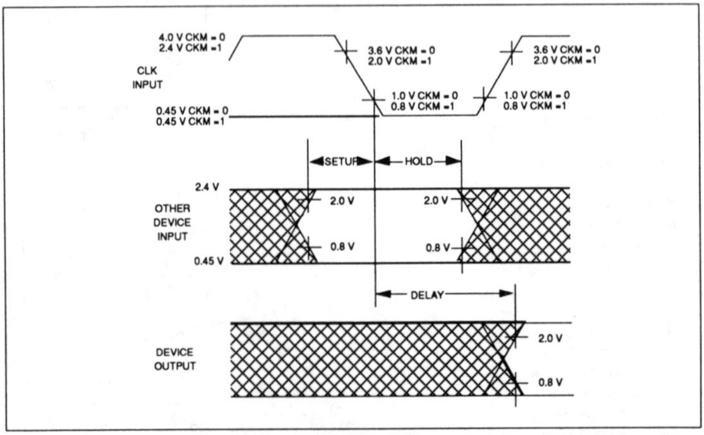

AC Setup, Hold and Delay Time Measurement—General

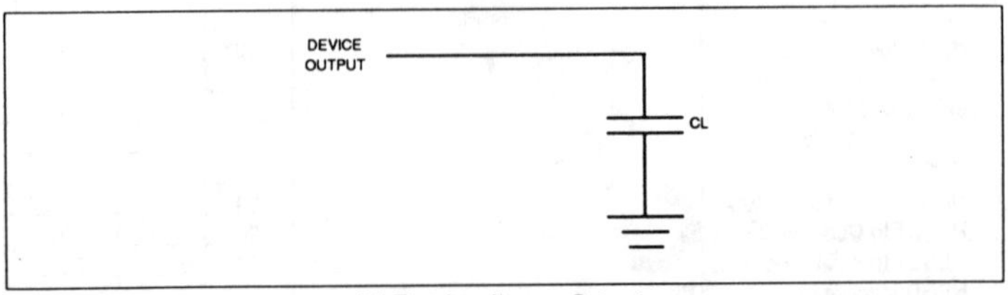

AC Test Loading on Outputs

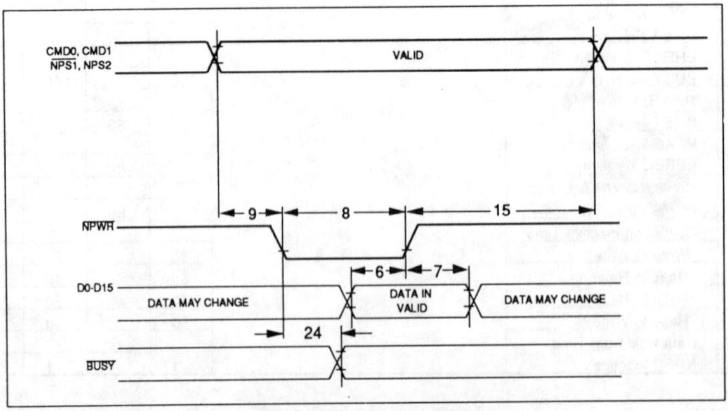

Write Timing from 80EC287

SWITCHING WAVEFORMS (continued)

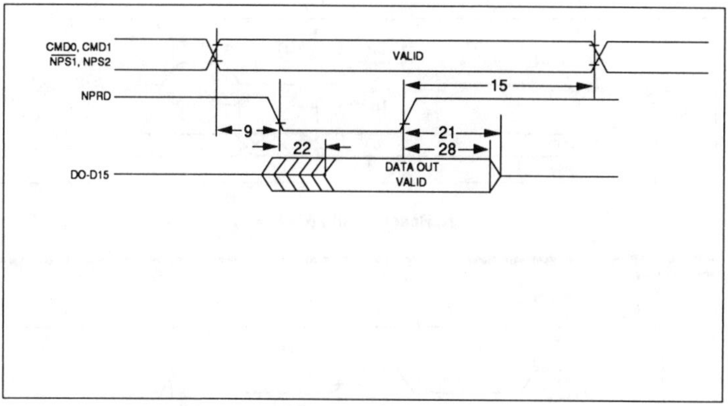

Read Timing from 80EC287

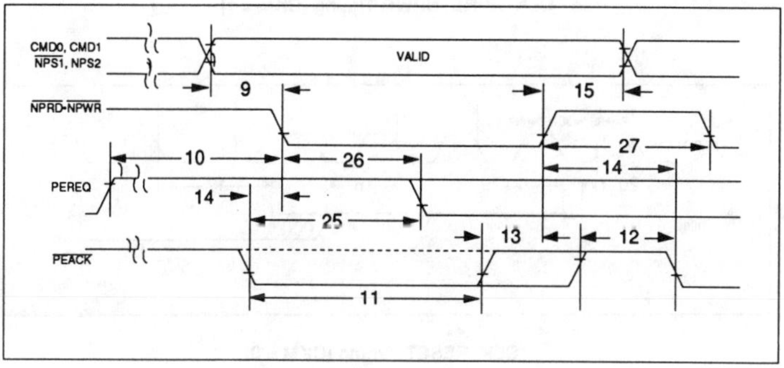

Data Channel Timing (Initiated by 80EC287)

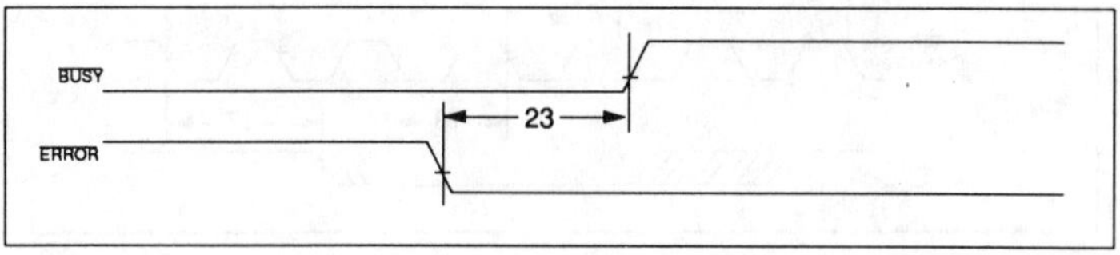

Error Output Timing

SWITCHING WAVEFORMS (continued)

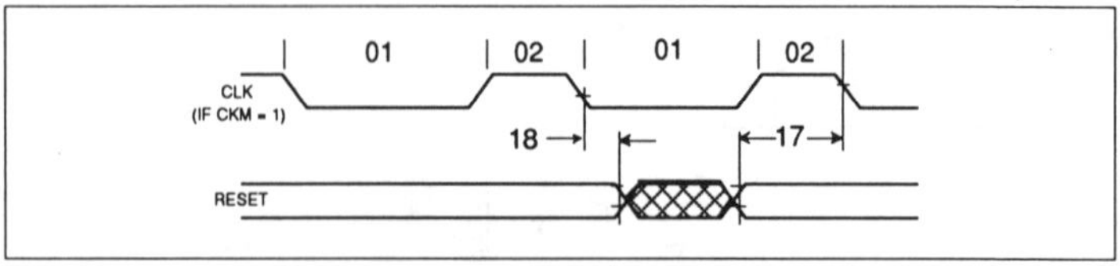

CLK, Reset Timing (CKM = 1)

NOTE: Reset, $\overline{NPWR}$, $\overline{NPRD}$ are inputs asynchronous to CLK. Timing requirements above are given for testing purposes only, to assure recognition at a specific CLK edge.

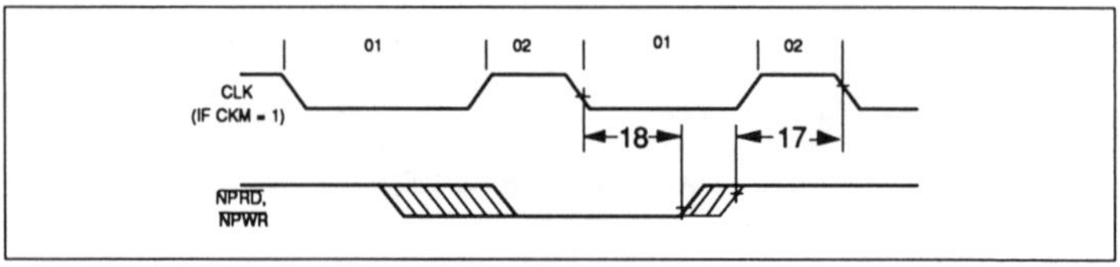

CLK, $\overline{NPRD}$, $\overline{NPWR}$ Timing (CKM = 1)

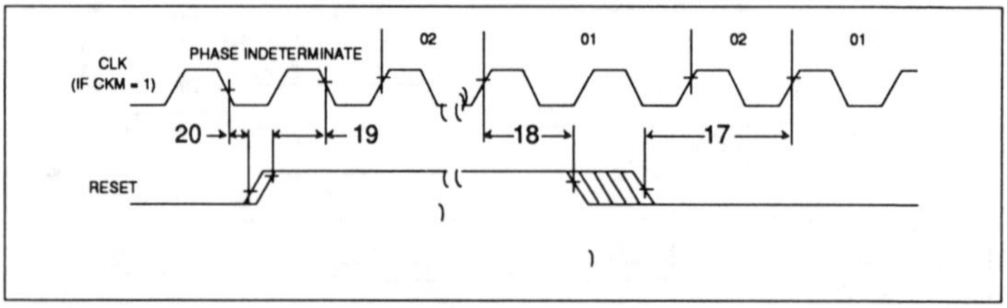

CLK, RESET Timing (CKM = 0)

NOTE: Reset must meet timing shown to guarantee known phase of internal ÷ 3 circuit.

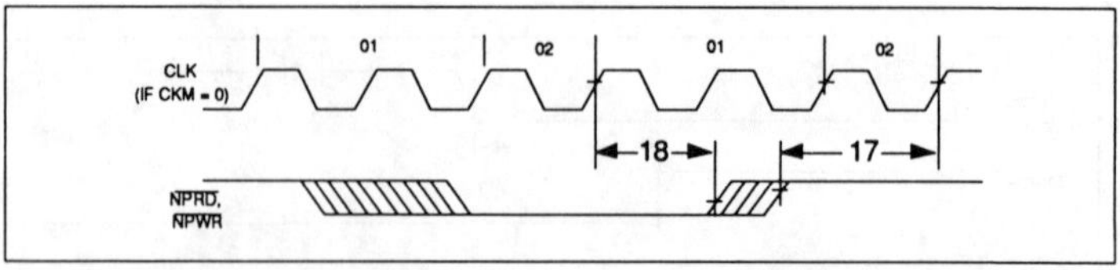

CLK, $\overline{NPRD}$, $\overline{NPWR}$ Timing (CKM = 0)

OVERVIEW

The IIT-2C87 is a high performance numerics processor extension that is plug and object-code compatible with the 80287. The IIT-2C87 is a low power CMOS device capable of operating at clock rates up to 20 MHz. The IIT-2C87 performs most of its functions in far fewer clock cycles than is required by the 80287. When combined with the faster clock frequency (the IIT-2C87 can operate on the same clock as the 80286), the floating point processor achieves performance at least two times faster than the 80287. When used with an 80286 processor the computing system fully conforms to the IEEE Floating Point Standard. The IIT-2C87 is packaged in a 40-pin ceramic package.

- ☐ Object code and plug compatible with the 80287 and 80C287A
- ☐ Low power CMOS device, ideal for lap-top applications
- ☐ High performance 80-bit internal architecture
- ☐ Implements ANSI/IEEE standard 754-1985 for binary floating point arithmetic
- ☐ Up to 200% faster than the 80287
- ☐ Upward object code compatible from 8087
- ☐ Expands 80286 data types to include 32-, 64-, 80 bit floating point, 32-, 64-, bit integers and 18-digit BCD operands
- ☐ Available in 40-pin dual in-line package
- ☐ Directly extends 80286 instructions set to include trigonometric, logarithmic, exponential and arithmetic instructions
- ☐ Full range transcendental operations for sine, cosine, tangent, arctangent and logarithm
- ☐ Built-in exception handling
- ☐ Operates in both real and protected mode of the 80286
- ☐ Thirty-two 80-bit numeric registers, 24 usable as 3 banks of 8 register stacks
- ☐ Built-in instruction to calculate 4x4 matrix transformation
- ☐ Operates at clock rates up to 20 MHz (can use 80286 clock)

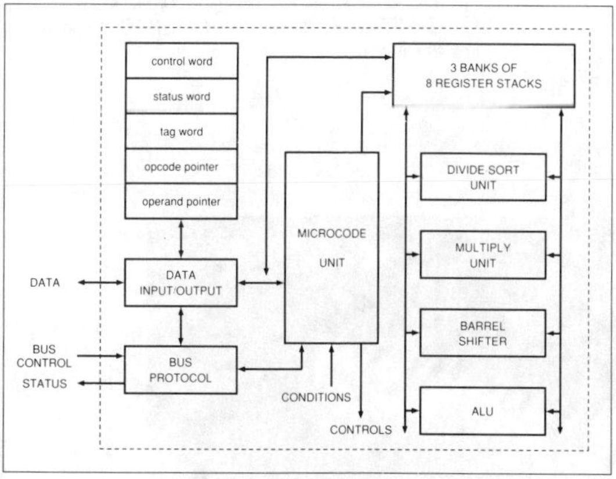

Figure 1. IIT-2C87 Block Diagram

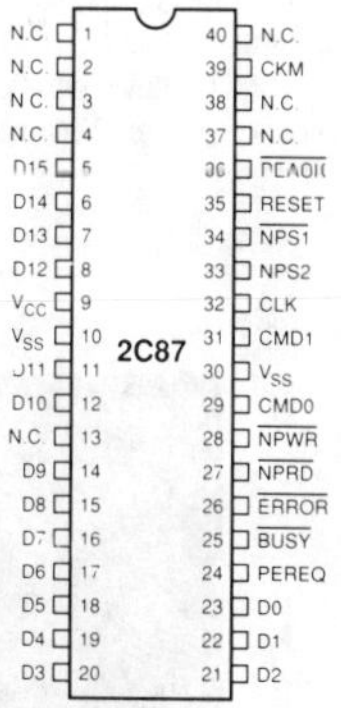

Figure 2. 2C87 Pin Configuration

ENHANCED PERFORMANCE

In addition to operating at clock speeds up to 20 MHz, the IIT-2C87 requires far fewer clock cycles than the 80287 in Instruction execution. Table 1 compares the range of clock cycles required to perform typical floating point instructions.

	CLOCK CYCLES REQUIRED	
INSTRUCTION	IIT-2C87	80287
ADD	15-17	70-100
MPY	19	90-145
DIV	48	193-203
SQRT	49	180-186
COMPARE	17	40-50
REM	58	15-190
TAN	196	30-540
LOG	235	900-1100

FUNCTIONALITY

The IIT-2C87 is object code and plug compatible with the 80287. The IIT-2C87 includes all of the instructions of the 80287. In addition the IIT-2C87 provides all the 80387 instructions and enhancements (SIN, COS, IEEE COMPARE, IEEE REMAINDER, larger range for transcendental functions).

The IIT-2C87 provides extra functions which are not available on the 80287.

There are thirty-two 80-bit floating point registers, 24 of which are usable as 3 banks of register stacks.

The IIT-2C87 includes a built-in instruction to calculate a 4x4 matrix transformation. This results in the capability to perform matrix transformations 6 to 8 times faster than the 80287.

FEATURES:

CMOS IMPLEMENTATION

The IIT-2C87 numeric co-processor is implemented in advanced 1.2 micron CMOS technology. The device dissipation is typical at 0.5 Watt. The advantages of low power 1.2 micron CMOS implementation include higher reliability and enhanced system performance. The IIT-2C87 is capable of operating at clock frequencies up to 20 MHz. The device may be operated using the 80286 clock.

The IIT-2C87 is ideally suited for LAP-TOP computer implementation.

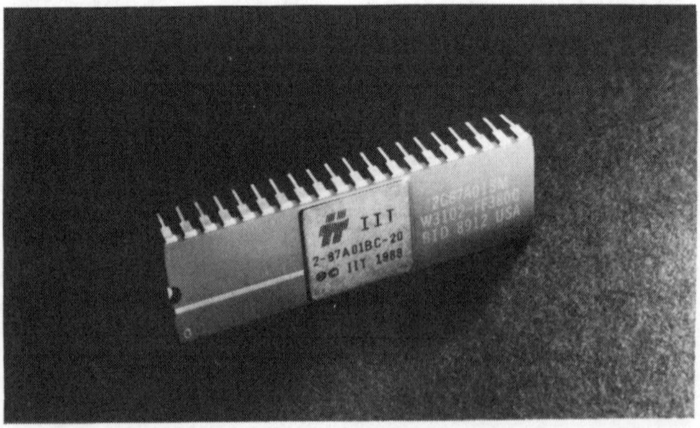

- **High Performance 80-Bit Internal Architecture**
- **Implements ANSI/IEEE Standard 754-1985 for Binary Floating-Point Arithmetic**
- **Six to Eleven Times 8087/80287 Performance**
- **Expands 386DX™ CPU Data Types to Include 32-, 64-, 80-Bit Floating Point, 32-, 64-Bit Integers and 18-Digit BCD Operands**
- **Directly Extends 386DX™ CPU Instruction Set to Include Trigonometric, Logarithmic, Exponential and Arithmetic Instructions for All Data Types**
- **Upward Object-Code Compatible from 8087 and 80287**
- **Full-Range Transcendental Operations for SINE, COSINE, TANGENT, ARCTANGENT and LOGARITHM**
- **Built-In Exception Handling**
- **Operates Independently of Real, Protected and Virtual-8086 Modes of the 386DX™ Microprocessor**
- **Eight 80-Bit Numeric Registers, Usable as Individually Addressable General Registers or as a Register Stack**
- **Available in 68-Pin PGA Package**
  (See Packaging Spec: Order #231369)

The Intel 387DX™ Math Coprocessor is a high-performance numerics coprocessor extension that extends the Intel386™ Architecture with floating point, extended integer and BCD data types. The 386DX™ Microprocessor and the 387DX Math Coprocessor computing system fully conforms to the ANSI/IEEE floating-point standard. Using a numerics oriented architecture, the 387DX NPX adds over seventy mnemonics to the 386DX Microprocessor instruction set, making the 386DX Microprocessor and the 387DX Math Coprocessor a complete solution for high-performance numerics processing. The 387DX NPX is implemented with 1 micron, high-speed CHMOS IV technology and packaged in a 68-pin ceramic pin grid array (PGA) package. The 386DX Microprocessor and the 387DX Math Coprocessor are upward object-code compatible from the 386DX Microprocessor and the 80287 Coprocessor, 80286/80287 and 8086/8087 computing systems.

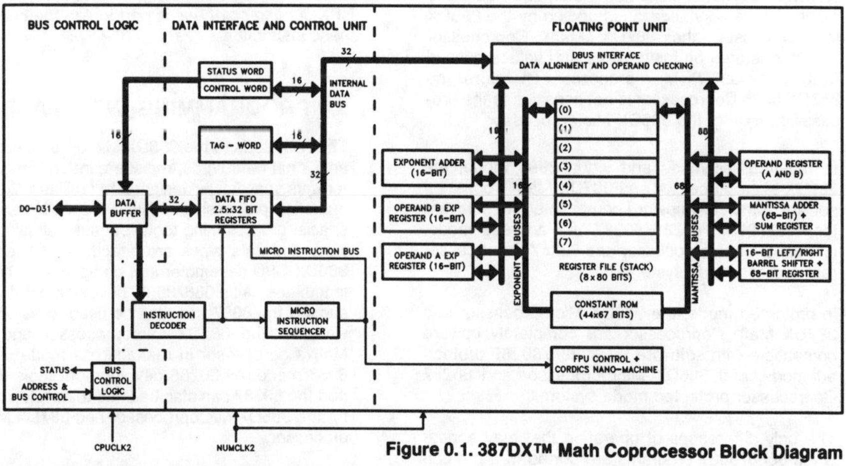

Figure 0.1. 387DX™ Math Coprocessor Block Diagram

1.0 FUNCTIONAL DESCRIPTION

The 387DX™ Numeric Coprocessor Extension (NPX) provides arithmetic instructions for a variety of numeric data types in 386DX™ Microprocessor and 387DX Math Coprocessor systems. It also executes numerous built-in transcendental functions (e.g. tangent, sine, cosine, and log functions). The 387DX Math Coprocessor effectively extends the register and instruction set of a 386DX Microprocessor system for existing data types and adds several new data types as well. Figure 1.1 shows the model of registers visible to 386DX Microprocessor and 387DX Math Coprocessor programs. Essentially, the 387DX Math Coprocessor can be treated as an additional resource or an extension to the 386DX Microprocessor. The 386DX Microprocessor together with a 387DX Math Coprocessor can be used as a single unified system, the 386DX Microprocessor and 387DX Math Coprocessor.

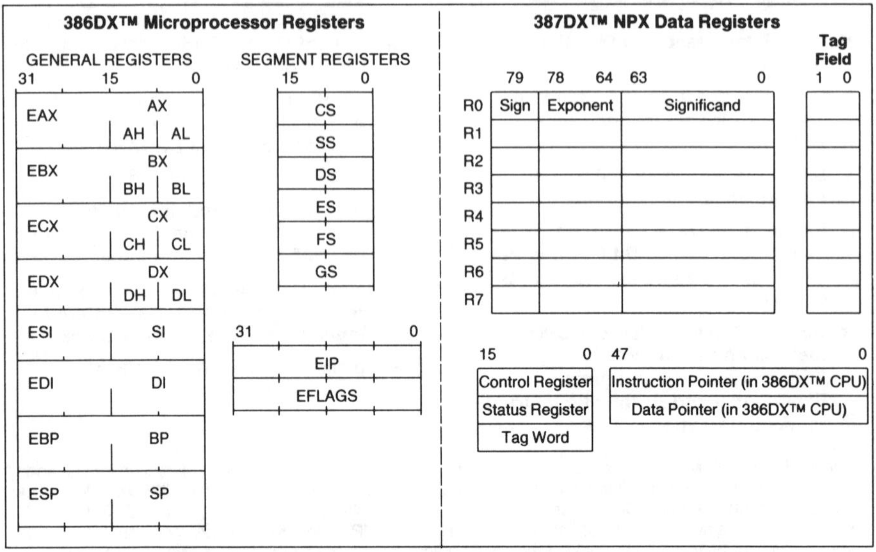

Figure 1.1. 386DX™ Microprocessor and 387DX™ Math Coprocessor Register Set

The 387DX Math Coprocessor works the same whether the 386DX Microprocessor is executing in real-address mode, protected mode, or virtual-8086 mode. All memory access is handled by the 386DX Microprocessor; the 387DX Math Coprocessor merely operates on instructions and values passed to it by the 386DX Microprocessor. Therefore, the 387DX Math Coprocessor is not sensitive to the processing mode of the 386DX Microprocessor.

In real-address mode and virtual-8086 mode, the 386DX Microprocessor and 387DX Math Coprocessor are completely upward compatible with software for 8086/8087, 80286/80287 real-address mode, and 386DX Microprocessor and 80287 Coprocessor real-address mode systems.

In protected mode, the 386DX Microprocessor and 387DX Math Coprocessor are completely upward compatible with software for 80286/80287 protected mode, and 386DX Microprocessor and 80287 Coprocessor protected mode systems.

The only differences of operation that may appear when 8086/8087 programs are ported to a protected-mode 386DX Microprocessor and 387DX Math Coprocessor system (*not* using virtual-8086 mode), is in the format of operands for the administrative instructions FLDENV, FSTENV, FRSTOR and FSAVE. These instructions are normally used only by exception handlers and operating systems, not by applications programs.

The 387DX Math Coprocessor contains three functional units that can operate in parallel to increase system performance. The 386DX Microprocessor can be transferring commands and data to the NPX *bus control logic* for the next instruction while the NPX *floating-point unit* is performing the current numeric instruction.

2.0 PROGRAMMING INTERFACE

The NPX adds to the 386DX Microprocessor system additional data types, registers, instructions, and interrupts specifically designed to facilitate high-speed numerics processing. To use the NPX requires no special programming tools, because all new instructions and data types are directly supported by the 386DX CPU assembler and compilers for high-level languages. All 8086/8088 development tools that support the 8087 can also be used to develop software for the 386DX Microprocessor and 387DX Math Coprocessor in real-address mode or virtual-8086 mode. All 80286 development tools that support the 80287 can also be used to develop software for the 386DX Microprocessor and 387DX Math Coprocessor.

All communication between the 386DX Microprocessor and the NPX is transparent to applications software. The CPU automatically controls the NPX whenever a numerics instruction is executed. All physical memory and virtual memory of the CPU are available for storage of the instructions and operands of programs that use the NPX. All memory addressing modes, including use of displacement, base register, index register, and scaling, are available for addressing numerics operands.

Section 6 at the end of this data sheet lists by class the instructions that the NPX adds to the instruction set of the 386DX Microprocessor system.

2.1 Data Types

Table 2.1 lists the seven data types that the 387DX NPX supports and presents the format for each type. Operands are stored in memory with the least significant digit at the lowest memory address. Programs retrieve these values by generating the lowest address. For maximum system performance, all operands should start at physical-memory addresses evenly divisible by four (doubleword boundaries); operands may begin at any other addresses, but will require extra memory cycles to access the entire operand.

Internally, the 387DX NPX holds all numbers in the extended-precision real format. Instructions that load operands from memory automatically convert operands represented in memory as 16-, 32-, or 64-bit integers, 32- or 64-bit floating-point numbers, or 18-digit packed BCD numbers into extended-precision real format. Instructions that store operands in memory perform the inverse type conversion.

2.2 Numeric Operands

A typical NPX instruction accepts one or two operands and produces a single result. In two-operand instructions, one operand is the contents of an NPX register, while the other may be a memory location. The operands of some instructions are predefined; for example FSQRT always takes the square root of the number in the top stack element.

Table 2.1. 387DX™ NPX Data Type Representation in Memory

Data Formats	Range	Precision	Most Significant Byte = Highest Addressed Byte (7 0 | 7 0 | 7 0 | 7 0 | 7 0 | 7 0 | 7 0 | 7 0 | 7 0 | 7 0)
Word Integer	$\pm 10^4$	16 Bits	(TWO'S COMPLEMENT) 15 … 0
Short Integer	$\pm 10^9$	32 Bits	(TWO'S COMPLEMENT) 31 … 0
Long Integer	$\pm 10^{18}$	64 Bits	(TWO'S COMPLEMENT) 63 … 0
Packed BCD	$\pm 10^{\pm 18}$	18 Digits	S | X | MAGNITUDE d_{17} d_{16} d_{15} d_{14} d_{13} d_{12} d_{11} d_{10} d_9 d_8 d_7 d_6 d_5 d_4 d_3 d_2 d_1 d_0; 79, 72 … 0
Single Precision	$\pm 10^{\pm 38}$	24 Bits	S | BIASED EXPONENT | SIGNIFICAND; 31, 23 (I▲) … 0
Double Precision	$\pm 10^{\pm 308}$	53 Bits	S | BIASED EXPONENT | SIGNIFICAND; 63, 52 (I▲) … 0
Extended Precision	$\pm 10^{\pm 4932}$	64 Bits	S | BIASED EXPONENT | I | SIGNIFICAND; 79, 64 63▲ … 0

NOTES:
(1) S = Sign bit (0 = positive, 1 = negative)
(2) d_n = Decimal digit (two per byte)
(3) X = Bits have no significance; 387DX™ NPX ignores when loading, zeros when storing
(4) ▲ = Position of implicit binary point
(5) I = Integer bit of significand; stored in temporary real, implicit in single and double precision
(6) Exponent Bias (normalized values):
Single: 127 (7FH)
Double: 1023 (3FFH)
Extended Real: 16383 (3FFFH)
(7) Packed BCD: $(-1)^S (D_{17} \ldots D_0)$
(8) Real: $(-1)^S (2^{E-BIAS}) (F_0\ F_1 \ldots)$

15							0
TAG (7)	TAG (6)	TAG (5)	TAG (4)	TAG (3)	TAG (2)	TAG (1)	TAG (0)

NOTE:
The index i of tag(i) is **not** top-relative. A program typically uses the "top" field of Status Word to determine which tag(i) field refers to logical top of stack.
TAG VALUES:
00 = Valid
01 = Zero
10 = QNaN, SNaN, Infinity, Denormal and Unsupported Formats
11 = Empty

Figure 2.1. 387DX™ NPX Tag Word

2.3 Register Set

Figure 1.1 shows the 387DX NPX register set. When an NPX is present in a system, programmers may use these registers in addition to the registers normally available on the 386DX CPU.

2.3.1 DATA REGISTERS

387DX NPX computations use the NPX's data registers. These eight 80-bit registers provide the equivalent capacity of twenty 32-bit registers. Each of the eight data registers in the NPX is 80 bits wide and is divided into "fields" corresponding to the NPXs extended-precision real data type.

The 387DX NPX register set can be accessed either as a stack, with instructions operating on the top one or two stack elements, or as a fixed register set, with instructions operating on explicitly designated registers. The TOP field in the status word identifies the current top-of-stack register. A "push" operation decrements TOP by one and loads a value into the new top register. A "pop" operation stores the value from the current top register and then increments TOP by one. Like the 386DX Microprocessor stacks in memory, the NPX register stack grows "down" toward lower-addressed registers.

Instructions may address the data registers either implicitly or explicitly. Many instructions operate on the register at the TOP of the stack. These instructions implicitly address the register at which TOP points. Other instructions allow the programmer to explicitly specify which register to user. This explicit register addressing is also relative to TOP.

2.3.2 TAG WORD

The tag word marks the content of each numeric data register, as Figure 2.1 shows. Each two-bit tag represents one of the eight numerics registers. The principal function of the tag word is to optimize the NPXs performance and stack handling by making it possible to distinguish between empty and nonempty register locations. It also enables exception handlers to check the contents of a stack location without the need to perform complex decoding of the actual data.

2.3.3 STATUS WORD

The 16-bit status word (in the status register) shown in Figure 2.2 reflects the overall state of the NPX. It may be read and inspected by CPU code.

Bit 15, the B-bit (busy bit) is included for 8087 compatibility only. It reflects the contents of the ES bit (bit 7 of the status word), not the status of the BUSY# output of the 387DX NPX.

Bits 13–11 (TOP) point to the 387DX NPX register that is the current top-of-stack.

The four numeric condition code bits (C_3–C_0) are similar to the flags in a CPU; instructions that perform arithmetic operations update these bits to reflect the outcome. The effects of these instructions on the condition code are summarized in Tables 2.2 through 2.5.

Bit 7 is the error summary (ES) status bit. This bit is set if any unmasked exception bit is set; it is clear otherwise. If this bit is set, the ERROR# signal is asserted.

Bit 6 is the stack flag (SF). This bit is used to distinguish invalid operations due to stack overflow or underflow from other kinds of invalid operations. When SF is set, bit 9 (C_1) distinguishes between stack overflow ($C_1 = 1$) and underflow ($C_1 = 0$).

Figure 2.2 shows the six exception flags in bits 5–0 of the status word. Bits 5–0 are set to indicate that the NPX has detected an exception while executing an instruction. A later section entitled "Exception Handling" explains how they are set and used.

Note that when a new value is loaded into the status word by the FLDENV or FRSTOR instruction, the value of ES (bit 7) and its reflection in the B-bit (bit 15) are not derived from the values loaded from memory but rather are dependent upon the values of the exception flags (bits 5–0) in the status word and their corresponding masks in the control word. If ES is set in such a case, the ERROR# output of the NPX is activated immediately.

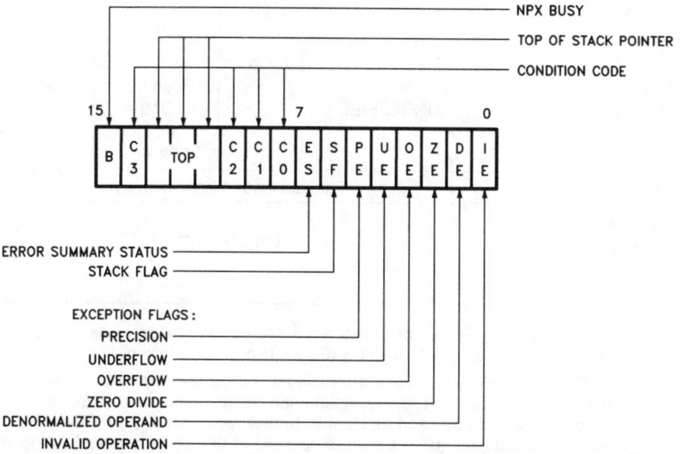

ES is set if any unmasked exception bit is set; cleared otherwise.
See Table 2.2 for interpretation of condition code.
TOP values:
000 = Register 0 is Top of Stack
001 = Register 1 is Top of Stack
•
•
•
111 = Register 7 is Top of Stack
For definitions of exceptions, refer to the section entitled "Exception Handling"

Figure 2.2. NPX Status Word

Table 2.2. Condition Code Interpretation

Instruction	C0 (S)	C3 (Z)	C1 (A)	C2 (C)
FPREM, FPREM1 (see Table 2.3)	Three least significant bits of quotient Q2	Q0	Q1 or O/U#	Reduction 0 = complete 1 = incomplete
FCOM, FCOMP, FCOMPP, FTST, FUCOM, FUCOMP, FUCOMPP, FICOM, FICOMP	Result of comparison (see Table 2.4)		Zero or O/U#	Operand is not comparable (Table 2.4)
FXAM	Operand class (see Table 2.5)		Sign or O/U#	Operand class (Table 2.5)
FCHS, FABS, FXCH, FINCSTP, FDECSTP, Constant loads, FXTRACT, FLD, FILD, FBLD, FSTP (ext real)	UNDEFINED		Zero or O/U#	UNDEFINED

FIST, FBSTP, FRNDINT, FST, FSTP, FADD, FMUL, FDIV, FDIVR, FSUB, FSUBR, FSCALE, FSQRT, FPATAN, F2XM1, FYL2X, FYL2XP1	UNDEFINED	Roundup or O/U#	UNDEFINED
FPTAN, FSIN FCOS, FSINCOS	UNDEFINED	Roundup or O/U#, undefined if C2 = 1	Reduction 0 = complete 1 = incomplete
FLDENV, FRSTOR	Each bit loaded from memory		
FLDCW, FSTENV, FSTCW, FSTSW, FCLEX, FINIT, FSAVE	UNDEFINED		

O/U#	When both IE and SF bits of status word are set, indicating a stack exception, this bit distinguishes between stack overflow (C1 = 1) and underflow (C1 = 0).
Reduction	If FPREM or FPREM1 produces a remainder that is less than the modulus, reduction is complete. When reduction is incomplete the value at the top of the stack is a partial remainder, which can be used as input to further reduction. For FPTAN, FSIN, FCOS, and FSINCOS, the reduction bit is set if the operand at the top of the stack is too large. In this case the original operand remains at the top of the stack.
Roundup	When the PE bit of the status word is set, this bit indicates whether the last rounding in the instruction was upward.
UNDEFINED	Do not rely on finding any specific value in these bits.

Table 2.3. Condition Code Interpretation after FPREM and FPREM1 Instructions

Condition Code					Interpretation after FPREM and FPREM1
C2	C3	C1	C0		
1	X	X	X		Incomplete Reduction: further interation required for complete reduction
	Q1	Q0	Q2	Q MOD8	
0	0	0	0	0	Complete Reduction: C0, C3, C1 contain three least significant bits of quotient
0	0	1	0	1	
0	1	0	0	2	
0	1	1	0	3	
0	0	0	1	4	
0	0	1	1	5	
0	1	0	1	6	
0	1	1	1	7	

Table 2.4. Condition Code Resulting from Comparison

Order	C3	C2	C0
TOP > Operand	0	0	0
TOP < Operand	0	0	1
TOP = Operand	1	0	0
Unordered	1	1	1

Table 2.5. Condition Code Defining Operand Class

C3	C2	C1	C0	Value at TOP
0	0	0	0	+ Unsupported
0	0	0	1	+ NaN
0	0	1	0	− Unsupported
0	0	1	1	− NaN
0	1	0	0	+ Normal
0	1	0	1	+ Infinity
0	1	1	0	− Normal
0	1	1	1	− Infinity
1	0	0	0	+ 0
1	0	0	1	+ Empty
1	0	1	0	− 0
1	0	1	1	− Empty
1	1	0	0	+ Denormal
1	1	1	0	− Denormal

2.3.4 INSTRUCTION AND DATA POINTERS

Because the NPX operates in parallel with the CPU, any errors detected by the NPX may be reported after the CPU has executed the ESC instruction which caused it. To allow identification of the failing numeric instruction, the 386DX Microprocessor and 387DX Math Coprocessor contains two pointer registers that supply the address of the failing numeric instruction and the address of its numeric memory operand (if appropriate).

The instruction and data pointers are provided for user-written error handlers. These registers are actually located in the 386DX CPU, but appear to be located in the NPX because they are accessed by the ESC instructions FLDENV, FSTENV, FSAVE, and FRSTOR. (In the 8086/8087 and 80286/80287, these registers are located in the NPX.) Whenever the 386DX CPU decodes a new ESC instruction, it saves the address of the instruction (including any prefixes that may be present), the address of the operand (if present), and the opcode.

The instruction and data pointers appear in one of four formats depending on the operating mode of the 386DX Microprocessor (protected mode or real-address mode) and depending on the operand-size attribute in effect (32-bit operand or 16-bit operand). When the 386DX Microprocessor is in virtual-8086 mode, the real-address mode formats are used. (See Figures 2.3 through 2.6.) The ESC instructions FLDENV, FSTENV, FSAVE, and FRSTOR are used to transfer these values between the 386DX Microprocessor registers and memory. Note that the value of the data pointer is *undefined* if the prior ESC instruction did not have a memory operand.

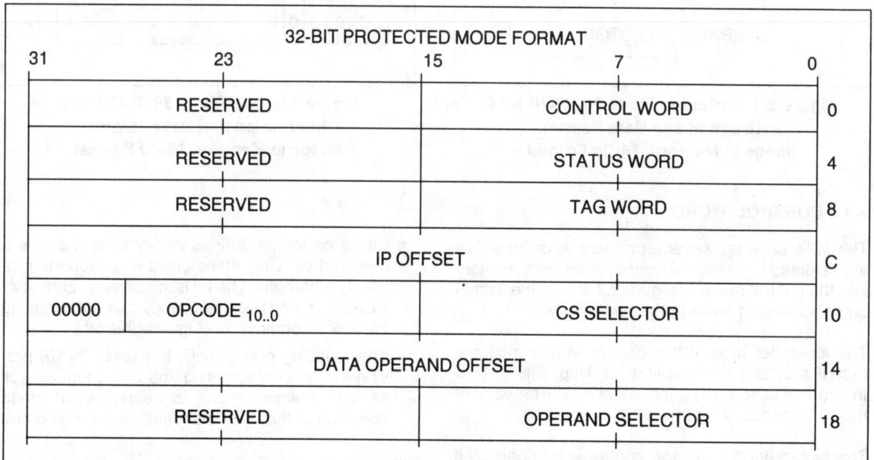

Figure 2.3. Protected Mode 387DX™ NPX Instruction and Data Pointer Image in Memory, 32-Bit Format

32-BIT REAL-ADDRESS MODE FORMAT

31	23	15	7 … 0	
RESERVED		CONTROL WORD		0
RESERVED		STATUS WORD		4
RESERVED		TAG WORD		8
RESERVED		INSTRUCTION POINTER 15..0		C
0000	INSTRUCTION POINTER 31..16	0	OPCODE 10..0	10
RESERVED		OPERAND POINTER 15..0		14
0000	OPERAND POINTER 31..16	0000	00000000	18

Figure 2.4. Real Mode 387DX™ NPX Instruction and Data Pointer Image in Memory, 32-Bit Format

16-BIT PROTECTED MODE FORMAT

15 … 7 … 0	
CONTROL WORD	0
STATUS WORD	2
TAG WORD	4
IP OFFSET	6
CS SELECTOR	8
OPERAND OFFSET	A
OPERAND SELECTOR	C

Figure 2.5. Protected Mode 387DX™ NPX Instruction and Data Pointer Image in Memory, 16-Bit Format

16-BIT REAL-ADDRESS MODE AND VIRTUAL-8086 MODE FORMAT

15		7 … 0	
CONTROL WORD			0
STATUS WORD			2
TAG WORD			4
INSTRUCTION POINTER 15..0			6
IP19.16	0	OPCODE 10..0	8
OPERAND POINTER 15..0			A
DP 19.16	0	0 0 0 0 0 0 0 0 0 0 0	C

Figure 2.6. Real Mode 387DX™ NPX Instruction and Data Pointer Image in Memory, 16-Bit Format

2.3.5 CONTROL WORD

The NPX provides several processing options that are selected by loading a control word from memory into the control register. Figure 2.7 shows the format and encoding of fields in the control word.

The low-order byte of this control word configures the NPX error and exception masking. Bits 5–0 of the control word contain individual masks for each of the six exceptions that the NPX recognizes.

The high-order byte of the control word configures the NPX operating mode, including precision and rounding.

- Bit 12 no longer defines infinity control and is a reserved bit. Only affine closure is supported for infinity arithmetic. The bit is initialized to zero after RESET or FINIT and is changeable upon loading the CW. Programs must ignore this bit.
- The rounding control (RC) bits (bits 11–10) provide for directed rounding and true chop, as well as the unbiased round to nearest even mode specified in the IEEE standard. Rounding control

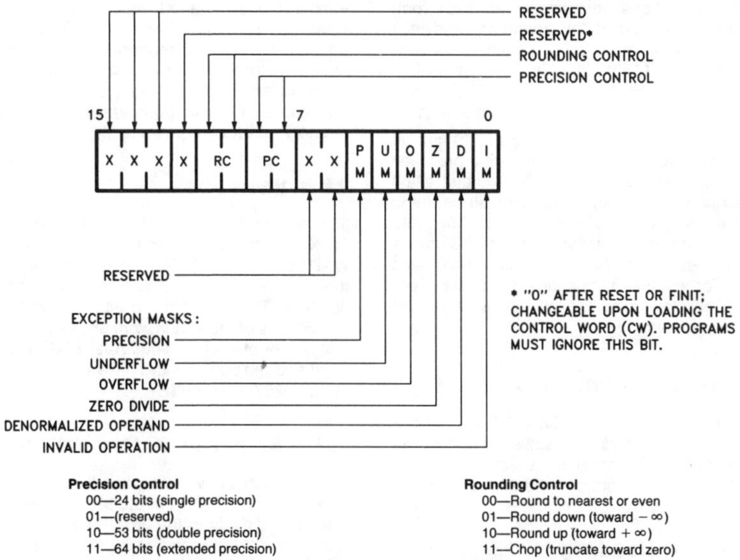

Figure 2.7. 387DX™ NPX Control Word

Table 2.6. 386DX™ Microprocessor Interrupt Vectors Reserved for NPX

Interrupt Number	Cause of Interrupt
7	An ESC instruction was encountered when EM or TS of the 386DX™ CPU control register zero (CR0) was set. EM = 1 indicates that software emulation of the instruction is required. When TS is set, either an ESC or WAIT instruction causes interrupt 7. This indicates that the current NPX context may not belong to the current task.
9	An operand of a coprocessor instruction wrapped around an addressing limit (0FFFFH for small segments, 0FFFFFFFFH for big segments, zero for expand-down segments) and spanned inaccessible addresses[a]. The failing numerics instruction is not restartable. The address of the failing numerics instruction and data operand may be lost; an FSTENV does not return reliable addresses. As with the 80286/80287, the segment overrun exception should be handled by executing an FNINIT instruction (i.e. an FINIT without a preceding WAIT). The return address on the stack does not necessarily point to the failing instruction nor to the following instruction. The interrupt can be avoided by never allowing numeric data to start within 108 bytes of the end of a segment.
13	The first word or doubleword of a numeric operand is not entirely within the limit of its segment. The return address pushed onto the stack of the exception handler points at the ESC instruction that caused the exception, including any prefixes. The 387DX™ NPX has not executed this instruction; the instruction pointer and data pointer register refer to a previous, correctly executed instruction.
16	The previous numerics instruction caused an unmasked exception. The address of the faulty instruction and the address of its operand are stored in the instruction pointer and data pointer registers. Only ESC and WAIT instructions can cause this interrupt. The 386DX™ CPU return address pushed onto the stack of the exception handler points to a WAIT or ESC instruction (including prefixes). This instruction can be restarted after clearing the exception condition in the NPX. FNINIT, FNCLEX, FNSTSW, FNSTENV, and FNSAVE cannot cause this interrupt.

a. An operand may wrap around an addressing limit when the segment limit is near an addressing limit and the operand is near the largest valid address in the segment. Because of the wrap-around, the beginning and ending addresses of such an operand will be at opposite ends of the segment. There are two ways that such an operand may also span inaccessible addresses: 1) if the segment limit is not equal to the addressing limit (e.g. addressing limit is FFFFH and segment limit is FFFDH) the operand will span addresses that are not within the segment (e.g. an 8-byte operand that starts at valid offset FFFC will span addresses FFFC-FFFF and 0000-0003; however addresses FFFE and FFFF are not valid, because they exceed the limit); 2) if the operand begins and ends in present and accessible pages but intermediate bytes of the operand fall in a not-present page or a page to which the procedure does not have access rights.

affects only those instructions that perform rounding at the end of the operation (and thus can generate a precision exception); namely, FST, FSTP, FIST, all arithmetic instructions (except FPREM, FPREM1, FXTRACT, FABS, and FCHS), and all transcendental instructions.

- The precision control (PC) bits (bits 9–8) can be used to set the NPX internal operating precision of the significand at less than the default of 64 bits (extended precision). This can be useful in providing compatibility with early generation arithmetic processors of smaller precision. PC affects only the instructions ADD, SUB, DIV, MUL, and SQRT. For all other instructions, either the precision is determined by the opcode or extended precision is used.

2.4 Interrupt Description

Several interrupts of the 386DX CPU are used to report exceptional conditions while executing numeric programs in either real or protected mode. Table 2.6 shows these interrupts and their causes.

2.5 Exception Handling

The 387DX NPX detects six different exception conditions that can occur during instruction execution. Table 2.7 lists the exception conditions in order of precedence, showing for each the cause and the default action taken by the NPX if the exception is masked by its corresponding mask bit in the control word.

Any exception that is not masked by the control word sets the corresponding exception flag of the status word, sets the ES bit of the status word, and asserts the ERROR# signal. When the CPU attempts to execute another ESC instruction or WAIT, exception 7 occurs. The exception condition must be resolved via an interrupt service routine. The 386DX Microprocessor and 387DX Math Coprocessor save the address of the floating-point instruction that caused the exception and the address of any memory operand required by that instruction.

2.6 Initialization

387DX NPX initialization software must execute an FNINIT instruction (i.e. an FINIT without a preceding WAIT) to clear ERROR#. After a hardware RESET, the ERROR# output is asserted to indicate that a 387DX NPX is present. To accomplish this, the IE and ES bits of the status word are set, and the IM bit in the control word is reset. After FNINIT, the status word and the control word have the same values as in an 80287 after RESET.

2.7 8087 and 80287 Compatibility

This section summarizes the differences between the 387DX NPX and the 80287. Any migration from the 8087 directly to the 387DX NPX must also take into account the differences between the 8087 and the 80287 as listed in Appendix A.

Many changes have been designed into the 387DX NPX to directly support the IEEE standard in hardware. These changes result in increased performance by eliminating the need for software that supports the standard.

2.7.1 GENERAL DIFFERENCES

The 387DX NPX supports only affine closure for infinity arithmetic, not projective closure. Bit 12 of the

Table 2.7. Exceptions

Exception	Cause	Default Action (if exception is masked)
Invalid Operation	Operation on a signaling NaN, unsupported format, indeterminate form ($0 * \infty$, 0/0, $(+\infty) + (-\infty)$, etc.), or stack overflow/underflow (SF is also set).	Result is a quiet NaN, integer indefinite, or BCD indefinite
Denormalized Operand	At least one of the operands is denormalized, i.e. it has the smallest exponent but a nonzero significand.	Normal processing continues
Zero Divisor	The divisor is zero while the dividend is a noninfinite, nonzero number.	Result is ∞
Overflow	The result is too large in magnitude to fit in the specified format.	Result is largest finite value or ∞
Underflow	The true result is nonzero but too small to be represented in the specified format, and, if underflow exception is masked, denormalization causes loss of accuracy.	Result is denormalized or zero
Inexact Result (Precision)	The true result is not exactly representable in the specified format (e.g. 1/3); the result is rounded according to the rounding mode.	Normal processing continues

Control Word (CW) no longer defines infinity control. It is a reserved bit; but it is initialized to zero after RESET or FINIT and is changeable upon loading the CW. Programs must ignore this bit.

Operands for FSCALE and FPATAN are no longer restricted in range (except for $\pm\infty$); F2XM1 and FPTAN accept a wider range of operands.

The results of transcendental operations may be slightly different from those computed by 80287.

In the case of FPTAN, the 387DX NPX supplies a true tangent result in ST(1), and (always) a floating point 1 in ST.

Rounding control is in effect for FLD *constant*.

Software cannot change entries of the tag word to values (other than empty) that do not reflect the actual register contents.

After reset, FINIT, and incomplete FPREM, the 387DX NPX resets to zero the condition code bits C_3–C_0 of the status word.

In conformance with the IEEE standard, the 387DX NPX does not support the special data formats: pseudozero, pseudo-NaN, pseudoinfinity, and unnormal.

2.7.2 EXCEPTIONS

A number of differences exist due to changes in the IEEE standard and to functional improvements to the architecture of the 387DX NPX:

1. When the overflow or underflow exception is masked, the 387DX NPX differs from the 80287 in rounding when overflow or underflow occurs. The 387DX NPX produces results that are consistent with the rounding mode.
2. When the underflow exception is masked, the 387DX NPX sets its underflow flag only if there is also a loss of accuracy during denormalization.
3. Fewer invalid-operation exceptions due to denormal operands, because the instructions FSQRT, FDIV, FPREM, and conversions to BCD or to integer normalize denormal operands before proceeding.
4. The FSQRT, FBSTP, and FPREM instructions may cause underflow, because they support denormal operands.
5. The denormal exception can occur during the transcendental instructions and the FXTRACT instruction.
6. The denormal exception no longer takes precedence over all other exceptions.
7. When the denormal exception is masked, the 387DX NPX automatically normalizes denormal operands. The 8087/80287 performs unnormal arithmetic, which might produce an unnormal result.
8. When the operand is zero, the FXTRACT instruction reports a zero-divide exception and leaves $-\infty$ in ST(1).
9. The status word has a new bit (SF) that signals when invalid-operation exceptions are due to stack underflow or overflow.
10. FLD *extended precision* no longer reports denormal exceptions, because the instruction is not numeric.
11. FLD *single/double precision* when the operand is denormal converts the number to extended precision and signals the denormalized operand exception. When loading a signaling NaN, FLD *single/double precision* signals an invalid-operand exception.
12. The 387DX NPX only generates quiet NaNs (as on the 80287); however, the 387DX NPX distinguishes between quiet NaNs and signaling NaNs. Signaling NaNs trigger exceptions when they are used as operands; quiet NaNs do not (except for FCOM, FIST, and FBSTP which also raise IE for quiet NaNs).
13. When stack overflow occurs during FPTAN and overflow is masked, both ST(0) and ST(1) contain quiet NaNs. The 80287/8087 leaves the original operand in ST(1) intact.
14. When the scaling factor is $\pm\infty$, the FSCALE (ST(0), ST(1)) instruction behaves as follows (ST(0) and ST(1) contain the scaled and scaling operands respectively):
    - FSCALE($0, \infty$) generates the invalid operation exception.
    - FSCALE(finite, $-\infty$) generates zero with the same sign as the scaled operand.
    - FSCALE(finite, $+\infty$) generates ∞ with the same sign as the scaled operand.

    The 8087/80287 returns zero in the first case and raises the invalid-operation exception in the other cases.
15. The 387DX NPX returns signed infinity/zero as the unmasked response to massive overflow/underflow. The 8087 and 80287 support a limited range for the scaling factor; within this range either massive overflow/underflow do not occur or undefined results are produced.

3.0 HARDWARE INTERFACE

In the following description of hardware interface, the # symbol at the end of a signal name indicates that the active or asserted state occurs when the signal is at a low voltage. When no # is present after the signal name, the signal is asserted when at the high voltage level.

3.1 Signal Description

In the following signal descriptions, the 387DX Math Coprocessor pins are grouped by function as follows:

1. Execution control—CPUCLK2, NUMCLK2, CKM,

Table 3.1. 387DX™ NPX Pin Summary

Pin Name	Function	Active State	Input/ Output	Referenced To
CPUCLK2	386DX™ CPU CLocK 2		I	
NUMCLK2	387DX™ NPX CLocK 2		I	
CKM	387DX™ NPX CLocKing Mode		I	
RESETIN	System reset	High	I	CPUCLK2
PEREQ	Processor Extension REQuest	High	O	CPUCLK2/STEN
BUSY#	Busy status	Low	O	CPUCLK2/STEN
ERROR#	Error status	Low	O	NUMCLK2/STEN
D31–D0	Data pins	High	I/O	CPUCLK2
W/R#	Write/Read bus cycle	Hi/Lo	I	CPUCLK2
ADS#	ADdress Strobe	Low	I	CPUCLK2
READY#	Bus ready input	Low	I	CPUCLK2
READYO#	Ready output	Low	O	CPUCLK2/STEN
STEN	STatus ENable	High	I	CPUCLK2
NPS1#	NPX select #1	Low	I	CPUCLK2
NPS2	NPX select #2	High	I	CPUCLK2
CMD0#	CoMmanD	Low	I	CPUCLK2
V_{CC} V_{SS}	**NOTE:** STEN is referenced to only when getting the output pins into or out of tristate mode.			

Table 3.2. 387DX™ NPX Pin Cross-Reference

ADS#	—	K7	D18	—	A8	STEN	—	L4
BUSY#	—	K2	D19	—	B9	W/R#	—	K4
CKM	—	J11	D20	—	B10			
CPUCLK24	—	K10	D21	—	A10	V_{CC}	—	A6, A9, B4,
CMD0#	—	L8	D22	—	B11			E1, F1, F10,
D0	—	H2	D23	—	C10			J2, K3, K5,
D1	—	H1	D24	—	D10			L7, L9
D2	—	G2	D25	—	D11			
D3	—	G1	D26	—	E10	V_{SS}	—	B2, B7, C11,
D4	—	D2	D27	—	E11			E2, F2, F11,
D5	—	D1	D28	—	G10			J1, J10, L5
D6	—	C2	D29	—	G11			
D7	—	C1	D30	—	H10	NO CONNECT	—	K9
D8	—	B1	D31	—	H11			
D9	—	A2	ERROR#	—	L2			
D10	—	B3	NPS1#	—	L6			
D11	—	A3	NPS2	—	K6			
D12	—	A4	NUMCLK2	—	K11			
D13	—	B5	PEREQ	—	K1			
D14	—	A5	READY#	—	K8			
D15	—	B6	READYO#	—	L3			
D16	—	A7	RESETIN	—	L10			
D17	—	B8						

RESETIN

2. NPX handshake—PEREQ, BUSY#, ERROR#
3. Bus interface pins—D31–D0, W/R#, ADS#, READY#, READYO#
4. Chip/Port Select—STEN, NPS1#, NPS2, CMD0#
5. Power supplies—V_{CC}, V_{SS}

Table 3.1 lists every pin by its identifier, gives a brief description of its function, and lists some of its characteristics. All output signals are tristate; they leave floating state only when STEN is active. The output buffers of the bidirectional data pins D31–D0 are also tristate; they leave floating state only in read cycles when the NPX is selected (i.e. when STEN, NPS1#, and NPS2 are all active).

Figure 3.1 and Table 3.2 together show the location of every pin in the pin grid array.

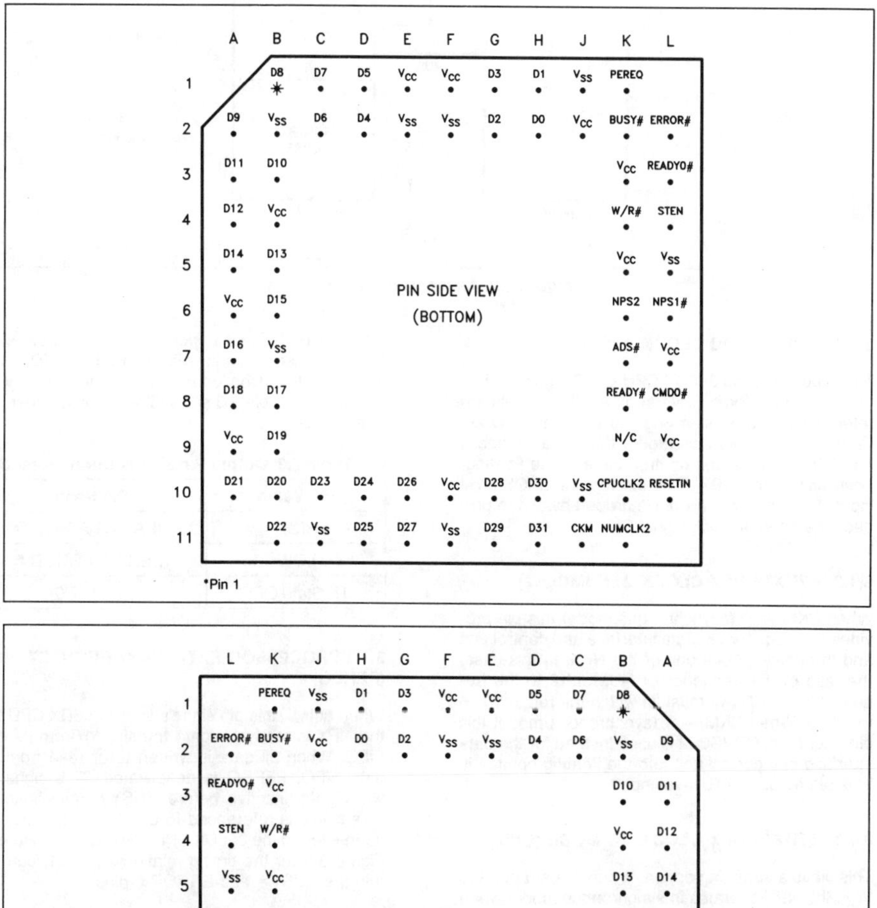

Figure 3.1. 387DX™ NPX Pin Configuration

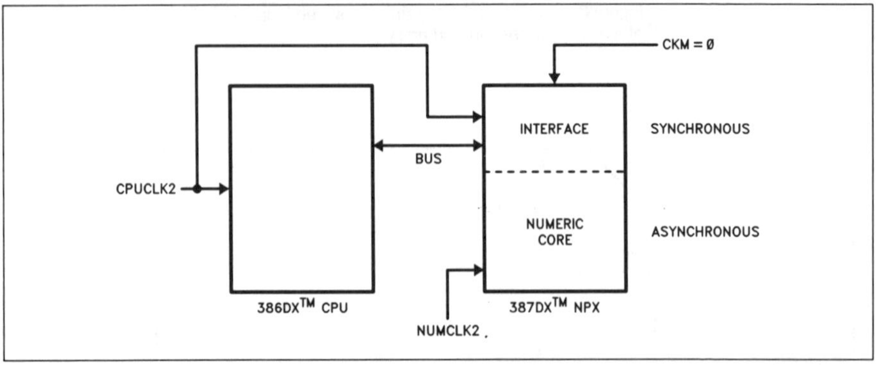

Figure 3.2. Asynchronous Operation

3.1.1 386DX™ CPU CLOCK 2 (CPUCLK2)

This input uses the 386DX CPU CLK2 signal to time the bus control logic. Several other NPX signals are referenced to the rising edge of this signal. When CKM = 1 (synchronous mode) this pin also clocks the data interface and control unit and the floating-point unit of the NPX. This pin requires MOS-level input. The signal on this pin is divided by two to produce the internal clock signal CLK.

3.1.2 387DX™ NPX CLOCK 2 (NUMCLK2)

When CKM = 0 (asynchronous mode) this pin provides the clock for the data interface and control unit and the floating-point unit of the NPX. In this case, the ratio of the frequency of NUMCLK2 to the frequency of CPUCLK2 must lie within the range 10:16 to 14:10. When CKM = 1 (synchronous mode) this pin is ignored; CPUCLK2 is used instead for the data interface and control unit and the floating-point unit. This pin requires TTL-level input.

3.1.3 387DX™ NPX CLOCKING MODE (CKM)

This pin is a strapping option. When it is strapped to V_{CC}, the NPX operates in synchronous mode; when strapped to V_{SS}, the NPX operates in asynchronous mode. These modes relate to clocking of the data interface and control unit and the floating-point unit only; the bus control logic always operates synchronously with respect to the 386DX Microprocessor.

3.1.4 SYSTEM RESET (RESETIN)

A LOW to HIGH transition on this pin causes the NPX to terminate its present activity and to enter a dormant state. RESETIN must remain HIGH for at least 40 NUMCLK2 periods. The HIGH to LOW transitions of RESETIN must be synchronous with CPUCLK2, so that the phase of the internal clock of the bus control logic (which is the CPUCLK2 divided by 2) is the same as the phase of the internal clock of the 386DX CPU. After RESETIN goes LOW, at least 50 NUMCLK2 periods must pass before the first NPX instruction is written into the 387DX NPX. This pin should be connected to the 386DX CPU RESET pin. Table 3.3 shows the status of other pins after a reset.

Table 3.3. Output Pin Status During Reset

Pin Value	Pin Name
HIGH	READYO#, BUSY#
LOW	PEREQ, ERROR#
Tri-State OFF	D31–D0

3.1.5 PROCESSOR EXTENSION REQUEST (PEREQ)

When active, this pin signals to the 386DX CPU that the NPX is ready for data transfer to/from its data FIFO. When all data is written to or read from the data FIFO, PEREQ is deactivated. This signal always goes inactive before BUSY# goes inactive. This signal is referenced to CPUCLK2. It should be connected to the 386DX CPU PEREQ input. Refer to Figure 3.8 for the timing relationships between this and the BUSY# and ERROR# pins.

3.1.6 BUSY STATUS (BUSY#)

When active, this pin signals to the 386DX CPU that the NPX is currently executing an instruction. This signal is referenced to CPUCLK2. It should be connected to the 386DX CPU BUSY# pin. Refer to Figure 3.8 for the timing relationships between this and the PEREQ and ERROR# pins.

3.1.7 ERROR STATUS (ERROR#)

This pin reflects the ES bits of the status register. When active, it indicates that an unmasked exception has occurred (except that, immediately after a reset, it indicates to the 386DX Microprocessor that a 387DX NPX is present in the system). This signal can be changed to inactive state only by the following instructions (without a preceding WAIT): FNINIT, FNCLEX, FNSTENV, and FNSAVE. This signal is referenced to NUMCLK2. It should be connected to the 386DX CPU ERROR# pin. Refer to Figure 3.8 for the timing relationships between this and the PEREQ and BUSY# pins.

3.1.8 DATA PINS (D31–D0)

These bidirectional pins are used to transfer data and opcodes between the 386DX CPU and 387DX NPX. They are normally connected directly to the corresponding 386DX CPU data pins. HIGH state indicates a value of one. D0 is the least significant data bit. Timings are referenced to CPUCLK2.

3.1.9 WRITE/READ BUS CYCLE (W/R#)

This signal indicates to the NPX whether the 386DX CPU bus cycle in progress is a read or a write cycle. This pin should be connected directly to the 386DX CPU W/R# pin. HIGH indicates a write cycle; LOW, a read cycle. This input is ignored if any of the signals STEN, NPS1#, or NPS2 is inactive. Setup and hold times are referenced to CPUCLK2.

3.1.10 ADDRESS STROBE (ADS#)

This input, in conjunction with the READY# input indicates when the NPX bus-control logic may sample W/R# and the chip-select signals. Setup and hold times are referenced to CPUCLK2. This pin should be connected to the 386DX CPU ADS# pin.

3.1.11 BUS READY INPUT (READY#)

This input indicates to the NPX when a 386DX CPU bus cycle is to be terminated. It is used by the bus-control logic to trace bus activities. Bus cycles can be extended indefinitely until terminated by READY#. This input should be connected to the same signal that drives the 386DX CPU READY# input. Setup and hold times are referenced to CPUCLK2.

3.1.12 READY OUTPUT (READYO#)

This pin is activated at such a time that write cycles are terminated after two clocks (except FLDENV and FRSTOR) and read cycles after three clocks. In configurations where no extra wait states are required, this pin must directly or indirectly drive the 386DX CPU READY# input. Refer to section 3.4 "Bus Operation" for details. This pin is activated only during bus cycles that select the NPX. This signal is referenced to CPUCLK2.

3.1.13 STATUS ENABLE (STEN)

This pin serves as a chip select for the NPX. When inactive, this pin forces BUSY#, PEREQ, ERROR#, and READYO# outputs into floating state. D31–D0 are normally floating and leave floating state only if STEN is active and additional conditions are met. STEN also causes the chip to recognize its other chip-select inputs. STEN makes it easier to do on-board testing (using the overdrive method) of other chips in systems containing the NPX. STEN should be pulled up with a resistor so that it can be pulled down when testing. In boards that do not use on-board testing, STEN should be connected to V_{CC}. Setup and hold times are relative to CPUCLK2. Note that STEN must maintain the same setup and hold times as NPS1#, NPS2, and CMD0# (i.e. if STEN changes state during a 387DX NPX bus cycle, it should change state during the same CLK period as the NPS1#, NPS2, and CMD0# signals).

3.1.14 NPX Select #1 (NPS1#)

When active (along with STEN and NPS2) in the first period of a 386DX CPU bus cycle, this signal indicates that the purpose of the bus cycle is to communicate with the NPX. This pin should be connected directly to the 386DX CPU M/IO# pin, so that the NPX is selected only when the 386DX CPU performs I/O cycles. Setup and hold times are referenced to CPUCLK2.

3.1.15 NPX SELECT #2 (NPS2)

When active (along with STEN and NPS1#) in the first period of an 386DX CPU bus cycle, this signal indicates that the purpose of the bus cycle is to communicate with the NPX. This pin should be connected directly to the 386DX CPU A31 pin, so that the NPX is selected only when the 386DX CPU uses one of the I/O addresses reserved for the NPX (800000F8 or 800000FC). Setup and hold times are referenced to CPUCLK2.

3.1.16 COMMAND (CMD0#)

During a write cycle, this signal indicates whether an opcode (CMD0# active) or data (CMD0# inactive) is being sent to the NPX. During a read cycle, it indicates whether the control or status register (CMD0# active) or a data register (CMD0# inactive) is being read. CMD0# should be connected directly to the A2 output of the 386DX Microprocessor. Setup and hold times are referenced to CPUCLK2.

3.2 Processor Architecture

As shown by the block diagram on the front page, the NPX is internally divided into three sections: the bus control logic (BCL), the data interface and control unit, and the floating point unit (FPU). The FPU (with the support of the control unit which contains the sequencer and other support units) executes all numerics instructions. The data interface and control unit is responsible for the data flow to and from the FPU and the control registers, for receiving the instructions, decoding them, and sequencing the microinstructions, and for handling some of the administrative instructions. The BCL is responsible for the 386DX CPU bus tracking and interface. The BCL is the only unit in the 387DX NPX that must run synchronously with the 386DX CPU; the rest of the NPX can run asynchronously with respect to the 386DX Microprocessor.

3.2.1 BUS CONTROL LOGIC

The BCL communicates solely with the CPU using I/O bus cycles. The BCL appears to the CPU as a special peripheral device. It is special in two respects: the CPU initiates I/O automatically when it encounters ESC instructions, and the CPU uses reserved I/O addresses to communicate with the BCL. The BCL does not communicate directly with memory. The CPU performs all memory access, transferring input operands from memory to the NPX and transferring outputs from the NPX to memory.

3.2.2 DATA INTERFACE AND CONTROL UNIT

The data interface and control unit latches the data and, subject to BCL control, directs the data to the FIFO or the instruction decoder. The instruction decoder decodes the ESC instructions sent to it by the CPU and generates controls that direct the data flow in the FIFO. It also triggers the microinstruction sequencer that controls execution of each instruction. If the ESC instruction is FINIT, FCLEX, FSTSW, FSTSW AX, or FSTCW, the control executes it independently of the FPU and the sequencer. The data interface and control unit is the one that generates the BUSY#, PEREQ and ERROR# signals that synchronize 387DX NPX activities with the 386DX CPU. It also supports the FPU in all operations that it cannot perform alone (e.g. exceptions handling, transcendental operations, etc.).

3.2.3 FLOATING POINT UNIT

The FPU executes all instructions that involve the register stack, including arithmetic, logical, transcendental, constant, and data transfer instructions. The data path in the FPU is 84 bits wide (68 significant bits, 15 exponent bits, and a sign bit) which allows internal operand transfers to be performed at very high speeds.

3.3 System Configuration

As an extension to the 386DX Microprocessor, the 387DX Math Coprocessor can be connected to the CPU as shown by Figure 3.3. A dedicated communication protocol makes possible high-speed transfer of opcodes and operands between the 386DX CPU and 387DX NPX. The 387DX NPX is designed so that no additional components are required for interface with the 386DX CPU. The 387DX NPX shares the 32-bit wide local bus of the 386DX CPU and

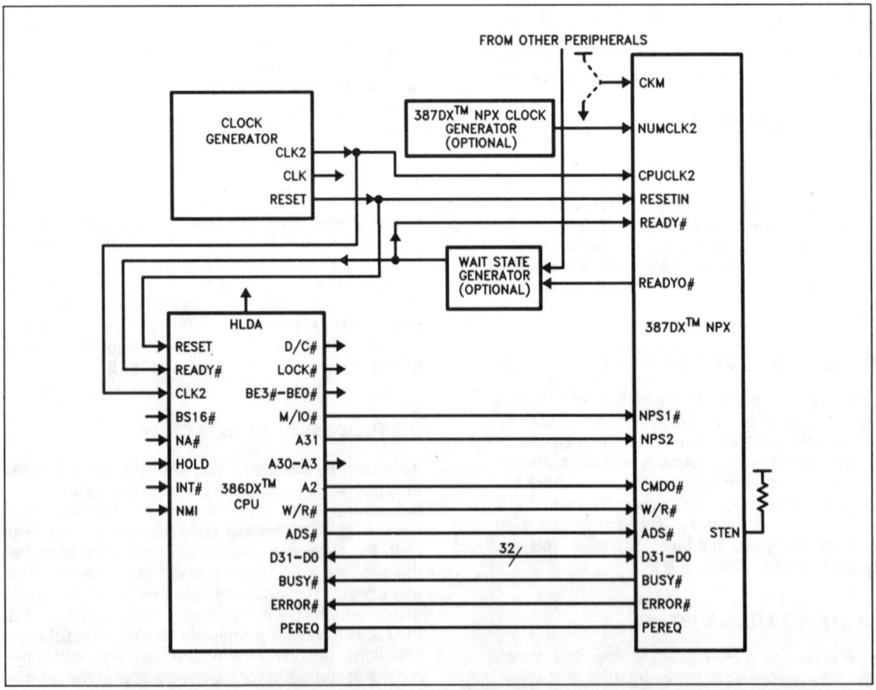

Figure 3.3. 386DX™ Microprocessor and 387DX™ Math Coprocessor System Configuration

Table 3.4. Bus Cycles Definition

STEN	NPS1#	NPS2	CMD0#	W/R#	Bus Cycle Type
0	x	x	x	x	NPX not selected and all outputs in floating state
1	1	x	x	x	NPX not selected
1	x	0	x	x	NPX not selected
1	0	1	0	0	CW or SW read from NPX
1	0	1	0	1	Opcode write to NPX
1	0	1	1	0	Data read from NPX
1	0	1	1	1	Data write to NPX

most control pins of the 387DX NPX are connected directly to pins of the 386DX Microprocessor.

3.3.1 BUS CYCLE TRACKING

The ADS# and READY# signals allow the NPX to track the beginning and end of the 386DX CPU bus cycles, respectively. When ADS# is asserted at the same time as the NPX chip-select inputs, the bus cycle is intended for the NPX. To signal the end of a bus cycle for the NPX, READY# may be asserted directly or indirectly by the NPX or by other bus-control logic. Refer to Table 3.4 for definition of the types of NPX bus cycles.

3.3.2 NPX ADDRESSING

The NPS1#, NPS2 and STEN signals allow the NPX to identify which bus cycles are intended for the NPX. The NPX responds only to I/O cycles when bit 31 of the I/O address is set. In other words, the NPX acts as an I/O device in a reserved I/O address space.

Because A_{31} is used to select the NPX for data transfers, it is not possible for a program running on the 386DX CPU to address the NPX with an I/O instruction. Only ESC instructions cause the 386DX Microprocessor to communicate with the NPX. The 386DX CPU BS16# input must be inactive during I/O cycles when A_{31} is active.

3.3.3 FUNCTION SELECT

The CMD0# and W/R# signals identify the four kinds of bus cycle: control or status register read, data read, opcode write, data write.

3.3.4 CPU/NPX Synchronization

The pin pairs BUSY#, PEREQ, and ERROR# are used for various aspects of synchronization between the CPU and the NPX.

BUSY# is used to synchronize instruction transfer from the 386DX CPU to the NPX. When the NPX recognizes an ESC instruction, it asserts BUSY#. For most ESC instructions, the 386DX CPU waits for the NPX to deassert BUSY# before sending the new opcode.

The NPX uses the PEREQ pin of the 386DX CPU to signal that the NPX is ready for data transfer to or from its data FIFO. The NPX does not directly access memory; rather, the 386DX Microprocessor provides memory access services for the NPX. Thus, memory access on behalf of the NPX always obeys the rules applicable to the mode of the 386DX CPU, whether the 386DX CPU be in real-address mode or protected mode.

Once the 386DX CPU initiates an NPX instruction that has operands, the 386DX CPU waits for PEREQ signals that indicate when the NPX is ready for operand transfer. Once all operands have been transferred (or if the instruction has no operands) the 386DX CPU continues program execution while the NPX executes the ESC instruction.

In 8086/8087 systems, WAIT instructions may be required to achieve synchronization of both commands and operands. In 80286/80287, 386DX Microprocessor and 387DX Math Coprocessor systems, WAIT instructions are required only for operand synchronization; namely, after NPX stores to memory (except FSTSW and FSTCW) or loads from memory. Used this way, WAIT ensures that the value has already been written or read by the NPX before the CPU reads or changes the value.

Once it has started to execute a numerics instruction and has transferred the operands from the 386DX CPU, the NPX can process the instruction in parallel with and independent of the host CPU. When the NPX detects an exception, it asserts the ERROR# signal, which causes a 386DX CPU interrupt.

3.3.5 SYNCHRONOUS OR ASYNCHRONOUS MODES

The internal logic of the 387DX NPX (the FPU) can either operate directly from the CPU clock (synchronous mode) or from a separate clock (asynchronous mode). The two configurations are distinguished by the CKM pin. In either case, the bus control logic (BCL) of the NPX is synchronized with the CPU clock. Use of asynchronous mode allows the 386DX CPU and the FPU section of the NPX to run at different speeds. In this case, the ratio of the frequency of NUMCLK2 to the frequency of CPUCLK2 must lie within the range 10:16 to 14:10. Use of synchronous mode eliminates one clock generator from the board design.

3.3.6 AUTOMATIC BUS CYCLE TERMINATION

In configurations where no extra wait states are required, READYO# can be used to drive the 386DX CPU READY# input. If this pin is used, it should be connected to the logic that ORs all READY outputs from peripherals on the 386DX CPU bus. READYO# is asserted by the NPX only during I/O cycles that select the NPX. Refer to section 3.4 "Bus Operation" for details.

3.4 Bus Operation

With respect to the bus interface, the 387DX NPX is fully synchronous with the 386DX Microprocessor. Both operate at the same rate, because each generates its internal CLK signal by dividing CPUCLK2 by two.

The 386DX CPU initiates a new bus cycle by activating ADS#. The NPX recognizes a bus cycle, if, during the cycle in which ADS# is activated, STEN, NPS1#, and NPS2 are all activated. Proper operation is achieved if NPS1# is connected to the M/IO# output of the 386DX CPU, and NPS2 to the A31 output. The 386DX CPU's A31 output is guaranteed to be inactive in all bus cycles that do not address the NPX (i.e. I/O cycles to other devices, interrupt acknowledge, and reserved types of bus cycles). System logic must not signal a 16-bit bus cycle via the 386DX CPU BS16# input during I/O cycles when A31 is active.

During the CLK period in which ADS# is activated, the NPX also examines the W/R# input signal to determine whether the cycle is a read or a write cycle and examines the CMD0# input to determine whether an opcode, operand, or control/status register transfer is to occur.

The 387DX NPX supports both pipelined and nonpipelined bus cycles. A nonpipelined cycle is one for which the 386DX CPU asserts ADS# when no other NPX bus cycle is in progress. A pipelined bus cycle is one for which the 386DX CPU asserts ADS# and provides valid next-address and control signals as soon as in the second CLK period after the ADS# assertion for the previous 386DX CPU bus cycle. Pipelining increases the availability of the bus by at least one CLK period. The NPX supports pipelined bus cycles in order to optimize address pipelining by the 386DX CPU for memory cycles.

Bus operation is described in terms of an abstract *state machine*. Figure 3.4 illustrates the states and state transitions for NPX bus cycles:

- T_I is the idle state. This is the state of the bus logic after RESET, the state to which bus logic returns after evey nonpipelined bus cycle, and the state to which bus logic returns after a series of pipelined cycles.
- T_{RS} is the READY# sensitive state. Different types of bus cycle may require a minimum of one or two successive T_{RS} states. The bus logic remains in T_{RS} state until READY# is sensed, at which point the bus cycle terminates. Any number of wait states may be implemented by delaying READY#, thereby causing additional successive T_{RS} states.
- T_P is the first state for every pipelined bus cycle.

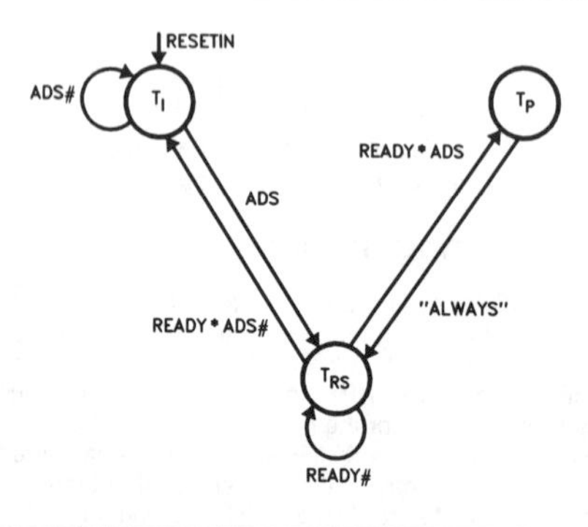

Figure 3.4. Bus State Diagram

The READYO# output of the 387DX NPX indicates when a bus cycle for the NPX may be terminated if no extra wait states are required. For all write cycles (except those for the instructions FLDENV and FRSTOR), READYO# is always asserted in the first T_{RS} state, regardless of the number of wait states. For all read cycles and write cycles for FLDENV and FRSTOR, READYO# is always asserted in the second T_{RS} state, regardless of the number of wait states. These rules apply to both pipelined and nonpipelined cycles. Systems designers must use READYO# in one of the following ways:

1. Connect it (directly or through logic that ORs READY signals from other devices) to the READY# inputs of the 386DX CPU and 387DX NPX.
2. Use it as one input to a wait-state generator.

The following sections illustrate different types of NPX bus cycles.

Because different instructions have different amounts of overhead before, between, and after operand transfer cycles, it is not possible to represent in a few diagrams all of the combinations of successive operand transfer cycles. The following bus-cycle diagrams show memory cycles between NPX operand-transfer cycles. Note however that, during the instructions FLDENV, FSTENV, FSAVE, and FRSTOR, some consecutive accesses to the NPX do not have intervening memory accesses. For the timing relationship between operand transfer cycles and opcode write or other overhead activities, see Figure 3.8.

3.4.1 NONPIPELINED BUS CYCLES

Figure 3.5 illustrates bus activity for consecutive nonpipelined bus cycles.

3.4.1.1 Write Cycle

At the second clock of the bus cycle, the 387DX NPX enters the T_{RS} (READY#-sensitive) state. During this state, the 387DX NPX samples the READY# input and stays in this state as long as READY# is inactive.

In write cycles, the NPX drives the READYO# signal for one CLK period beginning with the second CLK of the bus cycle; therefore, the fastest write cycle takes two CLK cycles (see cycle 2 of Figure 3.5). For the instructions FLDENV and FRSTOR, however, the NPX forces a wait state by delaying the activation of READYO# to the second T_{RS} cycle (not shown in Figure 3.5).

When READY# is asserted the NPX returns to the idle state, in which ADS# could be asserted again by the 386DX Microprocessor for the next cycle.

3.4.1.2 Read Cycle

At the second clock of the bus cycle, the NPX enters the T_{RS} state. See Figure 3.5. In this state, the NPX samples the READY# input and stays in this state as long as READY# is inactive.

At the rising edge of CLK in the second clock period of the cycle, the NPX starts to drive the D31–D0 outputs and continues to drive them as long as it stays in T_{RS} state.

In read cycles that address the NPX, at least one wait state must be inserted to insure that the 386DX CPU latches the correct data. Since the NPX starts driving the system data bus only at the rising edge of CLK in the second clock period of the bus cycle, not enough time is left for the data signals to propagate and be latched by the 386DX CPU at the falling edge of the same clock period. The NPX drives the READYO# signal for one CLK period in the third CLK of the bus cycle. Therefore, if the READYO# output is used to drive the 386DX CPU READY# input, one wait state is inserted automatically.

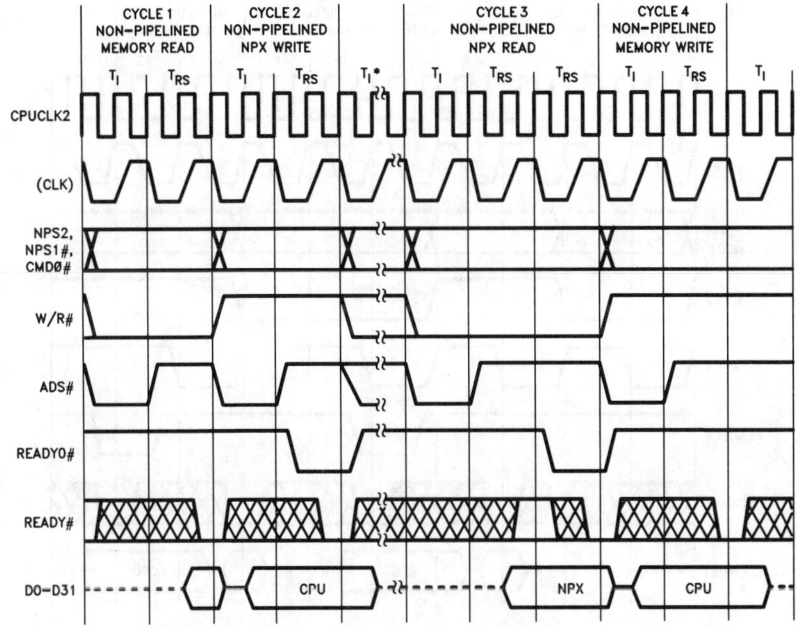

Cycles 1 & 2 represent part of the operand transfer cycle for instructions involving either 4-byte or 8-byte operand loads.
Cycles 3 & 4 represent part of the operand transfer cycle for a store operation.
*Cycles 1 & 2 could repeat here or T_I states for various non-operand transfer cycles and overhead.

Figure 3.5. Nonpipelined Read and Write Cycles

Because one wait state is required for NPX reads, the minimum is three CLK cycles per read, as cycle 3 of Figure 3.5 shows.

When READY# is asserted the NPX returns to the idle state, in which ADS# could be asserted again by the 386DX CPU for the next cycle. The transition from T_{RS} state to idle state causes the NPX to put the tristate D31–D0 outputs into the floating state, allowing another device to drive the system data bus.

3.4.2 PIPELINED BUS CYCLES

Because all the activities of the 387DX NPX bus interface occur either during the T_{RS} state or during the transitions to or from that state, the only difference between a pipelined and a nonpipelined cycle is the manner of changing from one state to another. The exact activities in each state are detailed in the previous section "Nonpipelined Bus Cycles".

When the 386DX CPU asserts ADS# before the end of a bus cycle, both ADS# and READY# are active during a T_{RS} state. This condition causes the NPX to change to a different state named T_P. The NPX activities in the transition from a T_{RS} state to a T_P state are exactly the same as those in the transition from a T_{RS} state to a T_I state in nonpipelined cycles.

T_P state is metastable; therefore, one clock period later the NPX returns to T_{RS} state. In consecutive pipelined cycles, the NPX bus logic uses only T_{RS} and T_P states.

Figure 3.6 shows the fastest transition into and out of the pipelined bus cycles. Cycle 1 in this figure represents a nonpipelined cycle. (Nonpipelined write cycles with only one T_{RS} state (i.e. no wait states) are always followed by another nonpipelined cycle, because READY# is asserted before the earliest possible assertion of ADS# for the next cycle.)

Figure 3.7 shows the pipelined write and read cycles with one additional T_{RS} states beyond the minimum required. To delay the assertion of READY# requires external logic.

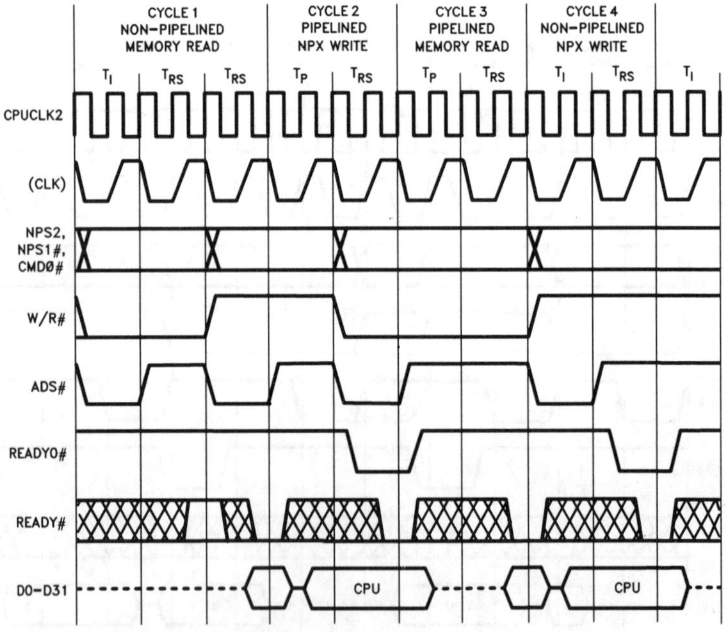

Cycle 1–Cycle 4 represent the operand transfer cycle for an instruction involving a transfer of two 32-bit loads in total. The opcode write cycles and other overhead are not shown.
Note that the next cycle will be a pipelined cycle if both READY# and ADS# are sampled active at the end of a T_{RS} state of the current cycle.

Figure 3.6. Fastest Transitions to and from Pipelined Cycles

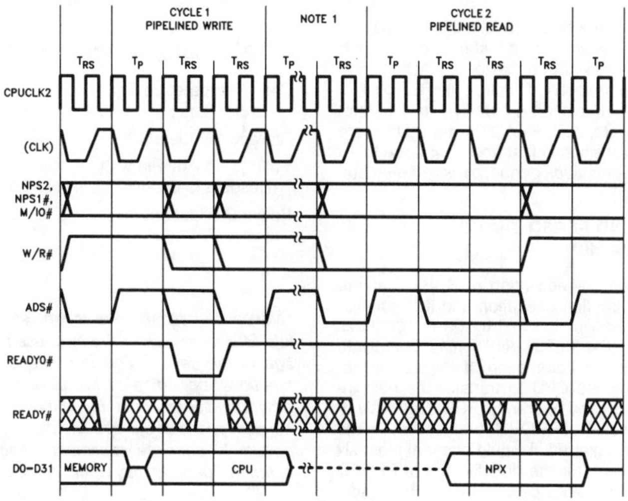

NOTE:
1. Cycles between operand write to the NPX and storing result.

Figure 3.7. Pipelined Cycles with Wait States

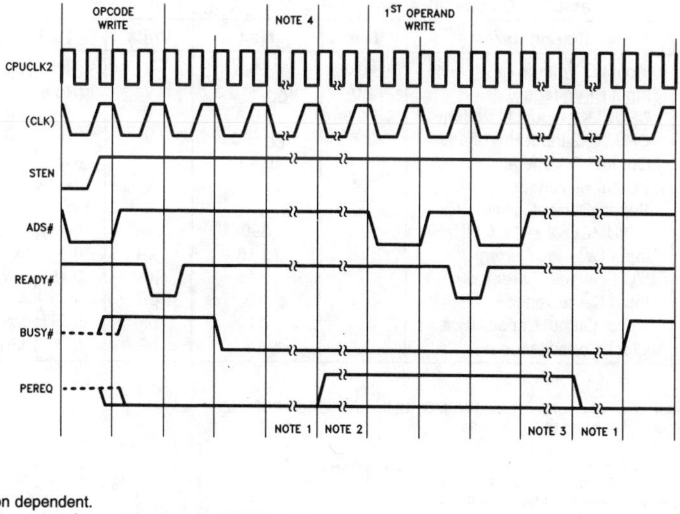

NOTES:
1. Instruction dependent.
2. PEREQ is an asynchronous input to the 386DX™ Microprocessor; it may not be asserted (instruction dependent).
3. More operand transfers.
4. Memory read (operand) cycle is not shown.

Figure 3.8. STEN, BUSY# and PEREQ Timing Relationship

3.4.3 BUS CYCLES OF MIXED TYPE

When the 387DX NPX bus logic is in the T_{RS} state, it distinguishes between nonpipelined and pipelined cycles according to the behavior of ADS# and READY#. In a nonpipelined cycle, only READY# is activated, and the transition is from T_{RS} to idle state. In a pipelined cycle, both READY# and ADS# are active and the transition is first from T_{RS} state to T_P state then, after one clock period, back to T_{RS} state.

3.4.4 BUSY# AND PEREQ TIMING RELATIONSHIP

Figure 3.8 shows the activation of BUSY# at the beginning of instruction execution and its deactivation after execution of the instruction is complete. When possible, the 387DX NPX may deactivate BUSY# prior to the completion of the current instruction allowing the CPU to transfer the next instruction's opcode and operands. PEREQ is activated in this interval. If ERROR# (not shown in the diagram) is ever asserted, it would occur at least six CPUCLK2 periods after the deactivation of PEREQ and at least six CPUCLK2 periods before the deactivation of BUSY#. Figure 3.8 shows also that STEN is activated at the beginning of a bus cycle.

4.0 ELECTRICAL DATA

4.1 Absolute Maximum Ratings*

Case Temperature T_C
Under Bias . . . . −65°C to +110°C

Storage Temperature . . . . −65°C to +150°C

Voltage on Any Pin with
Respect to Ground . . . . −0.5 to V_{CC} +0.5V

Power Dissipation 1.5W

**Notice:* *Stresses above those listed under "Absolute Maximum Ratings" may cause permanent damage to the device. This is a stress rating only and functional operation of the device at these or any other conditions above those indicated in the operational sections of this specification is not implied. Exposure to absolute maximum rating conditions for extended periods may affect device reliability.*

NOTICE: Specifications contained within the following tables are subject to change.

4.2 D.C. Characteristics

Table 5.1. DC Specifications T_C = 0° to 85°C, V_{CC} = 5V ± 5%

Symbol	Parameter	Min	Max	Units	Test Conditions
V_{IL}	Input LO Voltage	−0.3	+0.8	V	(Note 1)
V_{IH}	Input HI Voltage	2.0	V_{CC} + 0.3	V	(Note 1)
V_{CL}	CPUCLK2 Input LO Voltage	−0.3	+0.8	V	
V_{CH}	CPUCLK2 Input HI Voltage	3.7	V_{CC} +0.3	V	
V_{OL}	Output LO Voltage		0.45	V	(Note 2)
V_{OH}	Output HI Voltage	2.4		V	(Note 3)
I_{CC}	Supply Current				
	NUMCLK2 = 66.6 MHz(4)		390	mA	I_{CC} typ. = 250 mA
I_{LI}	Input Leakage Current		±15	μA	0V ≤ V_{IN} ≤ V_{CC}
I_{LO}	I/O Leakage Current		±15	μA	0.45V ≤ V_O ≤ V_{CC}
C_{IN}	Input Capacitance		10	pF	fc = 1 MHz
C_O	I/O or Output Capacitance		12	pF	fc = 1 MHz
C_{CLK}	Clock Capacitance		15	pF	fc = 1 MHz

NOTES:
1. This parameter is for all inputs, including NUMCLK2 but excluding CPUCLK2.
2. This parameter is measured at I_{OL} as follows:
   data = 4.0 mA
   READYO# = 2.5 mA
   ERROR#, BUSY#, PEREQ = 2.5 mA
3. This parameter is measured at I_{OH} as follows:
   data = 1.0 mA
   READYO# = 0.6 mA
   ERROR#, BUSY#, PEREQ = 0.6 mA
4. I_{CC} is measured at steady state, maximum capacitive loading on the outputs, and worst-case DC level at the inputs; CPUCLK2 at the same frequency as NUMCLK2.

4.3 A.C. Characteristics

Table 4.2a. Combinations of Bus Interface and Execution Speeds

Functional Block	80387DX-33
Bus Interface Unit (MHz)	33
Execution Unit (MHz)	33

Table 4.2b. Timing Requirements of the Execution Unit
T_C = 0°C to +85°C, V_{CC} = 5V ±5%

Pin	Symbol	Parameter	33 MHz Advance Min (ns)	33 MHz Advance Max (ns)	Test Conditions	Figure Reference
NUMCLK2	t1	Period	15	125	2.0V	4.1
NUMCLK2	t2a	High Time	6.25		2.0V	
NUMCLK2	t2b	High Time	4.5		3.7V	
NUMCLK2	t3a	Low Time	6.25		2.0V	
NUMCLK2	t3b	Low Time	4.5		0.8V	
NUMCLK2	t4	Fall Time		6	3.7V to 0.8V	
NUMCLK2	t5	Rise Time		6	0.8V to 3.7V	

Table 4.2c. Timing Requirements of the Bus Interface Unit
T_C = 0°C to +85°C, V_{CC} = 5V ±5%
(All measurements made at 1.5V and C_L = 50 pF unless otherwise specified)

Pin	Symbol	Parameter	33 MHz Advance Min (ns)	33 MHz Advance Max (ns)	Test Conditions	Figure Reference
CPUCLK2	t1	Period	15	125	2.0V	4.1
CPUCLK2	t2a	High Time	6.25		2.0V	
CPUCLK2	t2b	High Time	4.5		3.7V	
CPUCLK2	t3a	Low Time	6.25		2.0V	
CPUCLK2	t3b	Low Time	4.5		0.8V	
CPUCLK2	t4	Fall Time		4	3.7V to 0.8V	
CPUCLK2	t5	Rise Time		4	0.8V to 3.7V	
CPUCLK2/ NUMCLK2 *		Ratio	10/16	14/10		
READYO#	t7	Out Delay	3	17		4.2
READYO# (2)	t7	Out Delay	3	15		
PEREQ (1)	t7	Out Delay	4	25		
BUSY# (1)	t7	Out Delay	4	21		
BUSY# (1, 2)	t7	Out Delay	4	19		
ERROR# (1)	t7	Out Delay	4	25		
D31–D0	t8	Out Delay	0	37		4.3
D31–D0	t10	Setup Time	11			
D31–D0	t7	Hold Time	11			
D31–D0 (3)	t12*	Float Time	3	19		
PEREQ (3)	t13*	Float Time	1	30		4.5
BUSY# (3)	t13*	Float Time	1	30		
ERROR# (3)	t13*	Float Time	1	30		
READYO# (3)	t13*	Float Time	1	30		

*Float condition occurs when maximum output current becomes less than I_{LO} in magnitude. Float delay is not tested.

Table 4.2c. Timing Requirements of the Bus Interface Unit (Continued)
T_C = 0°C to +85°C, V_{CC} = 5V ±5%
(All measurements made at 1.5V and C_L = 50 pF unless otherwise specified)

Pin	Symbol	Parameter	33 MHz Advance		Test Conditions	Figure Reference
			Min (ns)	Max (ns)		
ADS#	t14	Setup Time	13			4.3
ADS#	t15	Hold Time	4			
W/R#	t14	Setup Time	13			
W/R#	t15	Hold Time	4			
READY#	t16	Setup Time	7			
READY#	t17	Hold Time	4			
CMD0#	t16	Setup Time	13			
CMD0#	t17	Hold Time	4			
NPS1# NPS2	t16	Setup Time	13			
NPS1# NPS2	t17	Hold Time	4			
STEN	t16	Setup Time	13			
STEN	t17	Hold Time	2			
RESETIN	t18	Setup Time	5			4.4
RESETIN	t19	Hold Time	3			

NOTES:
1. PEREQ, BUSY#, ERROR# Out Delay — 4 @ T_C = 0°C; 4 @ T_C = 85°C
2. Not tested at 25 pF.
3. Float delay is not tested. Float condition occurs when maximum output current becomes less than I_{LO} in magnitude.

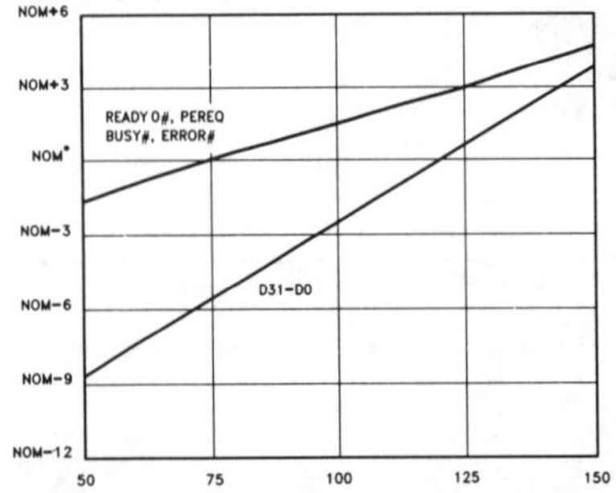

*nom - nominal value

NOTE:
This graph will not be linear outside of the C_L range shown.

Figure 4.0a. Typical Output Valid Delay vs Load Capacitance at Max Operating Temperature

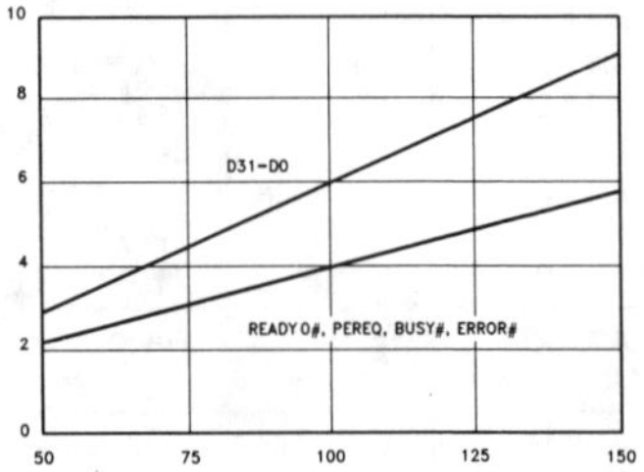

NOTE:
This graph will not be linear outside of the C_L range shown.

Figure 4.0b. Typical Output Rise Time vs Load Capacitance at Max Operating Temperature

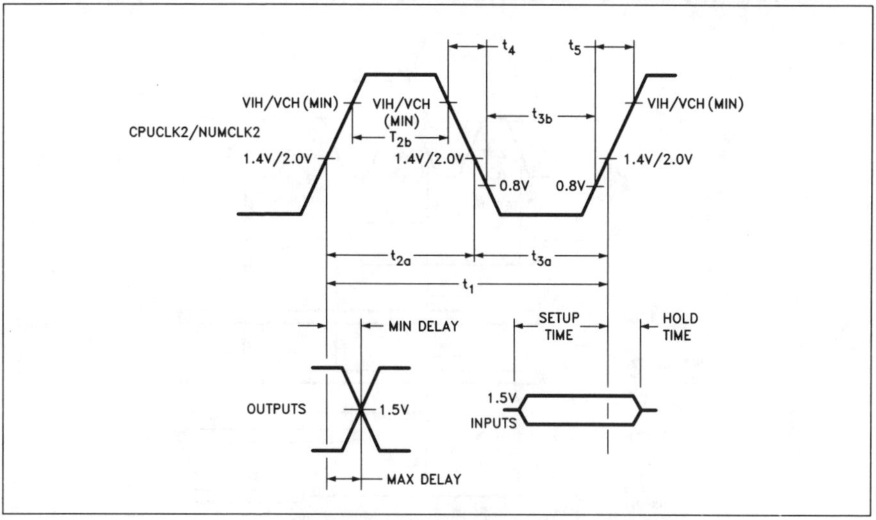

Figure 4.1. CPUCLK2/NUMCLK2 Waveform and Measurement Points for Input/Output A.C. Specifications

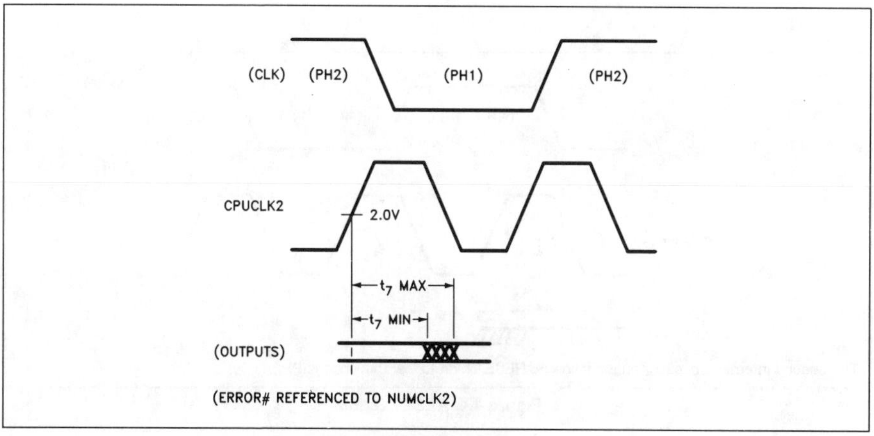

Figure 4.2. Output Signals

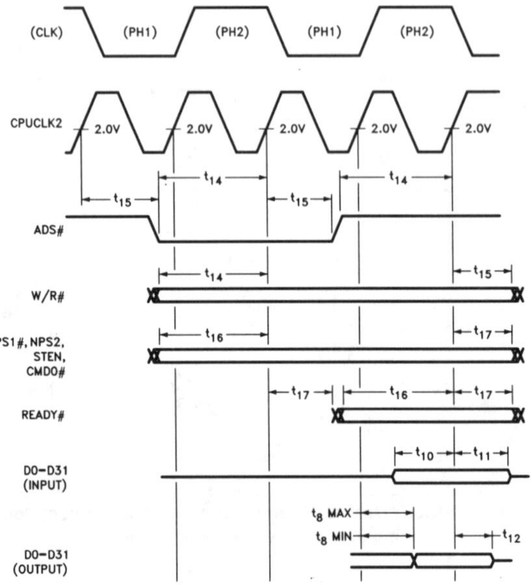

Figure 4.3. Input and I/O Signals

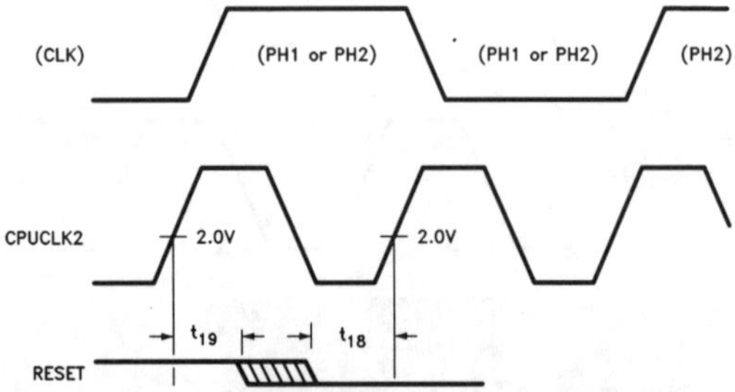

NOTE:
The second internal processor phase following RESET high to low transition is PH2.

Figure 4.4. RESET Signal

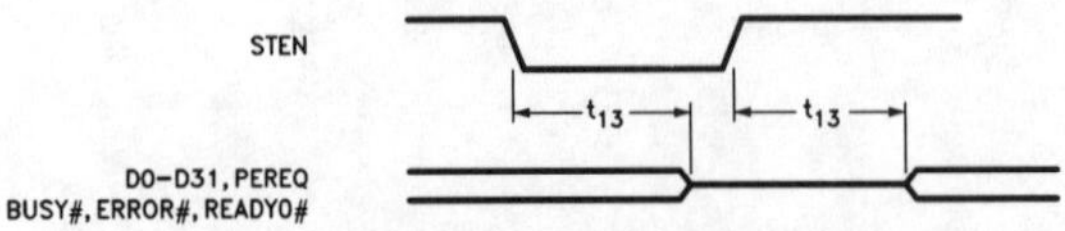

Figure 4.5. Float from STEN

Table 4.3. Other Parameters

Pin	Symbol	Parameter	Min	Max	Units
RESETIN	t30	Duration	40		NUMCLK2
RESETIN	t31	RESETIN Inactive to 1st Opcode Write	50		NUMCLK2
BUSY#	t32	Duration	6		CPUCLK2
BUSY#, ERROR#	t33	ERROR# (In) Active to BUSY# Inactive	6		CPUCLK2
PEREQ, ERROR#	t34	PEREQ Inactive to ERROR# Active	6		CPUCLK2
READY#, BUSY#	t35	READY# Active to BUSY# Active	4	4	CPUCLK2
READY#	t36	Minimum Time from Opcode Write to Opcode/Operand Write	6		CPUCLK2
READY#	t37	Minimum Time from Operand Write to Operand Write	8		CPUCLK2

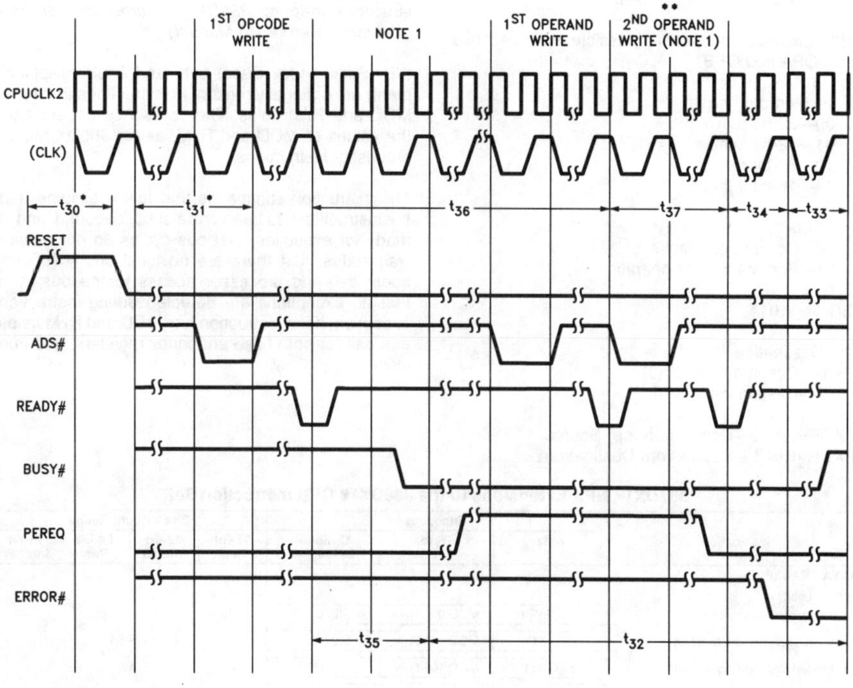

* In NUMCLK2's
** or last operand

NOTE:
1. Memory read (operand) cycle is not shown.

Figure 4.6. Other Parameters

	Instruction										Optional Fields	
	First Byte				Second Byte							
1	11011	OPA		1	MOD		1	OPB		R/M	SIB	DISP
2	11011	MF		OPA	MOD		OPB			R/M	SIB	DISP
3	11011	d	P	OPA	1	1	OPB			ST(i)		
4	11011	0	0	1	1	1	1	OP				
5	11011	0	1	1	1	1	1	OP				
	15–11	10	9	8	7	6	5	4 3		2 1 0		

5.0 387DX™ NPX EXTENSIONS TO THE 386DX™ CPU INSTRUCTION SET

Instructions for the 387DX NPX assume one of the five forms shown in the following table. In all cases, instructions are at least two bytes long and begin with the bit pattern 11011B, which identifies the ESCAPE class of instruction. Instructions that refer to memory operands specify addresses using the 386DX CPU addressing modes.

OP = Instruction opcode, possible split into two fields OPA and OPB

MF = Memory Format
- 00—32-bit real
- 01—32-bit integer
- 10—64-bit real
- 11—16-bit integer

P = Pop
- 0—Do not pop stack
- 1—Pop stack after operation

ESC = 11011

d = Destination
- 0—Destination is ST(0)
- 1—Destination is ST(i)

R XOR d = 0—Destination (op) Source
R XOR d = 1—Source (op) Destination

ST(i) = Register stack element *i*
- 000 = Stack top
- 001 = Second stack element
- •
- •
- •
- 111 = Eighth stack element

MOD (Mode field) and R/M (Register/Memory specifier) have the same interpretation as the corresponding fields of the 386DX Microprocessor instructions (refer to *386DX™ Microprocessor Programmer's Reference Manual*).

SIB (Scale Index Base) byte and DISP (displacement) are optionally present in instructions that have MOD and R/M fields. Their presence depends on the values of MOD and R/M, as for 386DX Microprocessor instructions.

The instruction summaries that follow assume that the instruction has been prefetched, decoded, and is ready for execution; that bus cycles do not require wait states; that there are no local bus HOLD request delaying processor access to the bus; and that no exceptions are detected during instruction execution. If the instruction has MOD and R/M fields that call for both base and index registers, add one clock.

387DX™ NPX Extensions to the 386DX™ CPU Instruction Set

Instruction	Encoding			Clock Count Range			
	Byte 0	Byte 1	Optional Bytes 2–6	32-Bit Real	32-Bit Integer	64-Bit Real	16-Bit Integer
DATA TRANSFER							
FLD = Load[a]							
Integer/real memory to ST(0)	ESC MF 1	MOD 000 R/M	SIB/DISP	18	35–42	23	42
Long integer memory to ST(0)	ESC 111	MOD 101 R/M	SIB/DISP	43–54			
Extended real memory to ST(0)	ESC 011	MOD 101 R/M	SIB/DISP	43			
BCD memory to ST(0)	ESC 111	MOD 100 R/M	SIB/DISP	69–97			
ST(i) to ST(0)	ESC 001	11000 ST(i)		12			
FST = Store							
ST(0) to integer/real memory	ESC MF 1	MOD 010 R/M	SIB/DISP	43	62–76	44	63–76
ST(0) to ST(i)	ESC 101	11010 ST(i)		11			

387DX™ NPX Extensions to the 386DX™ CPU Instruction Set (Continued)

Instruction	Encoding			Clock Count Range			
	Byte 0	Byte 1	Optional Bytes 2–6	32-Bit Real	32-Bit Integer	64-Bit Real	16-Bit Integer
FSTP = Store and Pop							
ST(0) to integer/real memory	ESC MF 1	MOD 011 R/M	SIB/DISP	43	62–76	44	63–76
ST(0) to long integer memory	ESC 111	MOD 111 R/M	SIB/DISP	65–82			
ST(0) to extended real	ESC 011	MOD 111 R/M	SIB/DISP	52			
ST(0) to BCD memory	ESC 111	MOD 110 R/M	SIB/DISP	134–190			
ST(0) to ST(i)	ESC 101	11011 ST (i)		11			
FXCH = Exchange							
ST(i) and ST(0)	ESC 001	11001 ST(i)		17			
COMPARISON							
FCOM = Compare							
Integer/real memory to ST(0)	ESC MF 0	MOD 010 R/M	SIB/DISP	25	45–52	27	58–62
ST(i) to ST(0)	ESC 000	11010 ST(i)		21			
FCOMP = Compare and pop							
Integer/real memory to ST	ESC MF 0	MOD 011 R/M	SIB/DISP	25	45–52	27	58–62
ST(i) to ST(0)	ESC 000	11011 ST(i)		21			
FCOMPP = Compare and pop twice							
ST(1) to ST(0)	ESC 110	1101 1001		21			
FTST = Test ST(0)	ESC 001	1110 0100		25			
FUCOM = Unordered compare	ESC 101	11100 ST(i)		21			
FUCOMP = Unordered compare and pop	ESC 101	11101 ST(i)		21			
FUCOMPP = Unordered compare and pop twice	ESC 010	1110 1001		21			
FXAM = Examine ST(0)	ESC 001	11100101		29–37			
CONSTANTS							
FLDZ = Load +0.0 into ST(0)	ESC 001	1110 1110		17			
FLD1 = Load +1.0 into ST(0)	ESC 001	1110 1000		22			
FLDPI = Load pi into ST(0)	ESC 001	1110 1011		36			
FLDL2T = Load $\log_2(10)$ into ST(0)	ESC 001	1110 1001		36			
FLDL2E = Load $\log_2(e)$ into ST(0)	ESC 001	1110 1010		36			
FLDLG2 = Load $\log_{10}(2)$ into ST(0)	ESC 001	1110 1100		35			
FLDLN2 = Load $\log_e(2)$ into ST(0)	ESC 001	1110 1101		38			
ARITHMETIC							
FADD = Add							
Integer/real memory with ST(0)	ESC MF 0	MOD 000 R/M	SIB/DISP	21–29	41–56	26–34	53–64
ST(i) and ST(0)	ESC d P 0	11000 ST(i)		18–26[b]			
FSUB = Subtract							
Integer/real memory with ST(0)	ESC MF 0	MOD 10 R R/M	SIB/DISP	21–29	41–56	26–34	53–64[c]
ST(i) and ST(0)	ESC d P 0	1110 R R/M		18–26[d]			
FMUL = Multiply							
Integer/real memory with ST(0)	ESC MF 0	MOD 001 R/M	SIB/DISP	24–32	50–71	28–53	63–74
ST(i) and ST(0)	ESC d P 0	1100 1 R/M		22–50[e]			
FDIV = Divide							
Integer/real memory with ST(0)	ESC MF 0	MOD 11 R R/M	SIB/DISP	85	107–114[f]	91	120–124[g]
ST(i) and ST(0)	ESC d P 0	1111 R R/M		80[h]			

387DX™ NPX Extensions to the 386DX™ CPU Instruction Set (Continued)

Instruction	Encoding			Clock Count Range
	Byte 0	Byte 1	Optional Bytes 2–6	
FSQRT[i] = Square root	ESC 001	1111 1010		104–111
FSCALE = Scale ST(0) by ST(1)	ESC 001	1111 1101		63–82
FPREM = Partial remainder	ESC 001	1111 1000		60–140
FPREM1 = Partial remainder (IEEE)	ESC 001	1111 0101		78–168
FRNDINT = Round ST(0) to integer	ESC 001	1111 1100		48–62
FXTRACT = Extract components of ST(0)	ESC 001	1111 0100		57–63
FABS = Absolute value of ST(0)	ESC 001	1110 0001		21
FCHS = Change sign of ST(0)	ESC 001	1110 0000		23–24
TRANSCENDENTAL				
FCOS[k] = Cosine of ST(0)	ESC 001	1111 1111		122–680
FPTAN[k] = Partial tangent of ST(0)	ESC 001	1111 0010		162–430i
FPATAN = Partial arctangent	ESC 001	1111 0011		250–420
FSIN[k] = Sine of ST(0)	ESC 001	1111 1110		121–680
FSINCOS[k] = Sine and cosine of ST(0)	ESC 001	1111 1011		150–650
F2XM1[l] = $2^{ST(0)} - 1$	ESC 001	1111 0000		167–410
FYL2X[m] = ST(1) * $\log_2$(ST(0))	ESC 001	1111 0001		99–436
FYL2XP1[n] = ST(1) * $\log_2$(ST(0) + 1.0)	ESC 001	1111 1001		210–447
PROCESSOR CONTROL				
FINIT = Initialize NPX	ESC 011	1110 0011		33
FSTSW AX = Store status word	ESC 111	1110 0000		13
FLDCW = Load control word	ESC 001	MOD 101 R/M	SIB/DISP	19
FSTCW = Store control word	ESC 101	MOD 111 R/M	SIB/DISP	15
FSTSW = Store status word	ESC 101	MOD 111 R/M	SIB/DISP	15
FCLEX = Clear exceptions	ESC 011	1110 0010		11
FSTENV = Store environment	ESC 001	MOD 110 R/M	SIB/DISP	103–104
FLDENV = Load environment	ESC 001	MOD 100 R/M	SIB/DISP	71
FSAVE = Save state	ESC 101	MOD 110 R/M	SIB/DISP	375–376
FRSTOR = Restore state	ESC 101	MOD 100 R/M	SIB/DISP	308
FINCSTP = Increment stack pointer	ESC 001	1111 0111		21
FDECSTP = Decrement stack pointer	ESC 001	1111 0110		22
FFREE = Free ST(i)	ESC 101	1100 0 ST(i)		18
FNOP = No operations	ESC 001	1101 0000		12

Shaded areas indicate instructions not available in 8087/80287.

NOTE:
a. When loading single- or double-precision zero from memory, add 5 clocks.
b. Add 3 clocks to the range when d = 1.
c. Add 1 clock to **each** range when R = 1.
d. Add 3 clocks to the range when d = 0.
e. typical = 52 (When d = 0, 46–54, typical = 49).
f. Add 1 clock to the range when R = 1.
g. 135–141 when R = 1.
h. Add 3 clocks to the range when d = 1.
i. $-0 \le ST(0) \le +\infty$.

j. These timings hold for operands in the range $|x| < \pi/4$. For operands not in this range, up to 76 additional clocks may be needed to reduce the operand.
k. $0 \leq |ST(0)| < 2^{63}$.
l. $-1.0 \leq ST(0) \leq 1.0$.
m. $0 \leq ST(0) < \infty, -\infty < ST(1) < +\infty$.
n. $0 \leq |ST(0)| < (2 - SQRT(2))/2, -\infty < ST(1) < +\infty$.

COMPATIBILITY BETWEEN THE 80287 AND THE 8087

The 80286/80287 operating in Real-Address mode will execute 8086/8087 programs without major modification. However, because of differences in the handling of numeric exceptions by the 80287 NPX and the 8087 NPX, exception-handling routines *may* need to be changed.

This appendix summarizes the differences between the 80287 NPX and the 8087 NPX, and provides details showing how 8086/8087 programs can be ported to the 80286/80287.

1. The NPX signals exceptions through a dedicated ERROR# line to the 80286. The NPX error signal does not pass through an interrupt controller (the 8087 INT signal does). Therefore, any interrupt-controller-oriented instructions in numeric exception handlers for the 8086/8087 should be deleted.
2. The 8087 instructions FENI/FNENI and FDISI/FNDISI perform no useful function in the 80287. If the 80287 encounters one of these opcodes in its instruction stream, the instruction will effectively be ignored—none of the 80287 internal states will be updated. While 8086/8087 containing these instructions may be executed on the 80286/80287, it is unlikely that the exception-handling routines containing these instructions will be completely portable to the 80287.
3. Interrupt vector 16 must point to the numeric exception handling routine.
4. The ESC instruction address saved in the 80287 includes any leading prefixes before the ESC opcode. The corresponding address saved in the 8087 does not include leading prefixes.
5. In Protected-Address mode, the format of the 80287's saved instruction and address pointers is different than for the 8087. The instruction opcode is not saved in Protected mode—exception handlers will have to retrieve the opcode from memory if needed.
6. Interrupt 7 will occur in the 80286 when executing ESC instructions with either TS (task switched) or EM (emulation) of the 80286 MSW set (TS = 1 or EM = 1). If TS is set, then a WAIT instruction will also cause interrupt 7. An exception handler should be included in 80286/80287 code to handle these situations.
7. Interrupt 9 will occur if the second or subsequent words of a floating-point operand fall outside a segment's size. Interrupt 13 will occur if the starting address of a numeric operand falls outside a segment's size. An exception handler should be included in 80286/80287 code to report these programming errors.
8. Except for the processor control instructions, all of the 80287 numeric instructions are automatically synchronized by the 80286 CPU—the 80286 automatically tests the BUSY# line from the 80287 to ensure that the 80287 has completed its previous instruction before executing the next ESC instruction. No explicit WAIT instructions are required to assure this synchronization. For the 8087 used with 8086 and 8088 processors, explicit WAITs are required before each numeric instruction to ensure synchronization. Although 8086/8087 programs having explicit WAIT instructions will execute perfectly on the 80286/80287 without reassembly, these WAIT instructions are unnecessary.
9. Since the 80287 does not require WAIT instructions before each numeric instruction, the ASM286 assembler does not automatically generate these WAIT instructions. The ASM86 assembler, however, automatically precedes every ESC instruction with a WAIT instruction. Although numeric routines generated using the ASM86 assembler will generally execute correctly on the 80286/80287, reassembly using ASM286 may result in a more compact code image.

   The processor control instructions for the 80287 may be coded using either a WAIT or No-WAIT form of mnemonic. The WAIT forms of these instructions cause ASM286 to precede the ESC instruction with a CPU WAIT instruction, in the identical manner as does ASM86.

3C87 Numeric Coprocessor

OVERVIEW

The IIT-3C87 is a high performance numeric co-processor that is plug and object-code compatible with the Intel 80387, and operates up to 50% faster in the same socket and at the same clock rates. The unique architecture of the IIT-3C87 requires far fewer co-processor clock cycles to perform the various math operations, resulting in superior performance in the same socket as the Intel 80387, yet maintains full software compatibility with the Intel 80387. Device Icc is 25% less than required by the Intel 80387 when operating under the same conditions, resulting in lower junction temperatures and consequently higher reliability.

- ☐ High performance 80-bit architecture
- ☐ Plug and object-code compatible with the 80387
- ☐ Up to 50% faster than the 80387
- ☐ CMOS implementation requires 25% less power than the 80387
- ☐ Thirty-two registers, three banks of eight available to the user
- ☐ Upward object-code compatible with the 8087 and 80287
- ☐ Implements ANSI/IEEE standard for binary floating point arithmetic
- ☐ Full range transcendental operations for sine, cosine, tangent, arctangent and logarithm
- ☐ Runs all 80387 software
- ☐ Available at 16, 20 and 25 MHz

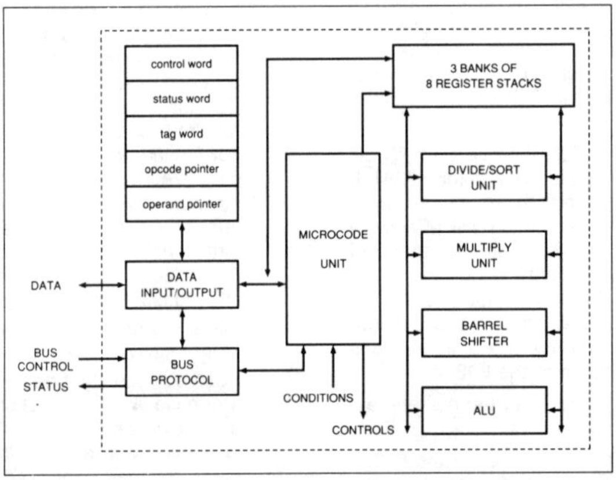

Figure 1. IIT-3C87 Block Diagram

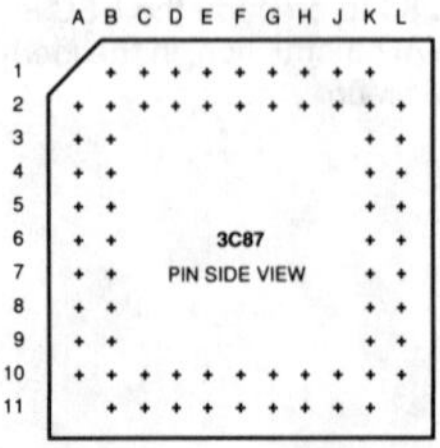

TABLE 1. 3C87 PIN CROSS REFERENCE

A2-D9	B3-D10	C10-D23	F2-V_{ss}	J1-V_{ss}	K9-NoConnect
A3-D11	B4-V_{cc}	C11-V_{ss}	F10-V_{cc}	J2-V_{cc}	K10-CPUCLK2
A4-D12	B5-D13	D1-D5	F11-V_{ss}	J10-V_{ss}	K11-NUMCLK2
A5-D14	B6-D15	D2-D4	G1-D3	J11-CKM	L2-ERROR#
A6-V_{cc}	B7-V_{ss}	D10-D24	G2-D2	K1-PEREQ	L3-READYO#
A7-D16	B8-D17	D11-D25	G10-D28	K2-BUSY#	L4-STEN
A8-D18	B9-D19	E1-V_{cc}	G11-D29	K3-Tie High	L5-V_{ss}
A9-V_{cc}	B10-D20	E2-V_{ss}	H1-D1	K4-W/R#	L6-NPS1#
A10-D21	B11-D22	E10-D26	H2-D0	K5-V_{cc}	L7-V_{cc}
B1-D8	C1-D7	E11-D27	H10-D30	K6-NPS2	L8-CMDO#
B2-V_{ss}	C2-D6	F1-V_{cc}	H11-D31	K7-ADS#	L9-Tie High
				K8-READY#	L10-RESETIN

ENHANCED PERFORMANCE

The IIT-3C87 numeric co-processor is available in speeds of 16, 20, and 25 MHz. The unique architecture of the device requires far fewer co-processor clock cycles for instruction execution. The result is a device which operates up to 50% faster than the 80387 in the same application. Table 2 compares the range of clock cycles required to perform typical floating point instructions.

TABLE 2. CLOCK CYCLES REQUIRED

INSTRUCTION	IIT-3C87	80387
ADD	11	31
MPY	15	57
DIV	44	88
SQRT	45	125
REM	54	155
TAN	192	726

FUNCTIONALITY

The IIT-3C87 is plug and object-code compatible with the Intel 80387 and is capable of running all software designed to support the 80387.

The IIT-3C87 provides extra functions which are not available on the 80387.

There are thirty-two 80-bit registers, 24 of which are available to the user as three stacks of eight registers.

FEATURES:

CMOS IMPLEMENTATION

The IIT-3C87 is implemented in 1.2 micron CMOS (16 and 20 MHz), and 1.0 micron CMOS technology (25 MHz). Device dissipation is typical at 0.6 Watt. The advantage is lower power dissipation than the Intel 80387 with corresponding improvement in reliability.

M3001 Real Time Clock

1. Summary

The M 3001 is a monolithic low power CMOS device intended to be used as a Real Time Clock for processor system applications. The internal circuit is clocked with a 32,768 Hz quartz crystal oscillator. Time information is stored in a 15 by 8 bit RAM. An 8 bit status word in the RAM stores the mode of operation programmed by the user. The 4 bit address and 8 bit data words are multiplexed via TTL compatible I/O pins. Write-in and read-out are performed as in a conventional RAM but additional interrupt facilities are also provided. The time information is in packed BCD format.

2. Features

- Easy to use like a RAM with fast access time
- Timings and levels compatible with most microprocessors
- Independent watch, alarm and timer functions
- Preset alarm time up to 1 month
- Repetitive alarm signals every month, day, hour, minute
- Timer up to 24 hours
- 4 bit address, 8 bit data in packed BCD format
- Busy output can be used as an 1Hz strobe for display control
- Very few external components needed, except crystal and battery, to keep time during power supply failure
- Different codes for "Cold-Start" and READY
- Watch counts from seconds to 99 years, indicates day of the week, and week number
- Automatic leap year correction
- Interrupt status available on the bus and on the IRQ pin
- IRQ also available during battery operation for "sleep and awake" conditions
- Test features

4. Pin Description

Pin	Name	Function
1	V_{BATT}	Battery back-up positive terminal
2	V_C	Positive chip supply terminal
3	XI	32.768Hz quartz connection
4	XO	32.768Hz quartz connection
5	V_{OSC}	Oscillator voltage
6	SYNC	Synchronisation input
7	$\overline{TE}$	Transfer enable input
8	$\overline{CS}$	Chip select input
9	$\overline{OE}$	Output enable input
10	R/$\overline{W}$	Read/Write select input
11	$\overline{A}$/D	Address/Data select input
12	V_{SS}	Ground terminal (Gnd)
13	I/O 0	
14	I/O 1	
15	I/O 2	
16	I/O 3	Data bus input/output lines (I/O 0 - I/O 7)
17	I/O 4	Address bus input lines (I/O 0 - I/O 3)
18	I/O 5	
19	I/O 6	
20	I/O 7	
21	$\overline{IRQ}$	Interrupt request line
22	$\overline{BUSY}$	Internal update cycle signal output
23	$\overline{PULSE}$	Programmable timing pulse output
24	V_{DD}	Positive supply terminal

3. Block Diagram

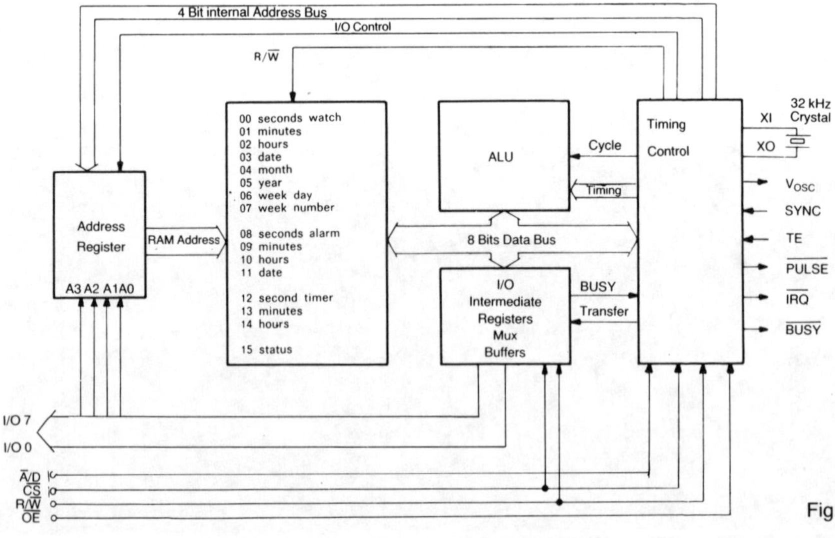

Fig. 1

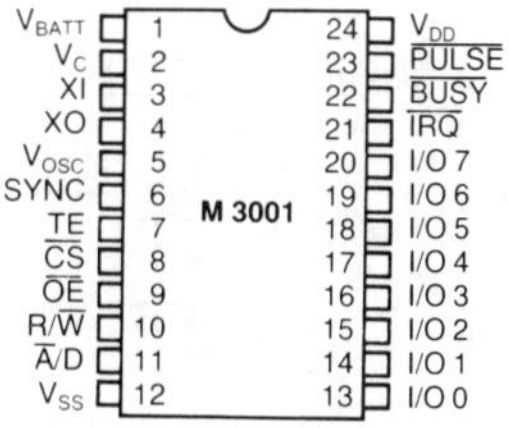

5. Absolute Maximum Ratings

Voltage V_C to V_{SS}	V_{MAX}	−0.3 to +8.0V
Voltage of any pin to V_{SS}	V_{MAX}	−0.4V
Voltage of any pin to V_C	V_{MAX}	+0.4V
Operating temperature range	T_A	−40 to +85°C
Storage temperature range	T_{STO}	−65 to +150°C

Stresses above these listed maximum ratings may cause permanent damage to the device. Exposure to absolute maximum rating conditions for extended periods may affect device reliability.

6. Handling Procedures

This device contains circuitry to protect the terminals against damage due to high static voltages or electrical fields; however, it is advised that normal precautions be taken to avoid application of any voltage higher than maximum rated voltages to the circuit. For proper operation it is recommended that all terminal voltages are constrained to the range $V_{SS} < V_{TERMINAL} < V_C - .1$, unless specially permitted. Unused inputs must always be tied to an appropriate logic voltage level (e.g. either V_{SS} or V_{DD}).

7. Functional Description

7.1. Power supply and data retention

The M 3001 may be powered with a supply voltage between 2 and 5.5V, backed up with a battery as indicated in Fig. 6 for power-down data retention. Because of the low power consumption of the device, lithium cells or standard rechargeable cells give years of effective life. When the transfer enable input TE goes to a low state, all inputs are disabled, the I/O lines and the outputs $\overline{BUSY}$ and $\overline{PULSE}$ are then set to a high impedance state. The open-drain output $\overline{IRQ}$ however will go to GND if an internal interrupt condition occurs. Thus it is possible to use the M 3001 in a "sleep and awake" condition to switch on the power system. Care should be taken that no parasitic current flows due to improper states of interfacing signal lines.

7.2. RAM

The 16 x 8 RAM is used to store all watch, alarm, timer and status data. The allocation of RAM addresses is shown in Table 1. All time data is stored in the "packed BCD format". The transfer of this data between the internal 8-bit bus and the I/O terminals is performed by the bidirectional I/O buffer. If the alarm and timer functions are not used, the RAM section allocated to the addresses 8 to E may be used as additional non-volatile system storage. In this case the data may assume any hexadecimal value. It should be noted however, that if the unused function is inadvertently activated by altering the status word, the stored data may be modified.

I/O Address Locations — Table 1

Address	Data	Group	Max. Value*	Operations
0	Seconds	WATCH	59	Time data
1	Minutes		59	incremented
2	Hours		23	under control of
3	Date		28, 29, 30, 31	status Bit 0
4	Month		12	
5	Year		99	
6	Week day		07	
7	Week no.		53	
8	Seconds	ALARM	59	Alarm data,
9	Minutes		59	providing an IRQ
A	Hours		23	under control of
B	Date		28, 29, 30, 31	status bit 1
C	Seconds	TIMER	59	Timer data
D	Minutes		59	incremented under
E	Hours		23	control of status bit 4
F	Status	STATUS		Control

* Only applicable to WATCH, ALARM and TIMER data.

7.3. Status word

The status word, stored at RAM address F, controls the timekeeping functions performed in the ALU section of the M 3001. The functions of the individual bits of the status word are shown in Table 2. The status word must be written after every break of the backup supply.

7.4. Data transfer

The interface between the M 3001 and the host microprocessor consists of eight bidirectional data lines D0 - D7, four control lines ($\overline{CS}$, $\overline{OE}$, R/$\overline{W}$ and $\overline{A}$/D), and an interrupt request line ($\overline{IRQ}$). Data and address information is separated by the address/data-input. Data present on the data bus is read from or written into the M 3001 depending on the status of the R/$\overline{W}$, $\overline{OE}$ and the $\overline{A}$/D inputs. The $\overline{OE}$ input activates the output buffers of the M 3001 during the read-out sequence. If the host processor has no appropriate output signal, $\overline{OE}$ should be connected to $\overline{CS}$.
Fig. 2a shows the flow diagram for a typical data transfer sequence with the general transfer signals shown in Fig. 4. The appropriate timings for read-out are presented in Fig. 5a; for write-in refer to Fig. 5b and 5c.
If consecutive transfers are executed (e.g. seconds, minutes, hours, date), no internal update will occur during this read-out procedure, if the time between two transfers is less than 2ms. Thus, if such procedures are repeated to look for an event or to refresh a display, the delay between two read-out procedures should be greater than 6ms, in order to enable an internal update cycle. However, maximum transfer time restrictions as described under 7.5 must be considered.

7.5. Internal update cycle

Every second, an internal time update occurs and lasts between 0.73ms and 6ms. During this update cycle, the $\overline{BUSY}$ output is low, and the data on the I/O lines will be "OFFH". The RAM is allocated to the ALU. If an external data transfer is already initiated (see Fig. 4), the internal update cycle is delayed for a maximum of one second. Then, the external transfer will be aborted.
The first time the M 3001 is powered-up, the access-code on the I/O lines is "OCOH". By this code a decision can be made whether the M 3001 has to be initialised or if the cold-start procedure may be omitted. After the first WRITE to the M 3001 the access-code changes to "OOOH" If this code is found immediately after power-up, then the back-up voltage has been functional.

Typical Program Sequence in Response to $\overline{IRQ}$

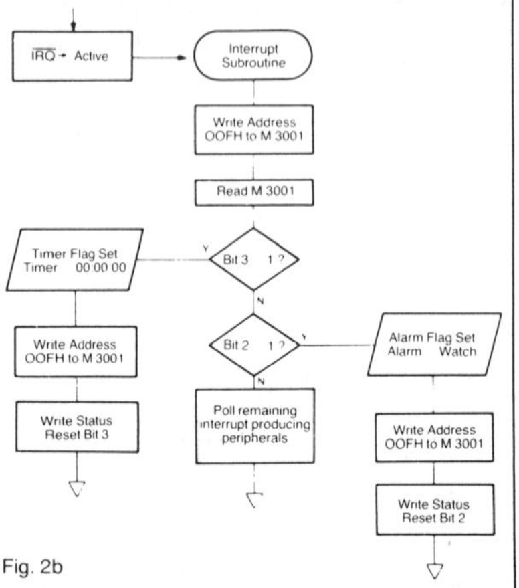

Fig. 2b

Note: "BUSY TEST" is not required provided that all accesses to the M 3001 are completed within 1 second of receipt of $\overline{IRQ}$.

Status Word Bit Allocations Table 2

Bit	Value	Function
0	0 / 1	Watch Stop / Watch Run
1	0 / 1	Alarm Disable / Alarm Enable
2	1	Alarm Flag: Alarm = Watch
3	1	Timer Flag: Timer = 0
4	0 / 1	Timer Stop / Timer Run
5, 6	00 / 01 / 10 / 11	256Hz / 1/SEC / 1/MIN / 1/HOUR — Frequency at $\overline{PULSE}$ output
7		Test Bit ("0" for normal operation)

Typical Data Transfer Sequence Fig. 2a

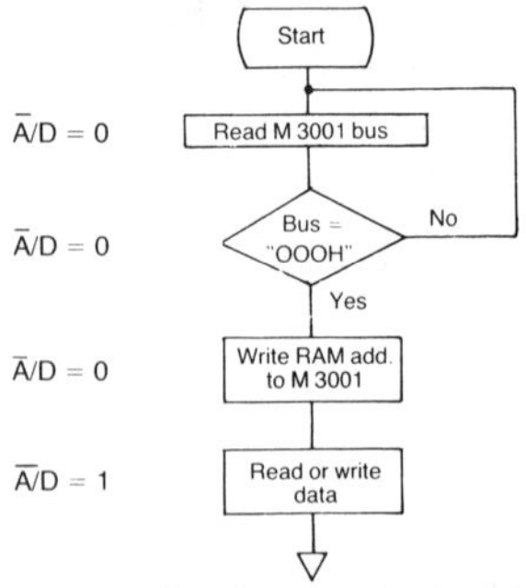

Access Codes (result of "READ M 3001 BUS")

"OFFH" = BUSY
"OCOH" = READY after POWER-UP (cold-start)
"OOOH" = READY

7.6. Alarm

An alarm date and time may be preset in RAM addresses 8 to B. During every update cycle, the ALU compares the contents of the watch addresses 0 to 3 with the preset alarm time 8 to B. When the watch data equals the alarm data and the alarm is enabled (status word bit 1), then the $\overline{IRQ}$ output goes low and the alarm flag (status word bit 2) is set. This status will remain until the alarm flag is acknowledged by resetting the interrupt flag.

If the alarm is activated (status word bit 1) and an alarm data (i.e. one of minutes, hours or date) is set to "OFFH" (hex), this register is not compared with the watch information. Thus, it is possible to achieve a "repeat" feature of the alarm without reprogramming the register.

7.7. Timer

By activating the status word bit 4 (timer run), the preset time data in RAM addresses C to E increments every second with the update cycle. When passing from 23:59:59 to 00:00:00, the timer flag (status word bit 3) is set and the $\overline{IRQ}$ output goes low until the flag is acknowledged.

7.8. $\overline{IRQ}$ output (open-drain output)

A low level on the interrupt request output $\overline{IRQ}$ indicates that either the preprogrammed alarm data matches the clock data, or that the timer data has incremented from 23:59:59 to 00:00:00, provided that the appropriate function is active. The output can be wire-ored to the system interrupt line. Once activated, $\overline{IRQ}$ will remain low until being acknowledged by clearing the appropriate interrupt flag of the status word. A typical program sequence in response to an $\overline{IRQ}$ signal is shown in Fig. 2b.

7.9. $\overline{PULSE}$ output

The $\overline{PULSE}$ output may be programmed with bits 5 and 6 of the status word to produce a negative pulse of 64μs width every second, minute or hour, while the watch is running. The 256Hz square wave option is available independently of the watch function. The timing of the output pulse waveforms is shown in Fig. 3.

7.10 SYNC input

If the SYNC input is set high for longer than 200μs, the watch will synchronize to the rising edge of this SYNC signal with a precision of $\pm$2ms. The seconds register is cleared and, if the content is $\geq$30, the minutes register will be incremented.

7.11. V_{OSC} pin

On this pin the voltage of the internal regulated oscillator is available. In standard applications this pin is left open. It may be used for test purposes (see 7.13).

7.12. Frequency tuning

The frequency of the oscillator can be tuned with the variable capacitor between XI and V_C (see fig. 6).

We recommand the use of ETA quartz crystals, and that the XI/XO pins are shielded with a ring connected to the V_C pad.

7.13. Test

From the various test features added to the M 3001, some may also be activated by the user. By setting bits 7 and 5 of the status word simultaneously high, all watch and timer data will increment in parallel at a rate of 1Hz depending on the status of bits 1 and 4 of the status word. To enter another test mode bit 7 of the status word must be set high and then the SYNC input tied high. The V_{OSC} pin should be connected to V_{SS}. This will bypass the first 5 divider stages and connect XI directly to the 1024Hz node of the divider chain. With a quartz being connected between XI and XO, all operations of the M 3001 will be accelerated 32 times. Higher speeds can be achieved by feeding XO directly from a pulse generator. One must exit from the test mode by setting bit 7 of the status word low. Every activation of $\overline{CS}$ will immediately exit the test mode, but the status word shall be properly rewritten. Further information on test features are available on request.

Electrical Specifications

(V_C = 5V, T_A = 0 – 85°C, unless otherwise specified.)

Parameter	Symbol	Test Conditions	Min.	Typ.	Max.	Units
Positive Supply Voltage	V_{DD}	wrt V_{SS}	2.5	5.5	6	V
Positive Chip Voltage	V_C	wrt V_{SS}	2.0	5	5.5	V
Total Supply Current	I_C	V_C = 5V, Inputs at V_C or V_{SS}		6	10	μA
		V_C = 3V, Inputs at V_C or V_{SS} TE at V_{SS}		4	8	μA
I/O Lines						
Input High Voltage	V_{IH}		2.4	0.5V_C	V_C	V
TE Input High Voltage	V_{IH} (TE)		V_{DD} – 1			V
Input Low Voltage	V_{IL}		V_{SS}		0.8	V
Output High Voltage	V_{OH}	I_{OH} = 3.2mA	4.0			V
Output High Voltage	V_{OH} (IRQ)	Open drain, I_L = 5μA (max.)			10	V
Output Low Voltage	V_{OL}	I_{OL} = 3.6mA			0.4	V
Input leakage Current TE	I_L	$V_{SS} < V_{TREN} < V_C$			1	μA
Input Currents for Inputs	I_{IN}	$\underline{V_{SS}} < \underline{V_{IN}} < V_C$			0.5	μA
3-State HI-Z Leakage Current	$I_{Hi\text{-}Z}$	$\overline{OE}$ or $\overline{CS}$ at V_{DD}			1	μA
Switching Characteristics		C_{LOAD} = 50pF				
Chip Select Duration	t_{CS}		0.15			μs
Time between 2 Transfers	t_W		1.0			μs
RAM Access Time	t_{ACC}			0.15	0.2	μs
Data Valid to High Impedance	$t_{Hi\text{-}Z}$				0.15	μs
Data Settle Time	t_{DW}		0.15			μs
TE Response Delay	t_{TE}				1	μs
Data Hold Time	t_{DH}		0			ns
Oscillator						
Starting Voltage	V_{START}	C_T = 20pF	1.8			V
Input Capacitance	C_{IN}	V_C = 0		3.7		pF
Output Capacitance	C_{OUT}	V_C = 0		25		pF
Build-up Time	T_{START}	C_T = 20pF		0.6	1	s
Stability	df / f	C_T = 5pF, 2V ≤ V_{BATT} ≤ 5V		0.2	0.5	ppm/V
Trimmer Capacitance	C_T		3		30	pF
Crystal Characteristics						
Frequency	f			32768		Hz
R_{QUARTZ}	R_Q			40	60	kΩ
C_O	C_O			1.5		fF
C_I	C_I			1.7		pF

Output Signals

T_{SEC} = 0.730ms
T_{MIN} = 1.04 to 1.16ms
T_{HOUR} = 1.34 to 1.58ms
T_{BUSY} = 0.73 to 6ms
PW = 64μs

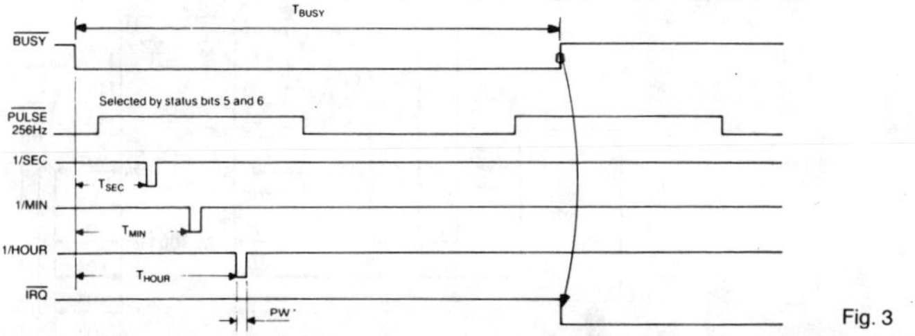

Fig. 3

Transfer Waveforms

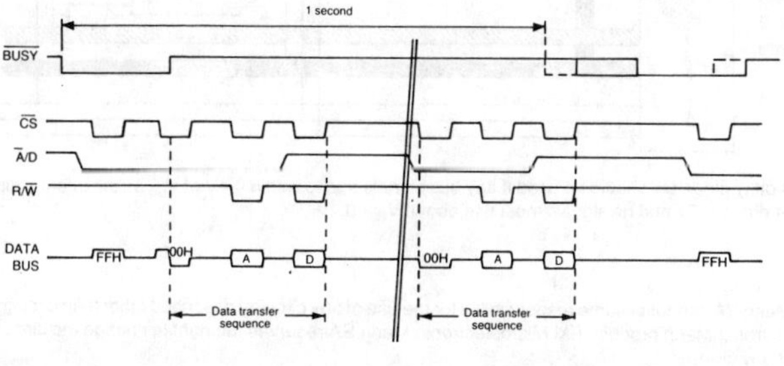

A = Address
D = Data

Fig. 4

Read Timing

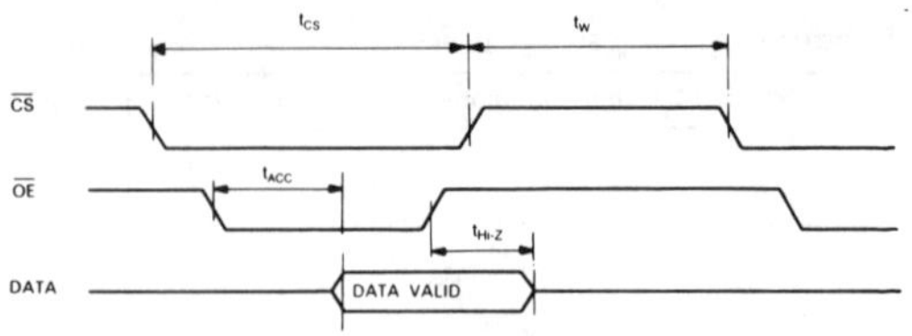

Fig. 5a

Write Timing 1
OE on the control bus

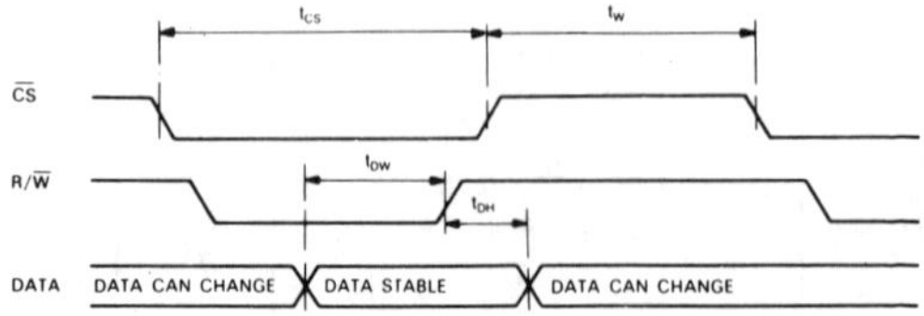

Fig. 5b

Write Timing 2
OE connected to CS

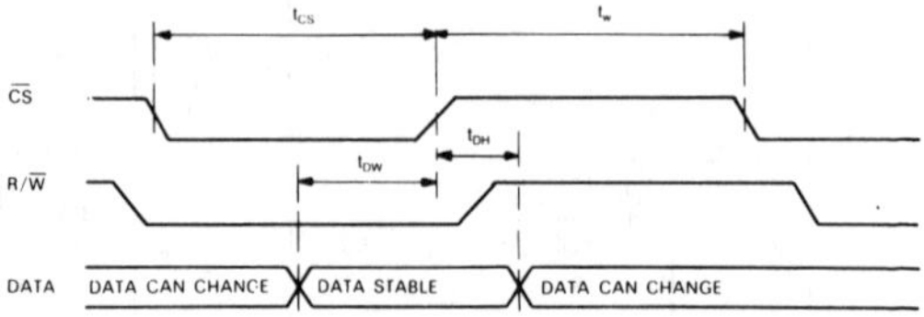

Fig. 5c

8. Typical Application and Test Configuration

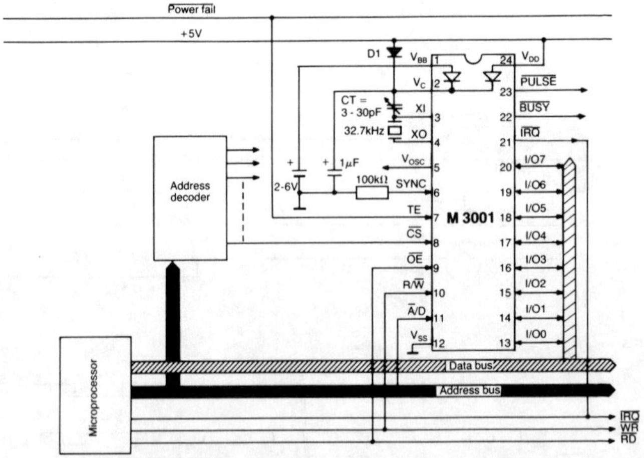

Fig. 6

A Schottky diode D1 should be used if any bus signals rise to within 0.4V of V_{DD} as the internal diode on pin 24 drops 0.7V and no signals must rise above V_C +0.4V.

Real Time Clock M3002

1. Summary

The M 3002 is a monolithic low power CMOS device intended to be used as a Real Time Clock for processor system applications. The internal circuit is clocked with a 32,768 Hz quartz crystal oscillator. Time information is stored in a 15 by 8 bit RAM. An 8 bit status word in the RAM stores the mode of operation programmed by the user. The 4 bit address and data words are multiplexed via TTL compatible I/O pins. Write-in and read-out are performed as in a conventional RAM but additional interrupt facilities are also provided. The time information is in BCD format.

2. Features

- Easy to use like a RAM with fast access time
- Timings and levels compatible with most microprocessors
- Independent watch, alarm and timer functions
- Preset alarm time up to 1 month
- Timer up to 24 hours
- Busy, interrupt and timing output signals provided
- 4 bit BCD format; display system compatible
- Busy output can be used as an 1Hz strobe for display control
- Low battery current
- Very few external components needed, except crystal and battery, to keep time during power supply failure
- Watch counts from seconds to 99 years, indicates day of the week, week number, and leap year
- Automatic leap year correction
- Interrupt status available on the bus and on the $\overline{IRQ}$ pin
- Synchronisation input to tune the device by an external time reference
- Test features added

4. Pin Description

Pin	Name	Function
1	V_{BB}	Negative battery terminal
2	XI	32,768 Hz quartz connection
3	XO	32,768 Hz quartz connection
4	$\overline{SYNC}$	Watch seconds synchronisation input
5	$R/\overline{W}$	Read/write select input
6	$\overline{OE}$	Output enable input
7	$\overline{CS}$	Chip select input
8	V_{SS}	Ground terminal (GND)
9	I/O 0	Data bus input/output lines, Address bus input lines
10	I/O 1	Data bus input/output lines, Address bus input lines
11	I/O 2	Data bus input/output lines, Address bus input lines
12	I/O 3	Data bus input/output lines, Address bus input lines
13	$\overline{IRQ}$	Interrupt request output
14	$\overline{BUSY}$	Internal update cycle signal output
15	$\overline{PULSE}$	Programmable timing pulse output
16	V_{DD}	Positive supply terminal

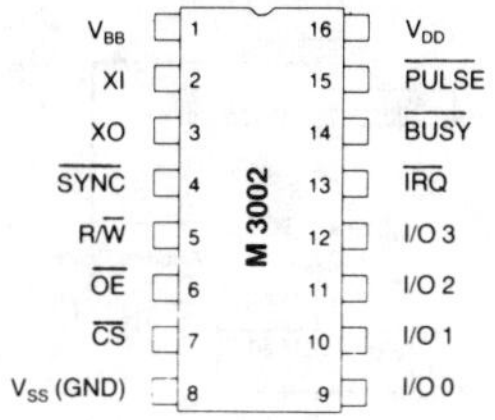

3. Block Diagram

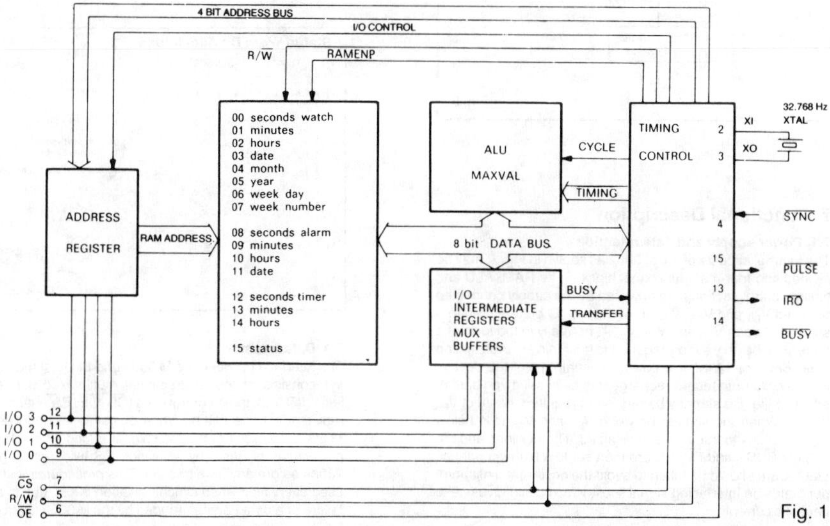

Fig. 1

5. Absolute Maximum Ratings

Voltage V_{DD} to V_{SS}	V_{MAX}	−0.3 to +8.0V
Voltage of any pin to V_{SS}	V_{MAX}	−0.3V
Voltage of any pin to V_{DD}	V_{MAX}	+0.3V
Operating temperature range	T_A	−40 to +85°C
Storage temperature range	T_{STO}	−65 to +150°C

Stresses beyond these listed maximum ratings may cause malfunction of or permanent damage to the device. Exposure to absolute maximum rating conditions for extended periods may affect device reliability.

6. Handling Procedures

This device contains circuitry to protect the terminals against damage due to high static voltages or electrical fields; however, it is advised that normal precautions be taken to avoid application of any voltage higher than maximum rated voltages to this circuit. For proper operation it is recommended that all terminal voltages are constrained to the range $V_{SS} < V_{TERMINAL} < V_{DD}$, unless specially permitted. Unused inputs must always be tied to an appropriate logic voltage level (e.g. either V_{SS} or V_{DD}).

Typical Data Transfer

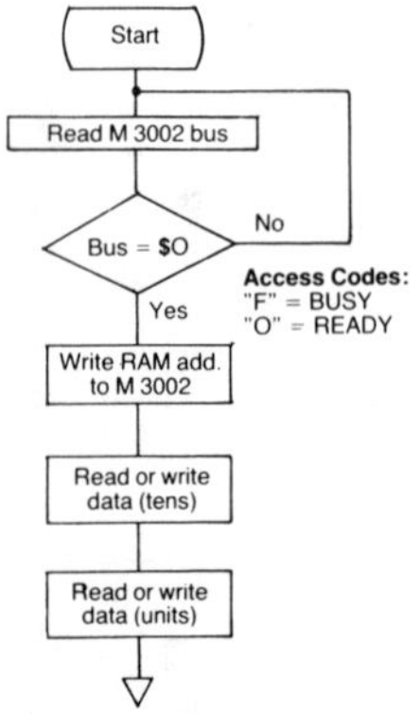

Fig. 2

7. Functional Description

7.1. Power supply and data retention

The internal circuitry of the M 3002 as shown in Fig. 1, may be divided into four main functional blocks. The RAM, ALU and timing control sections are powered by the supply connected between V_{DD} and V_{BB} (V_{BATT}), whilst the I/O buffers require a supply between V_{DD} and V_{SS}. V_{BATT}, normally in the form of a battery, is the only supply required to maintain accurate timing data. Because of the low power consumption of the device, lithium cells or standard rechargeable cells will give years of effective life. If a standby battery is not required, connect V_{BB} to V_{SS}. When the voltage between V_{DD} and V_{SS} falls below V_{BATT}, access to the device is disabled. The I/O lines and the outputs $\overline{BUSY}$ and $\overline{PULSE}$ are then set to a high impedance state. Care should be taken to avoid the occurrence of improper states on interfacing signal lines, which could give rise to parasitic currents.

7.2. RAM

The 16 x 8 RAM is used to store all watch, alarm, timer and status data. The allocation of RAM addresses is shown in Table 1. All time data is stored in the form of two 4-bit BCD words. The transfer of this data between the internal 8-bit bus and the I/O terminals is performed by the bidirectional I/O buffer and multiplexer. If the alarm and timer functions are not used, the RAM section allocated to the addresses 8 to E may be used as an additional non-volatile system storage. In this case the data may assume any hexadecimal value. It should be noted however, that if the unused function is inadvertently activated by altering the status word, the stored data may be modified.

7.3. Status word

The status word, stored at RAM address F, controls the time-keeping functions performed in the ALU section of the M 3002. The functions of the individual bits of the status word are shown in Table 2. The status word shall be written after every break of the backup supply.

I/O Address Locations Table 1

Address	Data	Group	Max. Value*	Operations
0	Seconds	WATCH	59	Time data
1	Minutes		59	incremented
2	Hours		23	under control of
3	Date		28, 29, 30, 31	status Bit 0
4	Month		12	
5	Year		99	
6	Week day		07	
7	Week no.		53	
8	Seconds	ALARM	59	Alarm data,
9	Minutes		59	providing an IRQ
A	Hours		23	under control of
B	Date		28, 29, 30, 31	status bit 1
C	Seconds	TIMER	59	Timer data
D	Minutes		59	incremented under
E	Hours		23	control of status bit 4
F	Status	STATUS		Control

* Only applicable to WATCH, ALARM and TIMER data.

Status Word Bit Allocations Table 2

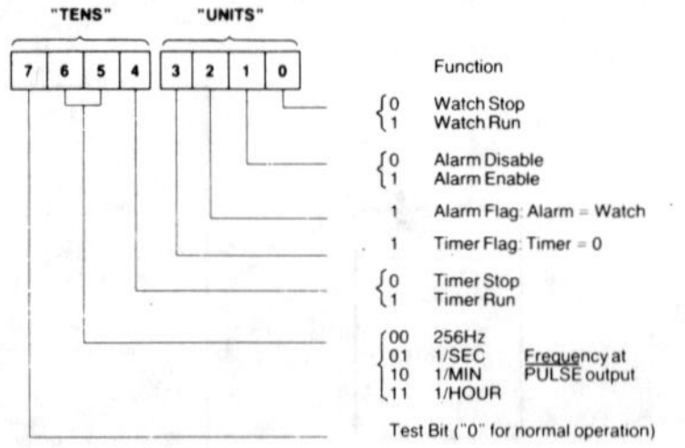

7.4. Data transfer

The interface between the M 3002 and the host microprocessor consists of four bidirectional multiplexed data/address lines (I/O 0-3), three control lines ($\overline{CS}$, $\overline{OE}$, R/$\overline{W}$), and an interrupt request line ($\overline{IRQ}$). When power is first applied to the M 3002, the state of the multiplexer is undefined. The multiplexer may be reset by activating $\overline{CS}$ twice for longer than 280ns before any data transfer. This procedure must also be used every time when synchronisation is lost, due to a power failure or a data transfer aborted by the M 3002. Data present

on the I/O lines is read from or written into the M 3002 depending on the status of the R/$\overline{W}$ and $\overline{OE}$ input signal. The $\overline{OE}$ input activates the output buffers of the M 3002 during the read-out sequence. If the host processor has no appropriate output signal, $\overline{OE}$ should be connected to $\overline{CS}$.
Fig. 2 shows the flow diagram for a typical data transfer sequence, with the general transfer signals shown in Fig. 4. The appropriate timings for read-out are presented in Fig. 5a; for write-in refer to Fig. 5b.

7.5. Internal update cycle

Every second, an internal time update occurs and lasts between 0.73ms and 6ms. During this update cycle, the multiplexer is reset, the $\overline{BUSY}$ output is low, and the data on the I/O lines will be "F". The RAM is allocated to the ALU. If an external data transfer is already initiated (see 7.4.), the internal update cycle is delayed for a maximum of one second. Then, the external transfer will be aborted.

7.6. Alarm

An alarm date and time may be preset in RAM addresses 8 to B. During every update cycle, the ALU compares the contents of the watch addresses 0 to 3 with the preset alarm time. When the watch data equals the alarm data and the alarm is enabled (status word bit 1), then the $\overline{IRQ}$ output goes low and the alarm flag (status word bit 2) is set. This status will remain until the alarm flag is acknowledged.

Typical Program Sequence in Response to $\overline{IRQ}$

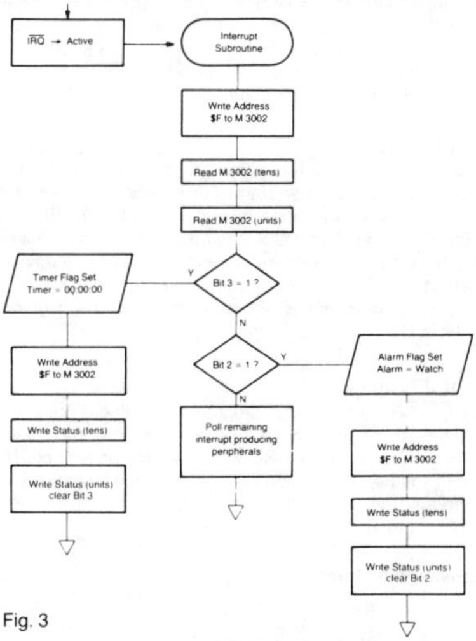

Fig. 3

Note: "BUSY TEST" is not required provided that all accesses to the M 3002 are completed within 1 second of receipt of IRQ.

Electrical Specifications

V_{DD} = 5V, V_{BATT} = 3V, T_A = 0 – 70°C, unless otherwise specified.

Parameter	Symbol	Test Conditions	Min.	Typ.	Max.	Units
Positive Supply Voltage	V_{DD}	wrt V_{SS}	2	5	5.5	V
Battery Current [1]	I_{DD}	$V_{BATT} = 5V, V_{DD} = V_{SS}$		12	20	µA
		$V_{BATT} = 3V, V_{DD} = V_{SS}$		5	8	µA
Total Supply Current [1]	I_{DD}	$V_{BATT} = 3V, V_{DD} - V_{SS} = 5V$ Inputs at V_{DD} or V_{SS}			10	µA
I/O Lines						
Input High Voltage	V_{IH}		2.4	$0.5V_{DD}$	V_{DD}	V
Input Low Voltage	V_{IL}		V_{SS}		0.8	V
Output High Voltage	V_{OH}	$I_{OH} = 2.0mA$	2.4			V
Output High Voltage for $\overline{IRQ}$	V_{OH}	100k pullup to V_{DD}	2.4			V
Output Low Voltage	V_{OL}	$I_{OL} = 3.2mA$			0.4	V
Input Leakage Current	I_L	$V_{SS} \leq V_{in} \leq V_{DD}$			1	µA
3-State HI-Z Leakage Current	I_{HI-Z}	OE or CS at V_{DD}			1	µA
Switching Characteristics		$C_L = 50pF$				
Chip Select Duration	t_{CS}	See Note	0.28			µs
Time between 2 Transfers	t_W		1.0			µs
Ram Access Time	t_{ACC}			0.15	0.27	µs
Data Valid to High Impedance	t_{DF}			0.18	0.3	µs
Data Settle Time	t_{DW}		0.2			µs
Data Hold Time	t_{DH}		0			µs
Oscillator						
Starting Voltage	V_{START}	$C_T = 18pF$	1.8			V
Input Capacitance	C_{IN}	Circuit unpowered		3.7		pF
Output Capacitance	C_{OUT}	Circuit unpowered		25		pF
Build up Time	T_{START}	$C_T = 18pF$		0.6	5	s
Stability	$\Delta f/f$	$C_T = 5pF, 2V \leq V_{BATT} \leq 5V$		5	10	ppm/V
Crystal Characteristics						
Frequency	F			32,768		Hz
R_{Quartz}	R_q			40	60	kΩ
C_O	C_O			1.5		pF
C_I	C_I			1.7		fF
Trimmer Capacitance	C_T		5		40	pF

Note: CS glitches even shorter than 0.2µs may be recorded by the M 3002 and cause malfunction.
[1] Current as tested in production with a simulated crystal waveform.

7.7. Timer

By activating the status word bit 4 (timer run), the preset time data in RAM addresses C to E increments every second with the update cycle. When passing from 23:59:59 to 00:00:00, the timer flag (status word bit 3) is set and the $\overline{IRQ}$ output goes low until the flag is acknowledged.

7.8. $\overline{IRQ}$ output

A low state on the interrupt request output $\overline{IRQ}$ indicates that either the preprogrammed alarm data matches the clock data, or that the timer data has incremented from 23:59:59 to 00:00:00, provided that the appropriate function is active. Once activated, $\overline{IRQ}$ will remain low until it is acknowledged by resetting the appropriate interrupt flag of the status word. A typical program sequence in response to an IRQ signal is shown in Fig. 3.

7.9. $\overline{PULSE}$ output

The $\overline{PULSE}$ output may be programmed with bits 5 and 6 of the status word to produce a negative pulse of 64μs width every second, minute or hour, while the watch is running. The 256Hz square wave option is available independently of the watch function. The timing of the output pulse waveforms is shown in Fig. 6.

7.10 $\overline{SYNC}$ input

If the $\overline{SYNC}$ input is set low for longer than 200μs, the watch will synchronize to the falling edge of this $\overline{SYNC}$ signal with a precision of ±2ms. The seconds register is cleared and, if the content is ≥30, the minutes register will be incremented.

7.11. Frequency tuning

The frequency of the oscillator can be tuned with the variable capacitor between XI and V_{DD}. A control signal in the form of a 256Hz square wave is available on the $\overline{PULSE}$ output (see 7.9.).

We recommend the use of ETA quartz crystals having C_L = 10pF, and that the XI / XO pins are shielded with a ring connected to V_{DD}.

7.12. Test

From the various test features added to the M 3002, some may also be activated by the user. A first test mode can be entered by setting bits 7 and 5 high with bit 6 immaterial, leaving input $\overline{SYNC}$ high. All watch and timer data will increment in parallel at the rate of 1Hz depending on the status of bits 1 and 4 of the status word. To enter the second test mode, bit 7 of the status word must be set high, bits 5 and 6 set low, and then the $\overline{SYNC}$ input tied low. This will bypass the first 5 divider stages and connect pin XI directly to the 1kHz node of the divider chain, which must be then driven by a signal generator. At 32'678 Hz,

Transfer Waveforms

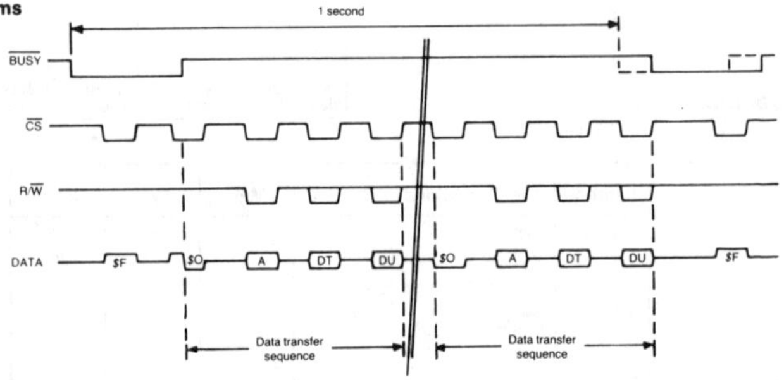

A = Address
DT = Data, tens
DU = Data, units

Fig. 4

Read Timing

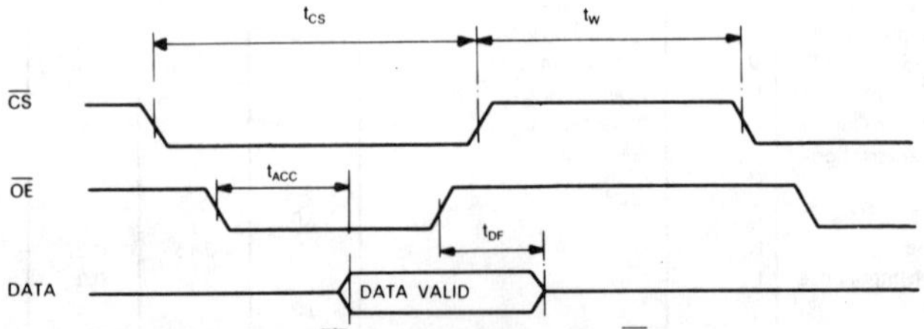

Fig. 5a

Note: If $\overline{CS}$ = 0 starts later than $\overline{OE}$ = 0, then t_{ACC} is referred to $\overline{CS}$.

Write Timing

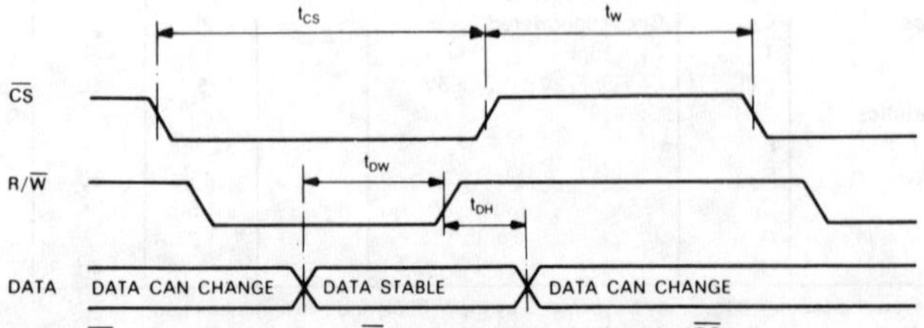

Fig. 5b

Note: If $\overline{CS}$ = 0 ends sooner than R/$\overline{W}$ = 0, t_{DW} and t_{DH} are referred to $\overline{CS}$.

the time counting will be speeded up by a factor of 32. Higher speeds can be achieved by speeding up the pulse generator. Modifying the status register as for the first test mode will combine both tests. To leave the test mode, set status bit 7 low. Every activation of $\overline{CS}$ will immediately exit the test mode, but the status word has to be properly rewritten.

Output Signals

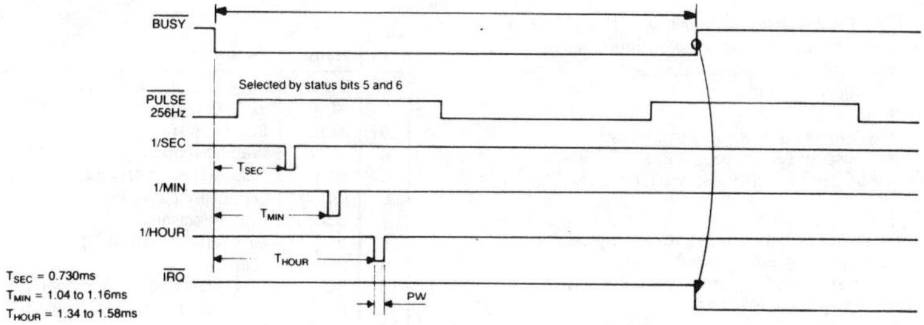

Fig. 6

8. Typical Application and Test Configuration

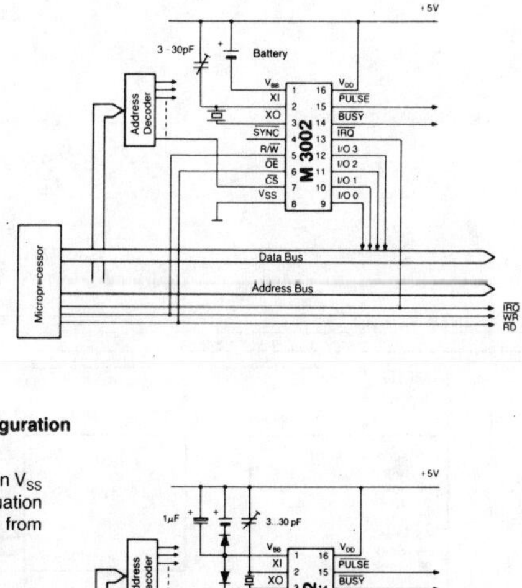

Fig. 7

8.1. Low Battery Current Configuration

Note: The 1 μF and 1k protect pin V_{SS} against excessive voltage fluctuation during violent switchovers to or from battery supply.

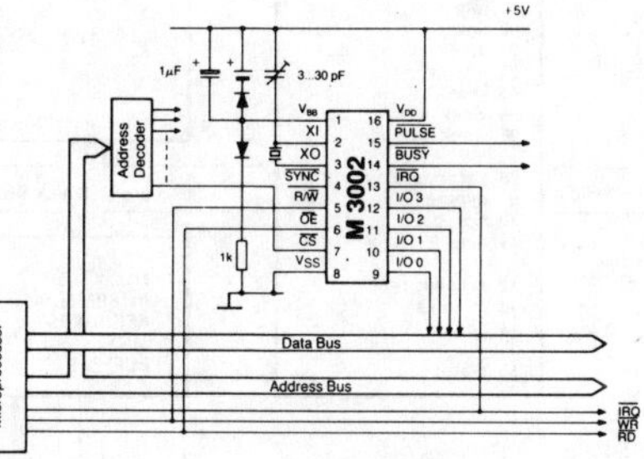

Fig. 8

M3003 Real Time Clock

1. Summary

The M 3003 is a monolithic low power CMOS device intended to be used as a Real Time Clock for processor system applications. The internal circuit is clocked with a 32,768 Hz quartz crystal oscillator. Time information is stored in a 15 by 8 bit RAM. An 8 bit status word in the RAM stores the mode of operation programmed by the user. The 4 bit address and data words are multiplexed via TTL compatible I/O pins. Write-in and read-out are performed as in a conventional RAM but additional interrupt facilities are also provided. The time information is in BCD format.

2. Features

- Easy to use like a RAM with fast access time
- Timings and levels compatible with most microprocessors
- Independent watch, alarm and timer functions
- Preset alarm time up to 1 month
- Timer up to 24 hours
- Busy, interrupt and timing output signals provided
- 4 bit BCD format; display system compatible
- Busy output can be used as an 1Hz strobe for display control
- Low standby battery current
- Very few external components needed, except crystal and battery, to keep time during power supply failure
- Watch counts from seconds to 99 years, indicates day of the week, week number, and leap year
- Automatic leap year correction
- Interrupt status available on the bus and on the $\overline{IRQ}$ pin
- $\overline{IRQ}$ also available during battery operation for "sleep and awake" conditions
- Synchronisation input to tune the device by an external time reference
- Test features added

4. Pin Description

Pin	Name	Function
1	V_{DD}	Positive supply terminal
2	XI	32,768 Hz quartz connection
3	XO	32,768 Hz quartz connection
4	SYNC	Watch seconds synchronisation input
5	R/W	Read/write select input
6	OE	Output enable input
7	CS	Chip select input
8	V_{SS}	Ground terminal (GND)
9	I/O 0	Data bus input/output lines, Address bus input lines
10	I/O 1	Data bus input/output lines, Address bus input lines
11	I/O 2	Data bus input/output lines, Address bus input lines
12	I/O 3	Data bus input/output lines, Address bus input lines
13	IRQ	Interrupt request output
14	BUSY	Internal update cycle signal output
15	PULSE	Programmable timing pulse output
16	TE	Transfer enable input

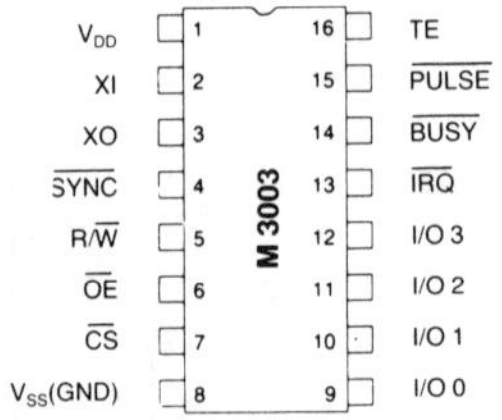

3. Block Diagram

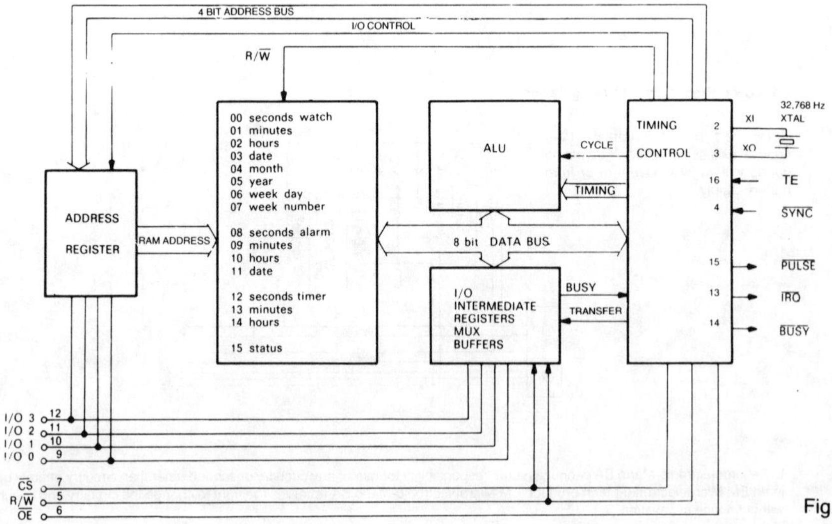

Fig. 1

5. Absolute Maximum Ratings

Voltage V_{DD} to V_{SS}	V_{MAX}	−0.3 to +8.0V
Voltage of any pin to V_{SS}	V_{MAX}	−0.3V
Voltage of any pin to V_{DD}	V_{MAX}	+0.5V
Operating temperature range	T_A	−40 to +85°C
Storage temperature range	T_{STO}	−65 to +150°C

Stresses above these listed maximum ratings may cause permanent damage to the device. Exposure to absolute maximum rating conditions for extended periods may affect device reliability.

6. Handling Procedures

This device contains circuitry to protect the terminals against damage due to high static voltages or electrical fields; however, it is advised that normal precautions be taken to avoid application of any voltage higher than maximum rated voltages to this circuit. For proper operation it is recommended that all terminal voltages are constrained to the range $V_{SS} < V_{TERMINAL} < V_{DD}$, unless specially permitted. Unused inputs must always be tied to an appropriate logic voltage level (e.g. either V_{SS} or V_{DD}).

Typical Data Transfer Sequence

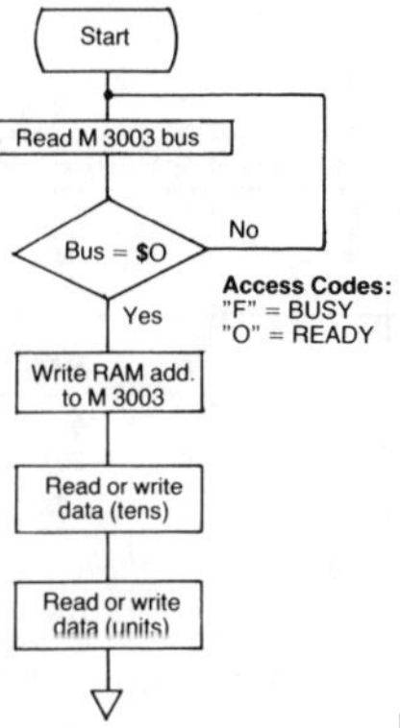

Fig. 2

7. Functional Description

7.1. Power supply and data retention

The M 3003 may be powered with a supply voltage between 2 and 5.5V, backed up with a battery as indicated in Fig. 7 for power-down data retention. Because of the low power consumption of the device, lithium cells or standard rechargeable cells give years of effective life. When the transfer enable input TE goes to a low state, all inputs are disabled, and the I/O lines and the outputs $\overline{BUSY}$ and $\overline{PULSE}$ are set to a high impedance state. The open-drain output $\overline{IRQ}$ will still go to GND if an internal interrupt condition occurs. Thus it is possible to use the M 3003 in a "sleep and awake" condition to switch on the power system. Care should be taken that no parasitic current flows due to improper states of interfacing signal lines.

7.2. RAM

The 16 x 8 RAM is used to store all watch, alarm, timer and status data. The allocation of RAM addresses is shown in Table 1. All time data is stored in the form of two 4-bit BCD words. The transfer of this data between the internal 8-bit bus and the I/O terminals is performed by the bidirectional I/O buffer and multiplexer. If the alarm and timer functions are not used, the RAM section allocated to the addresses 8 to E may be used as an additional non-volatile system storage. In this case the data may assume any hexadecimal value. It should be noted however, that if the unused function is inadvertently activated by altering the status word, the stored data may be modified.

7.3. Status word

The status word, stored at RAM address F, controls the timekeeping functions performed in the ALU section of the M 3003. The functions of the individual bits of the status word are shown in Table 2. The status word must be written after every break of the backup supply.

I/O Address Locations Table 1

Address	Data	Group	Max. Value*	Operations
0	Seconds	WATCH	59	Time data
1	Minutes		59	incremented
2	Hours		23	under control of
3	Date		28, 29, 30, 31	status Bit 0
4	Month		12	
5	Year		99	
6	Week day		07	
7	Week no.		53	
8	Seconds	ALARM	59	Alarm data,
9	Minutes		59	providing an IRQ
A	Hours		23	under control of
B	Date		28, 29, 30, 31	status bit 1
C	Seconds	TIMER	59	Timer data
D	Minutes		59	incremented under
E	Hours		23	control of status bit 4
F	Status	STATUS		Control

* Only applicable to WATCH, ALARM and TIMER data.

Status Word Bit Allocations Table 2

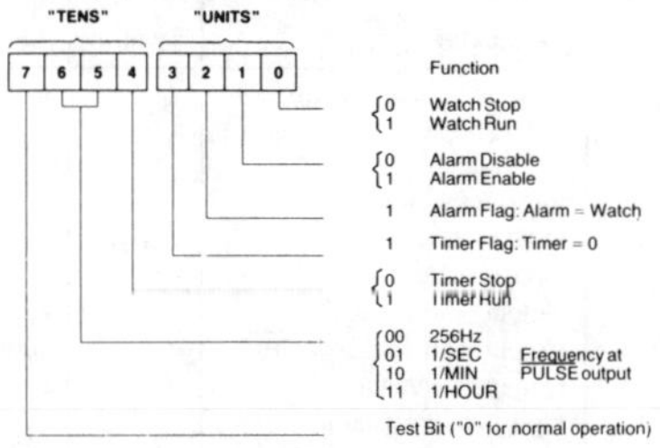

7.4. Data transfer

The interface between the M 3003 and the host microprocessor consists of four bidirectional multiplexed data/address lines (I/O 0-3), three control lines ($\overline{CS}$, $\overline{OE}$, R/$\overline{W}$), and an interrupt request line ($\overline{IRQ}$). When power is first applied to the M 3003, the state of the multiplexer is undefined. The multiplexer may be reset by activating $\overline{CS}$ twice for longer than 280ns before any data transfer. This procedure may also be used every time when synchronisation is lost, due to a power failure or a data transfer aborted by the M 3003. Data present on the I/O lines is read from or written into the M 3003 depending on the status of the R/$\overline{W}$ and $\overline{OE}$ input signal. The $\overline{OE}$ input activates the output buffers of the M 3003 during the read-out sequence. If the host processor has no appropriate output signal, $\overline{OE}$ should be connected to $\overline{CS}$.

Fig. 2 shows the flow diagram for a typical data transfer sequence, with the general transfer signals shown in Fig. 4. The appropriate timings for read-out are presented in Fig. 5a; for write-in refer to Fig. 5b.

If consecutive transfers are executed (e.g. seconds, minutes, hours, date), no internal update will occur during this procedure, if the time between two transfers is less than 2ms. Thus, if such procedures are repeated to look for an event or to refresh a display, the delay between two procedures should be greater than 6ms, in order to enable an internal update cycle. However, maximum transfer time restrictions as described under 7.5 must be considered.

7.5. Internal update cycle
Every second, an internal time update occurs and lasts between 0.73ms and 6ms. During this update cycle, the multiplexer is reset, the $\overline{BUSY}$ output is low, and the data on the I/O lines will be "F". The RAM is allocated to the ALU. If an external data transfer is already initiated (see 7.4.), the internal update cycle is delayed for a maximum of one second. Then, the external transfer will be aborted.

7.6. Alarm
An alarm date and time may be preset in RAM addresses 8 to B. During every update cycle, the ALU compares the contents of the watch addresses 0 to 3 with the preset alarm time. When the watch data equals the alarm data and the alarm is enabled (status word bit 1), then the $\overline{IRQ}$ output goes low and the alarm flag (status word bit 2) is set. This status will remain until the alarm flag is acknowledged.

7.7. Timer
By activating the status word bit 4 (timer run), the preset time data in RAM addresses C to E increments every second with the update cycle. When passing from 23:59:59 to 00:00:00, the timer flag (status word bit 3) is set and the $\overline{IRQ}$ output goes low until the flag is acknowledged.

Typical Program Sequence in Response to $\overline{IRQ}$

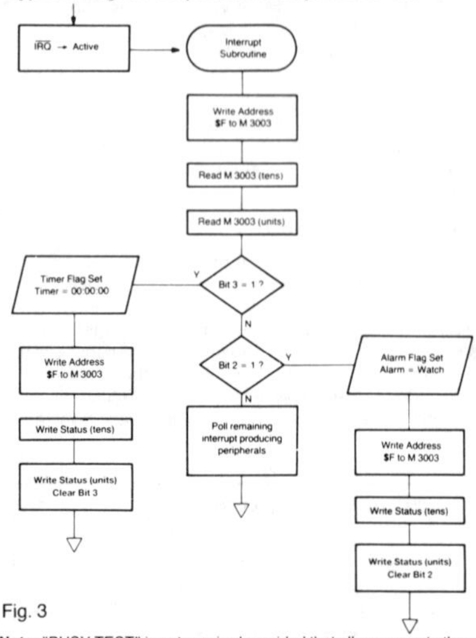

Fig. 3

Note: "BUSY TEST" is not required provided that all accesses to the M 3003 are completed within 1 second of receipt of IRQ.

Electrical Specifications

V_{DD} = 5V, T_A = 0 – 70°C, unless otherwise specified.

Parameter	Symbol	Test Conditions	Min.	Typ.	Max.	Units
Positive Supply Voltage	V_{DD}	wrt V_{SS}	2	5	5.5	V
Total Supply Current	I_{DD}	V_{DD} = 5V, Inputs at V_{DD} or V_{SS}		12	20	μA
		V_{DD} = 3V, Inputs at V_{DD} or V_{SS}		5	8	μA
Interface Lines						
Input High Voltage	V_{IH}		2.4		V_{DD}	V
Input Low Voltage	V_{IL}		V_{SS}		0.8	V
Output High Voltage	V_{OH}	I_{OH} = 2.0mA	2.4			V
Output High Voltage for $\overline{IRQ}$	V_{OH}	100k pull-up to V_{DD}	2.4			V
Output Low Voltage	V_{OL}	I_{OL} = 3.2mA			0.4	V
Input Leakage Current	I_L	$V_{SS} \leq V_{in} \leq V_{DD}$			1	μA
3-State HI-Z Leakage Current	$I_{HI\text{-}Z}$	OE or CS at V_{DD}			1	μA
Switching Characteristics		C_L = 50pF				
Chip Select Duration	t_{CS}	See Note	0.2			μs
Time between 2 Transfers	t_W		1.0			μs
Ram Access Time	t_{ACC}			0.15	0.2	μs
Data Valid to High Impedance	t_{DF}				0.18	μs
Data Settle Time	t_{DW}		0.2			μs
Data Hold Time	t_{DH}		0			μs
TE Response Delay	t_{TE}				0.18	μs
Oscillator						
Starting Voltage	V_{START}	C_T = 18pF	1.8			V
Input Capacitance	C_{IN}	V_{BATT} = 0		3.7		pF
Output Capacitance	C_{OUT}	V_{BATT} = 0		25		pF
Build up Time	T_{START}	C_T = 18pF		0.6	5	s
Stability	$\Delta f/f$	C_T = 5pF, 2V ≤ V_{BATT} ≤ 5V		5	10	ppm/V
Crystal Characteristics						
Frequency	F			32,768		Hz
R_{Quartz}	R_q			40	60	kΩ
C_O	C_O			1.5		pF
C_I	C_I			1.7		fF
Trimmer Capacitance	C_T		5		40	pF

Note: $\overline{CS}$ glitches even shorter than 0.2μs may be recorded by the M 3003 and cause malfunction

7.8. $\overline{\text{IRQ}}$ output

A low state on the interrupt request output $\overline{\text{IRQ}}$ indicates that either the preprogrammed alarm data matches the clock data, or that the timer data has incremented from 23:59:59 to 00:00:00, provided that the appropriate function is active. Once activated, $\overline{\text{IRQ}}$ will remain low until it is acknowledged by resetting the appropriate interrupt flag of the status word. A typical program sequence in response to an IRQ signal is shown in Fig. 3.

7.9. $\overline{\text{PULSE}}$ output

The $\overline{\text{PULSE}}$ output may be programmed with bits 5 and 6 of the status word to produce a negative pulse of 64μs width every second, minute or hour, while the watch is running. The 256Hz square wave option is available independently of the watch function. The timing of the output pulse waveforms is shown in Fig. 6.

7.10 $\overline{\text{SYNC}}$ input

If the $\overline{\text{SYNC}}$ input is set low for longer than 200μs, the watch will synchronize to the falling edge of this $\overline{\text{SYNC}}$ signal with a precision of $\pm$2ms. The seconds register is cleared and, if the content is $\geq$30, the minutes register will be incremented.

7.11. Frequency tuning

The frequency of the oscillator can be tuned with the variable capacitor between XI and V_{DD}. A control signal in the form of a 256Hz square wave is available on the $\overline{\text{PULSE}}$ output (see 7.10.).

We recommend the use of ETA quartz crystals, and that the XI / XO pins are shielded with a ring connected to V_{DD}.

7.12. Test

From the various test features added to the M 3002, some may also be activated by the user. A first test mode can be entered by setting bits 7 and 5 high with bit 6 immaterial, leaving input $\overline{\text{SYNC}}$ high. All watch and timer data will increment in parallel at the rate of 1Hz depending on the status of bits 1 and 4 of the status word. To enter the second test mode, bit 7 of the status word must be set high, bits 5 and 6 set low, and then the $\overline{\text{SYNC}}$ input tied low. This will bypass the first 5 divider stages and connect pin XI directly to the 1kHz node of the divider chain, which must be then driven by a signal generator. At 32'678 Hz, the time counting will be speeded up by a factor of 32. Higher speeds can be achieved by speeding up the pulse generator. Modifying the status register as for the first test mode will combine both tests. To leave the test mode, set status bit 7 low. Every activation of $\overline{\text{CS}}$ will immediately exit the test mode, but the status word has to be properly rewritten.

Transfer Waveforms

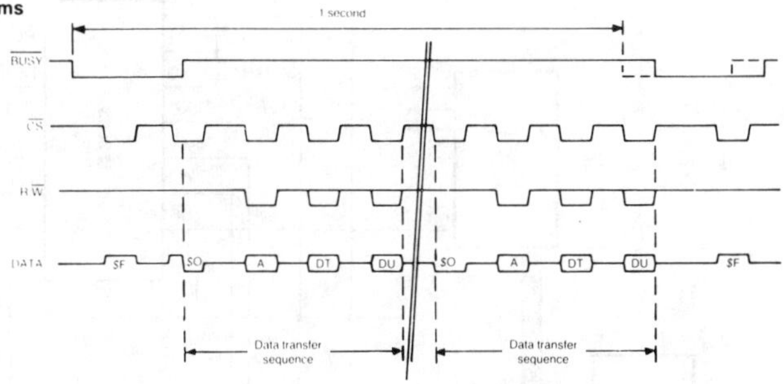

A Address
DT Data. tens
DU Data. units

Fig. 4

Read Timing

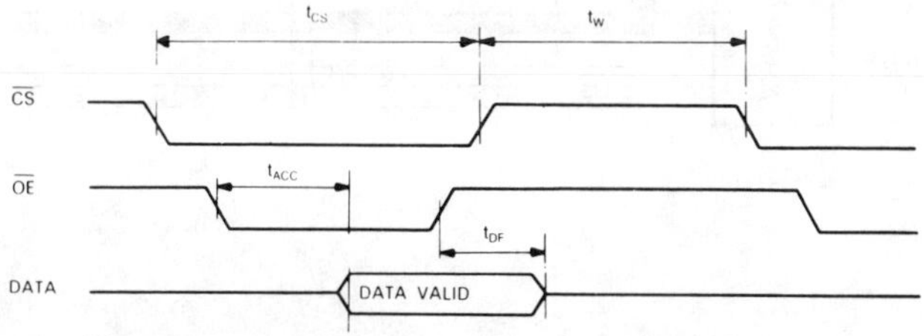

Fig. 5a

Note: If $\overline{\text{CS}} = 0$ starts later than $\overline{\text{OE}} = 0$, then t_{ACC} and t_{DF} are referred to $\overline{\text{CS}}$.

Write Timing

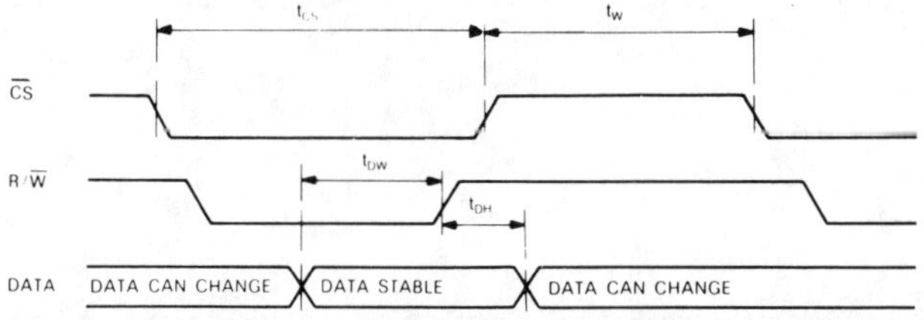

Fig. 5b

Note: If $\overline{\text{CS}} = 0$ ends sooner than $R/\overline{W} = 0$, t_{DW} and t_{DH} are referred to $\overline{\text{CS}}$.

Output Signals

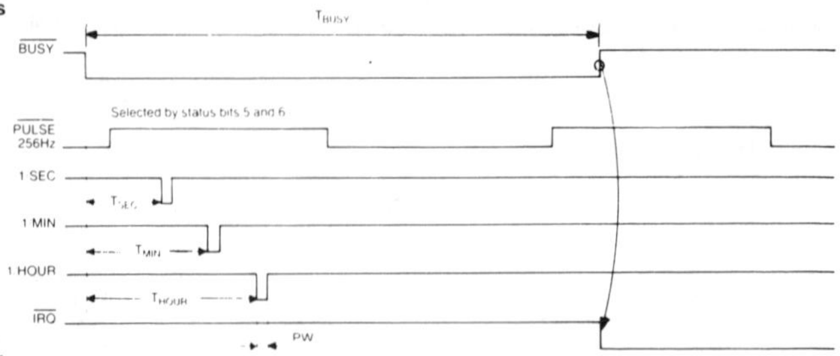

T_{SEC} 0.730ms
T_{MIN} 1.04 to 1.16ms
T_{HOUR} 1.34 to 1.58ms
T_{BUSY} 0.73 to 6ms
PW 64μs

Fig. 6

8. Typical Application and Test Configuration

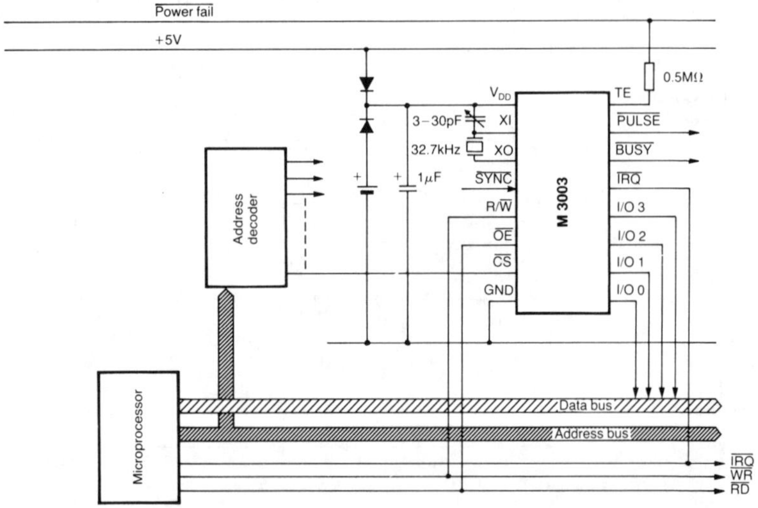

Fig. 7

Real Time Clock E 50-16

Description: This C-MOS circuit may be used as a real time clock or as an absolute time counter with battery back up and an external 32kHz quartz as time reference. The information transfer takes place serially on a 1-bit bi-directional I/O data line in synchronism with an external clock. Data exchange is controlled by the chip-select-signal. The internal time counting circuit operates at a minimum voltage of 1.5V. When a second supply of 5V is connected to another input terminal, all outputs are then available. All of the outputs are capable of driving one TTL unit load. The data I/O line is tri-state to enable it to work in microprocessor type environments. The data are in BCD format words.

Features

- Internal time counter requires one external battery cell only. Time is still running, even when supply voltage is removed from the circuit.
- All of the outputs lines can drive one TTL unit load with 5V supply connected.
- All input/time setting and output/time reading is performed through a single I/O line for minimum wiring costs.
- Accepts low impedance 32kHz crystals as time reference.
- Choice of: a) read/write
  b) selected time information
  c) continuous reading of all time data
- May be used in all microprocessor controlled or conventional electronic equipment, such as office calculators, electronic typewriters, industrial controls, TV equipment or others.
- Counts seconds, minutes, hours, date of the month, day of the week, month and year, with leap year correction.
- Available in a single 16 pin dual in-line package.
- To write or read time information, an external clock frequency of up to 150kHz may be used.
- Independent stop input for external control of time counting, for use as relative time counter.
- May also be used as a preset time counter, 24 hours by using the time pulse outputs.
- Easy connection to serial-in LCD drivers
- Independent outputs for sec., min., hour and day time pulses.
- Crystal frequency may be used to clock the data I/O and other external circuits.

Pin Assignments

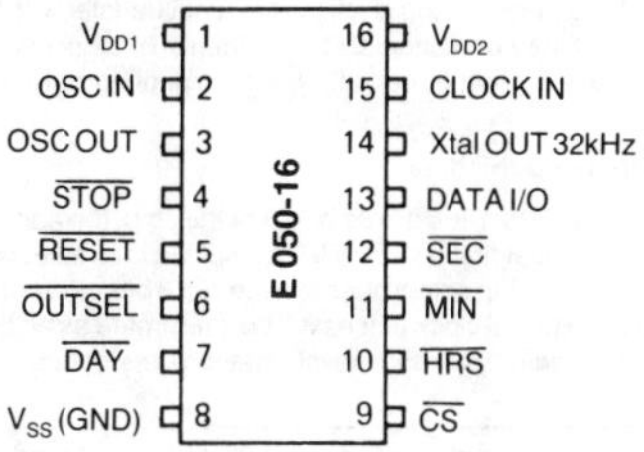

Pin	Name	Description
1	V_{DD1}	Back-up battery negative terminal (1.5 ... 3V)
2	OSC IN	32kHz quartz connection
3	OSC OUT	32kHz quartz connection
4	$\overline{\text{STOP}}$	Negative going I/P stop internal counting
5	$\overline{\text{RESET}}$	Negative going I/P to reset
6	$\overline{\text{OUTSEL}}$	Negative going I/P to read
7	$\overline{\text{DAY}}$	One negative pulse every day
8	V_{SS}	GROUND terminal (GND)
9	$\overline{\text{CS}}$	Negative going I/P to start read or write
10	$\overline{\text{HRS}}$	One negative pulse every hour
11	$\overline{\text{MIN}}$	One negative pulse every minute
12	$\overline{\text{SEC}}$	One negative pulse every second
13	I/O	Data input and output
14	Xtal OUT	32kHz crystal output
15	CLOCK I/P	External frequency input
16	V_{DD2}	Positive supply voltage (+5V)

Block Diagram

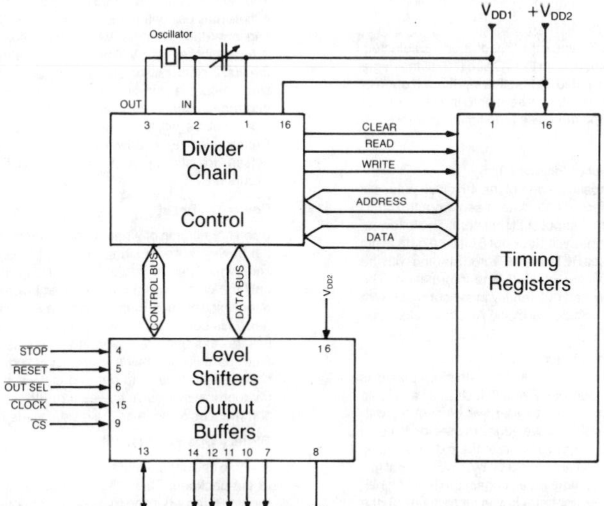

Operation

Bi-Directional Data Transfer (13)

Data transfer to and from the chip is accomplished through a single I/O data line (13), using external clock pulses (15). After the chip select input (9) has been activated (to a low level), a serial 3 bit address word will first be accepted by the chip to select particular timing information. A fourth bit selects read or write mode, thus specifying whether the selected timing information should be written into the circuit or read from it at pin 13. Using the following clock pulses, data transfer with the chip at pin 13 may be accomplished. When chip select is high the I/O line is high impedance, neither accepting nor giving out data.

Addressing the data

For serial data transfer into or out of the chip, the address and data line must first be activated by putting chip select to a low level. When chip select goes low the first 3 bits clocked into the chip by external clock pulses will be interpreted as an address. This determines which time information is selected.

Adress word	Bit configuration MSB		LSB	Selected time inform.	Counting capability
0	0	0	0	second	00...59
1	0	0	1	minute	00...59
2	0	1	0	hour	00...23
3	0	1	1	date	01..28/29..30/31
4	1	0	0	month	01...12
5	1	0	1	day of the week	01...07
6	1	1	0	year	00...99
7	1	1	1	continuous data transfer in the following sequence: hours, minutes, date, month, year, day of the week, seconds	

Read/Write Select

The fourth bit clocked into the chip by external clock will decide whether the time information has to be read or written:
X X X 1 reads time information from the chip
X X X 0 writes time information into the chip to set the time.

Outsel (6)

If this input is set to logic "0" and if the "read" mode is selected, the first bit of data will be sent onto the I/O pad (13) at the negative edge of the 5th clock pulse. When this input is left open or set to logic "1" the first bit of data is sent onto the I/O pad (13) at the negative edge of the 4th pulse (see timing diagrams).

Read Out Mode

a) Selective data read out (addresses 0...6)
If the I/P data at the positive edge of the 4th clock pulses is "1" (for read), the selected time data is sent from the internal time counter into the output shift registers. The following 8 external negative edges will clock out 8 bit time data at pin 13 organized in two 4 bit BCD format words starting with the least significant bit of the selected time information. The time information is clocked out serially in synchronism with the negative edge of the external clock. All further clock pulses are then ignored.

b) Continuous data read out (address 7)
If the I/P data at the positive edge of the 4th clock pulses is "1" (for read) and the address 7 was selected, all available time information (from second to year) will be sent out with the following 56 external negative edges of the clocfk, i.e. in synchronism with the negative edge of the external clock. Data transfer is then available in a 8 bit by 7 word serial format. The first bit of each time data is again the least significant bit. If chip select is kept at a low level (activated), the time data will be available every second, i.e. new timing information is available once a second. Interruption of data flow is accomplished by returning chip select to a high level state.

Write-In Mode

a) Selective data write-in (addresses 0...6)
If the I/P data at the positive edge of the 4th clock pulses is "0" (for write), time information can be clocked into the chip via pin 13 by means of external clock pulses at the clock I/P pin 15. The following 8 external clock pulses will clock the new timing information into the internal I/O shift register; all further clock pulse are then ignored until chip select goes high and then low again. The first bit clocked into the chip should be the most significant bit. The time information is transfered from the internal I/O shift register into the time counting circuit with the rising edge of the chip select signal; this defines the exact time at which the time information is updated.

b) Continuous data write-in (address 7)
This mode is similar to addresses 0...6, except that all 8 bit by 7 word time information is clocked into the chip in a predefined sequence; thus 60 clock pulses are required for a complete cycle after chip select goes low. Every 8 bit word should be available in the format that the most significant bit is clocked in first. In this mode it is not necessary to return chip select to a high level in order to write the information into the chip. This information is written into the chip only once for each low going chip select signal.

Chip Select (9)

Normally chip select is high. Chip select going low enables the data I/O line, and allows all data to be clocked in synchronism with the external clock. In the selective data write-in mode, the high going chip select edge transfers the data from the internal I/O shift register into the time counting network, thus specifying the exact time at which the time information is updated. Whenever chip select goes high the I/O line (13) goes into a high impedance state neither accepting nor giving out data.

Clock-In (15)

The positive going edge of the clock signal controls address and data input. The negative going edge controls data output. The clock is internally gated by the chip select signal (9). Clock pulses may be continuously connected to the chip without shifting any data in or out when chip select is at a high level. Address information will be clocked into the chip via pin 13 by the first 3 clock pulses after chip select goes low. At the fourth clock pulses a decision is made whether the selected time information should be read or written. The fifth and following clock pulses will then clock-in or clock-out the time data. During selective read/write modes the 61st and following clock pulses are also ignored until the next chip select high-low excursion.

Power-On Reset

Upon connection of a battery between pins 1 and 16, an internal power-on reset signal resets all counters to a specified condition. The O/P at the I/O pin (13) remains at a logic "1" until the chip select pin (9) is taken low and then high again; after which the next chip select can be used in the normal manner. This continuous logic "1" at the I/O pin indicates battery voltage has been removed at some time and that since this time the chip has never been accessed. This condition is a non-realistic time read-out and can easily be detected by a microprocessor as a power turn-off signal. Time counting commences as soon as the crystal starts oscillating.

Battery Operation (1, 16)

A single cell battery must be connected between pins 1 and 16 of the package. This voltage keeps the internal time counter running even when the 5V supply is removed. The battery may be replaced by a chargeable cell and appropriate current limiting circuitry and charging of the battery can be accomplished by the 5V supply.

Stop Input (4)

The circuit E 050/16 may also be used as a time counter with start/stop operation. When pin (4) is connected to logic "1" or left open circuit, the circuit will count time. When pin 4 is connected to logic "0" the circuit will stop counting time but will retain the most recent timing information.

Reset Input (5)

Reset of the internal time counting is performed by a negative going pulse at pin 5. When this pin is left open an internal pull-up resistor keeps the circuit in the counting mode. Reset to the individual registers is as shown:

00 second
00 minute
00 hour
01 date
01 month
01 day of the week
00 year

The width of the reset pulse should be not less than 14 μs. Time counting will remain static whilst the reset input is low.

Time Pulse Output (7, 10, 11, 12)

When stop input (4) is left open or connected to a logic "1" continuous output timing pulses are typically 32 μs wide and may be used to clock external circuitry every second, minute, hour or day, depending on the output pin. When address 7 is selected (continuous data), the pulse length is automatically changed, it then becomes 56 clock pulses long. The time pulse may then be used to gate or strobe the data from pin 13 into other external circuitry, i.e. display drivers with serial data input. Timing pulses will not be available, when stop (4) is at a low level. In order to return to 32 μs wide output pulses one of the selective data readouts must be performed.

32kHz Output (14)

This output is connected via an internal driver directly from the crystal oscillator. This squareware may be used to clock external CMOS circuitry, i.e. serial input display drivers connected to the data output pin. Pin 14 may be connected to clock in (15) in order to clock the internal address and data I/O. Pin 14 may also be used to measure the crystal frequency without loading the oscillator.

Supply Voltage (16)

A supply voltage of 5V may be supplied at pin 16, in order to input or output time information. If this voltage is removed the internal time counting still goes on when pin 16 has a battery cell connected and when using the crystal time base. When this voltage is removed, all input and output levels (except the data I/O line) remain at the level of the +Ve line through internal pull-up resistors. Thus, no zero going time output pulses are generated. The data I/O line is in a high impedance state without the 5V supply connected.

Electrical Specifications

Parameter	Conditions	Symbol	Min.	Typ.	Max.	Units
Temp. Range Storage		T_{St}	−65		+150	°C
Operating		T_A	−10	+25	+60	°C
Max. Voltage to any Pin	w.r.t. V_{SS}	V_{max}	−0.3		7.0	V
Positive Supply Voltage	w.r.t. V_{SS}	V_{DD2}	4.5	5	5.5	V
Battery Voltage ($V_{DD2}-V_{DD1}$)		V_{BATT}	1.5		3.6	V
Current Consumption	$V_{BATT}=1.5V$ $C_{IN}=20pF$	I_{DD1}		2	4	μA
	$V_{BATT}=3.6V$ $C_{IN}=20pF$	I_{DD1}		12	18	μA
	$V_{BATT}=3.6V$ $V_{DD2}=5V$	I_{DD2}		180	220	μA
I/O Lines						
All Inputs:		V_{IH}	2,4	$0{,}5V_{DD2}$	V_{DD2}	V
(4) (5) (9) (15)		V_{IL}	V_{SS}		0.8	V
All Outputs:	$I_{OH}=40\mu A$	V_{OH}	2.4			V
(7) (10) (11) (12) (13) (14)	$I_{OL}=1.6mA$	V_{OL}			0,4	V
Input Pad Impedance			100			kΩ
External Clock	$V_{DD1}=1.5V$	F_{EXT}	35			kHz
Frequency I/P	$V_{DD1}=2{,}4V$ see note [1]		150			kHz
Oscillator						
Oscillator Starting Voltage		V_{STA}	1.5			V
Oscillator Input Capacitance		C_{IN}		3		pF
Oscillator Output Capacitance		C_{OUT}		23		pF
Switching Characteristics						
Read Mode	$V_{BATT}=1.5V$					
Clock Rising Edge		t_{CLH}			1	μs
Clock Falling Edge		t_{CHL}			1	μs
Data Access Time		t_{ACC}		4	8	μs
Clock Pulse Width		t_{CLK}	14			μs
Clock Repetition Time	See note [2]	t_{FC}	28			μs
Write Mode	$V_{BATT}=1.5V$					
Clock Falling Edge		t_{CHL}			1	μs
Clock Rising Edge		t_{CLH}			1	μs
Clock Pulse Width		t_{CLK}	14			μs
Clock Repetition Time	See note [2]	t_{FC}	28			μs
Data Settle Time		t_S	−0.5			μs
Data Hold Time		t_H	0.5			μs

[1] See graph of voltage against operating frequency for typical performance characteristics.

[2] The seconds register is incremented every second in order to retain the correct time. Therefore any Data Transfer must be accomplished within 1 second.

Crystal (2+3)

Quartz: $f = 32\,768Hz$
$R_{quartz} = 40k\Omega$ typ., $60k\Omega$ max.
$C_O = 1.5pF$
$C_I = 1.7pF$

Frequency adjustment = ± 10ppm Trimmer: C_T: 3 to 12pF

Typical Performance Charakteristics

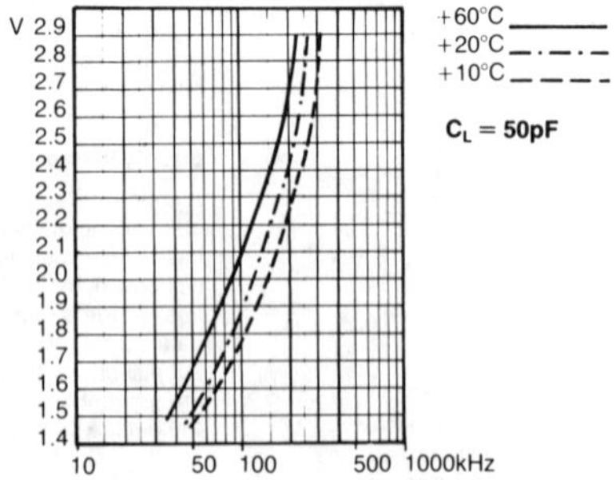

Supply voltage V_{DD1} against operating frequency

Clock and Data I/O Timing

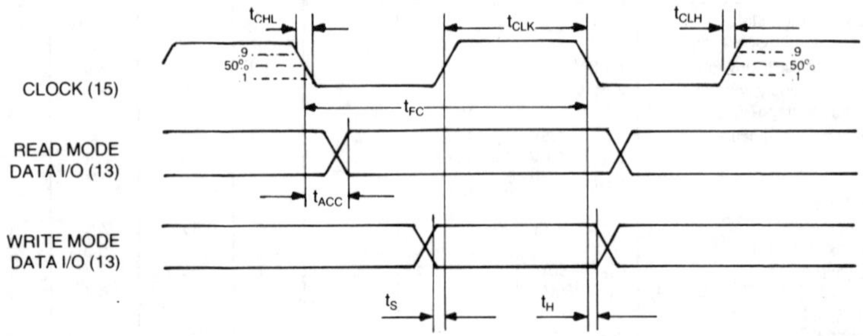

I/O Diagram 1

Single Read-Out / Write-In Mode

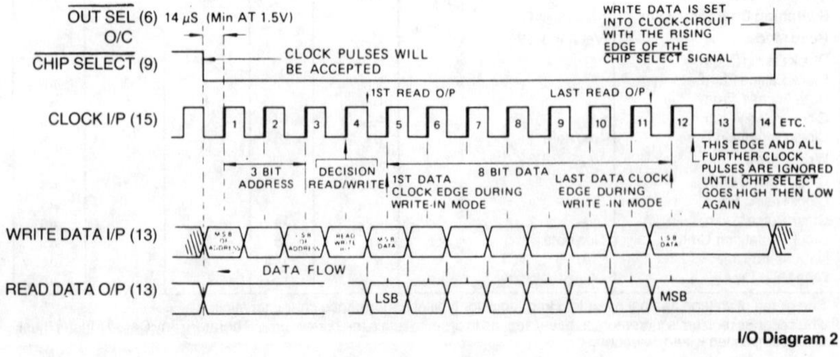

I/O Diagram 2

Continuous Read-Out / Write-In Mode

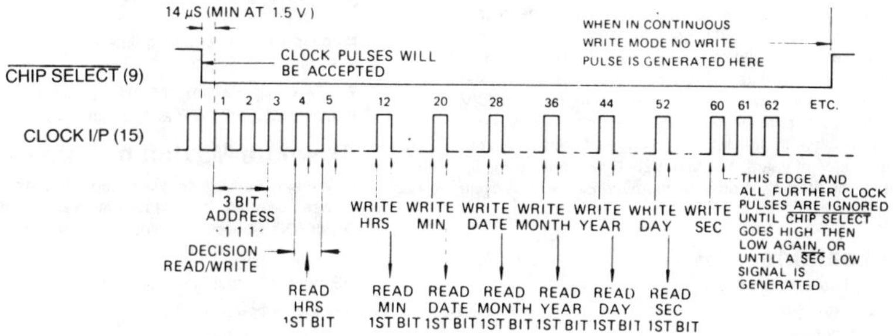

I/ODiagram 3

Single Read-Out Mode

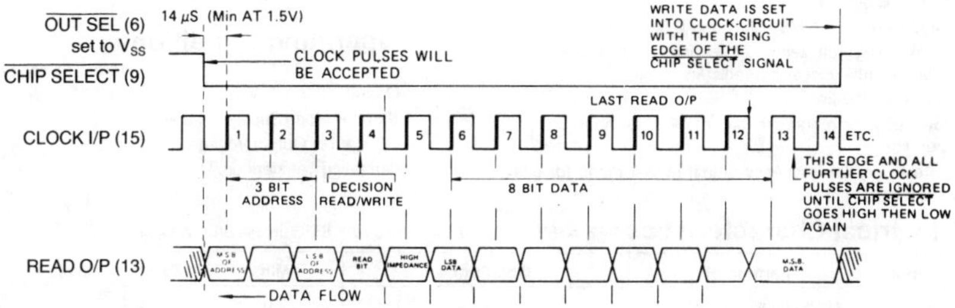

I/O Diagram 4

Continuous Read-Out Mode

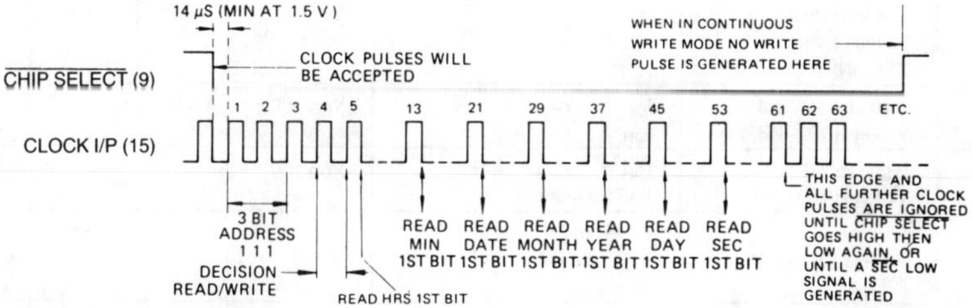

I/O Diagram 5

Continuous Read-Out / Write-In Mode

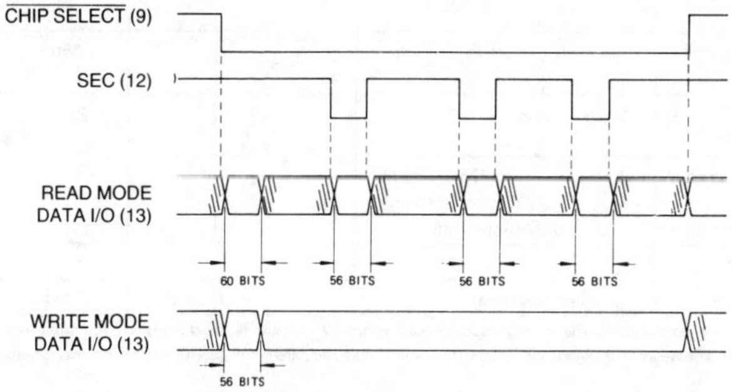

I/O Diagram 6

MM58274 Real Time Clock

General Description

The MM58274C is fabricated using low threshold metal gate CMOS technology and is designed to operate in bus oriented microprocessor systems where a real time clock and calendar function are required. The on-chip 32.768 kHz crystal controlled oscillator will maintain timekeeping down to 2.2V to allow low power standby battery operation. This device is pin compatible with the MM58174B but continues timekeeping up to tens of years. The MM58274C is a direct replacement for the MM58274 offering improved Bus access cycle times.

Applications

- Point of sale terminals
- Teller terminals
- Word processors
- Data logging
- Industrial process control

Features

- Same pin-out as MM58174A and MM58274B
- Timekeeping from tenths of seconds to tens of years in independently accessible registers
- Leap year register
- Hours counter programmable for 12 or 24-hour operation
- Buffered crystal frequency output in test mode for easy oscillator setting
- Data-changed flag allows simple testing for time rollover
- Independent interrupting time with open drain output
- Fully TTL compatible
- Low power standby operation (10μA at 2.2V)
- Low cost 16-pin DIP and 20-pin PCC

Absolute Maximum Ratings (Note 1)

If Military/Aerospace specified devices are required, please contact the National Semiconductor Sales Office/Distributors for availability and specifications.

DC Input or Output Voltage	$-0.3V$ to $V_{DD} + 0.3V$
DC Input or Output Diode Current	±5.0 mA
Storage Temperature, T_{STG}	−65°C to +150°C
Supply Voltage, V_{DD}	6.5V
Power Dissipation, P_D	500 mW
Lead Temperature (Soldering, 10 seconds)	260°

Operating Conditions

	Min	Max	Units
Operating Supply Voltage	4.5	5.5	V
Standby Mode Supply Voltage	2.2	5.5	V
DC Input or Output Voltage	0	V_{DD}	V
Operating Temperature Range	−40	85	°C

Electrical Characteristics $V_{DD} = 5V \pm 10\%$, T = −40°C to +85°C unless otherwise stated.

Symbol	Parameter	Conditions	Min	Typ	Max	Units
V_{IH}	High Level Input Voltage (except XTAL IN)		2.0			V
V_{IL}	Low Level Input Voltage (except XTAL IN)				0.8	V
V_{OH}	High Level Output Voltage (DB0–DB3)	$I_{OH} = -20\ \mu A$ $I_{OH} = -1.6$ mA	$V_{DD} - 0.1$ 3.7			V V
V_{OH}	High Level Output Voltage (INT)	$I_{OH} = -20\ \mu A$ (In Test Mode)	$V_{DD} - 0.1$			V
V_{OL}	Low Level Input Voltage (DB0–DB3, $\overline{INT}$)	$I_{OL} = 20\ \mu A$ $I_{OL} = 1.6$ mA			0.1 0.4	V V
I_{IL}	Low Level Input Current (AD0–AD3, DB0–DB3)	$V_{IN} = V_{SS}$ (Note 2)	−5		−80	μA
I_{IL}	Low Level Input Current ($\overline{WR}$, $\overline{RD}$)	$V_{IN} = V_{SS}$ (Note 2)	−5		−190	μA
I_{IL}	Low Level Input Current ($\overline{CS}$)	$V_{IN} = V_{SS}$ (Note 2)	−5		−550	μA
I_{OZH}	Ouput High Level Leakage Current ($\overline{INT}$)	$V_{OUT} = V_{DD}$			2.0	μA
I_{DD}	Average Supply Current	All $V_{IN} = V_{CC}$ or Open Circuit $V_{DD} = 2.2V$ (Standby Mode) $V_{DD} = 5.0V$ (Active Mode)		 4 	 10 1	 μA mA
C_{IN}	Input Capacitance			5	10	pF
C_{OUT}	Output Capacitance	(Outputs Disabled)		10		pF

Note 1: Absolute Maximum Ratings are those values beyond which damage to the device may occur. All voltages referenced to ground unless otherwise noted.

Note 2: The DB0–DB3 and AD0–AD3 lines all have active P-channel pull-up transistors which will source current. The $\overline{CS}$, $\overline{RD}$, and $\overline{WR}$ lines have internal pull-up resistors to V_{DD}.

AC Switching Characteristics

READ TIMING: DATA FROM PERIPHERAL TO MICROPROCESSOR $V_{DD} = 5V \pm 0.5V$, $C_L = 100$ pF

Symbol	Parameter	Commercial Specification $T_A = -40°C$ to $+85°C$			Units
		Min	Typ	Max	
t_{AD}	Address Bus Valid to Data Valid		390	650	ns
t_{CSD}	Chip Select On to Data Valid		140	300	ns
t_{RD}	Read Strobe On to Data Valid		140	300	ns
t_{RW}	Read Strobe Width (Note 3, Note 7)			DC	
t_{RA}	Address Bus Hold Time from Trailing Edge of Read Strobe	0			ns
t_{CSH}	Chip Select Hold Time from Trailing Edge of Read Strobe	0			ns
t_{RH}	Data Hold Time from Trailing Edge of Read Strobe	70	160		ns
t_{HZ}	Time from Trailing Edge of Read Strobe Until O/P Drivers are TRI-STATE®			250	ns

WRITE TIMING: DATA FROM MICROPROCESSOR TO PERIPHERAL $V_{DD} = 5V \pm 0.5V$

Symbol	Parameter	Commercial Specification $T_A = -40°C$ to $+85°C$			Units
		Min	Typ	Max	
t_{AW}	Address Bus Valid to Write Strobe ↗ (Note 4, Note 6)	400	125		ns
t_{CSW}	Chip Select On to Write Strobe ↗	250	100		ns
t_{DW}	Data Bus Valid to Write Strobe ↗	400	220		ns
t_{WW}	Write Strobe Width (Note 6)	250	95		ns
t_{WCS}	Chip Select Hold Time Following Write Strobe ↗	0			ns
t_{WA}	Address Bus Hold Time Following Write Strobe ↗	0			ns
t_{WD}	Data Bus Hold Time Following Write Strobe ↗	100	35		ns
t_{AWS}	Address Bus Valid Before Start of Write Strobe	70	20		ns

Note 3: Except for special case restriction: with interrupts programmed, max read strobe width of control register (ADDR 0) is 30 ms. See section on Interrupt Programming.

Note 4: All timings measured to the trailing edge of write strobe (data latched by the trailing edge of $\overline{WR}$).

Note 5: Input test waveform peak voltages are 2.4V and 0.4V. Output signals are measured to their 2.4V and 0.4V levels.

Note 6: Write strobe as used in the Write Timing Table is defined as the period when both chip select and write inputs are low, ie., $\overline{WS}$, = $\overline{CS}$ + $\overline{WR}$. Hence write strobe commences when both signals are low, and terminates when the first signal returns high.

Note 7: Read strobe as used in the Read Timing Table is defined as the period when both chip select and read inputs are low, ie., $\overline{RS}$ = $\overline{CS}$ + $\overline{RD}$.

Note 8: Typical numbers are at $V_{CC} = 5.0V$ and $T_A = 25°C$.

Switching Time Waveforms

Read Cycle Timing (Note 5)

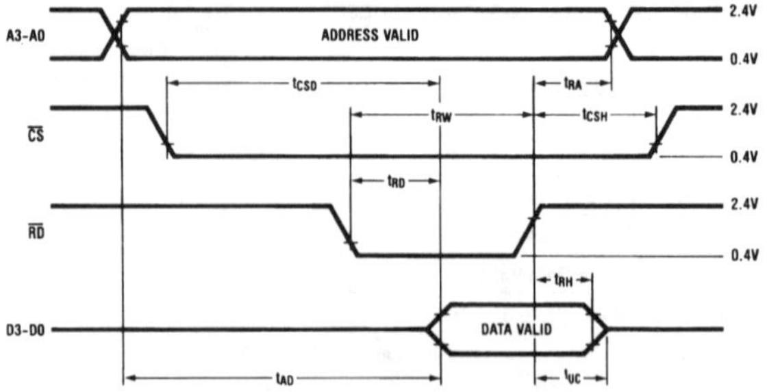

Write Cycle Timing (Note 5)

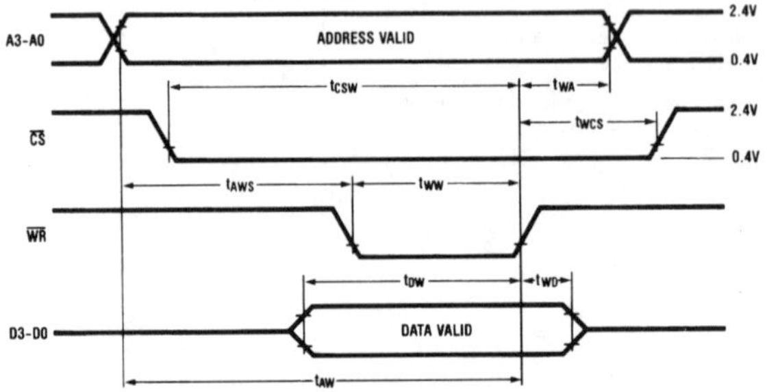

Functional Description

The MM58274C is a bus oriented microprocessor real time clock. It has the same pin-out as the MM58174A while offering extended timekeeping up to units and tens of years. To enhance the device further, a number of other features have been added including: 12 or 24 hours counting, a testable data-changed flag giving easy error-free time reading and simplified interrupt control.

A buffered oscillator signal appears on the interrupt output when the device is in test mode. This allows for easy oscillator setting when the device is initially powered up in a system.

The counters are arranged as 4-bit words and can be randomly accessed for time reading and setting. The counters output in BCD (binary coded decimal) 4-bit numbers. Any register which has less than 4 bits (e.g., days of week uses only 3 bits) will return to a logic 0 on any unused bits. When written to, the unused inputs will be ignored.

Writing a logic 1 to the clock start/stop control bit resets the internal oscillator divider chain and the tenths of seconds counter. Writing a logic 0 will start the clock timing from the nearest second. The time then updates every 100 ms with all counters changing synchronously. Time changing during a read is detected by testing the data-changed bit of the control register after completing a string of clock register reads.

Interrupt delay times of 0.1s, 0.5s, 1s, 5s, 10s, 30s or 60s can be selected with single or repeated interrupt outputs. The open drain output is pulled low whenever the interrupt timer times out and is cleared by reading the control register.

CIRCUIT DESCRIPTION

The block diagram in *Figure 1* shows the internal structure of the chip. The 16-pin package outline is shown in *Figure 2*.

Crystal Oscillator

This consists of a CMOS inverter/amplifier with an on-chip bias resistor. Externally a 20 pF capacitor, a 6 pF–36 pF trimmer capacitor and a crystal are required to complete the 32.768 kHz timekeeping oscillator circuit.

The 6 pF–36 pF trimmer fine tunes the crystal load impedance, optimizing the oscillator stability. When properly adjusted (i.e., to the crystal frequency of 32.768 kHz), the circuit will display a frequency variation with voltage of less than 3 ppm/V. When an external oscillator is used, connect to oscillator input and float (no connection) the oscillator output.

When the chip is enabled into test mode, the oscillator is gated onto the interrupt output pin giving a buffered oscillator output that can be used to set the crystal frequency when the device is installed in a system. For further information see the section on Test Mode.

Divider Chain

The crystal oscillator is divided down in three stages to produce a 10 Hz frequency setting pulse. The first stage is a non-integer divider which reduces the 32.768 kHz input to 30.720 kHz. This is further divided by a 9-stage binary ripple counter giving an output frequency of 60 Hz. A 3-stage Johnson counter divides this by six, generating a 10 Hz output. The 10 Hz clock is gated with the 32.768 kHz crystal frequency to provide clock setting pulses of 15.26 μs duration. The setting pulse drives all the time registers on the

FIGURE 1

Block Diagram

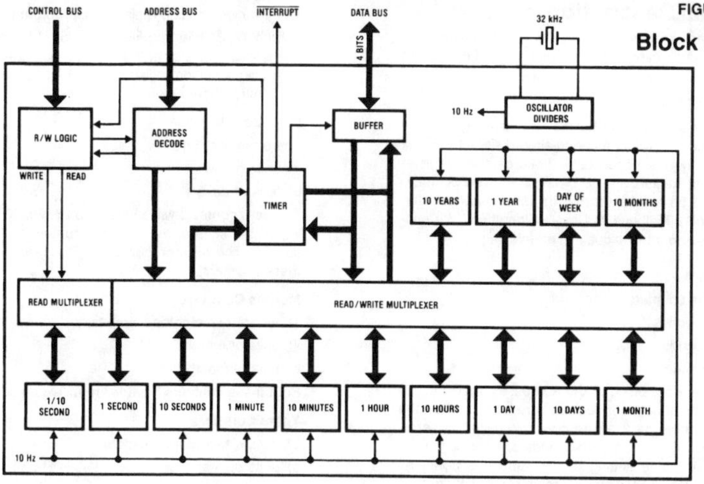

FIGURE 2

Connection Diagrams

Top View

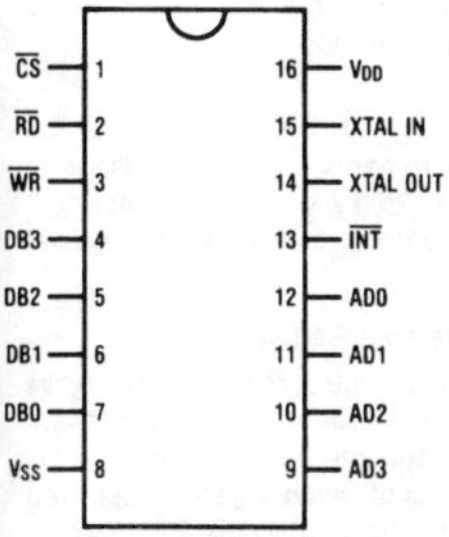

Dual-In-Line Package

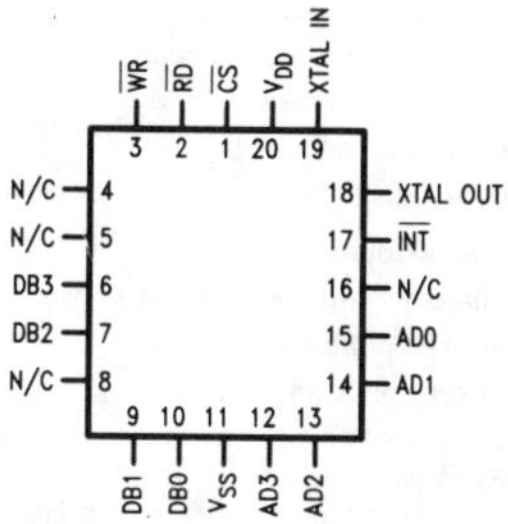

PCC Package

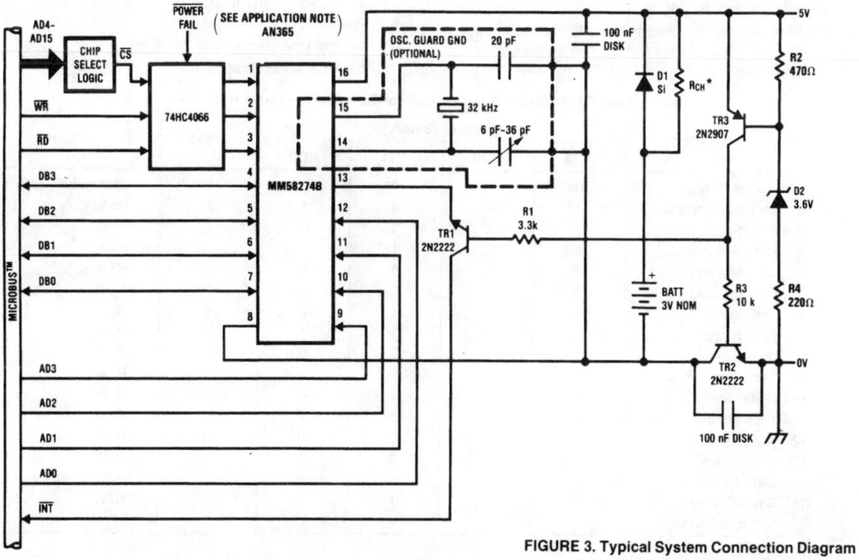

FIGURE 3. Typical System Connection Diagram

Functional Description (Continued)

device which are synchronously clocked by this signal. All time data and data-changed flag change on the falling edge of the clock setting pulse.

Data-Changed Flag

The data-changed flag is set by the clock setting pulse to indicate that the time data has been altered since the clock was last read. This flag occupies bit 3 of the control register where it can be tested by the processor to sense data-changed. It will be reset by a read of the control register. See the section, "Methods of Device Operation", for suggested clock reading techniques using this flag.

Seconds Counters

There are three counters for seconds:

a) tenths of seconds

b) units of seconds

c) tens of seconds.

The registers are accessed at the addresses shown in Table I. The tenths of seconds register is reset to 0 when the clock start/stop bit (bit 2 of the control register) is set to logic 1. The units and tens of seconds are set up by the processor, giving time setting to the nearest second. All three registers can be read by the processor for time output.

Minutes Counters

There are two minutes counters:

a) units of minutes

b) tens of minutes.

Both registers may be read to or written from as required.

Hours Counters

There are two hours counters:

a) units of hours

b) tens of hours.

Both counters may be accessed for read or write operations as desired.

In 12-hour mode, the tens of hours register has only one active bit and the top three bits are set to logic 0. Data bit 1 of the clock setting register is the AM/PM indicator; logic 0 indicating AM, logic 1 for PM.

When 24-hour mode is programmed, the tens of hours register reads out two bits of data and the two most significant bits are set to logic 0. There is no AM/PM indication and bit 1 of the clock setting register will read out a logic 0.

In both 12/24-hour modes, the units of hours will read out four active data bits. 12 or 24-hour mode is selected by bit 0 of the clock setting register, logic 0 for 12-hour mode, logic 1 for the 24-hour mode.

Days Counters

There are two days counters:

a) units of days

b) tens of days.

The days counters will count up to 28, 29, 30 or 31 depending on the state of the months counters and the leap year counter. The microprocessor has full read/write access to these registers.

Months Counters

There are two months counters:

a) units of months

b) tens of months.

Both these counters have full read/write access.

Years Counters

There are two years counters:

a) units of years

b) tens of years.

Both these counters have full read/write access. The years will count up to 99 and roll over to 00.

Day of Week Counter

The day of week counter increments as the time rolls from 23:59 to 00:00 (11:59 PM to 12:00 AM in 12-hour mode). It counts from 1 to 7 and rolls back to 1. Any day of the week may be specified as day 1.

Clock Setting Register/Interrupt Register

The interrupt select bit in the control register determines which of these two registers is accessible to the processor at address 15. Normal clock and interrupt timing operations will always continue regardless of which register is selected onto the bus. The layout of these registers is shown in Table II.

The clock setting register is comprised of three separate functions:

a) leap year counter: bits 2 and 3

b) AM/PM indicator: bit 1

TABLE I. Address Decoding of Real-Time Clock Internal Registers

Register Selected	Address (Binary)				(Hex)	Access
	AD3	AD2	AD1	AD0		
0 Control Register	0	0	0	0	0	Split Read and Write
1 Tenths of Seconds	0	0	0	1	1	Read Only
2 Units Seconds	0	0	1	0	2	R/W
3 Tens Seconds	0	0	1	1	3	R/W
4 Units Minutes	0	1	0	0	4	R/W
5 Tens Minutes	0	1	0	1	5	R/W
6 Unit Hours	0	1	1	0	6	R/W
7 Tens Hours	0	1	1	1	7	R/W
8 Units Days	1	0	0	0	8	R/W
9 Tens Days	1	0	0	1	9	R/W
10 Units Months	1	0	1	0	A	R/W
11 Tens Months	1	0	1	1	B	R/W
12 Units Years	1	1	0	0	C	R/W
13 Tens Years	1	1	0	1	D	R/W
14 Day of Week	1	1	1	0	E	R/W
15 Clock Setting/ Interrupt Registers	1	1	1	1	F	R/W

Functional Description (Continued)

c) 12/24-hour mode set: bit 0 (see Table IIA).

The leap year counter is a 2-stage binary counter which is clocked by the months counter. It changes state as the time rolls over from 11:59 on December 31 to 00:00 on January 1.

The counter should be loaded with the 'number of years since last leap year' e.g., if 1980 was the last leap year, a clock programmed in 1983 should have 3 stored in the leap year counter. If the clock is programmed during a leap year, then the leap year counter should be set to 0. The contents of the leap year counter can be read by the μP.

The AM/PM indicator returns a logic 0 for AM and a logic 1 for PM. It is clocked when the hours counter rolls from 11:59 to 12:00 in 12-hour mode. In 24-hour mode this bit is set to logic 0.

The 12/24-hour mode set determines whether the hours counter counts from 1 to 12 or from 0 to 23. It also controls the AM/PM indicator, enabling it for 12-hour mode and forcing it to logic 0 for the 24-hour mode. The 12/24-hour mode bit is set to logic 0 for 12-hour mode and it is set to logic 1 for 24-hour mode.

IMPORTANT NOTE: *Hours mode and AM/PM bits cannot be set in the same write operation. See the section on* Initialization (Methods of Device Operation) *for a suggested setting routine.*

All bits in the clock setting register may be read by the processor.

The interrupt register controls the operation of the timer for interrupt output. The processor programs this register for single or repeated interrupts at the selected time intervals.

The lower three bits of this register set the time delay period that will occur between interrupts. The time delays that can be programmed and the data words that select these are outlined in Table IIB.

Data bit 3 of the interrupt register sets for either single or repeated interrupts; logic 0 gives single mode, logic 1 sets for repeated mode.

Using the interrupt is described in the Device Operation section.

Control Register

There are three registers which control different operations of the clock:

a) the clock setting register

b) the interrupt register

c) the control register.

The clock setting and interrupt registers both reside at address 15, access to one or the other being controlled by the interrupt select bit; data bit 1 of the control register.

The clock setting register programs the timekeeping of the clock. The 12/24-hour mode select and the AM/PM indicator for 12-hour mode occupy bits 0 and 1, respectively. Data bits 2 and 3 set the leap year counter.

The interrupt register controls the operation of the interrupt timer, selecting the required delay period and either single or repeated interrupt.

The control register is responsible for controlling the operations of the clock and supplying status information to the processor. It appears as two different registers; one with write only access and one with read only access.

The write only register consists of a bank of four latches which control the internal processes of the clock.

The read only register contains two output data latches which will supply status information for the processor. Table III shows the mapping of the various control latches and status flags in the control register. The control register is located at address 0.

The write only portion of the control register contains four latches:

A logic 1 written into the test bit puts the device into test mode. This allows setting of the oscillator frequency as well as rapid testing of the device registers, if required. A more complete description is given in the Test Mode section. For normal operation the test bit is loaded with logic 0.

The clock start/stop bit stops the timekeeping of the clock and resets to 0 the tenths of seconds counter. The time of day may then be written into the various clock registers and the clock restarted synchronously with an external time source. Timekeeping is maintained thereafter.

TABLE IIA. Clock Setting Register Layout

Function	Data Bits Used				Comments	Access
	DB3	DB2	DB1	DB0		
Leap Year Counter	X	X			0 Indicates a Leap Year	R/W
AM/PM Indicator (12-Hour Mode)			X		0 = AM 1 = PM 0 in 24-Hour Mode	R/W
12/24-Hour Select Bit				X	0 = 12-Hour Mode 1 = 24-Hour Mode	R/W

TABLE IIB. Interrupt Control Register

Function	Comments	Control Word			
		DB3	DB2	DB1	DB0
No Interrupt	Interrupt output cleared, start/stop bit set to 1.	X	0	0	0
0.1 Second		0/1	0	0	1
0.5 Second		0/1	0	1	0
1 Second		0/1	0	1	1
5 Seconds	DB3 = 0 for single interrupt DB3 = 1 for repeated interrupt	0/1	1	0	0
10 Seconds		0/1	1	0	1
30 Seconds		0/1	1	1	0
60 Seconds		0/1	1	1	1

Timing Accuracy: single interrupt mode (all time delays): ±1 ms
Repeated Mode: ±1 ms on initial timeout, thereafter synchronous with first interrupt (i.e., timing errors do not accumulate).

Functional Description (Continued)

TABLE III. The Control Register Layout

Access (addr0)	DB3	DB2	DB1	DB0
Read From:	Data-Changed Flag	0	0	Interrupt Flag
Write To:	Test 0 = Normal 1 = Test Mode	Clock Start/Stop 0 = Clock Run 1 = Clock Stop	Interrupt Select 0 = Clock Setting Register 1 = Interrupt Register	Interrupt Start/Stop 0 = Interrupt Run 1 = Interrupt Stop

A logic 1 written to the start/stop bit halts clock timing. Timing is restarted when the start/stop bit is written with a logic 0.

The interrupt select bit determines which of the two registers mapped onto address 15 will be accessed when this address is selected.

A logic 0 in the interrupt select bit makes the clock setting register available to the processor. A logic 1 selects the interrupt register.

The interrupt start/stop bit controls the running of the interrupt timer. It is programmed in the same way as the clock start/stop bit; logic 1 to halt the interrupt and reset the timer, logic 0 to start interrupt timing.

When no interrupt is programmed (interrupt control register set to 0), the interrupt start/stop bit is automatically set to a logic 1. When any new interrupt is subsequently programmed, timing will not commence until the start/stop bit is loaded with 0.

In the single interrupt mode, interrupt timing stops when a timeout occurs. The processor restarts timing by writing logic 0 into the start/stop bit.

In repeated interrupt mode the interrupt timer continues to count with no intervention by the processor necessary.

Interrupt timing may be stopped in either mode by writing a logic 1 into the interrupt start/stop bit. The timer is reset and can be restarted in the normal way, giving a full time delay period before the next interrupt.

In general, the control register is set up such that writing 0's into it will start anything that is stopped, pull the clock out of test mode and select the clock setting register onto the bus. In other words, writing 0 will maintain normal clock operation and restart interrupt timing, etc.

The read only portion of the control register has two status outputs:

Since the MM58274C keeps real time, the time data changes asynchronously with the processor and this may occur while the processor is reading time data out of the clock.

Some method of warning the processor when the time data has changed must thus be included. This is provided for by the data-changed flag located in bit 3 of the control register. This flag is set by the clock setting pulse which also clocks the time registers. Testing this bit can tell the processor whether or not the time has changed. The flag is cleared by a read of the control register but not by any write operations. No other register read has any effect on the state of the data-changed flag.

Data bit 0 is the interrupt flag. This flag is set whenever the interrupt timer times out, pulling the interrupt output low. In a polled interrupt routine the processor can test this flag to determine if the MM58274C was the interrupting device. This interrupt flag and the interrupt output are both cleared by a read of the control register.

Reading the Time Registers

Using the data-changed flag technique supports microprocessors with block move facilities, as all the necessary time data may be read sequentially and then tested for validity as shown below.

1) Read the control register, address 0: *This is a dummy read to reset the data-changed flag (DCF) prior to reading the time registers.*

2) Read time registers: *All desired time registers are read out in a block.*

3) Read the control register and test DCF: *If DCF is cleared (logic 0), then no clock setting pulses have after occurred since step 1. All time data is guaranteed good and time reading is complete.*

If DCF is set (logic 1), then a time change has occurred since step 1 and time data may not be consistent. Repeat steps 2 and 3 until DCF is clear. The control read of step 3 will have reset DCF, automatically repeating the step 1 action.

Interrupt Programming

The interrupt timer generates interrupts at time intervals which are programmed into the interrupt register. A single interrupt after delay or repeated interrupts may be programmed. Table IIB lists the different time delays and the data words that select them in the interrupt register.

Once the interrupt register has been used to set up the delay time and to select for single or repeat, it takes no further part in the workings of the interrupt system. All activity by the processor then takes place in the control register.

Initializing:

1) Write 3 to the control register (AD0): *Clock timing continues, interrupt register selected and interrupt timing stopped.*

2) Write interrupt control word to address 15: *The interrupt register is loaded with the correct word (chosen from Table IIB) for the time delay required and for single or repeated interrupts.*

3) Write 0 or 2 to the control register: *Interrupt timing commences. Writing 0 selects the clock setting register onto the data bus; writing 2 leaves the interrupt register selected. Normal timekeeping remains unaffected.*

On Interrupt:

Read the control register and test for Interrupt Flag (bit 0).

If the flag is cleared (logic 0), then the device is not the source of the interrupt.

If the flag is set (logic 1), then the clock did generate an interrupt. The flag is reset and the interrupt output is cleared by the control register read that was used to test for interrupt.

Single Interrupt Mode:

When appropriate, write 0 or 2 to the control register to restart the interrupt timer.

Repeated Interrupt Mode:

Timing continues, synchronized with the control register write which originally started interrupt timing. No further intervention is necessary from the processor to maintain timing.

Functional Description (Continued)

In either mode interrupt timing can be stopped by writing 1 into the control register (interrupt start/stop set to 1). Timing for the full delay period recommences when the interrupt start/stop bit is again loaded with 0 as normal.

IMPORTANT NOTE: Using the interrupt timer places a constraint on the maximum Read Strobe width which may be applied to the clock. Normally all registers may be read from with a t_{RW} down to DC (i.e., $\overline{CS}$ and $\overline{RD}$ held continuously low). When the interrupt timer is active however, the maximum read strobe width that can be applied to the control register (Addr 0) is 30 ms.

This restriction is to allow the interrupt timer to properly reset when it times out. Note that it only affects reading of the control register—all other addresses in the clock may be accessed with DC read strobes, regardless of the state of the interrupt timer. Writes to any address are unaffected.

NOTES ON AC TIMING REQUIREMENTS

Although the Switching Time Waveforms show Microbus control signals used for clock access, this does not preclude the use of the MM58274C in other non-Microbus systems. *Figure 5* is a simplified logic diagram showing how the control signals are gated internally to control access to the clock registers. From this diagram it is clear that $\overline{CS}$ could be used to generate the internal data transfer strobes, with $\overline{RD}$ and $\overline{WR}$ inputs set up first. This situation is illustrated in *Figure 6*.

The internal data busses of the MM58274C are fully CMOS, contributing to the flexibility of the control inputs. When determining the suitability of any given control signal pattern for the MM58274B the timing specifications in AC Switching Characteristics should be examined. As long as these timings are met (or exceeded) the MM58274C will function correctly.

When the MM58274C is connected to the system via a peripheral port, the freedom from timing constraints allows for very simple control signal generation, as in *Figure 7*. For reading (*Figure 7a*), Address, $\overline{CS}$ and $\overline{RD}$ may be activated simultaneously and the data will be available at the port after t_{AD}-max (650 ns). For writing (*Figure 7b*), the address and data may be applied simultaneously; 70 ns later $\overline{CS}$ and $\overline{WR}$ may be strobed together.

Both of the flags and the interrupt output are reset by the trailing edge of the read strobe. The flag information is held latched during a control register read, guaranteeing that stable status information will always be read out by the processor.

Interrupt timeout is detected and stored internally if it occurs during a read of the control register, the interrupt output will then go low only after the read has been completed.

A clock setting pulse occurring during a control register read will *not* affect the data-changed flag since time data read out before or after the control read will not be affected by the time change.

METHODS OF DEVICE OPERATION

Test Mode

National Semiconductor uses test mode for functionally testing the MM58274C after fabrication and again after packaging. Test mode can also be used to set up the oscillator frequency when the part is first commissioned.

Figure 4 shows the internal clock connections when the device is written into test mode. The 32.768 kHz oscillator is gated onto the interrupt output to provide a buffered output for initial frequency setting. This signal is driven from a TRI-STATE output buffer, enabling easy oscillator setting in systems where interrupt is not normally used and there is no external resistor on the pin.

If an interrupt is programmed, the 32.768 kHz output is switched off to allow high speed testing of the interrupt timer. The interrupt output will then function as normal.

The clock start/stop bit can be used to control the fast clocking of the time registers as shown in *Figure 4*.

Initialization

When it is first installed and power is applied, the device will need to be properly initialized. The following operation steps are recommended when the device is set up (all numbers are decimal):

1) Disable interrupt on the processor to allow oscillator setting. Write 15 into the control register: *The clock and interrupt start/stop bits are set to 1, ensuring that the clock and interrupt timers are both halted. Test mode and the interrupt register are selected.*

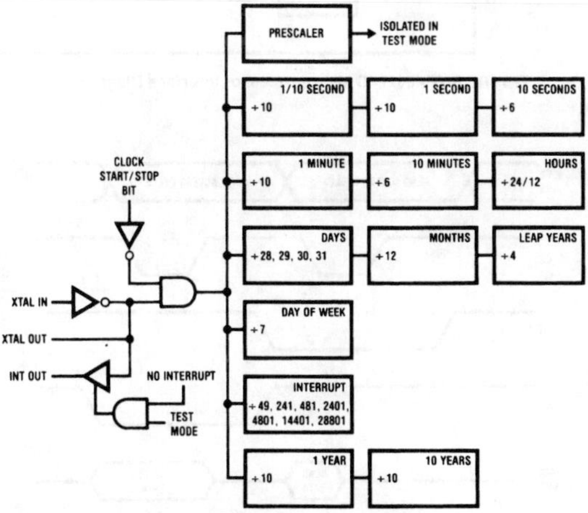

FIGURE 4. Test Mode Organization

Functional Description (Continued)

2) Write 0 to the interrupt register: *Ensure that there are no interrupts programmed and that the oscillator will be gated onto the interrupt output.*

3) Set oscillator frequency: *All timing has been halted and the oscillator is buffered out onto the interrupt line.*

4) Write 5 to the control register: *The clock is now out of test mode but is still halted. The clock setting register is now selected by the interrupt select bit.*

5) Write 0001 to all registers. This ensures starting with a valid BCD value in each register.

6) Set 12/24 Hours Mode: *Write to the clock setting register to select the hours counting mode required.*

7) Load Real-Time Registers: *All time registers (including Leap Years and AM/PM bit) may now be loaded in any order. Note that when writing to the clock setting register to set up Leap Years and AM/PM, the Hours Mode bit must not be altered from the value programmed in step 5.*

8) Write 0 to the control register: *This operation finishes the clock initialization by starting the time. The final control register write should be synchronized with an external time source.*

In general, timekeeping should be halted before the time data is altered in the clock. The data can, however, be altered at any time if so desired. Such may be the case if the user wishes to keep the clock corrected without having to stop and restart it; i.e., winter/summer time changing can be accomplished without halting the clock. This can be done in software by sensing the state of the data-changed flag and only altering time data just after the time has rolled over (data-changed flag set).

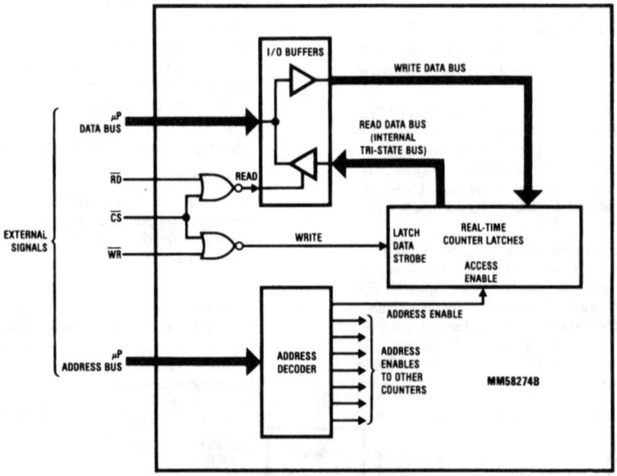

FIGURE 5. MM58274C Microprocessor Interface Diagram

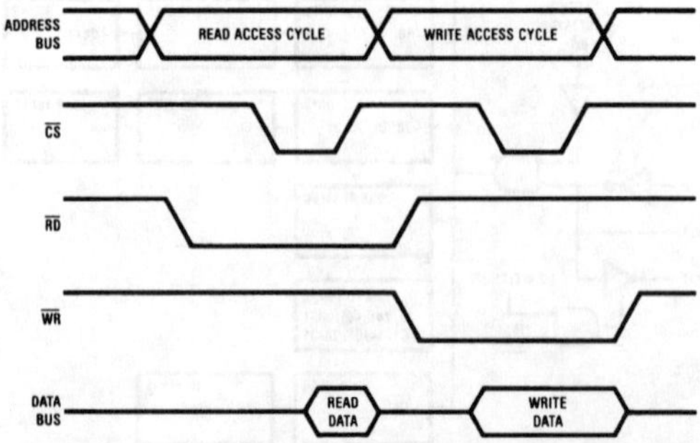

FIGURE 6. Valid MM58274C Control Signals Using Chip Select Generated Access Strobes

Functional Description (Continued)

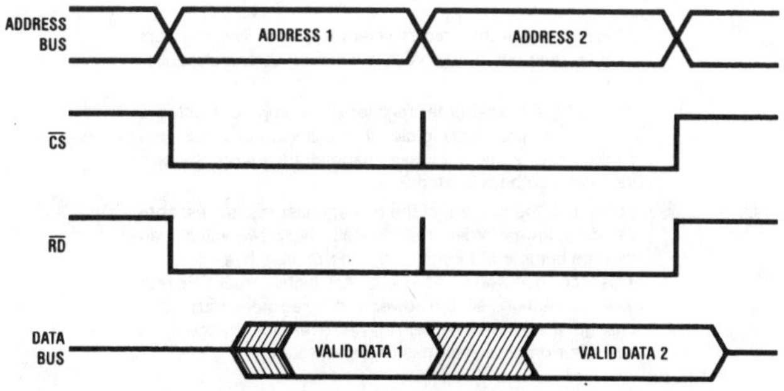

a. Port Generated Read Access—2 Addresses Read Out

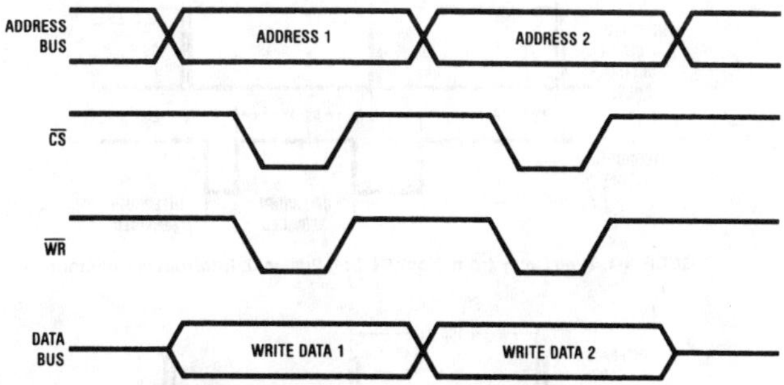

b. Port Generated Write Access—2 Addresses Written To

FIGURE 7. Simple Port Generated Control Signals

APPLICATION HINTS

Time Reading Using Interrupt

In systems such as point of sale terminals and data loggers, time reading is usually only required on a random demand basis. Using the data-changed flag as outlined in the section on methods of operation is ideal for this type of system. Some systems, however, need to sense a change in real time; e.g., industrial timers/process controllers, TV/VCR clocks, any system where real time is displayed.

The interrupt timer on the MM58274C can generate interrupts synchronously with the time registers changing, using software to provide the initial synchronization.

In single interrupt mode the processor is responsible for initiating each timing cycle and the timed period is accurate to ±1 ms.

In repeated interrupt mode the period from the initial processor start to the first timeout is also only accurate to ±1 ms. The following interrupts maintain accurate delay periods relative to the first timeout. Thus, to utilize interrupt to control time reading, we will use repeated interrupt mode.

In repeated mode the time period between interrupts is exact, which means that timeouts will always occur at the same point relative to the internal clock setting pulses. The case for 0.1s interrupts is shown in *Figure A-1*. The same is true for other delay periods, only there will be more clock setting pulses between each interrupt timeout. If we set up the interrupt timer so that interrupt always times out just after the clock setting pulse occurs (*Figure A-2*), then there is no need to test the data-changed flag as we know that the time data has just changed and will not alter again for another 100 ms.

This can be achieved as outlined below:

1) Follow steps 1 and 2 of the section on interrupt programming. In step 2 set up for repeated interrupt.

2) Read control register AD0: *This is a dummy read to reset the data-changed flag.*

3) Read control register AD0 until data-changed flag is set.

4) Write 0 or 2 to control register. Interrupt timing commences.

Time Reading with Very Slow Read Cycles

If a system takes longer than 100 ms to complete reading of all the necessary time registers (e.g., when CMOS processors are used) or where high level interpreted language routines are used, then the data-changed flag will always be set when tested and is of no value. In this case, the time registers themselves must be tested to ensure data accuracy.

The technique below will detect both time changing *between* read strobes (i.e., between reading tens of minutes and units of hours) and also time changing *during* read, which can produce invalid data.

1) Read and store the value of the *lowest* order time register required.

Functional Description (Continued)

2) Read out all the time registers required. The registers may be read out in any order, simplifying software requirements.

3) Read the lowest order register and compare it with the value stored previously in step 1. If it is still the same, then all time data is good. If it has changed, then store the new value and go back to step 2.

In general, the rule is that the first and last reads *must* both be of the lowest order time register. These two values can then be compared to ensure that no change has occurred. This technique works because for any higher order time register to change, all the lower order registers must also change. If the lowest order register does not change, then no higher order register has changed either.

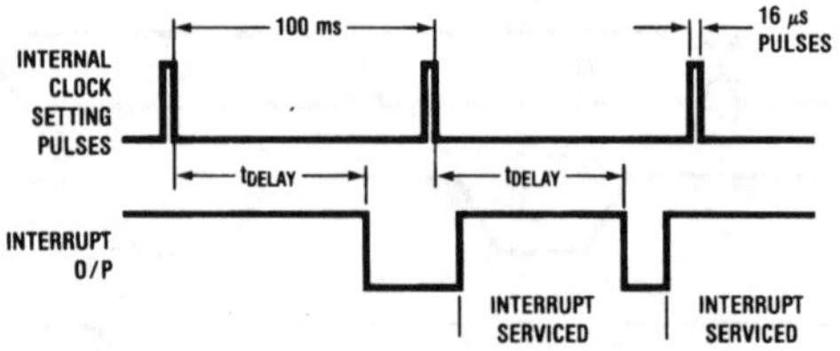

FIGURE A-1. Time Delay from Clock Setting Pulses to Interrupt is Constant

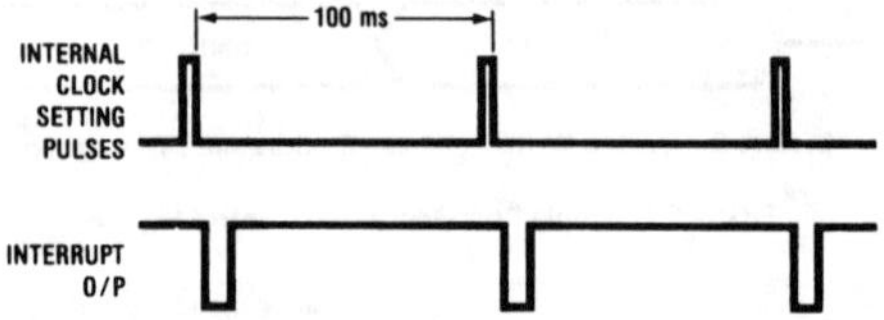

FIGURE A-2. Interrupt Timer Synchronized with Clock Setting Pulses

Features

- Full function real time clock/calendar
  - — 12/24 hour mode timekeeping
  - — Day of week and day of years counters
  - — Four selectable oscillator frequencies
  - — Parallel Resonant Oscillator
- Two 16-bit timers
  - — 10 MHz external clock frequency
  - — Programmable multi-function output
  - — Flexible re-trigger facilities
- Power fail features
  - — Internal power supply switch to external battery
  - — Power Supply Bus glitch protection
  - — Automatic log of time into RAM at power failure
- On-chip interrupt structure
  - — Periodic, alarm, timer and power fail interrupts
- Up to 44 bytes of CMOS RAM
- INTR/MFO pins programmable High/Low and push-pull or open drain

General Description

The DP8570A is intended for use in microprocessor based systems where information is required for multi-tasking, data logging or general time of day/date information. This device is implemented in low voltage silicon gate microCMOS technology to provide low standby power in battery back-up environments. The circuit's architecture is such that it looks like a contiguous block of memory or I/O ports. The address space is organized as 2 software selectable pages of 32 bytes. This includes the Control Registers, the Clock Counters, the Alarm Compare RAM, the Timers and their data RAM, and the Time Save RAM. Any of the RAM locations that are not being used for their intended purpose may be used as general purpose CMOS RAM.

Time and date are maintained from 1/100 of a second to year and leap year in a BCD format, 12 or 24 hour modes. Day of week, day of month and day of year counters are provided. Time is controlled by an on-chip crystal oscillator requiring only the addition of the crystal and two capacitors. The choice of crystal frequency is program selectable.

Two independent multifunction 10 MHz 16-bit timers are provided. These timers operate in four modes. Each has its own prescaler and can select any of 8 possible clock inputs. Thus, by programming the input clocks and the timer counter values a very wide range of timing durations can be achieved. The range is from about 400 ns (4.915 MHz oscillator) to 65,535 seconds (18 hrs., 12 min.).

Power failure logic and control functions have been integrated on chip. This logic is used by the TCP to issue a power fail interrupt, and lock out the μp interface. The time power fails may be logged into RAM automatically when $V_{BB} > V_{CC}$. Additionally, two supply pins are provided, and upon power failure detection, internal circuitry will automatically switch from the main supply to the battery supply. Status bits are provided to indicate initial application of battery power, system power, and low battery detect.

The DP8570A's interrupt structure provides four basic types of interrupts: Periodic, Alarm/Compare, Timer, and Power Fail. Interrupt mask and status registers enable the masking and easy determination of each interrupt.

One dedicated general purpose interrupt output is provided. A second interrupt output is available on the Multiple Function Output (MFO) pin. Each of these may be selected to generate an interrupt from any source. Additionally, the MFO pin may be programmed to be either as oscillator output or Timer 0's output.

Absolute Maximum Ratings (Notes 1 & 2)

If Military/Aerospace specified devices are required, please contact the National Semiconductor Sales Office/Distributors for availability and specifications.

Supply Voltage (V_{CC})	−0.5V to +7.0V
DC Input Voltage (V_{IN})	−0.5V to V_{CC} +0.5V
DC Output Voltage (V_{OUT})	−0.5V to V_{CC} + 0.5V
Storage Temperature Range	−65°C to +150°C
Power Dissipation (PD)	500 mW
Lead Temperature (Soldering, 10 sec.)	260°C

Operation Conditions

	Min	Max	Unit
Supply Voltage (V_{CC}) (Note 3)	4.5	5.5	V
Supply Voltage (V_{BB}) (Note 3)	2.2	$V_{CC}-0.4$	V
DC Input or Output Voltage (V_{IN}, V_{OUT})	0.0	V_{CC}	V
Operation Temperature (T_A)	−40	+85	°C
Electr-Static Discharge Rating TBD		1	kV

Block Diagram

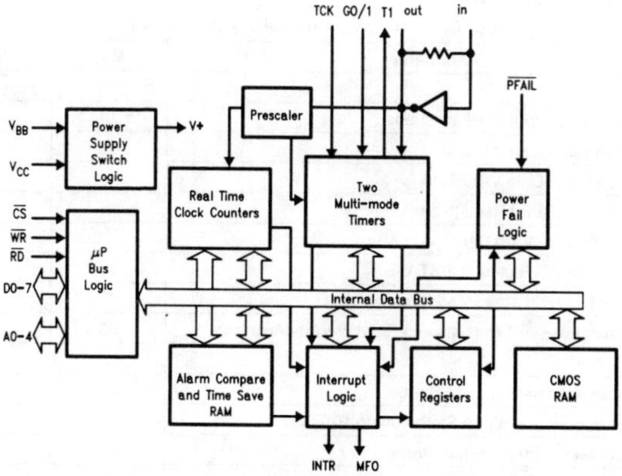

FIGURE 1

DC Electrical Characteristics

V_{CC} = 5V ±10%, V_{BB} = 3V, $V_{\overline{PFAIL}}$ > V_{IH}, C_L = 100 pF (unless otherwise specified)

Symbol	Parameter	Conditions	Min	Max	Units
V_{IH}	High Level Input Voltage (Note 4)	Any Inputs Except OSC IN, OSC IN with External Clock	2.0 V_{BB} −0.1		V V
V_{IL}	Low Level Input Voltage	All Inputs Except OSC IN OSC IN with External Clock		0.8 0.1	V V
V_{OH}	High Level Output Voltage (Excluding OSC OUT)	I_{OUT} = −20 μA I_{OUT} = −4.0 mA	V_{CC} −0.1 3.5		V V
V_{OL}	Low Level Output Voltage (Excluding OSC OUT)	I_{OUT} = 20 μA I_{OUT} = 4.0 mA		0.1 0.25	V V
I_{IN}	Input Current (Except OSC IN)	V_{IN} = V_{CC} or GND		±1.0	μA
I_{OZ}	Output TRI-STATE® Current	V_{OUT} = V_{CC} or GND		±5.0	μA
I_{LKG}	Output High Leakage Current T1, MFO, INTR Pins	V_{OUT} = V_{CC} or GND Outputs Open Drain		±5.0	μA
I_{CC}	Quiescent Supply Current (Note 7)	F_{OSC} = 32.768 kHz V_{IN} = V_{CC} or GND (Note 5) V_{IN} = V_{CC} or GND (Note 6) V_{IN} = V_{IH} or V_{IL} (Note 6)		260 1.0 12.0	μA mA mA
		F_{OSC} = 4.194304 MHz or 4.9152 MHz V_{IN} = V_{CC} or GND (Note 6) V_{IN} = V_{IH} or V_{IL} (Note 6)		8 20	mA mA
I_{CC}	Quiescent Supply Current (Single Supply Mode) (Note 7)	V_{BB} = GND V_{IN} = V_{CC} or GND F_{OSC} = 32.768 kHz F_{OSC} = 4.9152 MHz or 4.194304 MHz		80 7.5	μA mA
I_{BB}	Standby Mode Battery Supply Current (Note 8)	V_{CC} = GND F_{OSC} = 32.768 kHz F_{OSC} = 4.9152 MHz or 4.194304 MHz		10 400	μA μA
I_{BLK}	Battery Supply Leakage	2.2V ≤ V_{BB} ≤ 4.0V	−5	1.5	μA

Note 1: Absolute Maximum Ratings are those values beyond which damage to the device may occur.

Note 2: Unless otherwise specified all voltages are referenced to ground.

Note 3: For F_{OSC} = 4.194304 or 4.9152 MHz, V_{BB} minimum = 2.8V. In battery backed mode, V_{BB} ≤ V_{CC} − 0.4V.
Single Supply Mode: Data retention voltage is 2.2V min.
In single Supply Mode (Power connected to V_{CC} pin) 4.5V ≤ V_{CC} ≤ 5.5V.

Note 4: This parameter (V_{IH}) is not tested on all pins at the same time.

Note 5: This specification tests I_{CC} with all power fail circuitry disabled, by setting D7 of Interrupt Control Register 1 to 0.

Note 6: This specification tests I_{CC} with all power fail circuitry enabled, by setting D7 of Interrupt Control Register 1 to 1.

Note 7: This specification is tested with both the timers and OSC IN driven by a signal generator. Contents of the Test Register = 00(H), the MFO pin is not configured as buffered oscillator out and MFO, T1, INTR, are configured as open drain.

Note 8: This specification is tested with both the timers off, and only OSC IN is driven by a signal generator. Contents of the Test Register = 00(H) and the MFO pin is not configured as buffered oscillator out.

AC Electrical Characteristics

V_{CC} = 5V ±10%, V_{BB} = 3V, $V_{\overline{PFAIL}}$ > V_{IH}, C_L = 100 pF (unless otherwise specified)

Symbol	Parameter	Min	Max	Units
READ TIMING				
t_{AR}	Address Valid Prior to Read Strobe	20		ns
t_{RW}	Read Strobe Width (Note 9)	80		ns
t_{CD}	Chip Select to Data Valid Time		80	ns
t_{RAH}	Address Hold after Read (Note 10)	3		ns
t_{RD}	Read Strobe to Valid Data		70	ns
t_{DZ}	Read or Chip Select to TRI-STATE		60	ns
t_{RCH}	Chip Select Hold after Read Strobe	0		ns
t_{DS}	Minimum Inactive Time between Read or Write Accesses	50		ns
WRITE TIMING				
t_{AW}	Address Valid before Write Strobe	20		ns
t_{WAH}	Address Hold after Write Strobe (Note 10)	3		ns
t_{CW}	Chip Select to End of Write Strobe	90		ns
t_{WW}	Write Strobe Width (Note 11)	80		ns

t_{DW}	Data Valid to End of Write Strobe	50		ns
t_{WDH}	Data Hold after Write Strobe (Note 10)	3		ns
t_{WCH}	Chip Select Hold after Write Strobe	0		ns
TIMER 0/TIMER 1 TIMING				
F_{TCK}	Input Frequency Range	DC	10	MHz
t_{CK}	Propagation Delay Clock to Output		120	ns
t_{GO}	Propagation Delay G0 to G1 to Timer Output (Note 12)		100	ns
t_{PGW}	Pulse Width G0 or G1	25		ns

Note 9: Read Strobe width as used in the read timing table is defined as the period when both chip select and read inputs are low. Hence read commences when both signals are low and terminates when either signal returns high.

Note 10: Hold time is guaranteed by design but not production tested. This limit is not used to calculate outgoing quality levels.

Note 11: Write Strobe width as used in the write timing table is defined as the period when both chip select and write inputs are low. Hence write commences when both signals are low and terminates when either signal returns high.

Note 12: Timers in Mode 3.

AC Test Conditions

Input Pulse Levels	GND to 3.0V
Input Rise and Fall Times	6 ns (10%–90%)
Input and Output Reference Levels	1.3V
TRI-STATE Reference Levels (Note 14)	Active High +0.5V Active Low −0.5V

Note 13: C_L = 100 pF, includes jig and scope capacitance.

Note 14: S1 = V_{CC} for active low to high impedance measurements.
S1 = GND for active high to high impedance measurements.
S1 = open for all other timing measurements.

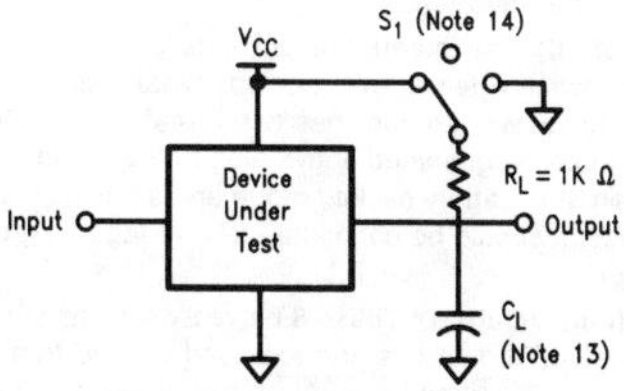

Capacitance (T_A = 25°C, f = 1 MHz)

Symbol	Parameter (Note 15)	Typ	Units
C_{IN}	Input Capacitance	5	pF
C_{OUT}	Output Capacitance	7	pF

Note 15: This parameter is not 100% tested.

Note 16: Output rise and fall times 25 ns max (10%–90%) with 100 pF load.

Timing Waveforms

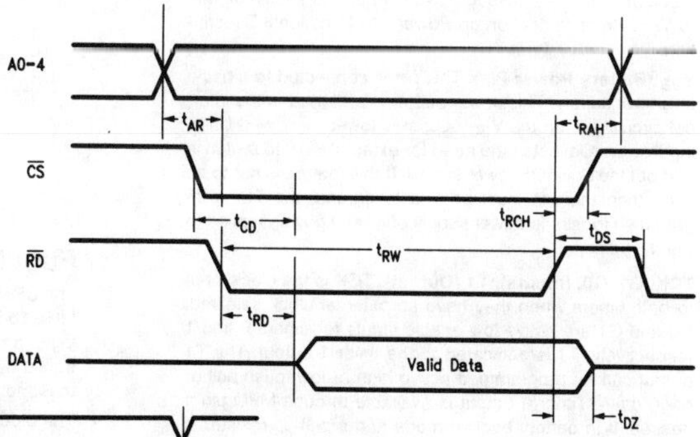

Read Timing Diagram

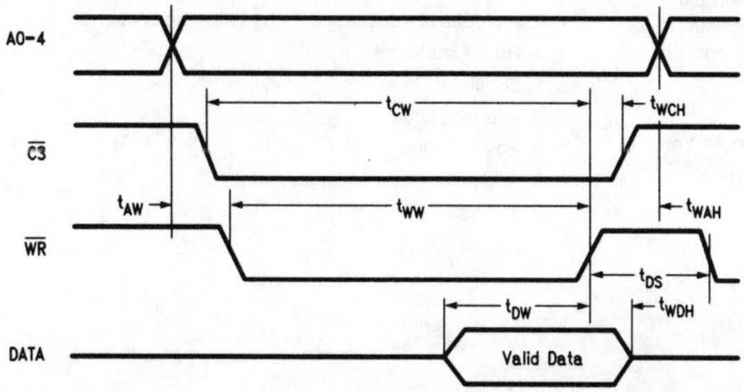

Write Timing Diagram

Pin Description

$\overline{CS}$, $\overline{RD}$, $\overline{WR}$ (Inputs): These pins interface to μP control lines. The $\overline{CS}$ pin is an active low enable for the read and write operations. Read and Write pins are also active low and enable reading or writing to the TCP. All three pins are disabled when power failure is detected. However, if a read or write is in progress at this time, it will be allowed to complete its cycle.

A0–A4 (Inputs): These 5 pins are for register selection. They individually control which location is to be accessed. These inputs are disabled when power failure is detected.

OSC IN (Input): OSC OUT (Output): These two pins are used to connect the crystal to the internal parallel resonant oscillator. The oscillator is always running when power is applied to V_{BB} and V_{CC}, and the correct crystal select bits in the Real Time Mode Register have been set.

MFO (Output): The multi-function output can be used as a second interrupt output for interrupting the μP. This pin can also provide an output for the oscillator or the internal Timer 0. The MFO output can be programmed active high or low, open drain or push-pull. If in battery backed mode and a pull-up resistor is attached, it should be connected to a voltage no greater than V_{BB}.

INTR (Output): The interrupt output is used to interrupt the processor when a timing event or power fail has occurred and the respective interrupt has been enabled. The INTR output can be programmed active high or low, push-pull or open drain. If in battery backed mode and a pull-up resistor is attached, it should be connected to a voltage no greater than V_{BB}.

D0–D7 (Input/Output): These 8 bidirectional pins connect to the host μP's data bus and are used to read from and write to the TCP. When the $\overline{PFAIL}$ pin goes low and a write is not in progress, these pins are at TRI-STATE.

$\overline{PFAIL}$ (Input): In battery backed mode, this pin can have a digital signal applied to it via some external power detection logic. When $\overline{PFAIL}$ = logic 0 the TCP goes into a lockout mode, in a minimum of 30 μs or a maximum of 63 μs unless lockout delay is programmed. In the single power supply mode, this pin is not useable as an input and should be tied to V_{CC}. Refer to section on Power Fail Functional Description.

V_{BB} (Battery Power Pin): This pin is connected to a back-up power supply. This power supply is switched to the internal circuitry when the V_{CC} becomes lower than V_{BB}. Utilizing this pin eliminates the need for external logic to switch in and out the back-up power supply. If this feature is not to be used then this pin must be tied to ground, the TCP programmed for single power supply only, and power applied to the V_{CC} pin.

TCK, G1, G0, (Inputs), T1 (Output): TCK is the clock input to both timers when they have an external clock selected. G0 and G1 are active low enable inputs for timers 0 and 1 respectively. T1 is dedicated to the timer 1 output. The T1 output can be programmed active high or low, push-pull or open drain. Timer 0 output is available through MFO pin if desired. If in battery backed mode and a pull-up resistor is attached to T1, it should be connected to a voltage no greater than V_{BB}.

V_{CC}: This is the main system power pin.

GND: This is the common ground power pin for both V_{BB} and V_{CC}.

Connection Diagrams

Dual-In-Line

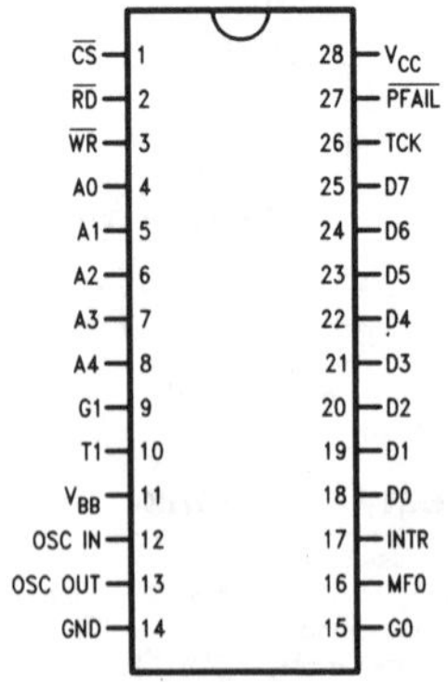

Top View

Plastic Chip Carrier

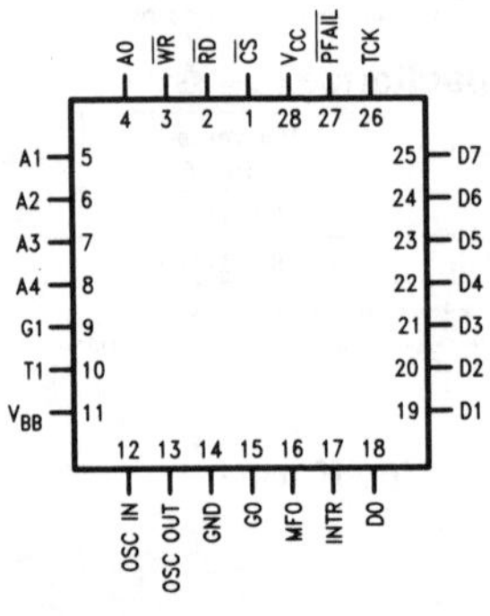

Top View

Functional Description

The DP8570A contains a fast access real time clock, two 10 MHz 16-bit timers, interrupt control logic, power fail detect logic, and CMOS RAM. All functions of the TCP are controlled by a set of nine registers. A simplified block diagram that shows the major functional blocks is given in *Figure 1*.

The blocks are described in the following sections:

1. Real Time Clock
2. Oscillator Prescaler
3. Interrupt Logic
4. Power Failure Logic
5. Additional Supply Management
6. Timers

Functional Description (Continued)

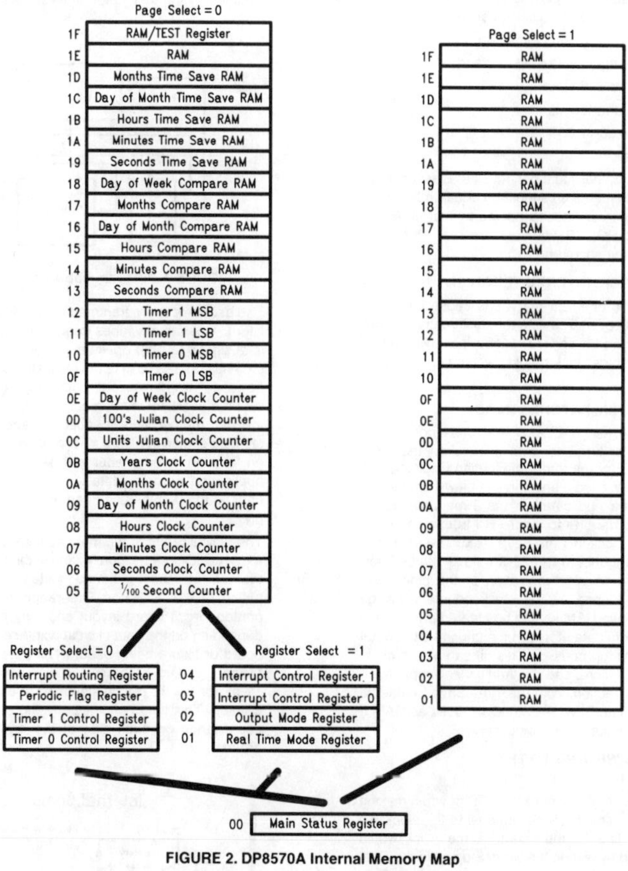

FIGURE 2. DP8570A Internal Memory Map

The memory map of the TCP is shown in the memory addressing table. The memory map consists of two 31 byte pages with a main status register that is common to both pages. A control bit in the Main Status Register is used to select either page. *Figure 2* shows the basic concept. Page 0 contains all the clock timer functions, while page 1 has scratch pad RAM. The control registers are split into two separate blocks to allow page 1 to be used entirely as scratch pad RAM. Again a control bit in the Main Status Register is used to select either control register block.

INITIAL POWER-ON of BOTH V_{BB} and V_{CC}

V_{BB} and V_{CC} may be applied in any sequence. In order for the power fail circuitry to function correctly, whenever power is off, the V_{CC} pin must see a path to ground through a maximum of 1 MΩ. The user should be aware that the control registers will contain random data. The first task to be carried out in an initialization routine is to start the oscillator by writing to the crystal select bits in the Real Time Mode Register. If the DP8570A is configured for single supply mode, an extra 50 μA may be consumed until the crystal select bits are programmed. The user should also ensure that the TCP is not in test mode (see register descriptions).

REAL TIME CLOCK FUNCTIONAL DESCRIPTION

As shown in *Figure 2*, the clock has 10 bytes of counters, which count from 1/100 of a second to years. Each counter counts in BCD and is synchronously clocked. The count sequence of the individual byte counters within the clock is shown later in Table VII. Note that the day of week, day of month, day of year, and month counters all roll over to 1. The hours counter in 12 hour mode rolls over to 1 and the AM/PM bit toggles when the hours rolls over to 12 (AM = 0, PM = 1). The AM/PM bit is bit D7 in the hours counter.

All other counters roll over to 0. Also note that the day of year counter is 12 bits long and occupies two addresses. Upon initial application of power the counters will contain random information.

READING THE CLOCK: VALIDATED READ

Since clocking of the counter occurs asynchronously to reading of the counter, it is possible to read the counter while it is being incremented (rollover). This may result in an incorrect time reading. Thus to ensure a correct reading of the entire contents of the clock (or that part of interest), it must be read without a clock rollover occurring. In general this can be done by checking a rollover bit. On this chip the periodic interrupt status bits can serve this function. The following program steps can be used to accomplish this.

1. Initialize program for reading clock.
2. Dummy read of periodic status bit to clear it.
3. Read counter bytes and store.
4. Read rollover bit, and test it.
5. If rollover occured go to 3.
6. If no rollover, done.

To detect the rollover, individual periodic status bits can be polled. The periodic bit chosen should be equal to the highest frequency counter register to be read. That is if only SECONDS through HOURS counters are read, then the SECONDS periodic bit should be used.

READING THE CLOCK: INTERRUPT DRIVEN

Enabling the periodic interrupt mask bits cause interrupts just as the clock rolls over. Enabling the desired update rate and providing an interrupt service routine that executes in less than 10 ms enables clock reading without checking for a rollover.

READING THE CLOCK: LATCHED READ

Another method to read the clock that does not require checking the rollover bit is to write a one into the Time Save Enable bit (D7) of the Interrupt Routing Register, and then to write a zero. Writing a one into this bit will enable the clock contents to be duplicated in the Time Save RAM. Changing the bit from a one to a zero will freeze and store the contents of the clock in Time Save RAM. The time then can be read without concern for clock rollover, since internal logic takes care of synchronization of the clock. Because only the bits used by the clock counters will be latched, the Time Save RAM should be cleared prior to use to ensure that random data stored in the unused bits do not confuse the host microprocessor. This bit can also provide time save at power failure, see the Additional Supply Management Functions section. With the Time Save Enable bit at a logical 0, the Time Save RAM may be used as RAM if the latched read function is not necessary.

INITIALIZING AND WRITING TO THE CALENDAR-CLOCK

Upon initial application of power to the TCP or when making time corrections, the time must be written into the clock. To correctly write the time to the counters, the clock would normally be stopped by writing the Start/$\overline{\text{Stop}}$ bit in the Real Time Mode Register to a zero. This stops the clock from counting and disables the carry circuitry. When initializing the clock's Real Time Mode Register, it is recommended that first the various mode bits be written while maintaining the Start/$\overline{\text{Stop}}$ bit reset, and then writing to the register a second time with the Start/$\overline{\text{Stop}}$ bit set.

The above method is useful when the entire clock is being corrected. If one location is being updated the clock need not be stopped since this will reset the prescaler, and time will be lost. An ideal example of this is correcting the hours for daylight savings time. To write to the clock "on the fly" the best method is to wait for the 1/100 of a second periodic interrupt. Then wait an additional 16 μs, and then write the data to the clock.

PRESCALER/OSCILLATOR FUNCTIONAL DESCRIPTION

Feeding the counter chain is a programmable prescaler which divides the crystal oscillator frequency to 32 kHz and further to 100 Hz for the counter chain (see *Figure 3*). The crystal frequency that can be selected are: 32 kHz, 32.768 kHz, 4.9152 MHz, and 4.194304 MHz.

Once 32 kHz is generated it feeds both timers and the clock. The clock and timer prescalers can be independently enabled by controlling the timer or clock Start/$\overline{\text{Stop}}$ bits.

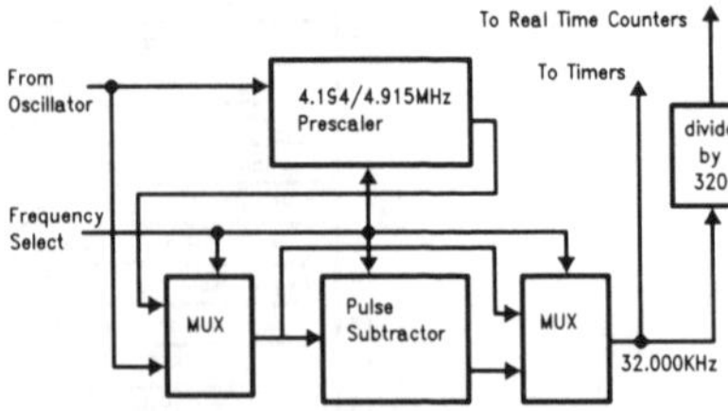

FIGURE 3. Programmable Clock Prescaler Block

The oscillator is programmed via the Real Time Mode Register to operate at various frequencies. The crystal oscillator is designed to offer optimum performance at each frequency. Thus, at 32.768 kHz the oscillator is configured as a low frequency and low power oscillator. At the higher frequencies the oscillator inverter is reconfigured. In addition to the inverter, the oscillator feedback bias resistor is included on chip, as shown in *Figure 4*. The oscillator input may be driven from an external source if desired. Refer to test mode application note for details. The oscillator stability is enhanced through the use of an on chip regulated power supply.

The typical range of trimmer capacitor (as shown in Oscillator Circuit Diagram *Figure 4*, and in the typical application) at the oscillator input pin is suggested only to allow accurate tuning of the oscillator. This range is based on a typical printed circuit board layout and may have to be changed depending on the parasitic capacitance of the printed circuit board or fixture being used. In all cases, the **load capacitance** specified by the crystal manufacturer (nominal value 11 pF for the 32.768 crystal) is what determines proper oscillation. This load capcitance is the series combination of capacitance on each side of the crystal (with respect to ground).

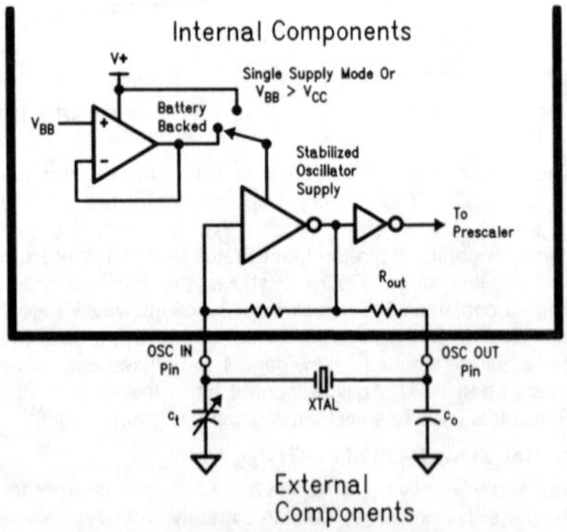

FIGURE 4. Oscillator Circuit Diagram

XTAL	C_o	C_t	R_{OUT} (Switched Internally)
32/32.768 kHz	47 pF	2 pF–22 pF	150 kΩ to 350 kΩ
4.194304 MHz	68 pF	0 pF–80 pF	500Ω to 900Ω
4.9152 MHz	68 pF	29 pF–49 pF	500Ω to 900Ω

Functional Description (Continued)

INTERRUPT LOGIC FUNCTIONAL DESCRIPTION

The TCP has the ability to coordinate processor timing activities. To enhance this, an interrupt structure has been implemented which enables several types of events to cause interrupts. Interrupts are controlled via two Control Registers in block 1 and two Status Registers in block 0. (See Register Description for notes on paging and also *Figure 5* and Table I.)

The interrupts are enabled by writing a one to the appropriate bits in Interrupt Control Register 0 and/or 1. Any of the interrupts can be routed to either the INTR pin or the MFO pin, depending on how the Interrupt Routing register is programmed. This, for example, enables the user to dedicate the MFO as a non-maskable interrupt pin to the CPU for power failure detection and enable all other interrupts to appear on the INTR pin. The polarity for the active interrupt can be programmed in the Output Mode Register for either active high or low, and open drain or push pull outputs.

TABLE I. Registers that are Applicable to Interrupt Control

Register Name	Register Select	Page Select	Address
Main Status Register	X	X	00H
Periodic Flag Register	0	0	03H
Interrupt Routing Register	0	0	04H
Interrupt Control Register 0	1	0	03H
Interrupt Control Register 1	1	0	04H
Output Mode Register	1	0	02H

The Interrupt Status Flag D0, in the Main Status Register, indicates the state of INTR and MFO outputs. It is set when either output becomes active and is cleared when all TCP interrupts have been cleared and no further interrupts are pending (i.e., both INTR and MFO are returned to their inactive state). This flag enables the TCP to be rapidly polled by the µP to determine the source of an interrupt in a wired—OR interrupt system.

Note that the Interrupt Status Flag will only monitor the state of the MFO output if it has been configured as an interrupt output (see Output Mode Register description). This is true, regardless of the state of the Interrupt Routing Register. Thus the Interrupt Status Flag provides a true reflection of all conditions routed to the external pins.

Status for the interrupts are provided by the Main Status Register and the Periodic Flag Register. Bits D1–D5 of the Main Status Register are the main interrupt bits.

These register bits will be set when their associated timing events occur. Enabled Alarm or Timer interrupts that occur will set its Main Status Register bit to a one. However, an external interrupt will only be generated if the appropriate Alarm or Timer interrupt enable bits are set (see *Figure 5*).

Disabling the periodic bits will mask the Main Status Register periodic bit, but not the Periodic Flag Register bits. The Power Fail Interrupt bit is set when the interrupt is enabled and a power fail event has occurred, and is not reset until the power is restored. If all interrupt enable bits are 0 no interrupt will be asserted. However, status still can be read from the Main Status Register in a polled fashion (see *Figure 5*).

To clear a flag in bits D2–D5 of the Main Status Register a 1 must be written back into the bit location that is to be cleared. For the Periodic Flag Register reading the status will reset all the periodic flags.

Interrupts Fall Into Four Categories:

1. The Timer Interrupts: For description see Timer Section.
2. The Alarm Compare Interrupt: Issued when the value in the time compared RAM equals the counter.
3. The Periodic Interrupts: These are issued at every increment of the specific clock counter signal. Thus, an interrupt is issued every minute, second, etc. Each of these interrupts occurs at the roll-over of the specific counter.
4. The Power Fail Interrupt: Issued upon recognition of a power fail condition by the internal sensing logic. The power failed condition is determined by the signal on the $\overline{\text{PFAIL}}$ pin. The internal power fail signal is gated with the chip select signal to ensure that the power fail interrupt does not lock the chip out during a read or write.

ALARM COMPARE INTERRUPT DESCRIPTON

The alarm/time comparison interrupt is a special interrupt similar to an alarm clock wake up buzzer. This interrupt is generated when the clock time is equal to a value programmed into the alarm compare registers. Up to six bytes can be enabled to perform alarm time comparisons on the counter chain. These six bytes, or some subset thereof, would be loaded with the future time at which the interrupt will occur. Next, the appropriate bits in the Interrupt Control Register 1 are enabled or disabled (refer to detailed description of Interrupt Control Register 1). The TCP then compares these bytes with the clock time. When all the enabled compare registers equal the clock time an alarm interrupt is issued, but only if the alarm compare interrupt is enabled can the interrupt be generated externally. Each alarm compare bit in the Control Register will enable a specific byte for comparison to the clock. Disabling a compare byte is the same as setting its associated counter comparator to an "always equal" state. For example, to generate an interrupt at 3:15 AM of every day, load the hours compare with 0 3 (BCD), the minutes compare with 1 5 (BCD) and the faster counters with 0 0 (BCD), and then disable all other compare registers. So every day when the time rolls over from 3:14:59.99, an interrupt is issued. This bit may be reset by writing a one to bit D3 in the Main Status Register at any time after the alarm has been generated.

If time comparison for an individual byte counter is disabled, that corresponding RAM location can then be used as general purpose storage.

PERIODIC INTERRUPTS DESCRIPTION

The Periodic Flag Register contains six flags which are set by real-time generated "ticks" at various time intervals, see *Figure 5*. These flags constantly sense the periodic signals and may be used whether or not interrupts are enabled. These flags are cleared by any read or write operation performed on this register.

To generate periodic interrupts at the desired rate, the associated Periodic Interrupt Enable bit in Interrupt Control Register 0 must be set. Any combination of periodic interrupts may be enabled to operate simultaneously. Enabled periodic interrupts will now affect the Periodic Interrupt Flag in the Main Status Register. The Periodic Route bit in the Interrupt Routing Register is used to route the periodic interrupt events to either the INTR output or the MFO output.

When a periodic event occurs, the Periodic Interrupt Flag in the Main Status Register is set, causing an interrupt to be generated. The µP clears both flag and interrupt by writing a "1" to the Periodic Interrupt Flag. The individual flags in the periodic Interrupt Flag Register do not require clearing to cancel the interrupt.

If all periodic interrupts are disabled and a periodic interrupt is left pending (i.e., the Periodic Interrupt Flag is still set), the Periodic Interrupt Flag will still be required to be cleared to cancel the pending interrupt.

Functional Description (Continued)

POWER FAIL INTERRUPTS DESCRIPTION

The Power Fail Status Flag in the Main Status Register monitors the state of the internal power fail signal. This flag may be interrogated by the μP, but it cannot be cleared; it is cleared automatically by the TCP when system power is restored. To generate an interrupt when the power fails, the Power Fail Interrupt Enable bit in Interrupt Control Register 1 is set.

The Power Fail Route bit determines which output the interrupt will appear on. Although this interrupt may not be cleared, it may be masked by clearing the Power Fail Interrupt Enable bit.

POWER FAILURE CIRCUITRY FUNCTIONAL DESCRIPTION

Since the clock must be operated from a battery when the main system supply has been turned off, the DP8570A provides circuitry to simplify design in battery backed systems. This circuitry switches over to the back up supply, and isolates the DP8570A from the host system. *Figure 6* shows a simplified block diagram of this circuitry, which consists of three major sections; 1) power loss logic: 2) battery switch over logic: and 3) isolation logic.

Detection of power loss occurs when $\overline{\text{PFAIL}}$ is low. Debounce logic provides a 30 μs–63 μs debounce time, which will prevent noise on the $\overline{\text{PFAIL}}$ pin from being interpreted as a system failure. After 30 μs–63 μs the debounce logic times out and a signal is generated indicating that system power is marginal and is failing. The Power Fail Interrupt will then be generated.

The user may choose to have this power failed signal lockout the TCP's data bus within 30 μs min/63 μs max or to delay the lock-out to enable μP access after power failure is detected. This delay is enabled by setting the delay enable bit in the Routing Register. Also, if the lock-out delay was not enabled the TCP will disconnect itself from the bus within 30 μs min → 63 μs max. If chip select is low when a power failure is detected, a safety circuit will ensure that if a read or write is held active continuously for greater than 30 μs after the power fail signal is asserted, the lock-out will be forced. If a lock-out delay is enabled, the DP8570A will remain active for 480 μs after power fail is detected. This will enable the μP to perform last minute bookkeeping before total system collapse. When the host CPU is finished accessing the TCP it may force the bus lock-out before 480 μs has elapsed by resetting the delay enable bit.

The battery switch over circuitry is completely independent of the $\overline{\text{PFAIL}}$ pin. A separate circuit compares V_{CC} to the V_{BB} voltage. As the main supply fails, the TCP will continue to operate from the V_{CC} pin until V_{CC} falls below the V_{BB} voltage. At this time, the battery supply is switched in, V_{CC} is disconnected, and the device is now in the standby mode. If indeterminate operation of the battery switch over circuit is to be avoided, then the voltage at the V_{CC} pin must not be allowed to equal the voltage at the V_{BB} pin.

After the generation of a lock-out signal, and eventual switch in of the battery supply, the pins of the TCP will be configured as shown in Table II. Outputs that have a pull-up resistor should be connected to a voltage no greater than V_{BB}.

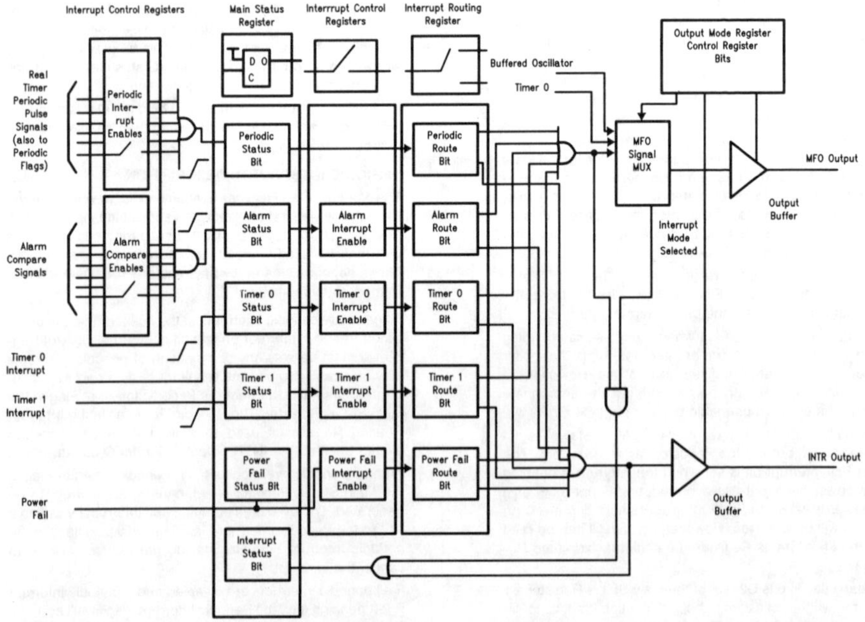

FIGURE 5. Interrupt Control Logic Overview

Functional Description (Continued)

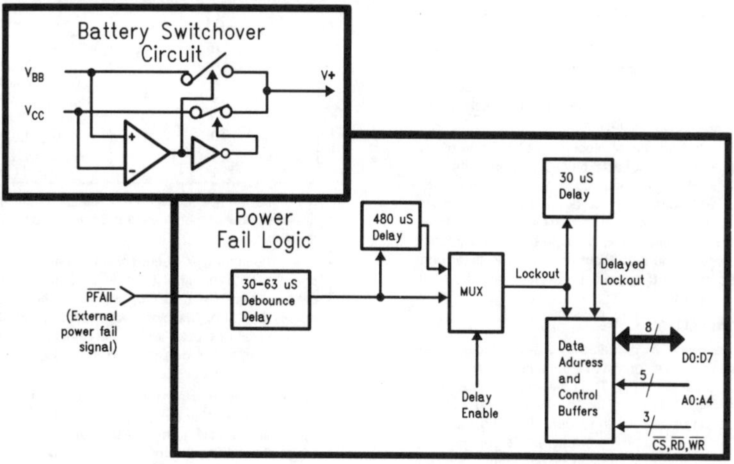

FIGURE 6. System-Battery Switchover (Upper Left), Power Fail and Lock-Out Circuits (Lower Right)

TABLE II. Pin Isolation during a Power Failure

Pin	PFAIL = Logic 0	Standby Mode $V_{BB} > V_{CC}$
CS, RD, WR	Locked Out	Locked Out
A0–A4	Locked Out	Locked Out
D0–D7	Locked Out	Locked Out
Oscillator	Not Isolated	Not Isolated
TCK, G0, G1	Not Isolated	Locked Out
PFAIL	Not Isolated	Not Isolated
INTR, MFO T1	Not Isolated	Open Drain

The Timer and Interrupt Power Fail Operation bits in the Real-Time Mode Register determine whether or not the timers and interrupts will continue to function after a power fail event.

As power returns to the system, the battery switch over circuit will switch back to V_{CC} power as soon as it becomes greater than the battery voltage. The chip will remain in the locked out state as long as PFAIL = 0. When PFAIL = 1 the chip is unlocked, but only after another 30 μs min → 63 μs max debounce time. The system designer must ensure that his system is stable when power has returned.

The power fail circuitry contains active linear circuitry that draws supply current from V_{CC}. In some cases this may be undesirable, so this circuit can be disabled by masking the power fail interrupt. The power fail input can perform all lock-out functions previously mentioned, except that no external interrupt will be issued. Note that the linear power fail circuitry is switched off automatically when using V_{BB} in standby mode.

LOW BATTERY, INITIAL POWER ON DETECT, AND POWER FAIL TIME SAVE

There are three other functions provided on the DP8570A to ease power supply control. These are an initial Power On detect circuit, which also can be used as a time keeping failure detect, a low battery detect circuit, and a time save on power failure.

On initial power up the Oscillator Fail Flag will be set to a one and the real time clock start bit reset to a zero. This indicates that an oscillator fail event has occurred, and time keeping has failed.

The Oscillator Fail flag will not be reset until the real-time clock is started. This allows the system to discriminate between an initial power-up and recovery from a power failure. If the battery backed mode is selected, then bit D6 of the Periodic Flag Register must be written low. This will not affect the contents of the Oscillator Fail Flag.

Another status bit is the low battery detect. This bit is set only when the clock is operating under the V_{CC} pin, and when the battery voltage is determined to be less than 2.1V (typical). When the power fail interrupt enable bit is low, it disables the power fail circuit and will also shut off the low battery voltage detection circuit as well.

To relieve CPU overhead for saving time upon power failure, the Time Save Enable bit is provided to do this automatically. (See also Reading the Clock: Latched Read.) The Time Save Enable bit, when set, causes the Time Save RAM to follow the contents of the clock. This bit can be reset by software, but if set before a power failure occurs, it will automatically be reset when the clock switches to the battery supply-(not when a power failure is detected by the PFAIL pin). Thus, writing a one to the Time Save bit enables both a software write or power fail write.

SINGLE POWER SUPPLY APPLICATIONS

The DP8570A can be used in a single power supply application. To achieve this, the V_{BB} pin must be connected to ground, and the power connected to V_{CC}. The Oscillator Failed/Single Supply bit in the Periodic Flag Register should be set to a logic 1, which will disable the oscillator battery reference circuit. The power fail interrupt should also be disabled. This will turn off the linear power fail detection circuits, and will eliminate any quiescent power drawn through these circuits. Until the crystal select bits are initialized, the DP8570A may consume about 50 μA due to arbitrary oscillator selection at power on.

(This extra 50 μA is not consumed if the battery backed mode is selected).

TIMER FUNCTIONAL DESCRIPTION

The DP8570A contains 2 independent multi-mode timers. Each timer is composed of a 16-bit negative edge triggered binary down counter and associated control. The operation is similar to existing μP peripheral timers except that several

Functional Description (Continued)

features have been enhanced. The timers can operate in four modes, and in addition, the input clock frequency can be selected from a prescaler over a wide range of frequencies. Furthermore, these timers are capable of generating interrupts as well as hardware output signals, and both the interrupt and timer outputs are fully programmable active high, or low, open drain, or push-pull.

Figure 7 shows the functional block diagram of one of the timers. The timer consists of a 16-bit counter, two 8-bit input registers, two 8-bit output registers, clock prescaler, mode control logic, and output control logic. The timer and the data registers are organized as two bytes for each timer. Under normal operations a read/write to the timer locations will read or write to the data input register. The timer contents can be read by setting the counter Read bit (RD) in the timer control register.

TIMER INITIALIZATION

The timer's operation is controlled by a set of registers, as listed in Table III. These consist of 2 data input registers and one control register per timer. The data input registers contain the timers count down value. The Timer Control Register is used to set up the mode of operation and the input clock rate. The timer related interrupts can be controlled by programming the Interrupt Routing Register and Interrupt Control Register 0. The timer outputs are configured by the Output Mode Register.

TABLE III. Timer Associated Registers

Register Name	Register Select	Page Select	Address
Timer 0 Data MSB	X	0	10H
Timer 0 Data LSB	X	0	0FH
Timer 0 Control Register	0	0	01H
Timer 1 Data MSB	X	0	12H
Timer 1 Data LSB	X	0	11H
Timer 1 Control Register	0	0	02H
Interrupt Routing Register	0	0	04H
Interrupt Control Reg. 0	1	0	03H
Output Mode Register	1	0	02H

All these registers must be initialized prior to starting the timer(s). The Timer Control Register should first be set to select the timer mode with the timer start/$\overline{\text{stop}}$ bit reset. Then when the timer is to be started the control register should be rewritten identically but with the start/$\overline{\text{stop}}$ bit set.

TIMER OPERATION

Each timer is capable of operation in one of four modes. As mentioned, these modes are programmed in each timer's Control Register which is described later. All four modes operate in a similar manner. They operate on the two 8-bit data words stored into the Data Input Register. At the beginning of a counting cycle the 2 bytes are loaded into the timer and the timer commences counting down towards zero. The exact action taken when zero is reached depends on the mode selected, but in general, the timer output will change state, and an interrupt will be generated if the timer interrupts are unmasked.

INPUT CLOCK SELECTION

The input frequency to the timers may be selected. Each timer has a prescaler that gives a wide selection of clocking rates. In addition, the DP8570A has a single external clock input pin that can be selected for either of the timers. Table IV shows the range of programmable clocks available and the corresponding setting in the Timer Control Register.

TABLE IV. Programmable Timer Input Clocks

C2	C1	C0	Selected Clock
0	0	0	External
0	0	1	Crystal Oscillator
0	1	0	(Crystal Oscillator)/4
0	1	1	93.5 µs (10.7 kHz)
1	0	0	1 ms (1 kHz)
1	0	1	10 ms (100 Hz)
1	1	0	1/10 Second (10 Hz)
1	1	1	1 Second (1 Hz)

Note that the second and third selections are not fixed frequencies, but depend on the crystal oscillator frequency chosen.

Since the input clock frequencies are usually running asynchronously to the timer Start/$\overline{\text{Stop}}$ control bit, a 1 clock cycle error may result. This error results when the Start/Stop occurs just after the clock edge (max error). To minimize this error on all clocks an independent prescaler is used for each timer and is designed so that its Start/Stop error is less than 1 clock cycle.

The count hold/gate bit in the Timer Control Register and the external enable pins, G0/G1, can be used to suspend the timer operation in modes 0, 1, and 2 (in mode 3 it is the trigger input). The external pin and the register bit are OR'ed together, so that when either is high the timers are suspended. Suspending the timer causes the same synchronization error that starting the timer does. The range of errors is specified in Table V.

TABLE V. Maximum Synchronization Errors

Clock Selected	Error
External	+ Ext. Clock Period
Crystal	+ 1 Crystal Clock Period
Crystal/4	+ 1 Crystal Clock Period
10.7 kHz	+ 32 µs
1 kHz	+ 32 µs
100 Hz	+ 32 µs
10 Hz	+ 32 µs
1 Hz	+ 32 µs

MODES OF OPERATION

Bits M0 and M1 in the Timer Control Registers are used to specify the modes of operation. The mode selection is described in Table VI.

TABLE VI. Programmable Timer Modes of Operation

M1	M0	Function	Modes
0	0	Single Pulse Generator	Mode 0
0	1	Rate Generator, Pulse Output	Mode 1
1	0	Square Wave Output	Mode 2
1	1	Retriggerable One Shot	Mode 3

MODE 0: SINGLE PULSE GENERATOR

When the timer is in this mode the output will be initially low if the Timer Start/$\overline{\text{Stop}}$ bit is low (stopped). When this mode is initiated the timer output will go high on the next falling edge of the prescaler's input clock, the contents of the input data registers are loaded into the timer. The output will stay high until the counter reaches zero. At zero the output is reset. The result is an output pulse whose duration is equal to the input clock period times the count value (N) loaded into the input data register. This is shown in *Figure 8*.

Pulse Width = Clock Period × N

An interrupt is generated when the zero count is reached. This can be used for one-time interrupts that are set to occur a certain amount of time in the future. In this mode the Timer Start/$\overline{\text{Stop}}$ bit (TSS) is automatically reset upon zero detection. This removes the need to reset TSS before starting another operation.

Functional Description (Continued)

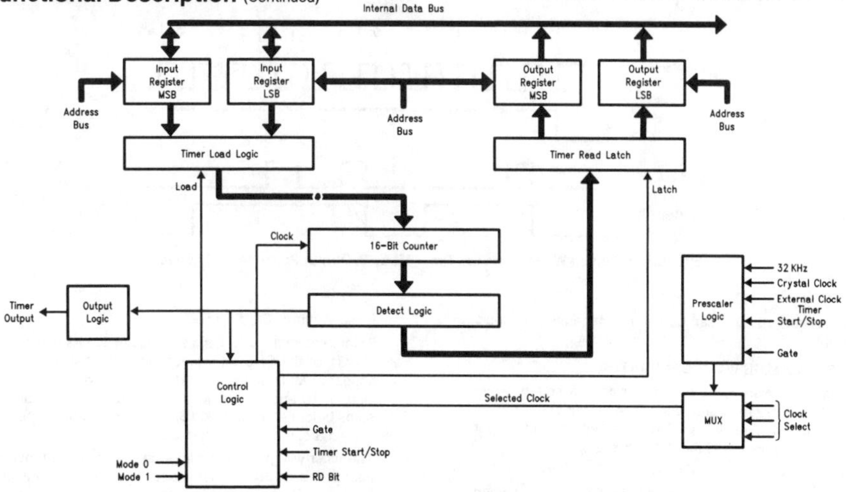

FIGURE 7. DP8570A Timer Block Diagram

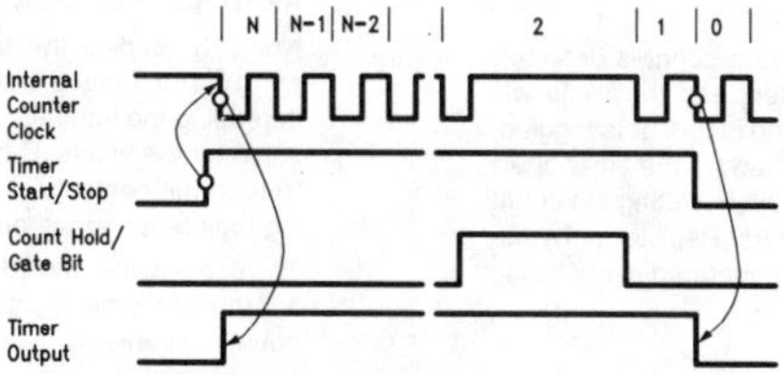

FIGURE 8. Typical Waveforms for Timer Mode 0 (Timer Output Programmed Active High)

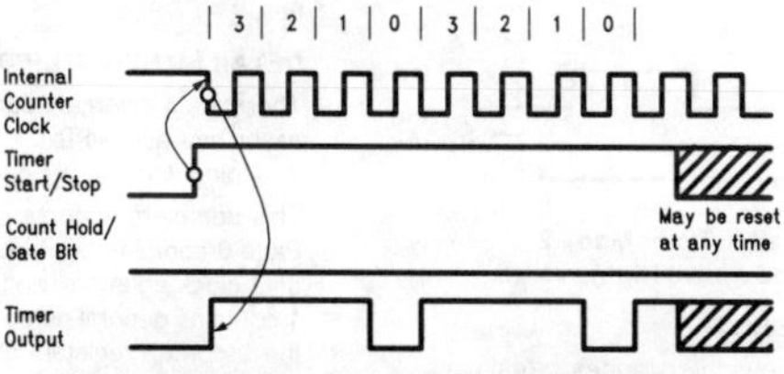

FIGURE 9. Timing Waveforms for Timer Mode 1 (Timer Output Programmed Active High)

The count down operation may be temporarily suspended either under software control by setting the Count Hold/ Gate bit in the timer register high, or in hardware by setting the G0 or G1 pin high.

The above discussion assumes that the timer outputs were programmed to be non-inverting outputs (active high). If the polarity of the output waveform is wrong for the application the polarity can be reversed by configuring the Output Mode Register. The drive configuration can also be programmed to be push pull or open drain.

MODE 1: RATE GENERATOR

When operating in this mode the timer will operate continuously. Before the timer is started its output is low. When the timer is started the input data register contents are loaded into the counter on the negative clock edge and the output is set high (again assuming the Output Mode Register is programmed active high). The timer will then count down to zero. Once the zero count is reached the output goes low for one clock period of the timer clock. Then on the next clock the counter is reloaded automatically and the count-down repeats itself. The output, shown in *Figure 9*, is a waveform whose pulse width and period is determined by N, the input register value, and the input clock period:

Period = (N + 1) (Clock Period)

Pulse Width = Clock Period

The G0 or G1 pin and the count hold/gate bit can be used to suspend the appropriate timer countdown when either is high. Again, the output polarity is controllable as in mode 0. If enabled, an interrupt is generated whenever the zero

Functional Description (Continued)

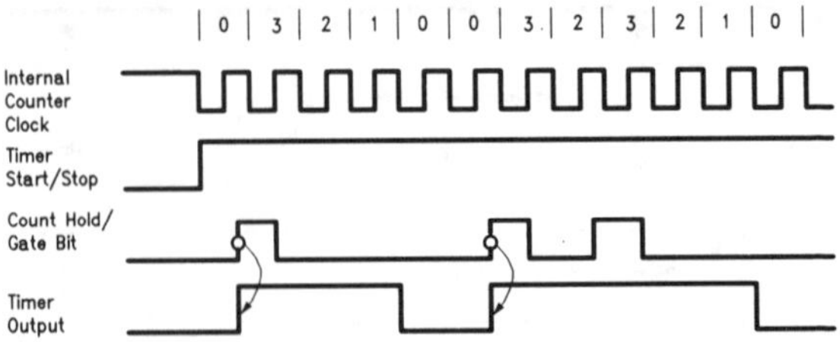

FIGURE 11. Timing Waveforms for Timer Mode 3, Output Programmed Active High

count is reached. This can be used to generate a periodic interrupt.

MODE 2: SQUARE WAVE GENERATOR

This mode is also cyclic but in this case a square wave rather than a pulse is generated. The output square wave period is determined by the value loaded into the timer input register. This period and the duty cycle are:

Period = 2(N + 1) (Clock Period)   Duty Cycle = 0.5

When the timer is stopped the output will be low, and when the Start/$\overline{\text{Stop}}$ bit is set high the timer's counter will be loaded on the next clock falling transition and the output will be set high.

The output will be toggled after the zero count is detected and the counter will then be reloaded, and the cycle will continue. Thus, every N + 1 counts the output gets toggled, as shown in *Figure 10*. Like the other modes the timer operation can be suspended either by software setting the count hold/gate bit (CHG) in the Timer Control Register or by using the gate pins. An interrupt will be generated every falling edge of the timer output, if enabled.

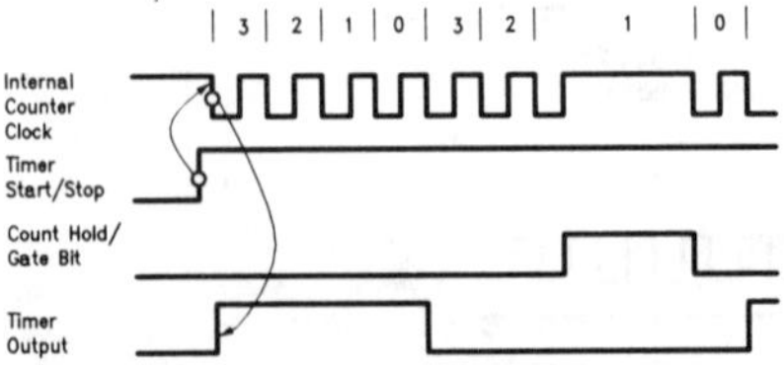

FIGURE 10. Timing Waveforms for Timer Mode 2 (Timer Output Programmed Active High)

MODE 3: RETRIGGERABLE ONE SHOT

This mode is different from the previous three modes in that this is the only mode which uses the external gate to trigger the output. Once the timer Start/$\overline{\text{Stop}}$ bit is set the output stays inactive, and nothing happens until a positive transition is received on the G1 or G0 pins, or the Count Hold/Gate (CHG) bit is set in the timer control register. When a transition ocurs the one shot output is set active immediately; the counter is loaded with the value in the input register on the next transition of the input clock and the countdown begins. If a retrigger occurs, regardless of the current counter value, the counters will be reloaded with the value in the input register and the counter will be restarted without changing the output state. See *Figure 11*. A trigger count can occur at any time during the count cycle and can be a hardware or software signal (G0, G1 or CHG). In this mode the timer will output a single pulse whose width is determined by the value in the input data register (N) and the input clock period.

Pulse Width = Clock Period × N

Before entering mode 3, if a spurious edge has occurred on G0/G1 or the CHG bit is set to logic 1, then a pulse will appear at MFO or T1 or INTR output pin when the timer is started. To ensure this does not happen, do the following steps before entering mode 3: Configure the timer for mode 0, load a count of zero, then start the timer.

The timer will generate an interrupt only when it reaches a count of zero. This timer mode is useful for continuous "watch dog" timing, line frequency power failure detection, etc.

READING THE TIMERS

Normally reading the timer data register addresses, 0FH and 10H for Timer 0 and 11H and 12H for Timer 1 will result in reading the input data register which contains the preset value for the timers. During timer operation it is often useful to read the contents of the 16-bit down counter. This reading may be an erroneous value of FFFFH.

To read a timer, the μP first sets the timer read bit in the appropriate Timer Control Register high. This will cause the counter's contents to be latched to 2–8 bit output registers, and will enable these registers to be read if the μP reads the timer's input data register addresses. On reading the LSB byte the timer read bit is internally reset and subsequent reads of the timer locations will return the input register values.

DETAILED REGISTER DESCRIPTION

There are 5 external address bits: Thus, the host microprocessor has access to 32 locations at one time. An internal switching scheme provides a total of 67 locations.

This complete address space is organized into two pages. Page 0 contains two blocks of control registers, timers, real time clock counters, and special purpose RAM, while page 1 contains general purpose RAM. Using two blocks enables the 9 control registers to be mapped into 5 locations. The only register that does not get switched is the Main Status Register. It contains the page select bit and the register select bit as well as status information.

A memory map is shown in *Figure 2* and register addressing in Table VII. They show the name, address and page locations for the DP8570A.

Functional Description (Continued)

TABLE VII. Register/Counter/RAM Addressing for DP8570A

A0-4	PS (Note 1)	RS (Note 2)	Description	
CONTROL REGISTERS				
00	X	X	Main Status Register	
01	0	0	Timer 0 Control Register	
02	0	0	Timer 1 Control Register	
03	0	0	Periodic Flag Register	
04	0	0	Interrupt Routing Register	
01	0	1	Real Time Mode Register	
02	0	1	Output Mode Register	
03	0	1	Interrupt Control Register 0	
04	0	1	Interrupt Control Register 1	
COUNTERS (CLOCK CALENDAR)				
05	0	X	1/100, 1/10 Seconds	(0–99)
06	0	X	Seconds	(0–59)
07	0	X	Minutes	(0–59)
08	0	X	Hours	(1–12, 0–23)
09	0	X	Days of Month	(1–28/29/30/31)
0A	0	X	Months	(1–12)
0B	0	X	Years	(0–99)
0C	0	X	Julian Date (LSB)	(1–99)
0D	0	X	Julian Date	(0–3)
0E	0	X	Day of Week	(1–7)
TIMER DATA REGISTERS				
0F	0	X	Timer 0 LSB	
10	0	X	Timer 0 MSB	
11	0	X	Timer 1 LSB	
12	0	X	Timer 1 MSB	
TIMER COMPARE RAM				
13	0	X	Sec Compare RAM	(0–59)
14	0	X	Min Compare RAM	(0–59)
15	0	X	Hours Compare RAM	(1–12, 0–23)
16	0	X	DOM Compare RAM	(1–28/29/30/31)
17	0	X	Months Compare RAM	(1–12)
18	0	X	DOW Compare RAM	(1–7)
TIME SAVE RAM				
19	0	X	Seconds Time Save RAM	
1A	0	X	Minutes Time Save RAM	
1B	0	X	Hours Time Save RAM	
1C	0	X	Day of Month Time Save RAM	
1D	0	X	Months Time Save RAM	
1E	0	1	RAM	
1F	0	X	RAM/Test Mode Register	
01–1F	1	X	2nd Page General Purpose RAM	

1 PS—Page Select (Bit D7 of Main Status Register)
2 RS—Register Select (Bit D6 of Main Status Register)

MAIN STATUS REGISTER

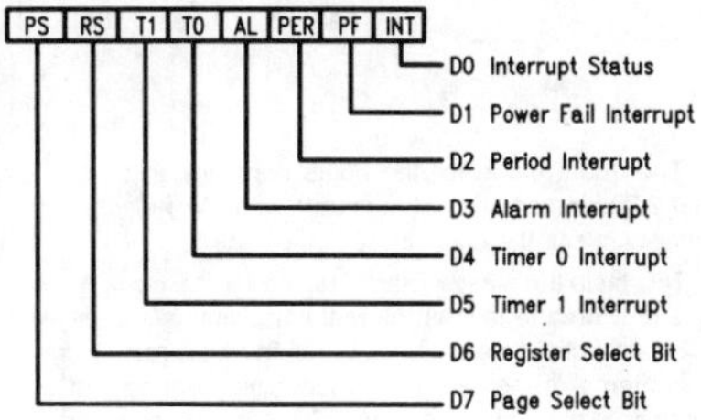

The Main Status Register is always located at address 0 regardless of the register block or the page selected.

D0: This read only bit is a general interrupt status bit that is taken directly from the interrupt pins. The bit is a one when an interrupt is pending on either the INTR pin or the MFO pin (when configured as an interrupt). This is unlike D3–D5 which can be set by an internal event but may not cause an interrupt. This bit is reset when the interrupt status bits in the Main Status Register are cleared.

D1–D5: These five bits of the Main Status Register are the main interrupt status bits. Any bit may be a one when any of the interrupts are pending. Once an interrupt is asserted the μP will read this register to determine the cause. These interrupt status bits are not reset when read. Except for D1, to reset an interrupt a one is written back to the corresponding bit that is being tested. D1 is reset whenever the $\overline{PFAIL}$ pin = logic 1. This prevents loss of interrupt status when reading the register in a polled mode. D1, D3–D5 are set regardless of whether these interrupts are masked or not by bits D6 and D7 of Interrupt Control Registers 0 and 1.

D6 and D7: These bits are Read/Write bits that control which register block or RAM page is to be selected. Bit D6 controls the register block to be accessed (see memory map). The memory map of the clock is further divided into two memory pages. One page is the registers, clock and timers, and the second page contains 31 bytes of general purpose RAM. The page selection is determined by bit D7.

TIMER 0 AND 1 CONTROL REGISTER

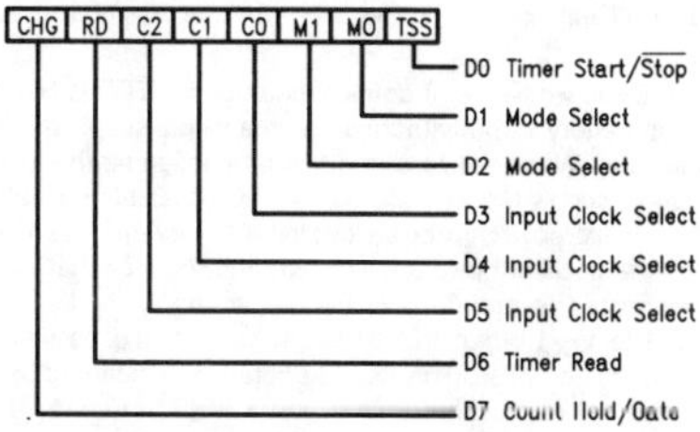

These registers control the operation of the timers. Each timer has its own register.

D0: This bit will Start (1) or Stop (0) the timer. When the timer is stopped the timer's prescaler and counter are reset, and the timer will restart from the beginning when started again. In mode 0 on time out the TSS bit is internally reset.

D1 and D2: These control the count mode of the timers. See Table VI.

D3–D5: These bits control which clock signal is applied to the timer's counter input. There is one external clock input pin (TCK) and either (or both) timer(s) can be selected to run off this pin: refer to Table IV for details.

D6: This is the read bit. If a one is written into this location it will cause the contents of the timer to be latched into a holding register, which can be read by the μP at any time. Reading the least significant byte of the timer will reset the RD bit. The timer read cycle can be aborted by writing RD to zero.

D7: The CHG bit has two mode dependent functions. In modes 0 through 2 writing a one to this bit will suspend the timer operation (without resetting the timer prescaler). However, in mode 3 this bit is used to trigger or re-trigger the count sequence as with the gate pins. If retriggering is desired using the CHG bit, it is not necessary to write a zero to this location prior to the re-trigger. The action of further writing a one to this bit will re-trigger the count.

Functional Description (Continued)

PERIODIC FLAG REGISTER

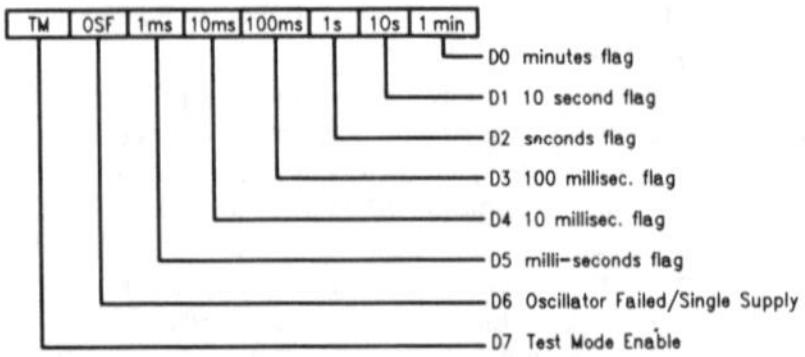

The Periodic Flag Register has the same bit for bit correspondence as Interrupt Control Register 0 except for D6 and D7. For normal operation (i.e., not a single supply application) this register must be written to on initial power up or after an oscillator fail event. D0–D5 are read only bits, D6 and D7 are read/write.

D0–D5: These bits are set by the real time rollover events: (Time Change = 1). The bits are reset when the register is read and can be used as selective data change flags.

D6: This bit performs a dual function. When this bit is read, a one indicates that an oscillator failure has occurred and the time information may have been lost. This bit is automatically set on initial power-up or an oscillator fail event. The oscillator fail flag is reset by writing a one to the clock start/$\overline{\text{stop}}$ bit in the Real Time Mode Register, with the crystal oscillating.

When D6 is written to, it defines whether the TCP is being used in battery standby (normal) or in a single supply mode application. When set to a one this bit configures the TCP for single supply mode applications. This bit is automatically set on initial power-up or an oscillator fail event. This disables the oscillator reference circuit, and requires that V_{BB} is connected to ground, and the single supply mode connected to V_{CC}. When this bit is set to zero, the oscillator reference is enabled. This allows operation in standard battery standby application.

D7: Writing a one to this bit enables the test mode register at location 1F (see Table VII). This bit should be forced to zero during initialization for normal operation. If the test mode has been entered, clear the test mode register before leaving test mode. (See separate test mode application note for further details.)

INTERRUPT ROUTING REGISTER

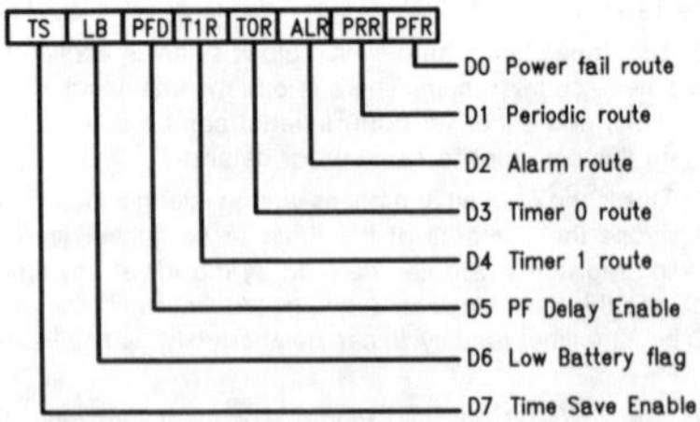

D0–D4: The lower 5 bits of this register are associated with the main interrupt sources created by this chip. The purpose of this register is to route the interrupts to either the MFO (multi-function pin), or to the main interrupt pin. When any bit is set the associated interrupt signal will be sent to the MFO pin, and when zero it will be sent to the INTR pin.

D5: The Delay Enable bit is used when a power fail occurs. If this bit is set, a 480 μs delay is generated internally before the μP interface is locked out. This will enable the μP to access the registers for up to 480 μs after it receives a power fail interrupt. After a power failure is detected but prior to the 480 μs delay timing out, the host μP may force immediate lock out by resetting the Delay Enable bit. Note if this bit is a 0 when power fails then after a delay of 30 μs min/63 μs max the μP cannot read the chip.

D6: This read only bit is set and reset by the voltage at the V_{BB} pin. It can be used by the μP to determine whether the battery voltage at the V_{BB} pin is getting too low. A comparator monitors the battery and when the voltage is lower than 2.1V (typical) this bit is set. The power fail interrupt must be enabled to check for a low battery voltage.

D7: Time Save Enable bit controls the loading of real-time-clock data into the Time Save RAM. When a one is written to this bit the Time Save RAM will follow the corresponding clock registers, and when a zero is written to this bit the time in the Time Save RAM is frozen. This eliminates any synchronization problems when reading the clock, thus negating the need to check for a counter rollover during a read cycle.

This bit must be set to a one prior to power failing to enable the Time Save feature. When the power fails this bit is automatically reset and the time is saved in the Time Save RAM.

REAL TIME MODE REGISTER

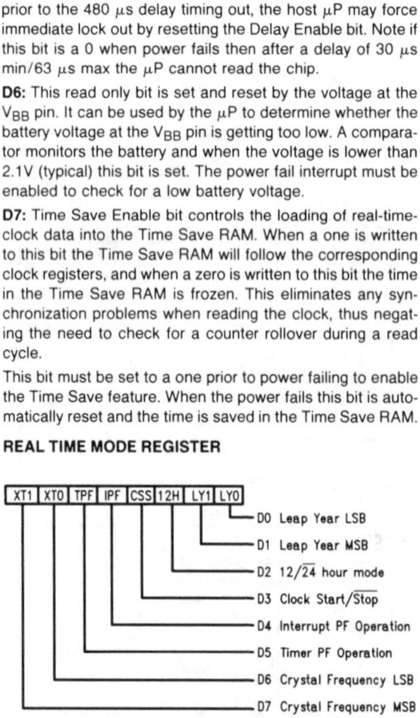

D0–D1: These are the leap year counter bits. These bits are written to set the number of years from the previous leap year. The leap year counter increments on December 31st and it internally enables the February 29th counter state. This method of setting the leap year allows leap year to occur whenever the user wishes to, thus providing flexibility in implementing Japanese leap year function.

LY1	LY0	Leap Year Counter
0	0	Leap Year Current Year
0	1	Leap Year Last Year
1	0	Leap Year 2 Years Ago
1	1	Leap Year 3 Years Ago

D2: The count mode for the hours counter can be set to either 24 hour mode or 12 hour mode with AM/PM indicator. A one will place the clock in 12 hour mode.

D3: This bit is the master Start/$\overline{\text{Stop}}$ bit for the clock. When a one is written to this bit the real time counter's prescaler and counter chain are enabled. When this bit is reset to zero the contents of the real time counter is stopped and the prescaler is cleared. When the TCP is initially powered up this bit will be held at a logic 0 until the oscillator starts functioning correctly after which this bit may be modified. If an oscillator fail event occurs, this bit will be reset to logic 0.

Functional Description (Continued)

D4: This bit controls the operation of the interrupt output in standby mode. If set to a one it allows Alarm, Periodic, and Power Fail interrupts to be functional in standby mode. Timer interrupts will also be functional provided that bit D5 is also set. Note that the MFO and INTR pins are configured as open drain in standby mode.

If bit D4 is set to a zero then interrupt control register 0 and bits D6 and D7 of interrupt control register 1 will be reset when the TCP enters the standby mode. They will have to be re-configured when system (V_{CC}) power is restored.

D5: This bit controls the operation of the timers in standby mode. If set to a one the timers will continue to function when the TCP is in standby mode. The input pins TCK, G0, G1 are locked out in standby mode, and cannot be used.

Therefore external control of the timers is not possible in standby mode. Note also that MFO and T1 pins are automatically reconfigured open drain during standby.

D6 and D7: These two bits select the crystal clock frequency as per the following table:

XT1	XT0	Crystal Frequency
0	0	32.768 kHz
0	1	4.194304 MHz
1	0	4.9152 MHz
1	1	32.000 kHz

All bits are Read/Write, and any mode written into this register can be determined by reading the register. On initial power up these bits are random.

OUTPUT MODE REGISTER

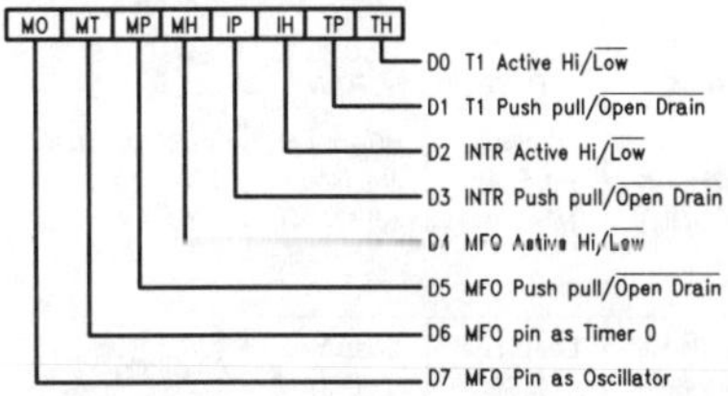

D0: This bit, when set to a one makes the T1 (timer 1) output pin active high, and when set to a zero, it makes this pin active low.

D1: This bit controls whether the T1 pin is an open drain or push-pull output. A one indicates push pull.

D2: This bit, when set to a one makes the INTR output pin active high, and when set to a zero, it makes this pin active low.

D3: This bit controls whether the INTR pin is an open drain or push-pull output. A one indicates push-pull.

D4: This bit, when set to a one makes the MFO output pin active high, and when set to a zero, it makes this pin active low.

D5: This bit controls whether the MFO pin is an open drain or push-pull output. A one indicates push-pull.

D6 and D7: These bits are used to program the signal appearing at the MFO output, as follows:

D7	D6	MFO Output Signal
0	0	2nd Interrupt
0	1	Timer 0 Waveform
1	X	Buffered Crystal Oscillator

INTERRUPT CONTROL REGISTER 0

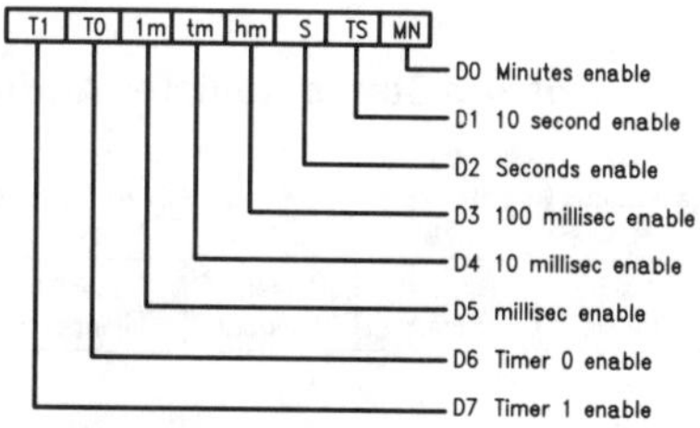

D0–D5: These bits are used to enable one of the selected periodic interrupts by writing a one into the appropriate bit. These interrupts are issued at the rollover of the clock. For example, the minutes interrupt will be issued whenever the minutes counter increments. In all likelihood the interrupt will be enabled asynchronously with the real time change. Therefore, the very first interrupt will occur in less than the periodic time chosen, but after the first interrupt all subsequent interrupts will be spaced correctly. These interrupts are useful when minute, second, real time reading, or task switching is required. When all six bits are written to a 0 this disables periodic interrupts from the Main Status Register and the interrupt pin.

D6 and D7: These are individual timer enable bits. A one written to these bits enable the timers to generate interrupts to the μP.

INTERRUPT CONTROL REGISTER 1

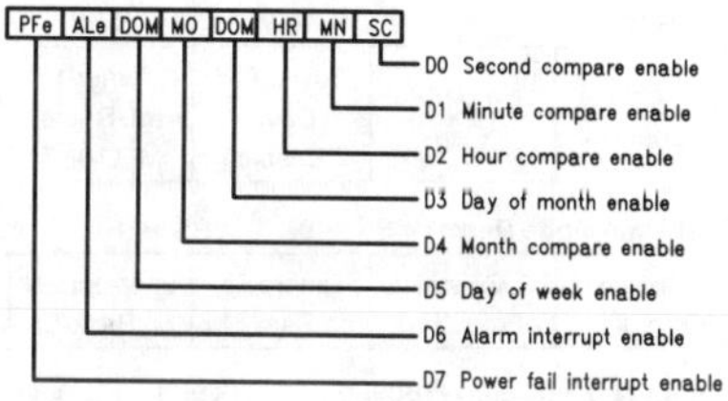

D0–D5: Each of these bits are enable bits which will enable a comparison between an individual clock counter and its associated compare RAM. If any bit is a zero then that clock-RAM comparator is set to the "always equal" state and the associated TIME COMPARE RAM byte can be used as general purpose RAM. However, to ensure that an alarm interrupt is not generated at bit D3 of the Main Status Register, all bits must be written to a logic zero.

D6: In order to generate an external alarm compare interrupt to the μP from bit D3 of the Main Status Register, this bit must be written to a logic 1.

D7: The MSB of this register is the enable bit for the Power Fail Interrupt. When this bit is set to a one an interrupt will be generated to the μP when $\overline{PFAIL} = 0$.

This bit also enables the low battery detection analog circuitry.

If the user wishes to mask the power fail interrupt, but utilize the analog circuitry, this bit should be enabled, and the Routing Register can be used to route the interrupt to the MFO pin. The MFO pin can then be left open or configured as the Timer 0 or buffered oscillator output.

Control and Status Register Address Bit Map

Main Status Register PS = 0 RS = 0 ADDRESS = 00H

D7	D6	D5	D4	D3	D2	D1	D0
R/W	**R/W**	**R[1]**	**R[1]**	**R[1]**	**R[1]**	**R[2]**	**R[3]**
Page Select	Register Select	Timer 1 Interrupt	Timer 0 Interrupt	Alarm Interrupt	Periodic Interrupt	Power Fail Interrupt	Interrupt Status

1. Reset by writing 1 to bit.
2. Set/reset by voltage at $\overline{\text{PFAIL}}$ pin.
3. Reset when all pending interrupts are removed.

Timer 0 Control Register PS = 0 RS = 0 Address = 01H

D7	D6	D5	D4	D3	D2	D1	D0
Count Hold Gate	Timer Read	Input Clock Select C2	Input Clock Select C1	Input Clock Select C0	Mode Select M1	Mode Select M0	Timer Start/$\overline{\text{Stop}}$

All Bits R/W

Timer 1 Control Register PS = 0 RS = 0 Address = 02H

D7	D6	D5	D4	D3	D2	D1	D0
Count Hold Gate	Timer Read	Input Clock Select C2	Input Clock Select C1	Input Clock Select C0	Mode Select M1	Mode Select M0	Timer Start/$\overline{\text{Stop}}$

All Bits R/W

Periodic Flag Register PS = 0 RS = 0 Address = 03H

D7	D6	D5	D4	D3	D2	D1	D0
R/W	**R/W[4]**	**R[5]**	**R[5]**	**R[5]**	**R[5]**	**R[5]**	**R[5]**
Test Mode	Osc. Fail/ Single Supply	1 ms Flag	10 ms Flag	100 ms Flag	Seconds Flag	10 Second Flag	Minute Flag

4. Read Osc fail Write 0 Batt-Backed Mode Write 1 Single Supply Mode
5. Reset by positive edge of read.

Interrupt Routing Register PS = 0 RS = 0 Address = 04H

D7	D6	D5	D4	D3	D2	D1	D0
R/W	**R[6]**	**R/W**	**R/W**	**R/W**	**R/W**	**R/W**	**R/W**
Time Save Enable	Low Battery Flag	Power Fail Delay Enable	Timer 1 Int. Route MFO/$\overline{\text{INT}}$	Timer 0 Int. Route MFO/$\overline{\text{INT}}$	Alarm Int. Route MFO/$\overline{\text{INT}}$	Periodic Int. Route MFO/$\overline{\text{INT}}$	Power Fail Int. Route MFO/$\overline{\text{INT}}$

6. Set and reset by V_{BB} voltage.

Real Time Mode Register PS = 0 RS = 1 Address = 01H

D7	D6	D5	D4	D3	D2	D1	D0
Crystal Freq. XT1	Crystal Freq. XT0	Timers EN on Back-Up	Interrupt EN on Back-Up	Clock Start/$\overline{\text{Stop}}$	12/$\overline{24}$ Hr. Mode	Leap Year MSB	Leap Year LSB

All Bits R/W

Output Mode Register PS = 0 RS = 1 Address = 02H

D7	D6	D5	D4	D3	D2	D1	D0
MFO as Crystal	MFO as Timer 0	MFO PP/$\overline{\text{OD}}$	MFO Active HI/$\overline{\text{LO}}$	INTR PP/$\overline{\text{OD}}$	INTR Active HI/$\overline{\text{LO}}$	T1 PP/$\overline{\text{OD}}$	T1 Active HI/$\overline{\text{LO}}$

All Bits R/W

Interrupt Control Register 0 PS = 0 RS = 1 Address = 03H

D7	D6	D5	D4	D3	D2	D1	D0
Timer 1 Interrupt Enable	Timer 0 Interrupt Enable	1 ms Interrupt Enable	10 ms Interrupt Enable	100 ms Interrupt Enable	Seconds Interrupt Enable	10 Second Interrupt Enable	Minute Interrupt Enable

All Bits R/W

Interrupt Control Register 1 PS = 0 RS = 1 Address = 04H

D7	D6	D5	D4	D3	D2	D1	D0
Power Fail Interrupt Enable	Alarm Interrupt Enable	DOW Interrupt Enable	Month Interrupt Enable	DOM Interrupt Enable	Hours Interrupt Enable	Minute Interrupt Enable	Second Interrupt Enable

All Bits R/W

Typical Application

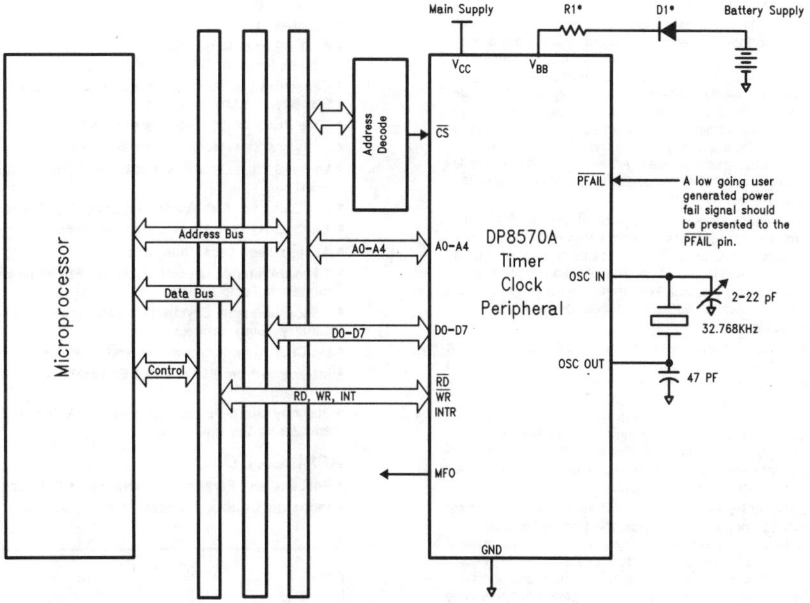

*These components may be necessary to meet UL requirements for lithium batteries. Consult battery manufacturer.

Typical Performance Characteristics

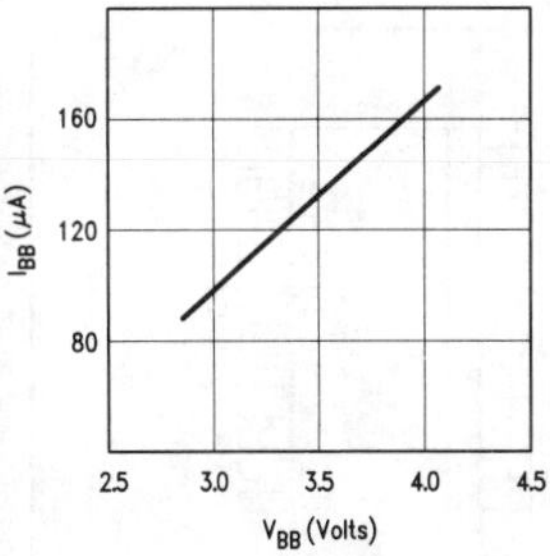

Standby Current vs Power Supply Voltage
F_{OSC} = 4.194304 MHz

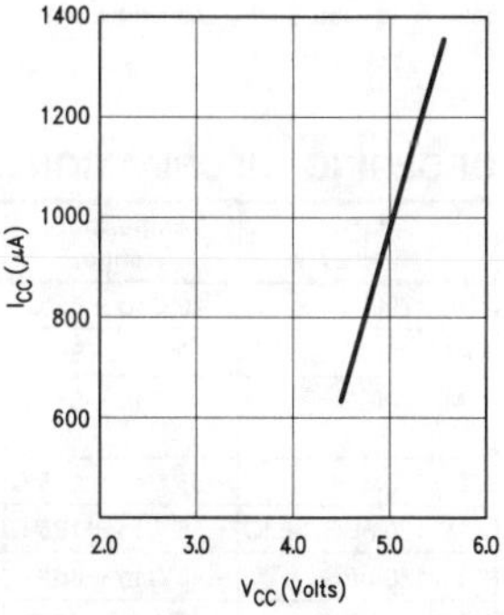

Operating Current vs Supply Voltage (Battery Backed Mode
F_{OSC} = 32.768 kHz)

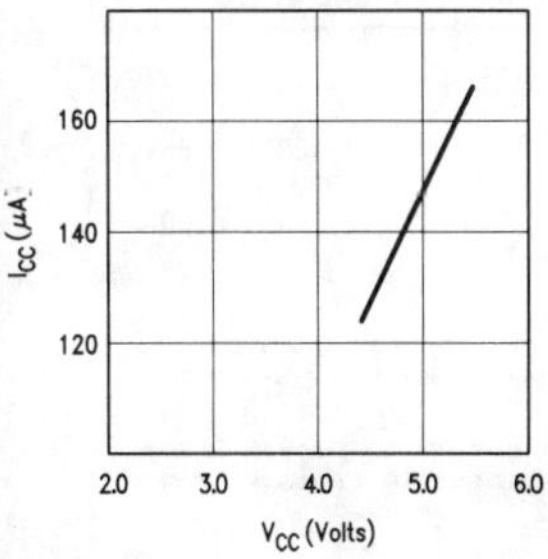

Operating Current vs Supply Voltage (Single Supply Mode
F_{OSC} = 32.768 kHz)

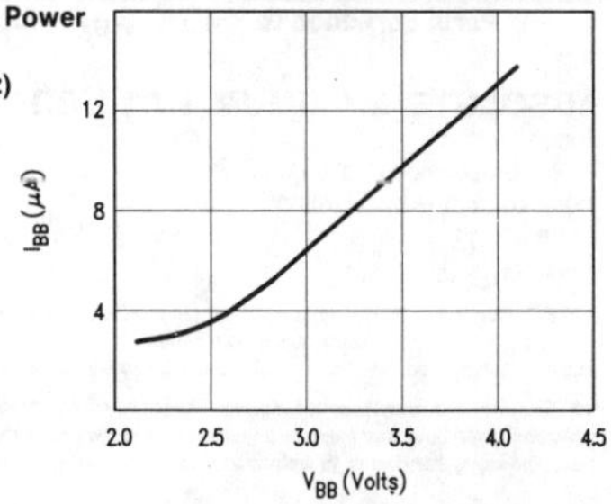

Standby Current vs Power Supply Voltage
(F_{OSC} = 32.768 kHz)

ICM7170 Real Time Clock

GENERAL DESCRIPTION

The ICM7170 real time clock is a microprocessor bus compatible peripheral, fabricated using Intersil's silicon gate CMOS LSI process. An 8-bit bidirectional bus is used for the data I/O circuitry. The clock is set or read by accessing the 8 internal separately addressable and programmable counters from 1/100 seconds to years. The counters are controlled by a pulse train divided down from a crystal oscillator circuit, and the frequency of the crystal is selectable with the on-chip command register. An extremely stable oscillator frequency is achieved through the use of an on-chip regulated power supply.

The device access time (t_{acc}) of 300ns eliminates the need for any microprocessor wait states or software overhead. Furthermore, the ALE (Address Latch Enable) input is provided for interfacing to microprocessors with a multiplexed address/data bus. With these two special features, the ICM7170 can be easily interfaced to any available microprocessor.

The ICM7170 generates two types of interrupts. The first type is the periodic interrupt (i.e., 100Hz, 10Hz, etc.) which can be programmed by the internal interrupt control register to provide 7 different output signals. The second type is the alarm interrupt. The alarm time is set by loading an on-chip 51-bit RAM that activates an interrupt output through a comparator. The alarm interrupt occurs when the real time counter and alarm RAM time are equal. A status register is available to indicate the interrupt source.

An on-chip Power-Down Detector eliminates the need for external components to support the battery back-up function. When a power-down or power failure occurs, internal logic switches the on-chip counters to battery back-up operation. Read/write functions become disabled and operation is limited to time-keeping and interrupt generation, resulting in low power consumption.

Internal latches prevent clock roll-over during a read cycle. Counter data is latched on the chip by reading the 100th-seconds counter and is held indefinitely until the counter is read again, assuring a stable and reliable time value.

ORDERING INFORMATION

Part Number	Temperature Range	Package
ICM7170IPG	−40°C to +85°C	24-Pin Plastic Dip
ICM7170IDG	−40°C to +85°C	24-Pin Ceramic
ICM7170IBG	−40°C to +85°C	24-Pin S.O.I.C. (Surface Mount)
ICM7170MDG	−55°C to +125°C	24-Pin Ceramic
ICM7170MDG/883C	−55°C to +125°C	24-Pin Ceramic
ICM7170AIPG	−40°C to +85°C	24-Pin Plastic Dip
ICM7170AIBG	−40°C to +85°C	24-Pin S.O.I.C.

"A" Parts Screened to <4 μA I_{STBY} @ 32 KHz

FEATURES

- **883B-Rev C Compliant**
- **8-Bit μP Bus Compatible —Multiplexed or Direct Addressing**
- **Regulated Oscillator Supply Ensures Frequency Stability and Low Power**
- **Time From 1/100 Seconds to 99 Years**
- **Software Selectable 12/24 Hour Format**
- **Latched Time Data Ensures No Roll-Over During Read**
- **Full Calendar With Automatic Leap Year Correction**
- **On-Chip Battery Backup Switchover Circuit**
- **Access Time Less Than 300ns**
- **4 Programmable Crystal Oscillator Frequencies over Industrial Temp Range**
- **3 Programmable Crystal Oscillator Frequencies over Military Temp Range**
- **On-Chip Alarm Comparator and RAM**
- **Interrupts from Alarm and 6 Selectable Periodic Intervals**
- **Standby Micro-Power Operation: 2μA Typ. at 3.0V and 32kHz Crystal**

APPLICATIONS

- **Portable and Personal Computers**
- **Data Logging**
- **Industrial Control Systems**
- **Point Of Sale**

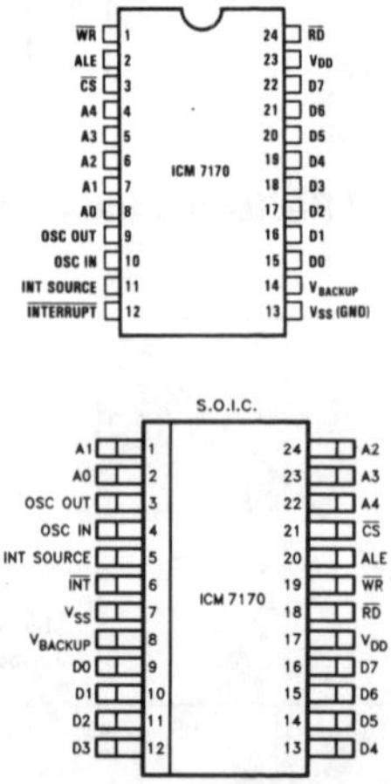

Figure 1: Pin Configurations

ABSOLUTE MAXIMUM RATINGS

Supply Voltage 8V
Power Dissipation (Note 1) 500mW
Input Voltage (Any Terminal)
(Note 2) .... V_{DD} +0.3V to V_{SS} −0.3V

Operating Temperature .... −40°C to +85°C
Storage Temperature .... −65°C to +150°C
Lead Temperature (Soldering, 10sec) .... 300°C

NOTE 1: T_A = 25°C.

NOTE 2: Due to the SCR structure inherent in the CMOS process, connecting any terminal at voltages greater than V_{DD} or less than V_{SS} may cause destructive device latchup. For this reason, it is recommended that no inputs from external sources not operating on the same power supply be applied to the device before its supply is established, and that in multiple supply systems, the supply to the ICM7170 be turned on first.

NOTE: *Stresses above those listed under "Absolute Maximum Ratings" may cause permanent damage to the device. These are stress ratings only and functional operation of the device at these or any other conditions above those indicated in the operational sections of the specifications is not implied. Exposure to absolute maximum rating conditions for extended periods may affect device reliability.*

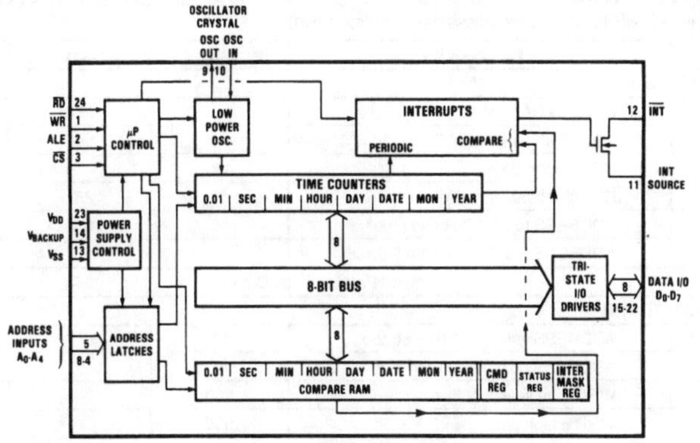

Figure 2: Functional Diagram

ELECTRICAL CHARACTERISTICS
DC CHARACTERISTICS

($T_A = -40°C$ to $+85°C$, $V_{DD} = +5V \pm 10\%$, $V_{BACKUP} = V_{DD}$, $V_{SS} = 0V$ unless otherwise specified)

Symbol	Parameter	Test Conditions		Specification Min	Specification Typ	Specification Max	Units
V_{DD}	V_{DD} Supply Range	$F_{OSC} = 32kHz$		1.9		5.5	V
		$F_{OSC} = 1, 2, 4MHz$		2.6		5.5	
$I_{STBY(1)}$	Standby Current	$F_{OSC} = 32kHz$ Pins 1–8, 15–22 & 24 = V_{DD} $V_{DD} = V_{SS}$; $V_{BACKUP} = V_{DD} - 3.0V$	7170		2.0	20.0	µA
			7170A		2.0	5.0	
$I_{STBY(2)}$	Standby Current	$F_{OSC} = 4MHz$ Pins 1–8, 15–22 & 24 = V_{DD} $V_{DD} = V_{SS}$; $V_{BACKUP} = V_{DD} - 3.0V$			20	150	µA
$I_{DD(1)}$	Operating Supply Current	$F_{OSC} = 32kHz$ Read/Write Operation at 100Hz			0.3	1.2	mA
$I_{DD(2)}$	Operating Supply Current	$F_{OSC} = 32kHz$ Read/Write Operation at 1MHz			1.0	2.0	mA
V_{IL}	Input low voltage (Except Osc.)	$V_{DD} = 5.0V$				0.8	V

Symbol	Parameter	Test Conditions		Specification Min	Specification Typ	Specification Max	Units
V_{IH}	Input high voltage (Except Osc.)	$V_{DD} = 5.0V$		2.4			V
V_{OL}	Output low voltage (Except Osc.)	$I_{OL} = 1.6mA$				0.4	V
V_{OH}	Output high voltage except $\overline{INTERRUPT}$ (Except Osc.)	$I_{OH} = -400\mu A$		2.4			V
I_{IL}	Input leakage current	$V_{IN} = V_{DD}$ or V_{SS}		−10	0.5	+10	µA
I_{OL}	Tristate leakage current (D_0–D_7)	$V_0 = V_{DD}$ or V_{SS}		−10	0.5	+10	µA
$V_{BATTERY}$	Backup Battery Voltage	$F_{OSC} = 1, 2, 4MHz$		2.6		$V_{DD} - 1.3$	V
$V_{BATTERY}$	Backup Battery Voltage	$F_{OSC} = 32kHz$		1.9		$V_{DD} - 1.3$	V
I_{OL}	Leakage current $\overline{INTERRUPT}$	$V_0 = V_{DD}$	INT SOURCE connected to V_{SS}		0.5	10	µA
$C_{I/O}$	CAPACITANCE D_0–D_7					8	pF
$C_{ADDRESS}$	CAPACITANCE A_0–A_4					6	pF
$C_{CONTROL}$	CAP. $\overline{RD}$, $\overline{WR}$, $\overline{CS}$ ALE					6	pF
C_{IN} Osc.	Total Osc. Input Cap.					3	pF

NOTE: All typical values have been characterized but are not tested.

AC CHARACTERISTICS

($T_A = -40°C$ to $+85°C$, $V_{DD} = +5V \pm 10\%$, $V_{BACKUP} = V_{DD}$, D_0–D_7 Load Capacitance = 150pF, $V_{IL} = 0.4V$, $V_{IH} = 2.8V$ unless otherwise specified)

Symbol	Parameter	Min	Max	Units
READ CYCLE TIMING				
t_{rd}	READ to DATA valid		250	ns
t_{acc}	ADDRESS valid to DATA valid		300	ns
t_{cyc}	READ cycle time	400		ns
t_{rx}	$\overline{RD}$ high to bus tristate*		25*	ns
t_{as}	ADDRESS to READ set up time*	50		ns
t_{ar}	ADDRESS HOLD time after READ*	0		ns
*Guaranteed Parameter by Design				
WRITE CYCLE TIMING				
t_{ad}	ADDRESS valid to WRITE strobe	50		ns
t_{wa}	ADDRESS hold time for WRITE	0		ns
t_{wl}	WRITE pulse width, low	100		ns
t_{wh}	WRITE high time	300		ns
t_{rh}	Read high time	150		ns
t_{dw}	DATA IN to WRITE set up time	100		ns
t_{wd}	DATA IN hold time after WRITE	30		ns
t_{cyc}	WRITE cycle time	400		ns
MULTIPLEXED MODE TIMING				
t_{ll}	ALE Pulse Width, High	50		ns
t_{al}	ADDRESS to ALE set up time	30		ns
t_{la}	ADDRESS hold time after ALE	30		ns

Capacitance values are maximum values and are sample tested only.

ICM 7170 ELECTRICAL CHARACTERISTICS (TEST SPECIFICATION) FOR MIL-STD-883 COMPLIANCE

ABSOLUTE MAXIMUM RATINGS

Supply Voltage 8V
Power Dissipation (Note 1)...................... 500mW
Input Voltage (Any Terminal)
.... $V_{DD} + 0.3V$ to $V_{SS} - 0.3V$
Operating Temperature .... −55°C to +125°C
Storage Temperature .... −65°C to +150°C
Lead Temperature (Soldering, 10 sec) .... 300°C

NOTE 1: $T_A = 25°C$.

NOTE: *Stresses above those listed under "Absolute Maximum Ratings" may cause permanent damage to the device. These are stress ratings only and functional operation of the device at these or any other conditions above those indicated in the operational sections of the specifications is not implied. Exposure to absolute maximum rating conditions for extended periods may affect device reliability.*

ELECTRICAL CHARACTERISTICS
DC CHARACTERISTICS

($V_{DD} = 5V \pm 10\%$, $V_{BACKUP} = V_{DD}$, $T_A = -55°C$ to $+125°C$, unless otherwise specified)

Symbol	Parameter	Test Conditions	Specification			Units
			Min	Typ	Max	
V_{DD}	V_{DD} Supply Range	F_{OSC} = 32kHz	1.9		5.5	V
		F_{OSC} = 1, 2MHz	2.6		5.5	
$I_{STBY(1)}$	Standby Current	F_{OSC} = 32 kHz All chip I/O to V_{DD} $V_{DD} = V_{SS}$: $V_{BACKUP} = V_{DD} - 3.0V$		2.0	40	μA
$I_{STBY(2)}$	Standby Current	F_{OSC} = 1, 2MHz All chip I/O to V_{DD}		30	200	μA
		7170A $V_{DD} = V_{SS}$: $V_{BACKUP} = V_{DD} - 3.0V$			5.0	
$I_{DD(1)}$	Operating Supply Current	F_{OSC} = 32 kHz Read/Write Operation at 100 Hz		0.3	1.2	mA
$I_{DD(2)}$	Operating Supply Current	F_{OSC} = 32 kHz Read/Write Operation at 1 MHz		1.0	2.0	mA
V_{IL}	Input Low Voltage (Except Osc.)	V_{DD} = 5.0V			0.8	V

PRELIMINARY
Specifications Subject to Change Without Notice

NOTE: All typical values have been characterized but are not tested.

V_{IH}	Input High Voltage (Except Osc.)	$V_{DD}=5.0V$		2.8			
V_{OL}	Output Low Voltage (Except Osc.)	$I_{OL}=1.6$ mA				0.5	V
V_{OH}	Output High Voltage Except INTERRUPT (Except Osc.)	$I_{OH}=400\mu A$		2.5			V
I_{IL}	Input Leakage Current	$V_{IN}=V_{DD}$ or V_{SS}		−10	0.5	+10	μA
I_{OL}	Tristate Leakage Current (D_0–D_7)	$V_{IN}=V_{DD}$ or V_{SS}		−10	0.5	+10	μA
$V_{BATTERY}$	Backup Battery Voltage	OSG = 32 kHz		1.9		$V_{DD}-1.5$	V
I_{OL}	Leakage Current INTERRUPT	$V_0=V_{DD}$ or V_{SS}	INT SOURCE connected to V_{SS}		0.5	10	μA

AC CHARACTERISTICS

(T_A = −55°C to +125°C, V_{DD} = 5V ±10%, V_{BACKUP} = V_{DD}, D_0–D_7 Load Capacitance = 150 pF, V_{IL} = 0.4V, V_{IH} = 3.20V unless otherwise specified)

Symbol	Parameter	Min	Max	Units
READ CYCLE TIMING				
t_{rd}	READ to DATA Valid		250	ns
t_{ACC}	ADDRESS Valid to DATA Valid		350	ns
t_{cyc}	READ Cycle Time	450		ns
t_{rx}	$\overline{RD}$ High to Bus Tristate		100	ns
t_{as}	ADDRESS to READ Set Up Time	100		ns
t_{ar}	ADDRESS HOLD Time after READ	50		ns
t_{rh}	READ High Time	200		ns
WRITE CYCLE TIMING				
t_{ad}	ADDRESS Valid to WRITE Strobe	100		ns
t_{wa}	ADDRESS Hold Time for WRITE	50		ns
t_{wl}	WRITE Pulse Low Width	125		ns
t_{wh}	WRITE Pulse Width High	325		ns
t_{dw}	DATA IN to WRITE Set Up Time	125		ns
t_{wd}	DATA IN Hold Time after WRITE	60		ns
t_{cyc}	WRITE Cycle Time	450		ns
MULTIPLEXED MODE TIMING				
t_{ll}	ALE Width	50		ns
t_{al}	ADDRESS to ALE Set Up Time	30		ns
t_{la}	ADDRESS Hold Time after ALE	40		ns

NOTE: All typical values have been characterized but are not tested.

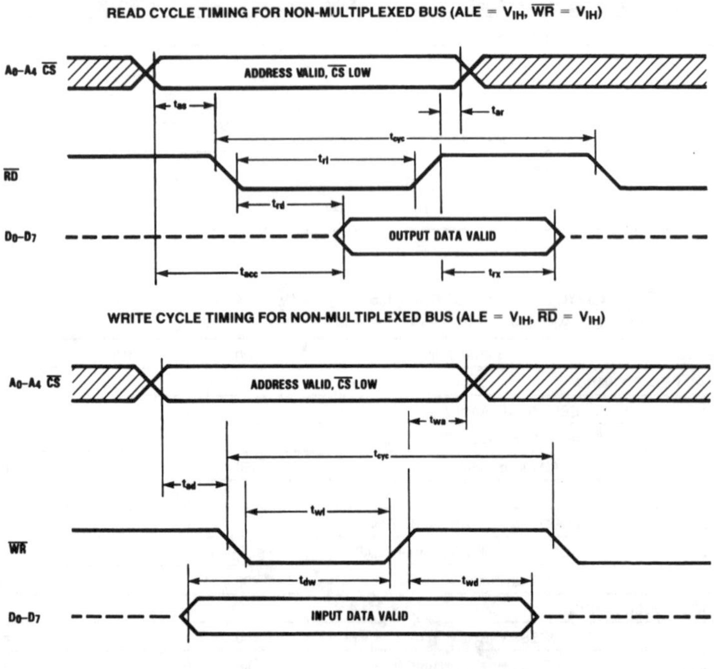

Figure 3: Timing Diagrams — Nonmultiplexed Bus

Table 1

Signal	Pin	Description
$\overline{WR}$	1	$\overline{\text{Write}}$ input
ALE	2	Address latch enable input
$\overline{CS}$	3	$\overline{\text{Chip select}}$ input
A4-A0	4-8	Address inputs
OSC OUT	9	Oscillator output
OSC IN	10	Oscillator input
INT SOURCE	11	Interrupt source
$\overline{INTERRUPT}$	12	$\overline{\text{Interrupt}}$ output
V_{SS}(GND)	13	Digital common
V_{BACKUP}	14	Battery negative side
D0-D7	15-22	Data I/O
V_{DD}	23	Positive digital supply
$\overline{RD}$	24	$\overline{\text{Read}}$ input

DETAILED DESCRIPTION

Oscillator

This circuit uses a regulated CMOS Pierce oscillator, for maximum accuracy, stability, and low-power consumption. Externally, one crystal and two capacitors are required. One of the capacitors is variable and is used to trim or tune the oscillator output. Typical values for these capacitors are C_{IN} = 15pF and C_{OUT} = 10 − 35pF, or approximately double the recommended C_{LOAD} for the crystal being used. Both capacitors must be connected from the respective oscillator pins to V_{DD} for maximum stability.

The oscillator output is divided down to 4000Hz by one of four selected ratios, via a variable prescaler. The ICM7170 can use any one of four different low-cost crystals: 4.194304MHz, 2.097152MHz, 1.048576MHz, or 32.768kHz. The ICM7170MDG is available with 3 crystal frequency options only. (4.194304 MHz is not avail. with military version.) The command register must be programmed for the frequency of the crystal chosen, and this in turn will determine the prescaler's divide ratio.

Command Register frequency selection is written to the D0 and D1 bits at address 11H and the 12 or 24 hour format is determined by bit D2, as shown in Table 4.

NOTE: All typical values have been characterized but are not tested.

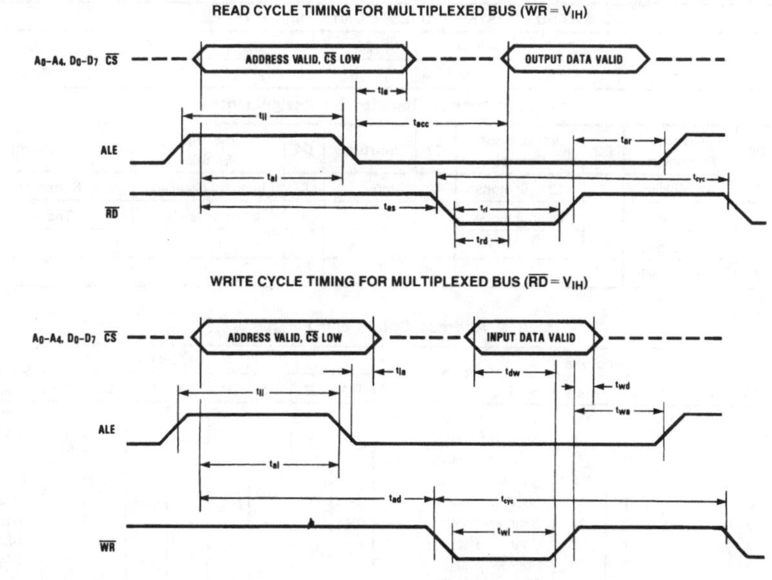

NOTE: The A0 to A4 address inputs may be connected to the D0 to D4 data lines when a multiplexed bus is used.

Figure 4: Timing Diagrams — Multiplexed Bus

The 4000Hz signal is divided down further to 100Hz, which is used as the clock for the counters. Time and calendar information is provided by 8 consecutive addressable, programmable counters: 100ths of seconds, seconds, minutes, hours, day of week, date, month, and year. The data is in binary format and is configured into 8 bits per digit. See Table 4 for address information. Any unused bits are held at logic "0" during a read and ignored during a write operation.

Alarm Compare RAM

On the chip are 51 bits of Alarm Compare RAM grouped into words of different lengths. These are used to store the time, ranging from 100ths of seconds to years, for comparison to the real-time counters. Each counter has a corresponding RAM word. In the Alarm Mode an interrupt is generated when the current time is equal to the alarm time. The RAM contents are compared to the counters on a word by word basis. If a comparison to a particular counter is unnecessary, then the appropriate 'M' bit in Compare RAM should be set to logic "1".

The 'M' bit, referring to Mask bit, causes a particular RAM word to be masked off or ignored during a compare. Table 4 shows addresses and Mask bit information.

Periodic Interrupts

The interrupt output can be programmed for 6 periodic signals: 100 Hz, 10 Hz, once per second, once per minute, once per hour, or once per day. The 100 Hz and 10 Hz interrupts have instantaneous errors of ±2.5% and ±0.15% respectively. This is because non-integer divider circuitry is used to generate these signals from the crystal frequency, which is a power of 2. The time average of these errors over a 1 second period, however, is zero. Consequently, the 100 Hz or 10 Hz interrupts are not suitable as an aid in tuning the oscillator; the 1 second interrupt must be used instead.

The periodic interrupts can occur concurrently and in addition to alarm interrupts. They are controlled by bits in the interrupt mask register, and are enabled by setting the appropriate bit to a "1" as shown in Table 5. Bits D0 through D6 in the mask register, in conjunction with bits D0 through D6 of the status register, control the generation of interrupts according to Figure 5.

The interrupt status register, when read, indicates the cause of the interrupt and resets itself on the rising edge of the RD signal. When any of the counters having a corresponding bit in the status register roll over to zero, that bit is set to a "1" regardless of whether the corresponding bit in the interrupt mask register is set or not. This also applies to the alarm compare bit.

Consequently, when the status register is read it will always indicate which counters have rolled over to zero and if an alarm compare occurred, since the last time it was read. This requires some special software considerations. If a slow interrupt is enabled (i.e. hourly or daily), the program must always check the slowest interrupt that has been enabled first, because all the other lower order bits in the status register will be set to "1" as well. Bit D7 is the global interrupt bit, and when set to a "1", indicates that the 7170 did indeed generate a hardware interrupt. This is useful when other interrupting devices in addition to the 7170 are attached to the system microprocessor, and all devices must be polled to determine which one generated the interrupt.

NOTE: All typical values have been characterized but are not tested.

Table 2: Command Register Format

COMMAND REGISTER ADDRESS (10001b, 11h) WRITE-ONLY							
D7	D6	D5	D4	D3	D2	D1	D0
n/a	n/a	Test	Int.	Run	12/24	Freq	Freq

Table 3: Command Register Bit Assignments

D1	D0	Crystal Frequency	D2	24/12 Hour Format	D3	Run/Stop	D4	Interrupt Enable	D5	Test Bit
0	0	32.768kHz	0	12 hour mode	0	Stop	0	Interrupt disabled	0	Normal Mode
0	1	1.048576MHz	1	24 hour mode	1	Run	1	Interrupt enable	1	Test Mode
1	0	2.097152MHz								
1	1	4.194304MHz								

Table 4: Address Codes and Functions

Address						Function	DATA								Value
A4	A3	A2	A1	A0	HEX		D7	D6	D5	D4	D3	D2	D1	D0	
0	0	0	0	0	00	Counter-1/100 seconds	–	.	.	.	.	.	.	.	0-99
0	0	0	0	1	01	Counter-hours	–	–	–	.	.	.	.	.	0-23
						12 Hour Mode	*	–	–	–	.	.	.	.	1-12
0	0	0	1	0	02	Counter-minutes	–	–	.	.	.	.	.	.	0-59
0	0	0	1	1	03	Counter-seconds	–	–	.	.	.	.	.	.	0-59
0	0	1	0	0	04	Counter-month	–	–	–	–	.	.	.	.	1-12
0	0	1	0	1	05	Counter-date	–	–	–	.	.	.	.	.	1-31
0	0	1	1	0	06	Counter-year	–	.	.	.	.	.	.	.	0-99
0	0	1	1	1	07	Counter-day of week	–	–	–	–	–	.	.	.	0-6
0	1	0	0	0	08	RAM-1/100 seconds	M	.	.	.	.	.	.	.	0-99
0	1	0	0	1	09	RAM-hours	–	M	–	.	.	.	.	.	0-23
						12 hour Mode	*	M	–	–	.	.	.	.	1-12
0	1	0	1	0	0A	RAM-minutes	M	–	.	.	.	.	.	.	0-59
0	1	0	1	1	0B	RAM-seconds	M	–	.	.	.	.	.	.	0-59
0	1	1	0	0	0C	RAM-month	M	–	–	–	.	.	.	.	1-12
0	1	1	0	1	0D	RAM-date	M	–	–	.	.	.	.	.	1-31
0	1	1	1	0	0E	RAM-year	M	.	.	.	.	.	.	.	0-99
0	1	1	1	1	0F	RAM-day of week	M	–	–	–	–	.	.	.	0-6
1	0	0	0	0	10	Interrupt Status and Mask Register	+	.	.	.	.	.	.	.	
1	0	0	0	1	11	Command register	–	–	.	.	.	.	.	.	

NOTES: Address 10010 to 11111 (12h to 1Fh) are unused.
'+' Unused bit for Interrupt Mask Register, MSB bit for Interrupt Status Register.
'–' Indicates unused bits.
'*' AM/PM indicator bit in 12 hour format. Logic "0" indicates AM, logic "1" indicates PM.
'M' Alarm compare for particular counter will be enabled if bit is set to logic "0".

Table 5: Interrupt and Status Registers Format

INTERRUPT MASK REGISTER ADDRESS (10000b, 10h) WRITE-ONLY							
D7	D6	D5	D4	D3	D2	D1	D0
Not Used	Day	Hour	Min.	Sec.	1/10 sec.	1/100 sec.	Alarm

INTERRUPT STATUS REGISTER ADDRESS (10000b, 10h) READ-ONLY							
D7	D6	D5	D4	D3	D2	D1	D0
Global Interrupt	Day	Hour	Min.	Sec.	1/10 sec.	1/100 sec.	Alarm

NOTE: All typical values have been characterized but are not tested.

Interrupt Operation

The interrupt output N-channel MOSFET is active at all times when the Interrupt Enable bit is set (bit 4 of the Command Register), and operates in both the standby and battery backup modes.

Since system power is usually applied between V_{DD} and V_{SS}, the user can connect the Interrupt Source (pin #11) to V_{SS}. This allows the Interrupt Output to turn on only while system power is applied and will not be pulled to V_{SS} during standby operation. If interrupts are required only during standby operation, then the interrupt source pin should be connected to the battery's negative side (V_{BACKUP}). In this configuration, for example, the interrupt could be used to turn on power for a cold boot.

Power-Down Detector

The ICM7170 contains an on-chip power-down detector that eliminates the need for external components to support the battery-backup switchover function, as shown in Figure 6. Whenever the voltage from the V_{SS} pin to the V_{BACKUP} pin is less than approximately 1.0V (the V_{th} of the N-channel MOSFET), the data bus I/O buffers in the 7170 are automatically disabled and the chip cannot be read or written to. This prevents random data from the microprocessor being written to the clock registers as the power supply is going down.

Actual switchover to battery operation occurs when the voltage on the V_{BACKUP} pin is within ±50 mV of V_{SS}. This switchover uncertainty is due to the offset voltage of the CMOS comparator that is used to sense the battery voltage. During battery backup, device operation is limited to timekeeping and interrupt generation only, thus achieving micropower current drain. If an external battery-backup switchover circuit is being used with the 7170, the V_{BACKUP} pin should be tied to the V_{DD} pin. The same also applies if standby battery operation is not required.

Time Synchronization

Time synchronization is achieved through bit D3 of the Command Register, which is used to enable or disable the 100Hz clock from the counters. A logic "1" allows the counters to function and a logic "0" disables the counters. To accurately set the time, a logic "0" should be written into D3 and then the desired times entered into the appropriate counters. The clock is then started at the proper time by writing a logic "1" into D3 of the Command Register.

Latched Data

To prevent ambiguity while the processor is gathering data from the registers, the ICM7170 incorporates data latches and a transparent transition delay circuit.

By accessing the 100ths of seconds counter an internal store signal is generated and data from all the counters is stored into a 36-bit latch. A transition delay circuit will delay a 100Hz transition during a READ cycle. The data stored by the latches is then available for further processing until the 100ths of seconds counter is read again.

Control Lines

The $\overline{RD}$, $\overline{WR}$, and $\overline{CS}$ signals are active low inputs. Data is placed on the bus from counters or registers when $\overline{RD}$ is a logic "0". Data is transferred to counters or registers when $\overline{WR}$ is a logic "0". $\overline{RD}$ and $\overline{WR}$ must be accompanied by a logical "0" $\overline{CS}$ as shown in Figures 3 and 4. The 7170 will also work satisfactorily with $\overline{CS}$ grounded. This access also to be controlled by $\overline{RD}$ and $\overline{WR}$ only.

With the ALE (Address Latch Enable) input, the ICM7170 can be interfaced directly to microprocessors that use a multiplexed address/data bus by connecting the address lines A0-A4 to the data lines D0-D4. To address the chip, the address is placed on the bus and ALE is strobed. On the falling edge, the address and $\overline{CS}$ information is read into the address latch and buffer. $\overline{RD}$ and $\overline{WR}$ are used in the same way as on a non-multiplexed bus. If a non-multiplexed bus is used, ALE should be connected to V_{DD}.

Test Mode

The test mode is entered by setting D5 of the Command Register to a logic "1". This connects the 100Hz counter to the oscillator's output. The peak-to-peak voltage used to drive osc. out should not be greater than the oscillator's regulated voltage. The signal must be referenced to V_{DD}.

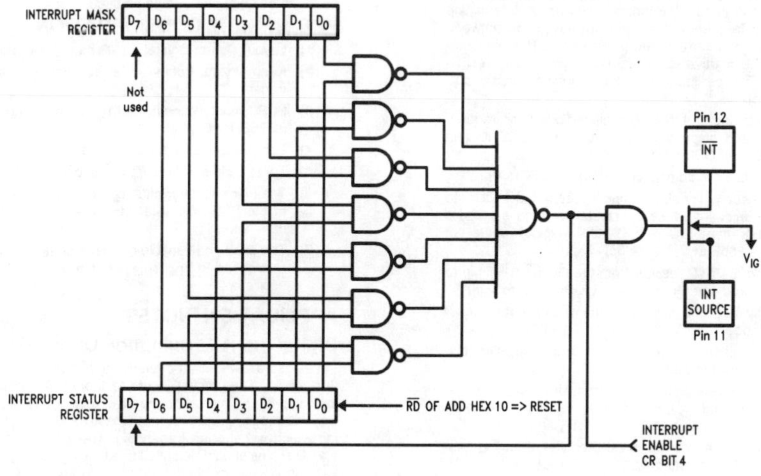

Figure 5: Interrupt Output Circuit

INTERSIL'S SOLE AND EXCLUSIVE WARRANTY OBLIGATION WITH RESPECT TO THIS PRODUCT SHALL BE THAT STATED IN THE WARRANTY ARTICLE OF THE CONDITION OF SALE. THE WARRANTY SHALL BE EXCLUSIVE AND SHALL BE IN LIEU OF ALL OTHER WARRANTIES, EXPRESS, IMPLIED OR STATUTORY, INCLUDING THE IMPLIED WARRANTIES OF MERCHANTABILITY AND FITNESS FOR A PARTICULAR USE.

NOTE: All typical values have been characterized but are not tested.

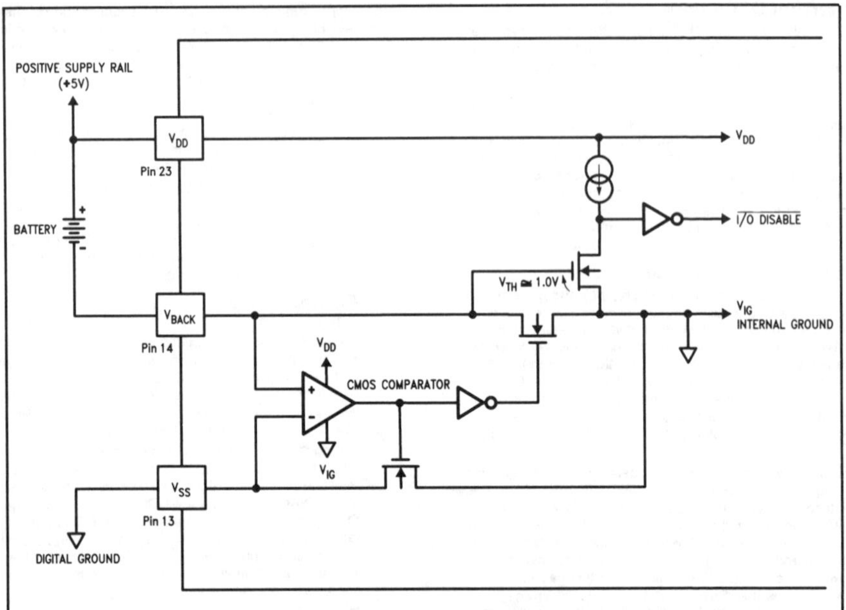

Figure 6: Simplified 7170 Battery Backup Circuit

Oscillator Tuning

Oscillator tuning should not be attempted by direct monitoring of the oscillator pins, unless very specialized equipment is used. External connections to the oscillator pins cause capacitive loading of the crystal, and shift the oscillator frequency. As a result, the precision setting being attempted is corrupted. One indirect method of determining the oscillator frequency is to measure the period between interrupts on the Interrupt Output pin (#12). This measurement must be relative to the falling edges of the $\overline{\text{INTERRUPT}}$ pin. The oscillator set-up and tuning can be performed as follows:

1) Select one of 4, readily-available oscillator frequencies and place the crystal between OSC IN (pin #10) and OSC OUT (pin #9).
2) Connect a fixed capacitor from OSC IN to V_{DD}.
3) Connect a variable capacitor from OSC OUT to V_{DD}. In cases where the crystal selected is a 32kHz Statek type (C_L=9pF), the typical value of C_{IN}=15pF and C_{OUT}=5pf–35pF.
4) Place a 4.7KΩ resistor from the $\overline{\text{INTERRUPT}}$ pin to V_{DD}, and connect the INT SOURCE pin to V_{SS}.
5) Apply 5V power and insure the clock is not in standby mode.
6) Write all 0's to the Interrupt Mask Register, disabling all interrupts.
7) Write to the Command Register with the desired oscillator frequency, Hours mode (12 hour or 24 hour), Run="1", Interrupt Enable="1", and Test="0".
8) Write to the Interrupt Mask Register, enabling one-second interrupts only.
9) Monitor the $\overline{\text{INTERRUPT}}$ output pin with a precision period counter and trim the OSC OUT capacitor for a reading of 1.000000 seconds. The period counter must be triggered on the falling edge of the interrupt output for this measurement to be accurate.
10) Read the Interrupt Status Register. This action resets the interrupt output back to a logic "1" level.
11) Repeat steps 9 and 10 with a software loop. A suitable computer should be used.

PCB DESIGN CONSIDERATION

1) Layout Quartz Crystal traces as short as possible.
2) Keep Crystal traces as far as possible from other traces.
3) PCB must accept both Saronix and Statek 32.768kHz Crystals.
4) Completely surround crystal traces with V_{DD} trace.
5) Try to keep oscillator traces on one side of the PCB.
6) Trimmer capacitor must be accessible from the top of the PCB after it is inserted into the appropriate connector.
7) The fixed and variable oscillator capacitors must be referenced to V_{DD}. V_{SS} is not an AC ground for the oscillator.

APPLICATION NOTES

Digital Input Termination During Backup

To ensure low current drain during battery backup operation, none of the digital inputs to the 7170 should be allowed to float. This keeps the input logic gates out of their transition region, and prevents crossover current from flowing which will shorten battery life. The address, data, $\overline{\text{CS}}$, and ALE pins should be pulled to either V_{DD} or V_{SS}, and the $\overline{\text{RD}}$ and $\overline{\text{WR}}$ inputs should be pulled to V_{DD}. This is necessary whether the internal battery switchover circuit is used or not.

NOTE: All typical values have been characterized but are not tested.

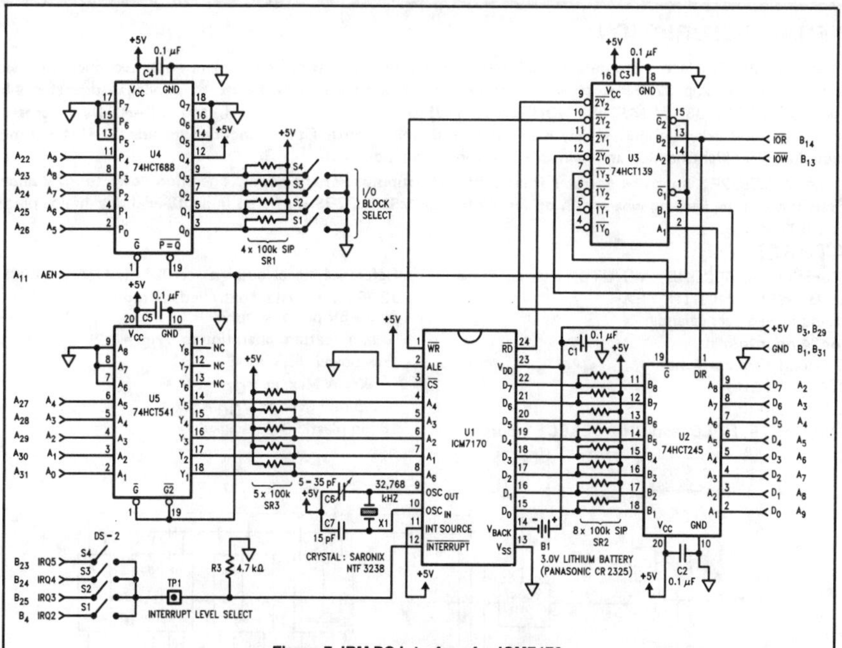

Figure 7: IBM PC Interface for ICM7170

IBM/PC Evaluation Circuit

Figure 7 shows the schematic of a board that has been designed to plug into an IBM PC or compatible computer. It features full buffering of all 7170 address and data lines, and switch selectable I/O block select. A provision for setting the priority level of the 7170 periodic interrupt has also been added.

Batteries	Crystals
Panasonic	Statek 32kHz CX-IV
Rayovac	SARONIX 32kHz NTF3238

NOTE: All typical values have been characterized but are not tested.

MSM5832RS Real Time Clock

GENERAL DESCRIPTION

The MSM5832RS is a metal-gate CMOS Real Time Clock/Calendar for use in bus-oriented microprocessor applications. The on-chip 32.768Hz crystal controlled oscillator time base is divided to provide addressable 4-bit I/O data of SECONDS, MINUTES, HOURS, DAY-OF-WEEK, DATE, MONTH, and YEAR. Data access is controlled by 4-bit address, chip select, read, write and hold inputs. Other functions include 12H/24H format selection, leap year identification and manual ±30 second correction.

The MSM5832RS normally operates from a 5V ±5% supply. Battery backup operation down to 2.2V allows continuation of time keeping when main power is off. The MSM5832RS is offered in an 18-lead dual-in-line plastic (RS suffix) package.

FEATURES

- 7 Function — SECOND, MINUTE, HOUR, DAY, DAY-OF-WEEK, MONTH, YEAR
- Automatic leap year calendar
- 12 or 24 hour format
- ±30 second error correction
- 4-BIT DATA BUS
- 4-BIT ADDRESS
- READ, WRITE, HOLD, and CHIP SELECT inputs
- Reference signal outputs — 1024, 1, 1/60, 1/3600Hz
- 32.768kHz crystal controlled operation
- Single 5V power supply
- Back-up battery operation to V_{DD} = 2.2V
- Low power dissipation
  90 μW Max. at V_{DD} = 3V
  2.5 mW Max. at V_{DD} = 5V
- 18 pin plastic DIP package

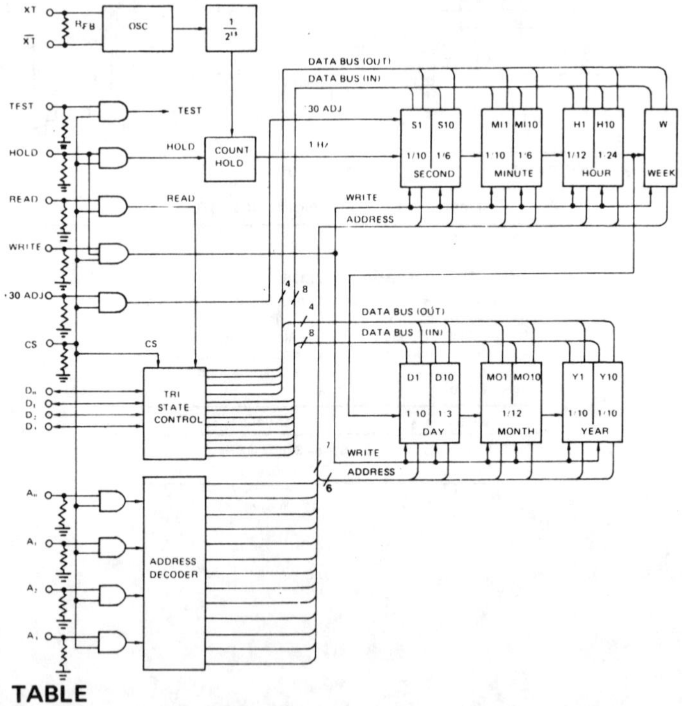

REGISTER TABLE

Address Input				Register Name	Data Input/Output				Data Limit	Remarks
A_0	A_1	A_2	A_3		D_0	D_1	D_2	D_3		
0	0	0	0	S1	*	*	*	*	0 ~ 9	S1 or S10 are reset to zero irrespective of input data D0—D3 when write instruction is executed with address selection.
1	0	0	0	S10	*	*	*		0 ~ 5	

0	1	0	0	MI1	*	*	*	*	0 ~ 9	
1	1	0	0	MI10	*	*	*		0 ~ 5	
0	0	1	0	H1	*	*	*	*	0 ~ 9	
1	0	1	0	H10	*	*	†	†	0 ~ 1 / 0~2	D2 = "1" for PM D3 = "1" for 24 hour format D2 = "0" for AM D3 = "0" for 12 hour format
0	1	1	0	W	*	*	*		0 ~ 6	
1	1	1	0	D1	*	*	*	*	0 ~ 9	
0	0	0	1	D10	*	*	†		0 ~ 3	D2 = "1" for 29 days in month 2 D2 = "0" for 28 days in month 2 (2)
1	0	0	1	MO1	*	*	*	*	0 ~ 9	
0	1	0	1	MO10	*				0 ~ 1	
1	1	0	1	Y1	*	*	*	*	0 ~ 9	
0	0	1	1	Y10	*	*	*	*	0 ~ 9	

(1) *data valid as "0" or "1".
Blank does not exist (unrecognized during a write and held at "0" during a read)
†data bits used for AM/PM, 12/24 HOUR and leap year.

(2) If D2 previously set to "1", upon completion of month 2 day 29, D2 will be internally reset to "0".

Table 1

DC CHARACTERISTICS

(V_{CC} = 5V ±5%; T_A = –30 to +85°C)

Parameter	Symbol	Min.	Typ.	Max.	Unit	Conditions
Input Current (1)	I_{IH}	10	25	50	μA	V_{IN}=5V, V_{DD}=5V
	I_{IL}	–	–	-1	μA	V_{IN} = 0V
Data I/O Leakage Current	I_{LD}	-10	–	10	μA	$V_{I/O}$ = 0 to V_{DD} CS = "0"
Output Low Voltage	V_{OL}	–	–	0.4	V	I_O = 1.6 mA, CS = "1", READ = "1"
Output Low Current	I_{OL}	1.6	–	–	mA	V_O = 0.4V, CS = "1", READ = "1"
Operating Supply Current	I_{DDS}	–	15	30	μA	V_{CC} = 3V, Ta = 25°C
	I_{DD}	–	100	500	μA	V_{CC} = 5V, Ta = 25°C

(1) XT, $\overline{XT}$ and D_0 ~ D_3 excluded.

OPERATING CONDITIONS

Parameter	Symbol	Min.	Typ.	Max.	Unit	Conditions
Supply Voltage	V_{DD}	4.5	5	7	V	
Standby Supply Voltage	V_{DH}	2.2	–	7	V	
Input Signal Level	V_{IH}	3.6	–	V_{DD}	V	V_{DD} = 5V ± 5% Respect to GND
	V_{IL}	–0.3	–	0.8	V	
Crystal Oscillator Freq.	f(XT)	–	32.768	–	kHz	
Operating Temperature	T_{OP}	–30	–	+85	°C	

ABSOLUTE MAXIMUM RATINGS

Rating	Symbol	Value	Unit
Supply voltage	V_{DD}	$-0.3 \sim 7.0$	V
Input voltage	V_I	$-0.3 \sim V_{DD} + 0.3$	V
Data I/O voltage	$V_{\overline{O}}$	$-0.3 \sim V_{DD} + 0.3$	V
Storage Temperature	Tstg	$-55 \sim 150$	°C

SWITCHING CHARACTERISTICS

(1) READ mode (V_{DD} = 5V ±5%, Ta = 25°C)

Parameter	Symbol	Condition	MIN	TYP	MAX	Unit
HOLD Set-up Time	t_{HS}	——	150	–	–	μs
HOLD Hold Time	t_{HH}	——	0	–	–	μs
HOLD Pulse Width	t_{HW}	——	–	–	990	ms
HOLD "L" Hold Time	t_{HL}	——	130	–	–	μs
READ Hold Time	t_{RH}	——	0	–	–	μs
READ Set-up Time	t_{RS}	——	0	–	–	μs
READ Access Time	t_{RA}	$R_{PULL\text{-}UP}$ = 5KΩ C_L = 15pF	–	–	6	μs
ADDRESS Set-up Time	t_{AS}	——	3	–	–	μs
ADDRESS Hold Time	t_{AH}	——	0.2	–	–	μs
READ Pulse Width	t_{RW}	$R_{PULL\text{-}UP}$ = 5KΩ C_L = 15pF	2	–	–	μs
DARA Access Time	t_{AC}	$R_{PULL\text{-}UP}$ = 5KΩ C_L = 15pF	–	–	0.6	μs
OUTPUT Disable Time	t_{OFF}	$R_{PULL\text{-}UP}$ = 5KΩ C_L = 15 pF	–	–	0.6	μs
CS Enable Delay Time	t_{CS1}	——	–	–	0.6	μs
CS Disable Delay Time	t_{CS2}	——	–	–	0.6	μs

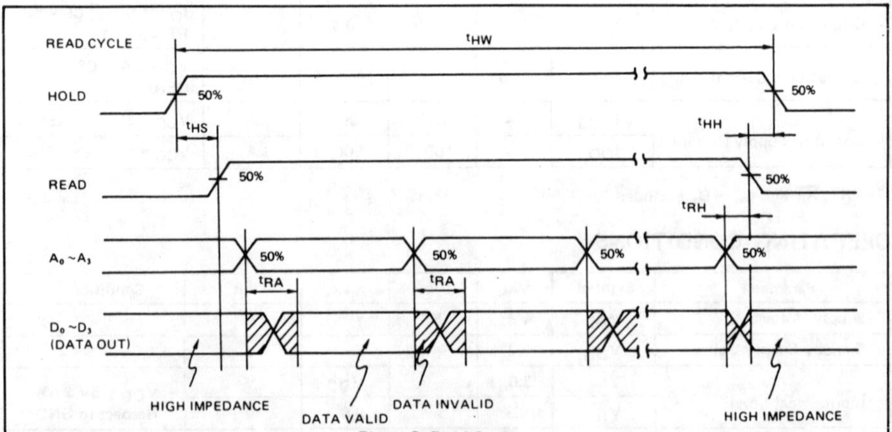

Figure 3 Read Cycle

Notes: 1. A Read occurs during the overlap of a high CS and a high READ.
2. CS may be a permanent "1", or may be coincident with HOLD pulse.

SWITCHING CHARACTERISTICS

(2) WRITE mode

(V_{DD} = 5V ±5%, Ta = 25°C)

Parameter	Symbol	Condition	MIN	TYP	MAX	Unit
HOLD Set-up Time	t_{HS}	———	150	–	–	μs
HOLD Bold Time	t_{HH}	———	0	–	–	μs
HOLD Pulse Width	t_{HW}	———	–	–	990	ms
HOLD "L" Hold Time	t_{HL}	———	130	–	–	μs
ADDRESS Pulse Width	t_{AW}	———	1.7	–	–	μs
Data Pulse Width	t_{DW}	———	1.7	–	–	μs
DATA Set-up Time	t_{DS}	———	0.5	–	–	μs
DATA Hold Time	t_{DH}	———	0.2	–	–	μs
WRITE Pulse Width	t_{WW}	———	1.0	–	–	μs
CS Enable Delay Time	t_{CS1}	———	–	–	0.6	μs
CS Disoble Delay Time	t_{CS2}	———	–	–	0.6	μs

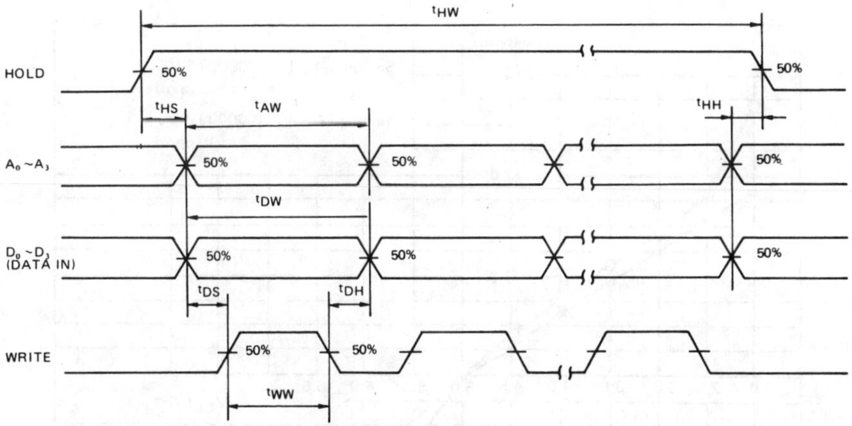

Figure 4 Write Cycle

Notes: 1. A WRITE occurs during the overlap of a high CS, a high HOLD and a high WRITE.
2. CS may be permanent "1", or may be coincident with HOLD pulse.

OSCILLATOR FREQUENCY DEVIATIONS

Frequency Deviation vs Temperature

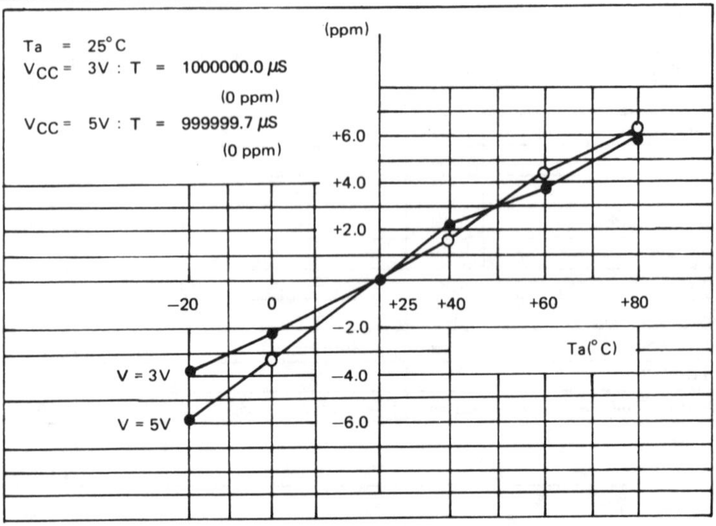

Figure 1

Frequency Deviation vs Supply Voltage

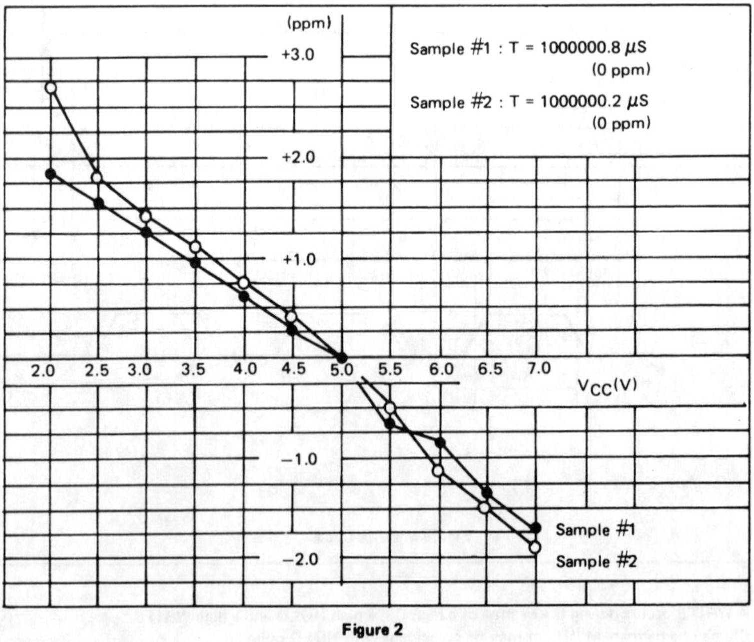

Figure 2

A0 to A3	:	Address Inputs
WRITE	:	Write Enable
READ	:	Read Enable
HOLD	:	Count Hold
CS	:	Chip Select
D0 to D3	:	Data Input Output
TEST	:	Test Input
±30 ADJ	:	±30 Second Correction Input
XT & $\overline{XT}$	:	xtal oscillator connections
V_{DD}	:	+5V Supply
GND	:	Ground

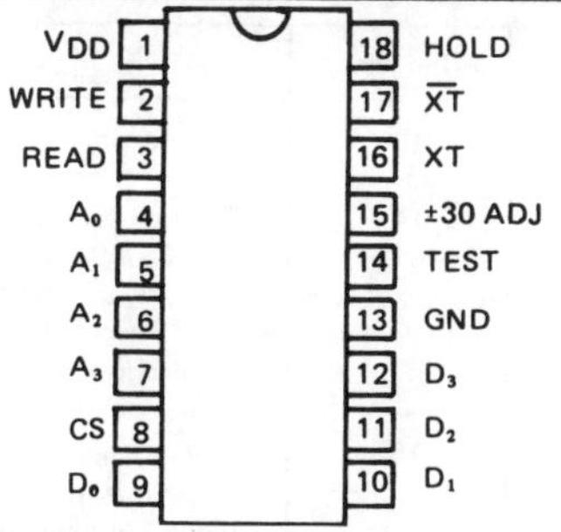

PIN CONFIGURATION

PIN DESCRIPTION

Name	Pin No.	Description
V_{DD}	1	Power supply pin. Application circuits for power supply are described in Figure 9.
WRITE	2	Data write pin. Data write cycle is described in Figure 4.
READ	3	Data read pin. Data read cycle is described in Figure 3.
$A_0 \sim A_3$	4 ~ 7	Address input pins used to select internal counters for read/write operations. The address is specified by 4-bit binary code as shown in Table 1.
C S	8	Chip slect pin which is required to interface with the external circuit. HOLD, WRITE, READ, ±30ADJ, TEST, $D_0 \sim D_3$ and $A_0 \sim A_3$ pins are activated if CS is set at H level, while all of these pins are disabled if CS is set at L level.
$D_0 \sim D_3$	9 ~ 12	Data input/output pins (bidirectional bus). As shown in Figure 5, external pull-up registers of 4.7 kΩ ~ 10 kΩ are required by the open-drain NMOS output. D_3 is the MSB, while D_0 is the LSB

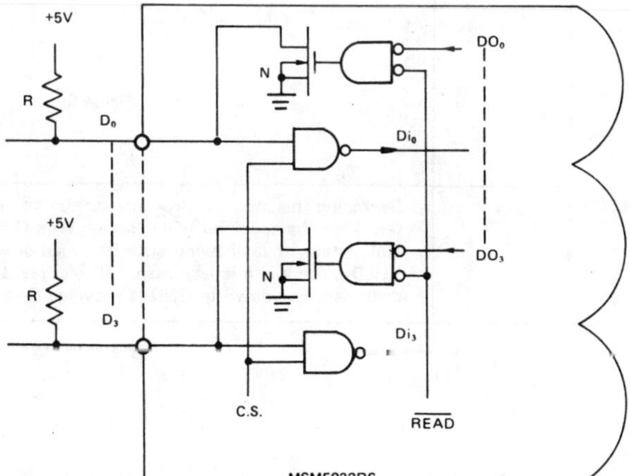

Figure 5

Name	Pin No.	Description
GND	13	Ground pin.
TEST	14	Test pin. Normally this pin should be left open or should be set at ground level. With CS at V_{DD}, pulses to V_{DD} on the TEST input will directly clock the S_1, MI_{10}, W, D_1 and Y_1 counters, depending on which counter is addressed (W and D_1 are selected by D_1 address in this mode only). Roll-over to next counter is enabled in this mode.
±30ADJ	15	This pin is used to adjust the time within the extent of ± 30 seconds. If this pin is set at H level when the seconds digits are 0 ~ 29, the seconds digits are cleared to 0. If this pin is set at H level when the seconds digits are 30 ~ 59, the second digits will be cleared to 0 and the minutes digits will be increased by +1. To enable this function, 31.25 ms or more width's pulse should be input to this pin.
XT	16	Oscillator pin. 32.768 kHz crystal, capacitor and trimmer condensor for frequency adjustment connected to these pins. See Figure 6. As for oscillator frequency deviation, refer to Figure 1 and Figure 2. If an external clock is to be used for the MSM5832RS's oscillation source, the external clock is to be input to XT, and $\overline{XT}$ should be left open. 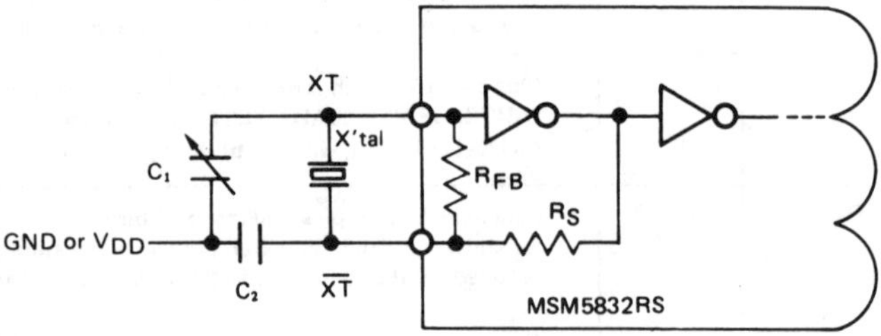 **Figure 6**
$\overline{XT}$	17	
HOLD	18	Switching this input to V_{DD} inhibits the internal 1 Hz clock to the S1 counter. After the specified HOLD set-up time (150 μs), all counters will be in a static state, thus allowing error-free read or write operations. So long as the HOLD pulse width is less than 990 ms, real time accuracy will be undisturbed. Pull-down to GND is provided by an internal resistor.

REFERENCE SIGNAL OUTPUT PIN

Condition	Output	Reference Frequency	Pulse Width
HOLD = L	D_0 (1)	1024 Hz	duty 50%
READ = H	D_1	1 Hz	122.1 μS
CS = H	D_2	1/60 Hz	122.1 μS
$A_0 \sim A_3$ = H	D_3	1/3600 Hz	122.1 μS

(1) 1024 Hz signal at D_0 not dependent on HOLD input level.

APPLICATION EXAMPLE

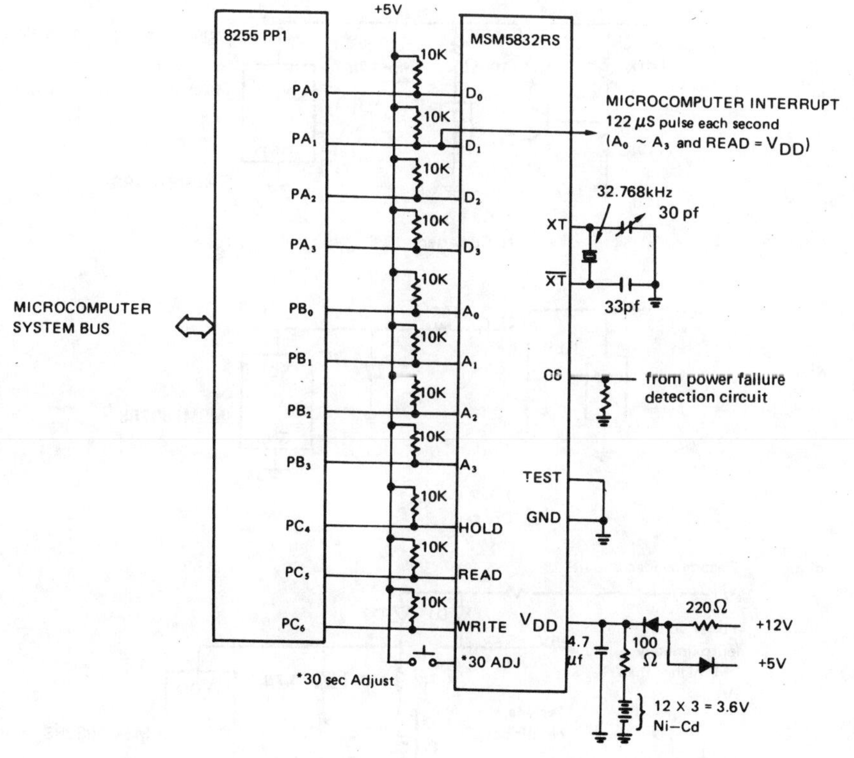

Figure 7

APPLICATION CIRCUIT – POWER SUPPLY CIRCUIT

Open or ground unused pins (pins other than the XT, $\overline{XT}$, D0–D3, and $\overline{BUSY}$ pins).

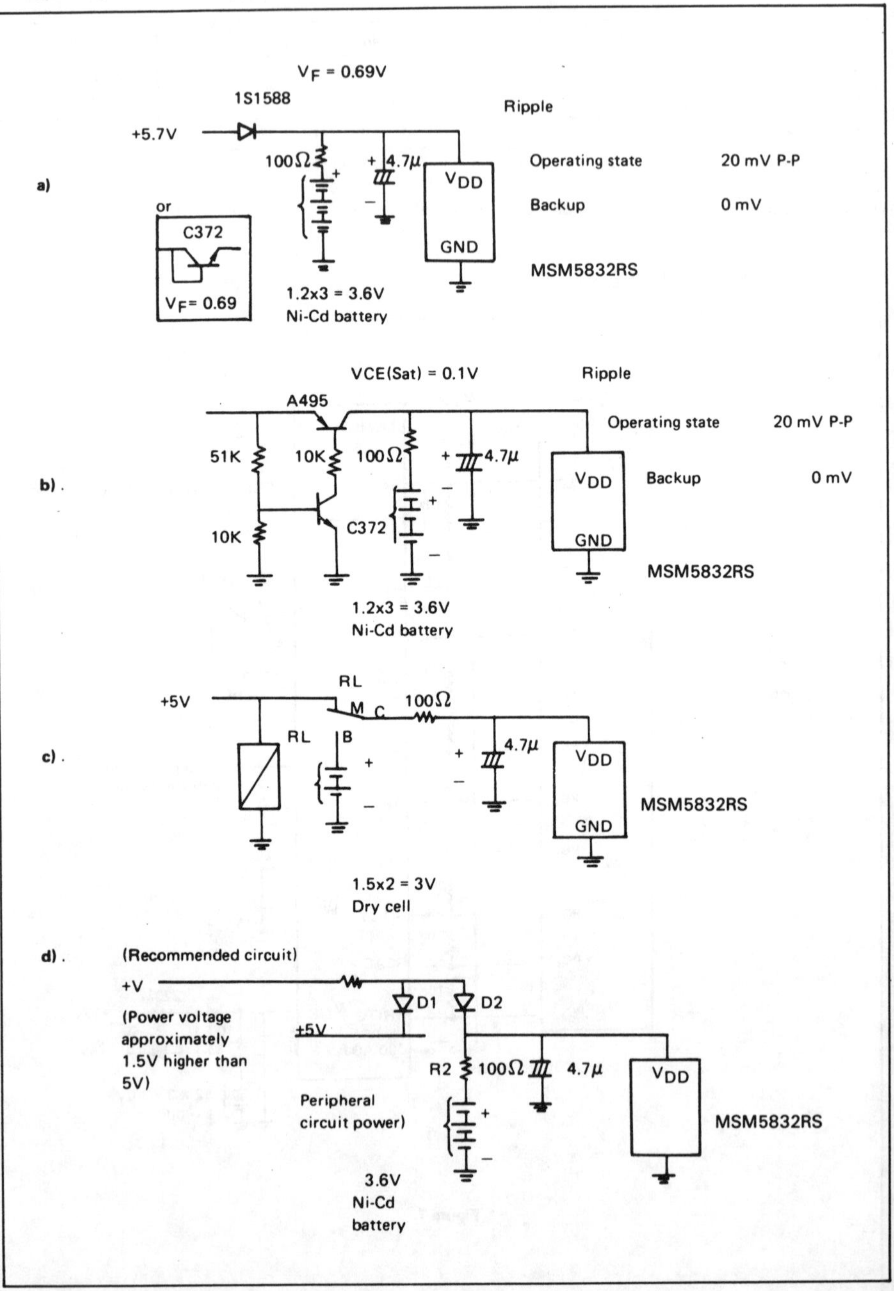

Note: Use the same diodes for D1 and D2 to reduce the level difference between +5V and V_{DD} of the MSM5832RS.

Real Time Clock MSM58321RS

GENERAL DESCRIPTION

The MSM58321RS is a metal gate CMOS Real Time Clock/Calendar with a battery backup function for use in bus-oriented microprocessor applications.

The 4-bit bidirectional bus line method is used for the data I/O circuit; the clock is set, corrected, or read by accessing the memory.

The time is read with 4-bit DATA I/O, ADDRESS WRITE, READ, and $\overline{\text{BUSY}}$; it is written with 4-bit DATA I/O, ADDRESS WRITE, WRITE, and $\overline{\text{BUSY}}$.

FEATURES

- 7 Function-Second, Minute, Hour, Day, Day-of-Week, Month, Year
- Automatic leap year calender
- 12/24 hour format
- Frequency divider 5-poststage reset
- Reference signal output
- 32.768kHz crystal controlled operation
- Single 5V power supply
- Back-up battery operation to V_{DD} = 2.2V
- Low power dissipation
  - 90μW max. at V_{DD} = 3V
  - 2.5mW max. at V_{DD} = 5V
- 16 pin plastic DIP package

FUNCTIONAL BLOCK DIAGRAM

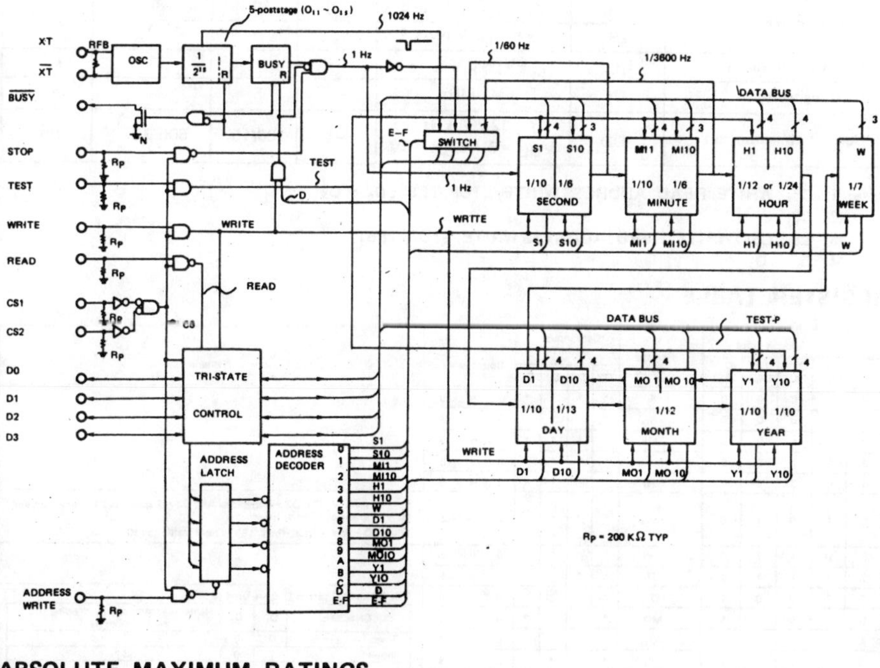

ABSOLUTE MAXIMUM RATINGS

Parameter	Symbol	Condition	Rating	Unit
Power voltage	V_{DD}	Ta = 25°C	−0.3 ~ 7	V
Input voltage	V_I	Ta = 25°C	GND−0.3 ~ V_{DD} + 0.3	V
Output voltage	V_O	Ta = 25°C	GND−0.3 ~ V_{DD} + 0.3	V
Storage temperature	Tstg	–	−55 ~ +150	°C

OPERATING CONDITIONS

Parameter	Symbol	Condition	Rating	Unit
Power voltage	V_{DD}	–	4.5 ~ 7	V
Date hold voltage	V_{DH}	–	2.2 ~ 7	V
Crystal frequency	f(XT)	–	32.768	kHz
Operating temperature	Top	–	–30 ~ +85	°C

Note: The data hold voltage guarantees the clock operations, though it does not guarantee operations outside the IC and data input/output.

DC CHARACTERISTICS

(V_{DD} = 5 V ±5%, Ta = –30 ~ +85°C)

Parameter	Symbol	Condition	Min.	Typ.	Max.	Unit
H input voltage	V_{IH1}	– Note 1	3.6	–	–	V
	V_{IH2}	– Note 2	V_{DD}–0.5	–	–	
L input voltage	V_{IL}	–	–	–	0.8	V
L output voltage	V_{OL}	I_O = 1.6 mA	–	–	0.4	V
L output current	I_{OL}	V_O = 0.4 V	1.6	–	–	mA
H input current	I_{IH1}	V_1 = V_{DD}V Note 3	10	30	80	μA
	I_{IH_2}	V_1 = V_{DD}V Note 4	–	–	1	
L input current	I_{IL}	V_I = 0 V	–	–	–1	μA
Input capacity	C_I	f = 1 MHz	–	5	–	pF
Current consumption	I_{DD}	f = 32.768 kHz V_{DD} = 5V/V_{DD} = 3V	–	100/15	500/30	μA

Note: 1. CS_2, WRITE, READ, ADDRESS WRITE, STOP, TEST, D_0 ~ D_3
2. CS_1
3. CS_1, CS_2, WRITE, READ, ADDRESS WRITE, STOP, TEST
4. D_0 ~ D_3

REGISTER TABLE

Address	Address input				Register Name	Data input/output				Count value	Remarks
	D_0 (A_0)	D_1 (A_1)	D_2 (A_2)	D_3 (A_3)		D_0	D_1	D_2	D_3		
0	0	0	0	0	S_1	•	•	•	•	0 ~ 9	
1	1	0	0	0	S_{10}	•	•	•		0 ~ 5	
2	0	1	0	0	MI_1	•	•	•	•	0 ~ 9	
3	1	1	0	0	MI_{10}	•	•	•		0 ~ 5	
4	0	0	1	0	H_1	•	•	•	•	0 ~ 9	
5	1	0	1	0	H_{10}	•	•	•	⊙	0~1 or 0~2	D2 = 1 specifies PM, D2 = 0 specifies AM, D3 = 1 specifies 24-hour timer, and D3 = 0 specifies 12-hour timer. When D3 = 1 is written, the D2 bit is reset inside the IC.
6	0	1	1	0	W	•	•	•		0 ~ 6	
7	1	1	1	0	D_1	•	•	•	•	0 ~ 9	
8	0	0	0	1	D_{10}	•	•	◉	◉	0 ~ 3	The D2 and D3 bits in D10 are used to select a leap year.
9	1	0	0	1	MO_1	•	•	•	•	0 ~ 9	
A	0	1	0	1	MO_{10}	•				0 ~ 1	
B	1	1	0	1	Y_1	•	•	•	•	0 ~ 9	
C	0	0	1	1	Y_{10}	•	•	•	•	0 ~ 9	
D	1	0	1	1							A selector to reset 5 poststages in the $1/2^{15}$ frequency divider and the BUSY circuit. They are reset when this code is latched with ADDRESS LATCH and the WRITE input goes to 1.
E~F	0/1	1	1	1							A selector to obtain reference signal output. Reference signals are output to D0 – D3 when this code is latched with ADDRESS LATCH and READ input goes to 1.

Calendar	D_2	D_3	Remainder obtained by dividing the year number by 4
Gregorian calendar	0	0	0
Showa	1	0	3
	0	1	2
	1	1	1

Notes: (1) There are no bits in blank fields for data input/output. 0 signals are output by reading and data is not stored by writing because there are no bits.
(2) The bit with marked ⊙ is used to select the 12/24-hour timer and the bits marked ◉ are used to select a leap year. These three bits can be read or written.
(3) When signals are input to bus lines D0 – D3 and ADDRESS WRITE goes to 1 for address input, ADDRESS information is latched with ADDRESS LATCH.

SWITCHING CHARACTERISTICS

(1) WRITE mode

(V_{DD} = 5 V ±5%, Ta = 25°C)

Parameter	Symbol	Condition	Min.	Typ.	Max.	Unit
CS setup time	t_{CS}	–	0	–	–	μs
CS Hold time	t_{CH}	–	0	–	–	μs
Address setup time	t_{AS}	–	0	–	–	μs
Address write pulse width	t_{AW}	–	0.5	–	–	μs
Address hold time	t_{AH}	–	0.1	–	–	μs
Data setup time	t_{DS}	–	0	–	–	μs
Write pulse width	t_{WW}	–	2	–	–	μs
Data hold time	t_{DH}	–	0	–	–	μs

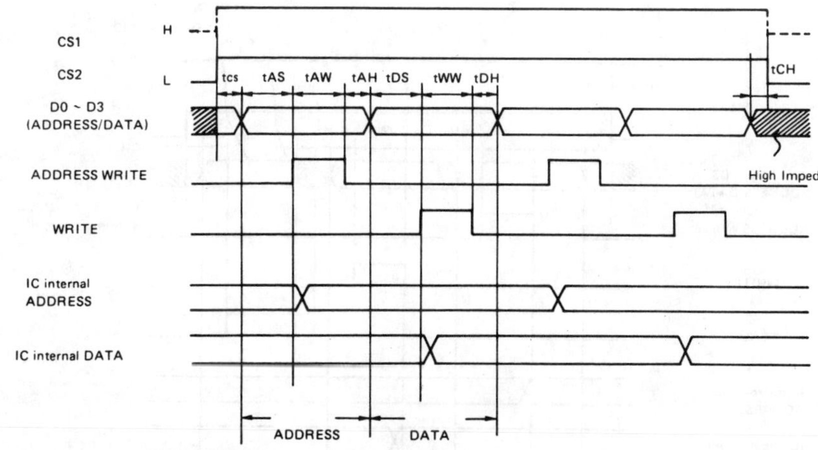

Write Cycle

Note: ADDRESS WRITE and WRITE inputs are activated by the level, not by the edge.

(2) READ mode

(V_{DD} = 5 V ±5%, Ta = 25°C)

Parameter	Symbol	Condition	Min.	Typ.	Max.	Unit
CS setup time	t_{CS}	–	0	–	–	μs
CS Hold time	t_{CH}	–	0	–	–	μs
Address setup time	t_{AS}	–	0	–	–	μs
Address write pulse width	t_{AW}	–	0.5	–	–	μs
Address hold time	t_{AH}	–	0.1	–	–	μs
Read access time	t_{RA}	–	–	–	see Note 1	μs
Read delay time	t_{DD}	–	–	–	1	μs
Read inhibit time	t_{RI}	–	0	–	–	μs

Note 1. $t_{RA} = 1\ \mu s + CR \ln \left(\frac{V_{DD}}{V_{DD} - V_{IH}\,min} \right)$

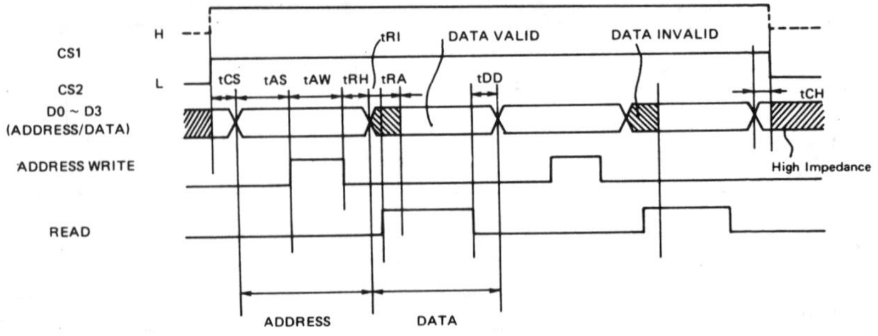

Read Cycle

Note: ADDRESS WRITE and READ inputs are activated by the level, not by the edge.

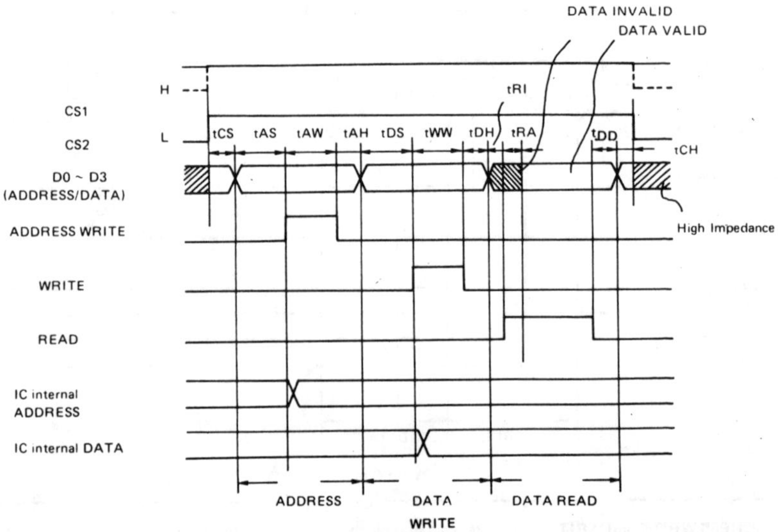

Read & Write Cycle

(3) WRITE & READ mode

Parameter	Symbol	Condition	Min.	Typ.	Max.	Unit
CS setup time	t_{CS}	–	0	–	–	μs
CS hold time	t_{CH}	–	0	–	–	μs
Address setup time	t_{AS}	–	0	–	–	μs
Address write pulse width	t_{AW}	–	0.5	–	–	μs
Address hold time	t_{AH}	–	0.1	–	–	μs
Data setup time	t_{DS}	–	0	–	–	μs
Write pulse width	t_{WW}	–	2	–	–	μs
Data hold time	t_{DH}	–	0	–	–	μs
Read access time	t_{RA}	–	–	–	see Note 1	μs

Read delay time	t_{DD}	–	–	–	1	μs
Read inhibit time	t_{RI}	–	0	–	–	μs

Note 1. $t_{RA} = 1\,\mu s + CR \ln\left(\frac{V_{DD}}{V_{DD} - V_{IH}\,min}\right)$

PIN CONFIGURATION

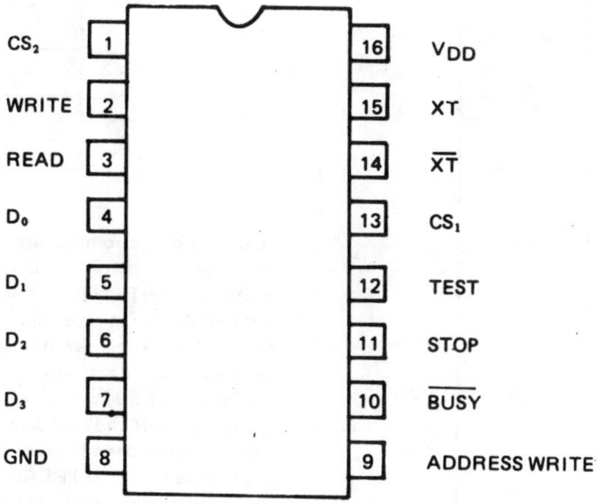

PIN DESCRIPTION

Name	Pin No.	Description
CS_2	1	Chip select pins. These pins enable the interface with the external circuit when both of these pins are set at H level simultanuously.
CS_1	13	If one of these pins is set at L level, STOP, TEST, WRITE, READ, ADDRESS WRITE pins and $D_0 \sim D_3$ pins are inactivated. Since the threshold voltage VT for the CS_1 pin is higher than that for other pins, it should be connected to the detector of power circuit and peripherals and CS_2 is to be connected to the microcontroller.
WRITE	2	WRITE pin is used to write data; it is activated when it is at the H level. Data bus data inside the IC is loaded to the object digit while this WRITE pin is at the H level, not at the WRITE input edge. Refer to Figure 2 below.
		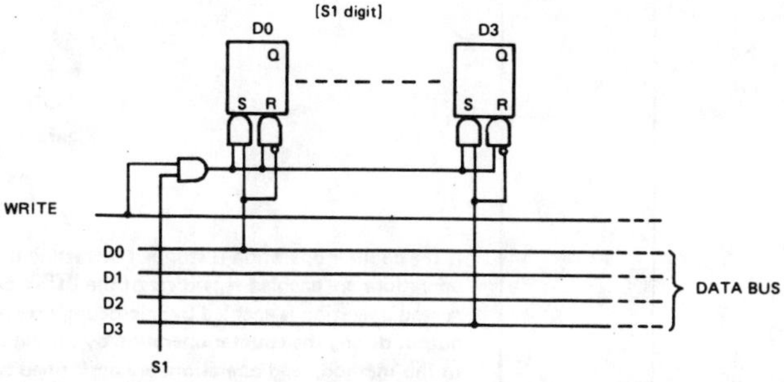

Name	Pin No.	Descrip
READ	3	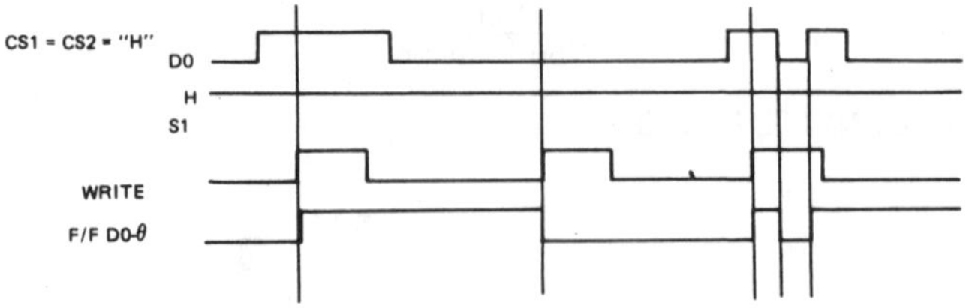 **Figure 2** READ pin is used to read data; it is activated when it is at the H level. Address contents are latched with ADDRESS LATCH inside the IC at the D0 – D3 and ADDRESS WRITE pins to select the object digit, then an H-level signal is input to the READ pin to read data. If a count operation is continued by setting the STOP input to the L level, read operation must be performed, in principle, while the $\overline{BUSY}$ output is at the H level. While the $\overline{BUSY}$ output is at the L level, count operations are performed by digit counters and read data is not guaranteed, therefore, read operations are inhibited in this period. Figure 3 shows a time chart of the $\overline{BUSY}$ output, 1 Hz signal inside the IC, and READ input. A read operation is stopped temporarily within a period of 244 μs from the $\overline{BUSY}$ output trailing edge and it is restarted when the $\overline{BUSY}$ output goes to the H level again.
		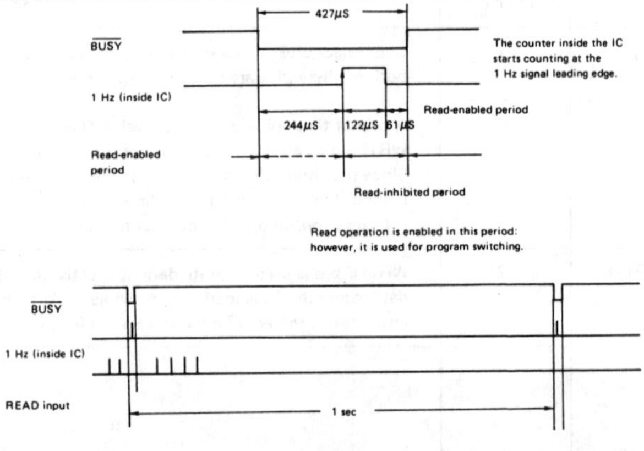 **Figure 3** If the counter operation is stopped by setting the STOP input to the H level, read operations are enabled regardless of the $\overline{BUSY}$ output. A read operation is enabled by microcomputer software regardless of the $\overline{BUSY}$ output during the counter operation by setting the STOP input to the L level. In this method, read operations are performed two or more times continuously and data that matches twice is used as guaranteed data.

Name	Pin No.	Description
$D_0 \sim D_3$	4~7	Data input/output pins. (Bidirectional bus). The output is a open-drain type and 4.7 kΩ ~ 10 kΩ pull-up registers are required utilize these pins as output pins.
GND	8	Ground pin.
ADDRESS WRITE	9	ADDRESS WRITE pin is used to load address information from the D0 – D3 I/O bus pins to the ADDRESS LATCH inside the IC; it is activated when it is at the H level. This input is activated by the level, not by the edge. Figure 4 shows the relationships between the D0 address input, ADDRESS WRITE input, and ADDRESS LATCH input/output. 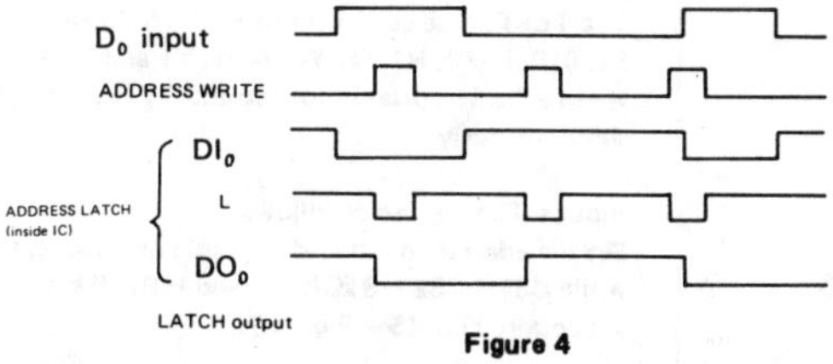 Figure 4
$\overline{BUSY}$	10	$\overline{BUSY}$ pin outputs the IC operation state. It is N-channel MOSFET open-drain output. An external pull-up resistor of 4.7 kΩ or more must be connected (see Figure 5) to use the $\overline{BUSY}$ output. The signals are output in negative logics. If the oscillator oscillates at 32.768 kHz, the frequency is always 1 Hz regardless of the CS1 and CS2 unless the D output of the ADDRESS DECODER inside the IC is H (CODE = H•L•H•H) and CS1 = CS2 = WRITE = H. Figure 6 shows the $\overline{BUSY}$ output time chart. 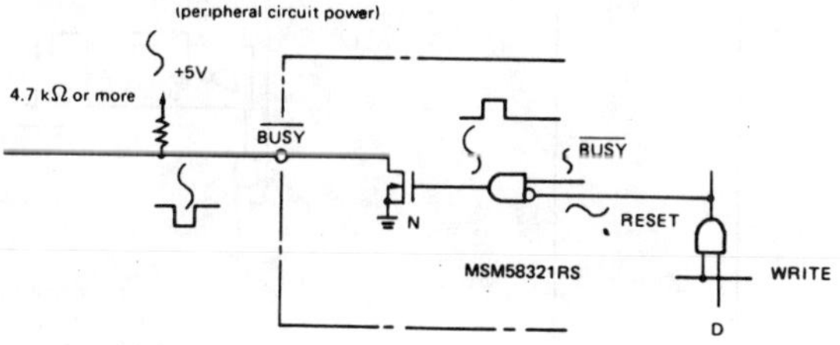 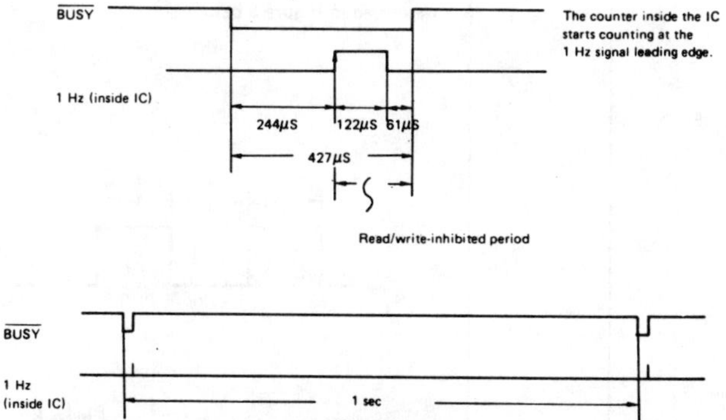 Figure 6

<table>
<tr><th>Name</th><th>Pin No.</th><th>Description</th></tr>
<tr><td>STOP</td><td>11</td><td>The STOP pin is used to input on/off control for a 1 Hz signal. When this pin goes to the H level, 1 Hz signals are inhibited and counting for all digits succeeding the S1 digit is stopped. When this pin goes to the L level, normal operations are performed; the digits are counted up. This STOP input controls stopping digit counting. Writing of external data in digits can be assured by setting the STOP input to the H level to stop counting, then writing sequentially from the low-order digits.</td></tr>
<tr><td>TEST</td><td>12</td><td>The TEST pin is used to test this IC; it is normally open or connected to GND. It is recommended to connect it to GND to safeguard against malfunctions from noise.
The TEST pulse can be input to the following nine digits:
S1, S10, MI10, H1, D1(W), M01, Y1 and Y10
When a TEST pulse is input to the D1 digit, the W digit is also counted up simultaneously.

Input a TEST pulse as follows:
Set the address to either digit explained above, then input a pulse to the TEST pin while CS1 = CS2 = STOP = H and WRITE = L. The specified and succeeding digits are counted up. (See Figure 7)

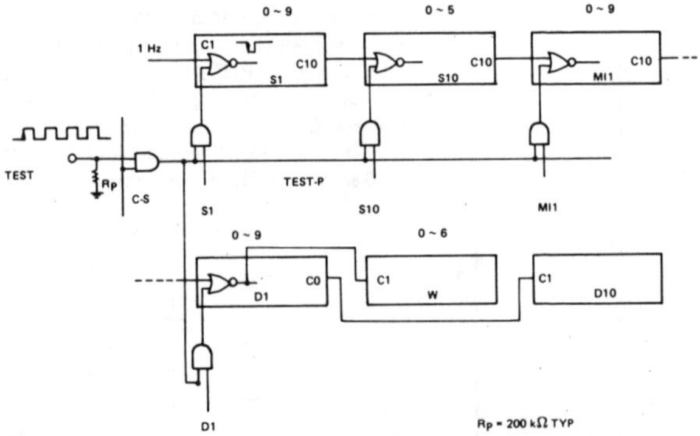

Figure 7

A digit is counted up at the leading edge (changing point from L to H) of a TEST pin input pulse. The pulse condition for TEST pin input at V_{DD} = 5 V ±5% is described in Figure 8 below.

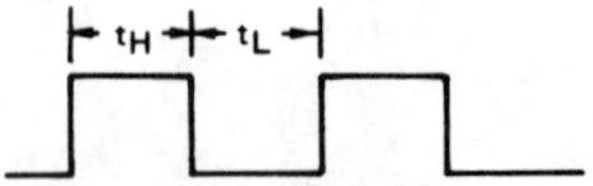

t_H = 10μS MIN
t_L =10μS MIN

Figure 8</td></tr>
</table>

<table>
<tr><th>Name</th><th>Pin No.</th><th>Description</th></tr>
<tr><td>$\overline{XT}$
XT</td><td>14
15</td><td>Oscillator pin. A 32.768kHz crystal oscillator, capacitor and trim capacitor for frequency adjustment are to be connected as shown in Figure 8 below.

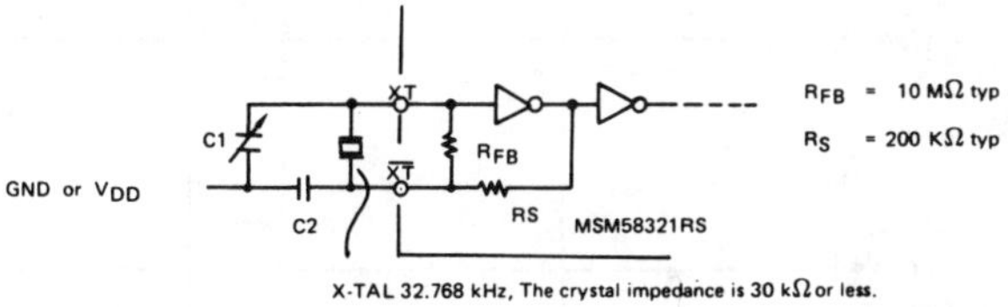

Figure 8

If an external clock is to be used for MSM58321RS's oscillation source, the external clock is to be input to XT, while $\overline{XT}$ should be left open. Refer to the Figure 9 below.

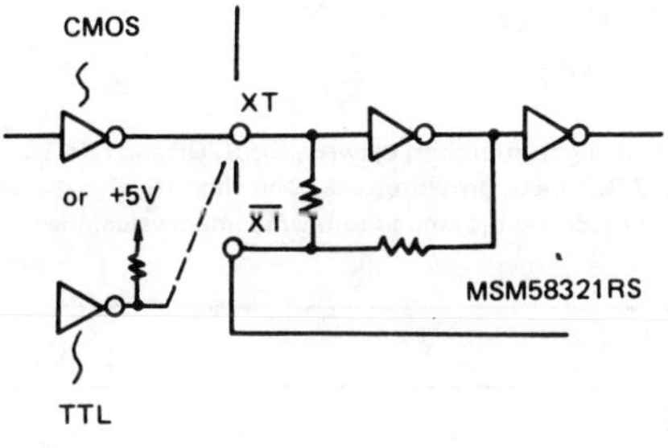

Figure 9</td></tr>
<tr><td>V_{DD}</td><td>16</td><td>Power supply pin. Refer to the application circuit.</td></tr>
</table>

REFERENCE SIGNAL OUTPUT

Reference signals are output from the D0 – D3 pins under the following conditions:

Conditions	Output pin	Reference signal frequency	Pulse width	Output logic
WRITE = L	D_0	1024 Hz	488.3 µs	Positive logic
READ = H	D_1	1 Hz	122.1 µs	Negative logic
CS1 = CS2 = H	D_2	1/60 Hz	122.1 µs	Negative logic
ADDRESS = E or F	D_3	1/3600 Hz	122.1 µs	Negative logic

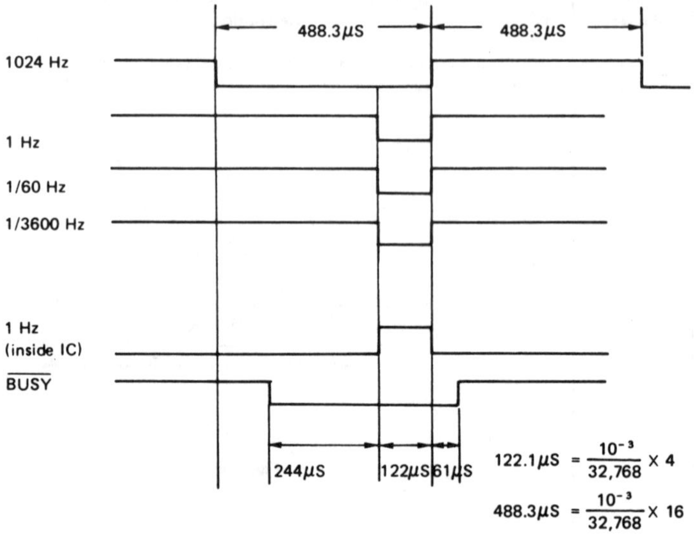

Figure 10

APPLICATION NOTES

■ WRITE and STOP

Note that the timing relationships between the STOP and WRITE inputs vary by the related digit when counting is stopped by the STOP input to write data. The time (t_{SH}) between the STOP input leading edge and WRITE input trailing edge for each digit is limited to the minimum value. (See Figure 11)

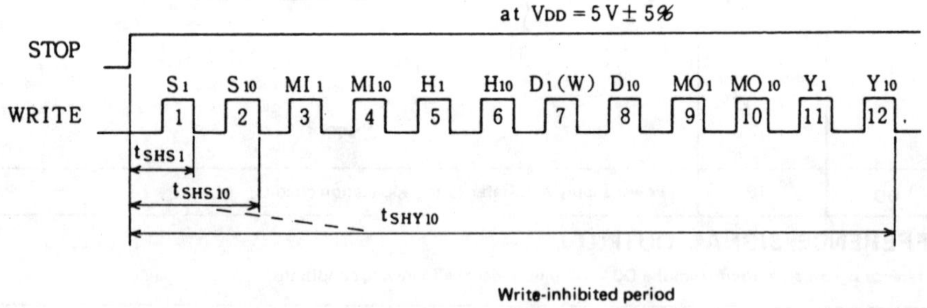

Figure 11

t_{SHS1} = 1 μs, t_{SHS10} = 2 μs, t_{SHMI1} = 3 μs, t_{SHM10} = 4 μs, t_{SHH1} = 5 μs
t_{SHH10} = 6 μs, t_{SHD1} = 7 μs, $t_{SHW'}$ = 7 μs, t_{SHD10} = 8 μs, t_{SHMO1} = 9 μs
t_{SHMO10} = 10 μs, t_{SHY1} = 11 μs, t_{SHY10} = 12 μs.

If a count operation is continued by setting the STOP input to the L level, write operation must be performed, in principle, while the $\overline{\text{BUSY}}$ output is at the H level. While the $\overline{\text{BUSY}}$ output is at the L level, count operations are performed by the digit counters and write operation is inhibited, but there is a marginal period of 244 μs from the $\overline{\text{BUSY}}$ output trailing edge. If the $\overline{\text{BUSY}}$ output goes to the L level during a write operation, the write operation is stopped temporarily within 244 μs and it is restarted when the $\overline{\text{BUSY}}$ output goes to the H level again. Figure 12 shows a time chart of $\overline{\text{BUSY}}$ output, 1 Hz signal inside the IC, and WRITE input.

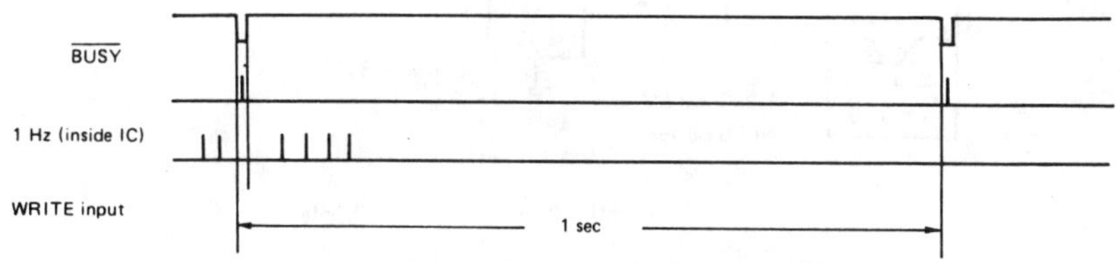

Figure 12

Frequency divider and $\overline{\text{BUSY}}$ circuit reset

If A0—A3 = H•L•H•H is input to ADDRESS DECODER, the DECODER output (D) goes to the H level. If CS1 = CS2 = H and WRITE = H in this state, the 5 poststages in the 15-stage frequency divider and the $\overline{\text{BUSY}}$ circuit are reset.

In this period, the $\overline{\text{BUSY}}$ output remains at the H level and the 1 Hz signal inside the IC remains at the L level, and counting is stopped. If this reset is inactivated while the oscillator operates, the $\overline{\text{BUSY}}$ output goes to the L level after 1000.1221 ±31.25 ms and the 1 Hz signal inside the IC goes to the H level after 1000.3663 ±31.25 ms. These times are not the same because the first ten stages in the 15-stage frequency divider are not reset. (See Figure 13)

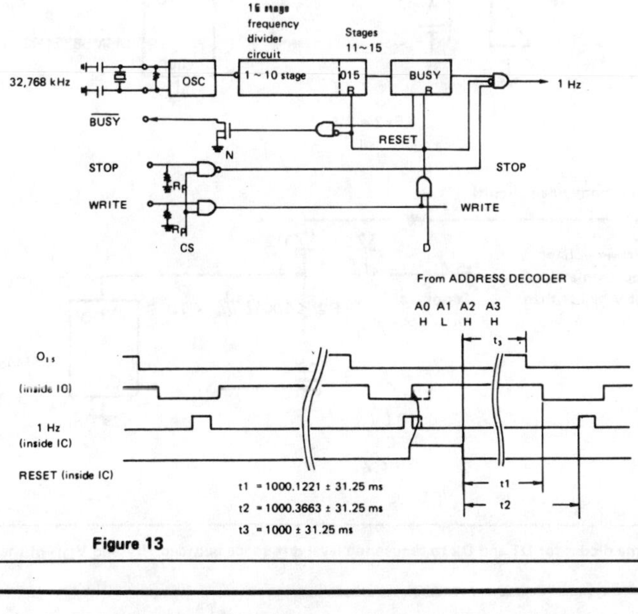

Figure 13

APPLICATION EXAMPLE - POWER SUPPLY CIRCUIT

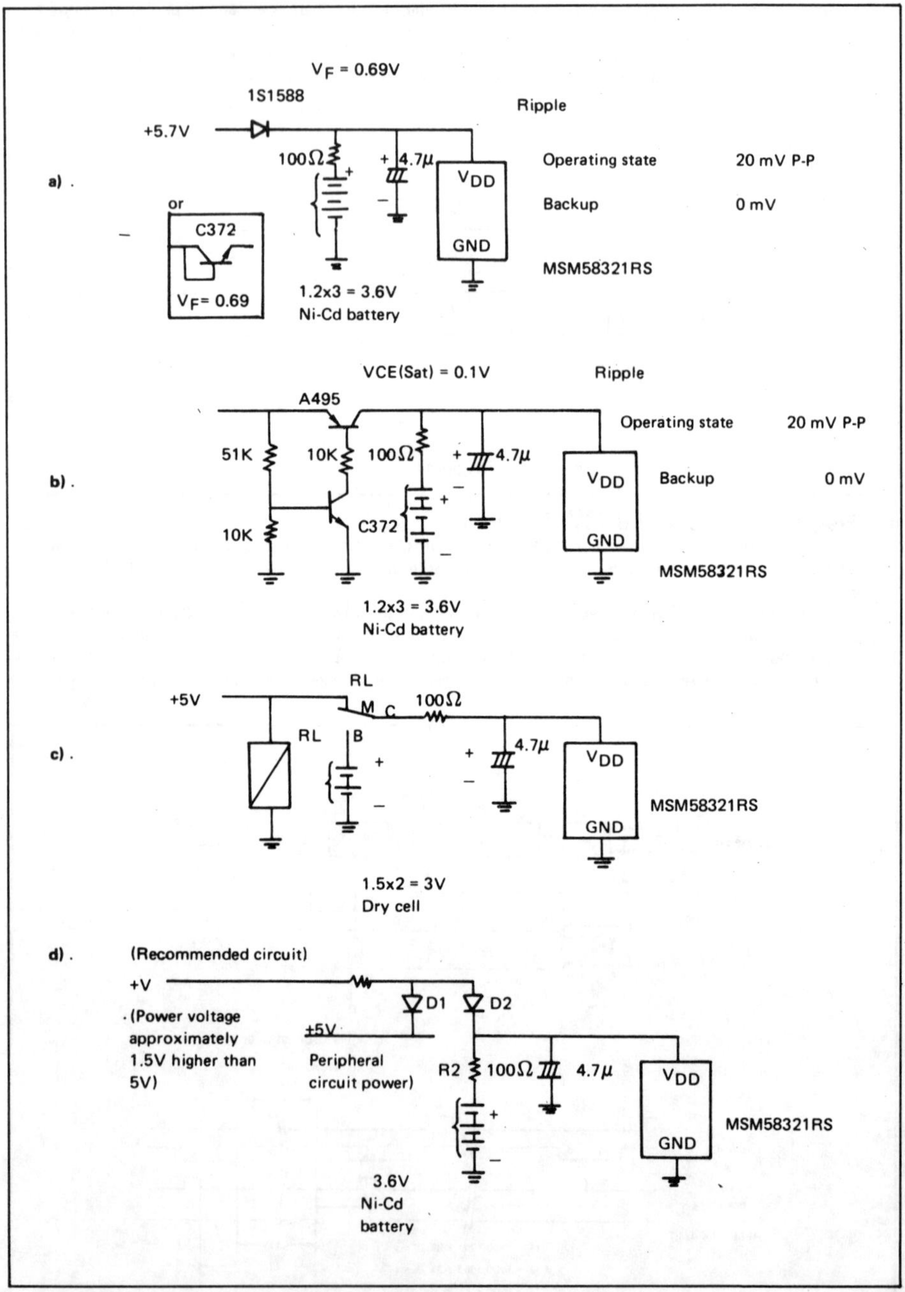

Note: Use the same diodes for D1 and D2 to reduce the level difference between +5V and V_{DD} of the MSM58321RS.

■ Selection of leap year

This IC is designed to select leap year automatically.

Four types of leap years can be selected by writing a select signal in the D2 and D3 bits of the D10 digit (CODE = L•L•L•H). (See Table 1 for the functions.)

Gregorian calendar, Japanese Showa, or other calendars can be set arbitrarily in the Y1 and Y2 digits of this IC. There is a leap year every four years and the year number varies according to whether the Gregorian calendar or Showa is used. There are four combinations of year numbers and leap years. (See the Table below).

No. 1: Gregorian calendar year. The remainder obtained by dividing the leap year number by 4 is 0.
No. 2: Showa year. The remainder obtained by dividing the leap year number by 4 is 3.
No. 3: The remainder obtained by dividing the leap year number by 4 is 2.
No. 4: The remainder obtained by dividing the leap year number by 4 is 1.

No. 1	Calendar	D10 digit		Remainder obtained by dividing the leap year number by 4	Leap years (examples)
		D2	D3		
1	Gregorian	L	L	0	1980, 1984, 1988, 1992, 1996, 2000, 2004
2	Showa	H	L	3	(83) (87) (91) (95) (99) 55, 59, 63, 67, 71, 75, 79
3		L	H	2	82, 86, 90, 94, 98, 102, 106
4		H	H	1	81, 85, 89, 93, 97, 101, 105

RTC58321 Real Time Clock

Features

Built-in crystal oscillator

- eliminates need for external components
- eliminates design time
- reduces board space

Low current consumption

Low-voltage battery backup function

4-bit bidirectional multiplexed address/data bus

Counter start, stop and reset functions

12 or 24 hour format, automatic leap year selection

Interrupt signal outputs: 1024, 1, 1/60, 1/3600 Hz

Standard 16-pin DIP, pin-compatible with MSM 58321RS

Description

The RTC-58321 Real Time Clock Module incorporates a CMOS real time clock and a complete crystal oscillator in a standard 16-pin DIP. The combination of the real time clock and crystal oscillator in one package eliminates the need for an external crystal, resistors, and capacitors, resulting in a substantial reduction in design time and board space, as well as procurement, inventory, testing, and assembly costs. Application note available upon request.

Electrical Characteristics

Operating Ranges

Item	Symbol	Conditions	Range	Units
Supply voltage	V_{DD}	———	4.5~5.5	V
Data-holding voltage[1]	V_{DH}	———	2.2~5.5	V
Crystal frequency	f_0	———	32.768	kHz
Operating temperature	T_{OP}	———	−10~+60	℃

[1]Guarantees continued clock operation only.

Absolute Maximum Ratings

Item	Symbol	Conditions	Rated Value	Units
Supply voltage	V_{DD}	Ta=25℃	−0.3~7	V
Input voltage	V_I	Ta=25℃	GND−0.3~V_{DD}+0.3	V
Output voltage	V_O	Ta=25℃	GND−0.3~V_{DD}+0.3	V
Storage temperature	Tstg	———	−30~+80	℃

Electrical Characteristics

V_{DD}=5V±5% Ta=−10~+60℃

Item	Symbol	Conditions	MIN	TYP	MAX	Unit
H. input voltage[1,2]	V_{IH1}	—	3.6	—	—	V
	V_{IH2}	—	V_{DD}−0.5	—	—	V
L. input voltage	V_{IL}	—	—	—	0.8	V
L. output voltage	V_{OL}	I_O=1.6mA	—	—	0.4	V
L. output current	I_{OL}	V_O=0.4V	1.6	—	—	mA
H. input current[3]	I_{IH}	V_I=5V	10	30	80	μA
L. input current[3]	I_{IL}	V_I=0V	—	—	−1	μA
D_0~D_3 terminals input off-leak current	I_{LIH} I_{LIL}	V_I=5V V_I=0V	—	—	1 −1	μA
Input capacity	C_I	f=1MHz	—	5	—	pF
Current consumption	I_{OP}	Ta=25℃ V_{DD}=5V/V_{DD}=3V	—	16.5/6.2	30.0/10.0	μA
Accuracy[4]	Δt/t	Ta=25℃ V_{DD}=5V	—	—	±4.5	sec/day

[1]CS2 WRITE, READ, ADDRESS-WRITE, STOP, TEST, D_0~D_3 terminals
[2]CS1 terminals
[3]CS1, CS2, WRITE, READ, ADDRESS-WRITE, STOP, TEST terminals
[4]Tighter accuracy available, contact factory
Specifications subject to change without notice

Function Table

Internal Counter	Address	Address Input D_3 (A_3)	D_2 (A_2)	D_1 (A_1)	D_0 (A_0)	Address Output D_3	D_2	D_1	D_0	Count Value	Remarks
S_1	0	L	L	L	L	*	*	*	*	0~9	
S_{10}	1	L	L	L	H		*	*	*	0~5	
MI_1	2	L	L	H	L	*	*	*	*	0~9	
MI_{10}	3	L	L	H	H		*	*	*	0~5	
H_1	4	L	H	L	L	*	*	*	*	0~9	
H_{10}	5	L	H	L	H	*1	*	*	*	0~1 0~2	D2:H for p.m., L for a.m., D3:H for 24-hour clock, L for 12-hour clock. When D3 H is written, the D2 bit is reset inside the IC and remains constantly at L.
W	6	L	H	H	L		*	*	*	0~6	
D_1	7	L	H	H	H	*	*	*	*	0~9	
D_{10}	8	H	L	L	L	*2	*2	*	*	0~3	D2 and D3 in the D10line are for leap year selection
MO_1	9	H	L	L	H	*	*	*	*	0~9	
MO_{10}	A	H	L	H	L				*	0~1	
Y_1	B	H	L	H	H	*	*	*	*	0~9	
Y_{10}	C	H	H	L	L	*	*	*	*	0~9	
	D	H	H	L	H						These selections are for resetting the 5-stage and the BUSY circuit after the $1/2^{15}$ frequency stage. Resetting is activated by latching this code on to the address latch and setting the WRITE input to H.
	E | F	H	H	H	L/H	1/3600 Hz	1/60 Hz	1 Hz	1024 Hz		These selections are for obtaining standard signals. By latching this code on to the address latch and setting READ to H, the standard signals will be output at D_0~D_3.

Calendar	D_3	D_2	Remainder when divided years by 4
Western	L	L	0
Japanese	L	H	3
	H	L	2
	H	H	1

Note 1. The blank spaces in the data input/output columns indicate that there are no bits. When READ is performed, the L level is output. When WRITE is performed nothing will be stored in the memory because thre are no bits.

Note 2: The bit indicated by the symbol *1 is for selecting the 12hr/24hr clock and those indicated by *2 are for leap year selection. READ and WRITE are possible with all three bits.

Note 3: For address input, send a signal to the D_0~D_3 bus line, then input ADDRESS WRITE. The ADDRESS data will be latched on to the address latch.

Write & Read Timing

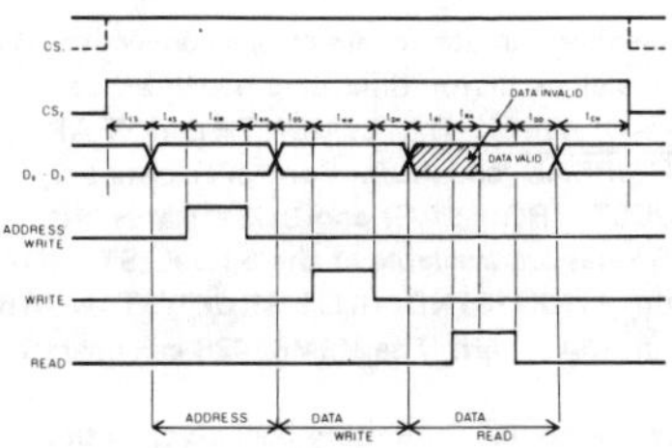

(Ta = 25°C V_{DD} = 5V ± 5%)

Item	Symbol	MIN	TYP	MAX	Units
CS set-up time	t_{CS}	0	—	—	μS
Address set-up time	t_{AS}	0	—	—	μS
Address write pulse range	t_{AW}	0.5	—	—	μS
Address hold time	t_{AH}	0.1	—	—	μS
Data set-up time	t_{DS}	0	—	—	μS
Write pulse range	t_{WW}	2	—	—	μS
Data hold time	t_{DH}	0	—	—	μS
Read inhibit time	t_{RI}	0	—	—	μS
Read access time	t_{RA}	—	—	*	μS
Read delay time	t_{DD}	—	—	1	μS
CS hold time	t_{CH}	0	—	—	μS

* $t_{RA} = 1\mu S + CR\ln\left(\frac{V_{DD}}{V_{DD}-V_{IH}}\right)$

C: Data line wiring capacity
R: Pull-up resistance value
V_{IH}: "H" input voltage of the IC connected to the data line
ln: Natural logarithms

Specifications subject to change without notice.

Circuit Diagram

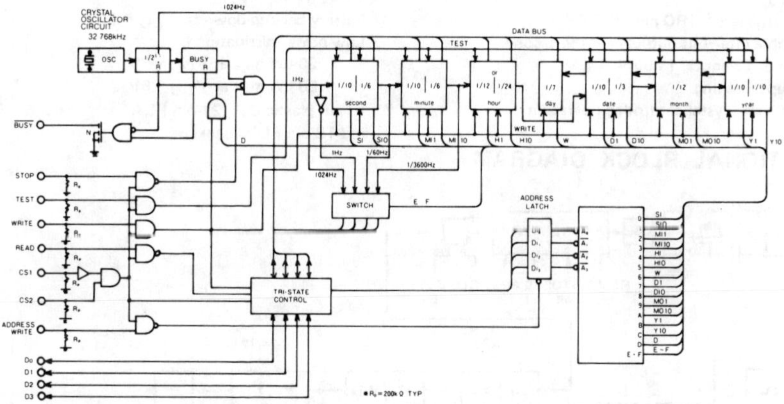

Pin Connections

(Top View)

(Top View)

1. CS_2	16. V_{DD}
2. WRITE	15. NC
3. READ	14. NC
4. D_0	13. CS_1
5. D_1	12. TEST
6. D_2	11. STOP
7. D_3	10. $\overline{BUSY}$
8. V_{SS}	9. ADDRESS WRITE

NC: Do not connect externally.

MSM6242BRS Real Time Clock

GENERAL DESCRIPTION

The MSM6242B is a silicon gate CMOS Real Time Clock/Calendar for use in direct bus-connection Microprocessor/Microcomputer applications. An on-chip 32.768KHz crystal oscillator time base is divided to provide addressable 4-bit I/O data for SECONDS, MINUTES, HOURS, DAY OF WEEK, DATE, MONTH and YEAR. Data access is controlled by 4-bit address, chip selects ($\overline{CS0}$, CS1), $\overline{WRITE}$, $\overline{READ}$, and ALE. Control Registers D, E and F provide for 30 SECOND error adjustment, INTERRUPT REQUEST (IRQ FLAG) and BUSY status bits, clock STOP, HOLD, and RESET FLAG bits, 4 selectable INTERRUPTS rates are available at the STD.P (STANDARD PULSE) output utilizing Control Register inputs T0, T1 and the ITRPT/STND (INTERRUPT/STANDARD). Masking of the interrupt output (STD.P) can be accomplished via the MASK bit. The MSM6242B can operate in a 12/24 hour format and Leap Year timing is automatic.

The MSM6242B normally operates from a 5V ± 10% supply at –30 to 85° C. Battery backup operation down to 2.0V allows continuation of time keeping when main power is off. The MSM6242B is offered in a 18-pin plastic DIP, a 24-pin FLAT package, and a 18-pin PLCC package.

FEATURES

DIRECT MICROPROCESSOR/MICROCONTROLLER BUS CONNECTION

TIME	MONTH	DATE	YEAR	DAY OF WEEK
23:59:59	12	31	80	7

- 4-bit data bus
- 4-bit address bus
- $\overline{READ}$, $\overline{WRITE}$, ALE and CHIP SELECT INPUTS
- Status registers – IRQ and BUSY
- Selectable interrupt outputs – 1/64 second, 1 second, 1 minute, 1 hour
- Interrupt masking
- 32.768KHz crystal controlled operation
- 12/24 hour format
- Auto leap year
- ±30 second error correction
- Single 5V supply
- Battery backup down to V_{DD} = 2.0V
- Low power dissipation:
  20 µW max at V_{DD} = 2V
  150 µW max at V_{DD} = 5V
- 18-pin plastic DIP, 24-pin FLAT and 18-pin PLCC package

FUNCTIONAL BLOCK DIAGRAM

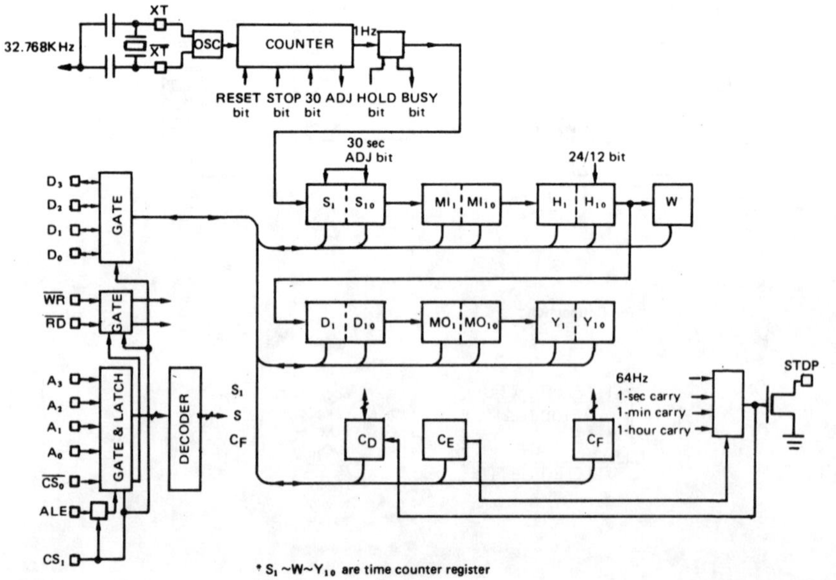

* S_1~W~Y_{10} are time counter register
* C_D~C_F are control register

ELECTRICAL CHARACTERISTICS

ABSOLUTE MAXIMUM RATINGS

Parameter	Symbol	Condition	Rating	Unit
Power Supply Voltage	V_{DD}	Ta = 25°C	–0.3~ 7	V
Input Voltage	V_I		GND – 0.3~V_{DD} + 0.3	V
Output Voltage	V_O		GND – 0.3~V_{DD} + 0.3	V
Storage Temperature	T_{STG}		–55~ +150	°C

OPERATING CONDITIONS

Parameter	Symbol	Condition	Rating	Unit
Power Supply Voltage	V_{DD}	–	4 ~ 6	V
Standby Supply Voltage	V_{BAK}	–	2 ~ 6	
Crystal Frequency	$f_{(XT)}$	–	32.768	kHz
Operating Temperature	T_{OP}	–	–30~+85	°C

D.C. CHARACTERISTICS

V_{DD} = 5V ± 10%, T_A = –30 ~ +85

Parameter	Symbol	Condition		Min.	Typ.	Max.	Unit	Applicable Terminal
"H" Input Voltage	$V_{IH}1$	–		2.2	–	–	V	All input terminals except CS_1
"L" Input Voltage	$V_{IL}1$	–		–	–	0.8		
Input Leak Current	$I_{LK}1$	V_I = V_{DD}/0V		–	–	1/–1	μA	Input terminals other than D_0 ~ D_3
Input Leak Current	$I_{LK}2$			–	–	10/–10		D_0 ~ D_3
"L" Output Voltage	$V_{OL}1$	I_{OL} = 2.5mA		–	–	0.4	V	D_0 ~ D_3
"H" Output Voltage	V_{OH}	I_{OH} = –400μA		2.4	–	–		
"L" Output Voltage	$V_{OL}2$	I_{OL} = 2.5mA		–	–	0.4	V	STD.P
OFF Leak Current	I_{OFFLK}	V = V_{DD}/0V		–	–	10	μA	
Input Capacitance	C_I	Input frequency 1MHz		–	5	–	PF	All input terminals
Current Consumption	$I_{DD}1$	$f_{(xt)}$ = 32.768 KHz T_a=25°C	V_{DD} = 5V	–	–	30	μA	V_{DD}
Current Consumption	$I_{DD}2$		V_{DD} = 2V	–	–	10		
"H" Input Voltage	$V_{IH}2$	V_{DD} = 2~5.5V		4/5V_{DD}	–	–	V	CS_1
"L" Input Voltage	$V_{IL}2$			–	–	1/5V_{DD}		

REGISTER TABLE

Address Input	Address Input A_3	A_2	A_1	A_0	Register Name	Data D_3	D_2	D_1	D_0	Count value	Description
0	0	0	0	0	S_1	S_8	S_4	S_2	S_1	0 ~ 9	1-second digit register
1	0	0	0	1	S_{10}	*	S_{40}	S_{20}	S_{10}	0 ~ 5	10-second digit register
2	0	0	1	0	MI_1	mi_8	mi_4	mi_2	mi_1	0 ~ 9	1-minute digit register
3	0	0	1	1	MI_{10}	*	mi_{40}	mi_{20}	mi_{10}	0 ~ 5	10-minute digit register
4	0	1	0	0	H_1	h_8	h_4	h_2	h_1	0 ~ 9	1-hour digit register
5	0	1	0	1	H_{10}	*	PM/ AM	h_{20}	h_{10}	0 ∿ 2 or 0 ∿ 1	PM/AM, 10-hour digit register
6	0	1	1	0	D_1	d_8	d_4	d_2	d_1	0 ~ 9	1-day digit register
7	0	1	1	1	D_{10}	*	*	d_{20}	d_{10}	0 ~ 3	10-day digit register
8	1	0	0	0	MO_1	mo_8	mo_4	mo_2	mo_1	0 ~ 9	1-month digit register
9	1	0	0	1	MO_{10}	*	*	*	MO_{10}	0 ~ 1	10-month digit register
A	1	0	1	0	Y_1	y_8	y_4	y_2	y_1	0 ~ 9	1-year digit register
B	1	0	1	1	Y_{10}	y_{80}	y_{40}	y_{20}	y_{10}	0 ~ 9	10-year digit register
C	1	1	0	0	W	*	w_4	w_2	w_1	0 ~ 6	Week register
D	1	1	0	1	C_D	30 sec. ADJ	IRQ FLAG	BUSY	HOLD	–	Control Register D
E	1	1	1	0	C_E	t_1	t_0	ITRPT /STND	MASK	–	Control Register E
F	1	1	1	1	C_F	TEST	24/12	STOP	REST	–	Control Register F

REST = RESET
ITRPT/STND = INTERRUPT/STANDARD

Note 1) – Bit * does not exist (unrecognized during a write and held at "0" during a read).
Note 2) – Be sure to mask the AM/PM bit when processing 10's of hour's data.
Note 3) – BUSY bit is read only. The IRQ FLAG bit can only be set to a "0". Setting the IRQ FLAG to a "1" is done by hardware.

Figure 1. Register Table

SWITCHING CHARACTERISTICS

(1) WRITE mode (ALE = V_{DD})

(V_{DD} = 5V ± 10% = Ta = –30 ~ +85°C)

Parameter	Symbol	Condition	Min.	Max.	Unit
CS_1 Set up Time	t_{C1S}	–	1000	–	ns
CS_1 Hold Time	t_{C1H}	–	1000	–	ns
Address Stable Before WRITE	t_{AW}	–	20	–	ns
Address Stable After WRITE	t_{WA}	–	10	–	ns
WRITE Pulse Width	t_{WW}	–	120	–	ns
Data Set up Time	t_{DS}	–	100	–	ns
Data Hold Time	t_{DH}	–	10	–	ns

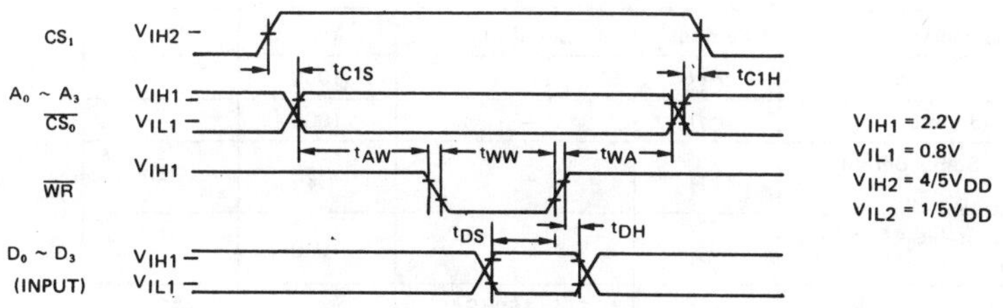

Figure 4. Write Cycle – (ALE = VDD)

(2) WRITE mode (With use of ALE)

(V_{DD} = 5 V ± 10%, Ta = –3C)

Parameter	Symbol	Condition	Min.	Max.	Unit
CS₁ Set up Time	t_{CIS}	–	1000	–	ns
Address Set up Time	t_{AS}	–	25	–	
Address Hold Time	t_{AH}	–	25	–	
ALE Pulse Width	t_{AW}	–	40	–	
ALE Before WRITE	t_{ALW}	–	10	–	
WRITE Pulse Width	t_{WW}	–	120	–	
ALE After WRITE	t_{WAL}	–	20	–	
DATA Set up Time	t_{DS}	–	100	–	
DATA Hold Time	t_{DH}	–	10	–	
CS₁ Hold Time	t_{C1H}	–	1000	–	

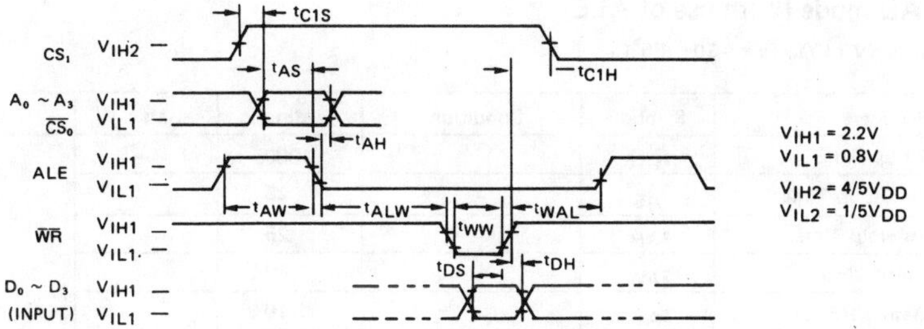

Figure 5. Write Cycle – (With Use of ALE)

(3) READ mode (ALE = V_{DD})

(V_{DD} = 5V ± 10%, Ta = –30 ~ +85°C)

Parameter	Symbol	Condition	Min.	Max.	Unit
CS_1 Set up Time	t_{C1S}	–	1000	–	ns
CS_1 Hold Time	t_{C1H}	–	1000	–	
Address Stable Before READ	t_{AR}	–	20	–	
Address Stable After READ	t_{RA}	–	0	–	
$\overline{RD}$ to Data	t_{RD}	C_L = 150pF	–	120	
Data Hold	t_{DR}	–	0	–	

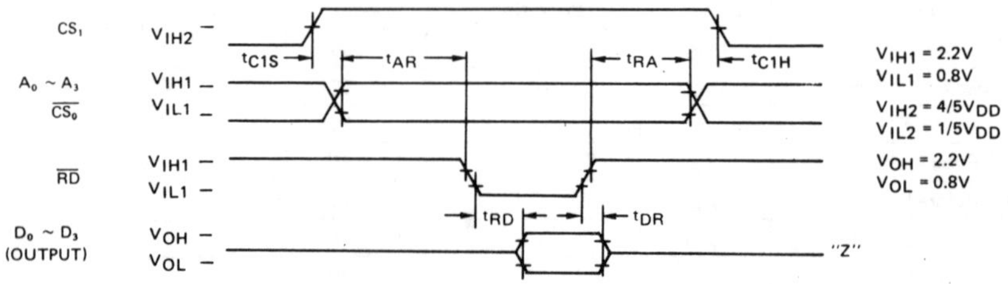

Figure 6. Read Cycle – (ALE = VDD)

(4) READ mode (With use of ALE)

(V_{DD} = 5V ±10%, Ta = –30~+85°C)

Parameter	Symbol	Condition	Min.	Max.	Unit
CS_1 Set up Time	t_{C1S}	–	1000	–	ns
Address Set up Time	t_{AS}	–	25	–	
Address Hold Time	t_{AH}	–	25	–	
ALE Pulse Width	t_{AW}	–	40	–	
ALE Before READ	t_{ALR}	–	10	–	
ALE after READ	t_{RAL}	–	10	–	
RD to Data	t_{RD}	C_L = 150pF	–	120	
DATA Hold	t_{DR}	–	0	–	
CS_1 Hold Time	t_{C1H}	–	1000	–	

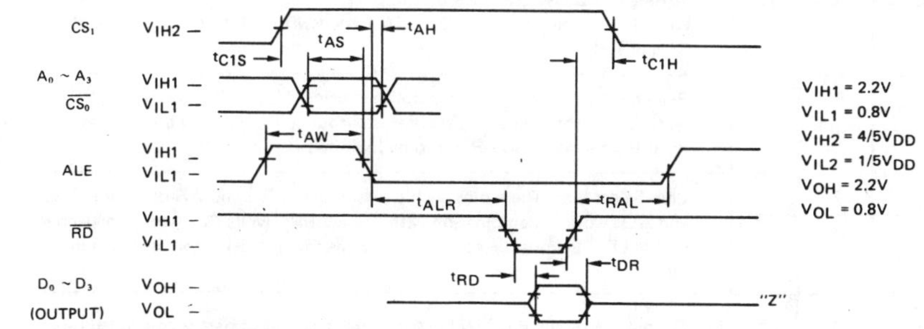

Figure 7. Read Cycle – (With Use of ALE)

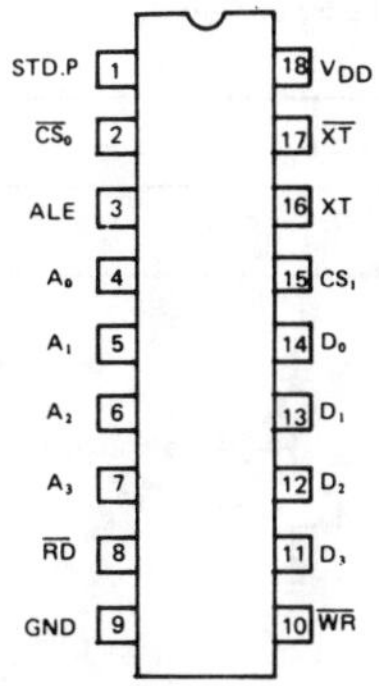

18 pin Plastic DIP Package

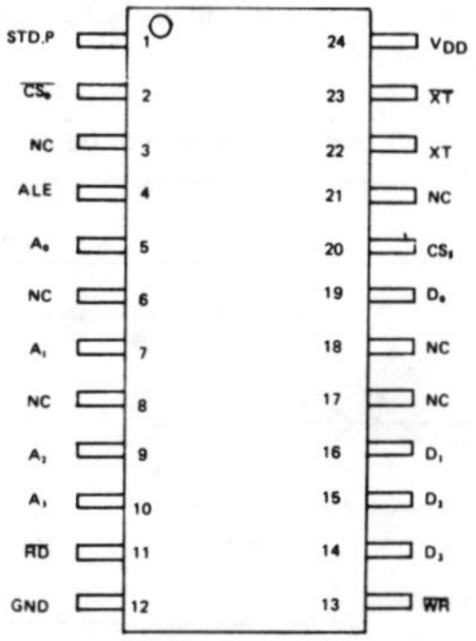

24 pin Plastic Flat Package

A0-A3:	Address input
D0-D3:	Data input/output
$\overline{CS0}$, $\overline{CS_1}$	CHIP SELECTS 0, 1
$\overline{RD}$:	READ enable
$\overline{WR}$:	WRITE enable
ALE:	Address latch enable
STD.P:	Standard pulse output
XT, $\overline{XT}$:	XTAL oscillator input/output
VDD:.	+5V supply
VSS:	ground

PIN CONFIGURATION

PIN DESCRIPTION

Name	Pin No. RS	Pin No. GS	Description
D_0	14	19	Data Input/Output pins to be directly connected to a microcontroller bus for reading and writing of the clock/calendar's registers and control registers. D0 = LSB and D3 = MSB.
D_1	13	16	
D_2	12	15	
D_3	11	14	
A_0	4	5	Address input pin for use by a microcomputer to select internal clock/calendar's registers and control registers for Read/Write operations (See Function Table Figure 1). Address input pins A0-A3 are used in combination with ALE for addressing registers.
A_1	5	7	
A_2	6	9	
A_3	7	10	
ALE	3	4	Address Latch Enable pin. This pin enables writing of address data when ALE = 1 and $\overline{CSO}$ = 0; address data is latched when ALE = 0 Microcontroller/Microprocessors having an ALE output should connect to this pin; otherwise it should be connected at V_{DD}.

$\overline{WR}$	10	13	Writing of data is performed by this pin. When CS_1 = 1 and $\overline{CS_0}$ = 0, $D_0 \sim D_3$ data is written into the register at the rising edge of $\overline{WR}$.
$\overline{RD}$	8	11	Reading of register data is accomplished using this pin. When CS_1 = 1, $\overline{CS_0}$ = 0 and $\overline{RD}$ = 0, the data of the register is output to $D_0 \sim D_3$. If both $\overline{RD}$ and $\overline{WR}$ are set at 0 simaltanuously, $\overline{RD}$ is to be inhibited.
$\overline{CS_0}$	2	2	Chip Select Pins. These pins enable/disable ALE, $\overline{RD}$ and $\overline{WR}$ operation. $\overline{CS_0}$ and ALE work in combination with one another, while CS_1 work independent with ALE. CS_1 must be connected to power failure detection as shown in Figure 18.
CS_1	15	20	
STD.P	1	1	Output pin of N-CH OPEN DRAIN type. The output data is controlled by the D_1 data content of C_E register. This pin has a priority to $\overline{CS_0}$ and CS_1. Refer to Figure 9 and FUNCTIONAL DESCRIPTION OF REGISTERS.
XT	16	22	32.768 kHz crystal is to be connected to these pins. When an external clock of 32.768 kHz is to be used for MSM6242's oscillation source, either CMOS output or pull-up TTL output is to be input from XT, while $\overline{XT}$ should be left open.
$\overline{XT}$	17	23	
V_{DD}	18	24	Power supply pin. +2 ~ +6V power is to be applied to this pin.
GND	9	12	Ground pin.

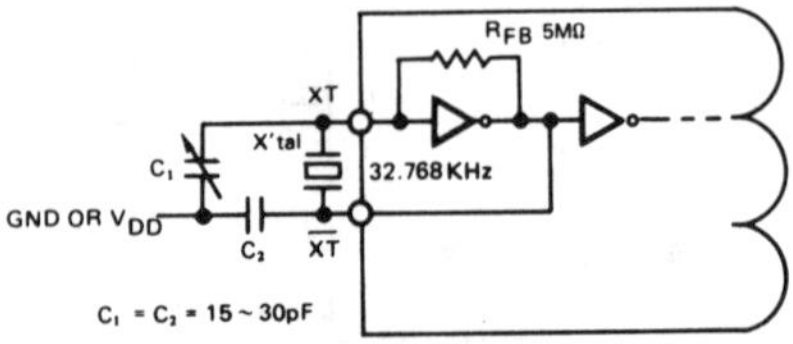

The impedance of the crystal should be less than 30kΩ

Figure 8. Oscillator Circuit

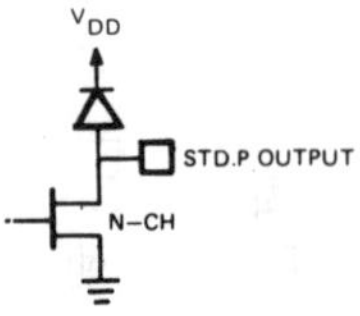

Figure 9.

FUNCTIONAL DESCRIPTION OF REGISTERS

- **S_1, S_{10}, MI_1, MI_{10}, H_1, H_{10}, D_1, D_{10}, $M\overline{O}_1$, $M\overline{O}_{10}$, Y_1, Y_{10}, W**

a) These are abbreviations for SECOND1, SECOND10, MINUTE1, MINUTE10, HOUR1, HOUR10, DAY1, DAY10, MONTH1, MONTH10, YEAR1, YEAR10, and WEEK. These values are in BCD notation.

b) All registers are logically positive. For example, (S8, S4, S2, S1) = 1001 which means 9 seconds.

c) If data is written which is out of the clock register data limits, it can result in erroneous clock data being read back.

d) PM/AM, h_{20}, h_{10}
In the mode setting of 24-hour mode, PM/AM bit is ignored, while in the setting of 12-hour mode h_{20} is to be set. Otherwise it causes a discrepancy. In reading out the PM/AM bit in the 24-hour mode, it is continuously read out as 0. In reading out h_{20} bit in the 12-hour mode, 0 is written into this bit first, then it is continuously read out as 0 unless 1 is being written into this bit.

e) Registers Y1, Y10, and Leap Year. The MSM6242B is designed exclusively for the Christian Era and is capable of identifying a leap year automatically. The result of the setting of a non-existant day of the month is shown in the following example: If the date February 29 or November 31, 1985, was written, it would be changed automatically to Match 1, or December 1, 1985 at the exact time at which a carry pulse occurs for the day's digit.

f) The Register W data limits are 0–6 (Table 1 shows a possible data definition).

TABLE 1

W_4	W_2	W_1	Day of Week
0	0	0	Sunday
0	0	1	Monday
0	1	0	Tuesday
0	1	1	Wednesday
1	0	0	Thursday
1	0	1	Friday
1	1	0	Saturday

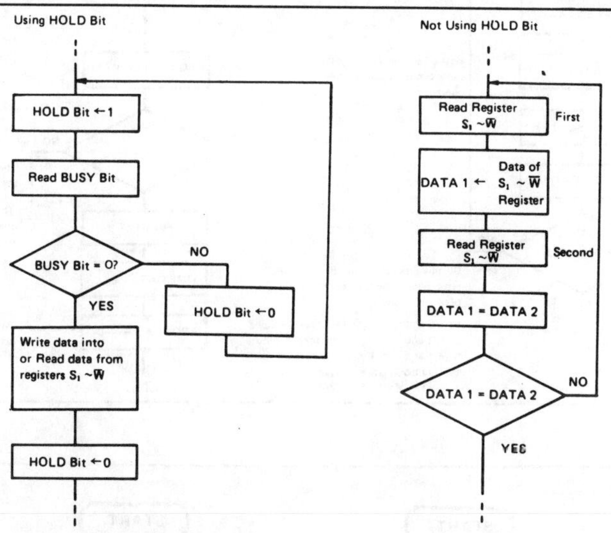

Figure 10. Reading and Writing of Registers $S_1 \sim \overline{W}$

■ CD REGISTER (Control D Register)

a) HOLD (D0) – Setting this bit to a "1" inhibits the 1Hz clock to the S1 counter, at which time the Busy status bit can be read. When Busy = 0, register's $S_1 \sim \overline{W}$ can be read or written. During this procedure if a carry occurs the S1 counter will be incremented by 1 second after HOLD = 0 (this condition is guaranteed as long as HOLD = 1 does not exceed 1 second in duration). If CS1 = 0 then HOLD = 0 irrespective of any condition.

b) BUSY (D1) – Status bit which shows the interface condition with microcontroller/microprocessors. As for the method of writing into and reading from $S_1 \sim \overline{W}$ (address $\phi \sim$ C), refer to the flow chart described in Figure 10.

c) IRQ FLAG (D2) – This status bit corresponds to the output level of the STD.P output. When STD.P = 0, then IRQ = 1; when STD.P =1, then IRQ = 0. The IRQ FLAG indicates that an interrupt has occurred to the microcomputer if IRQ = 1. When D0 of register C_E (MASK) = 0, then the STD.P output changes according to the timing set by D3 (t_1) and D2 (t_0) of register E. When D1 of register E (ITRPT/STND) = 1 (interrupt mode), the STD.P output remains low until the IRQ FLAG is written to a "0". When IRQ = 1 and timing for a new interrupt occurs, the new interrupt is ignored. When ITRPT/STND = 0 (Standard Pulse Output mode) the STD.P output remains low until either "0" is written to the IRQ FLAG; otherwise, the IRQ FLAG automatically goes to "0" after 7.8125 ms.

When writing the HOLD or 30 second adjust bits of register D, it is necessary to write the IRQ FLAG bit to a "1".

d) ±30 ADJ (D3) – When 30-second adjustment is necessary, a "1" is written to bit D3 during which time the internal clock registers should not be read from or written to 125µs after bit D3 = 1 it will automatically return to a "0", and at that time reading or writing of registers can occur.

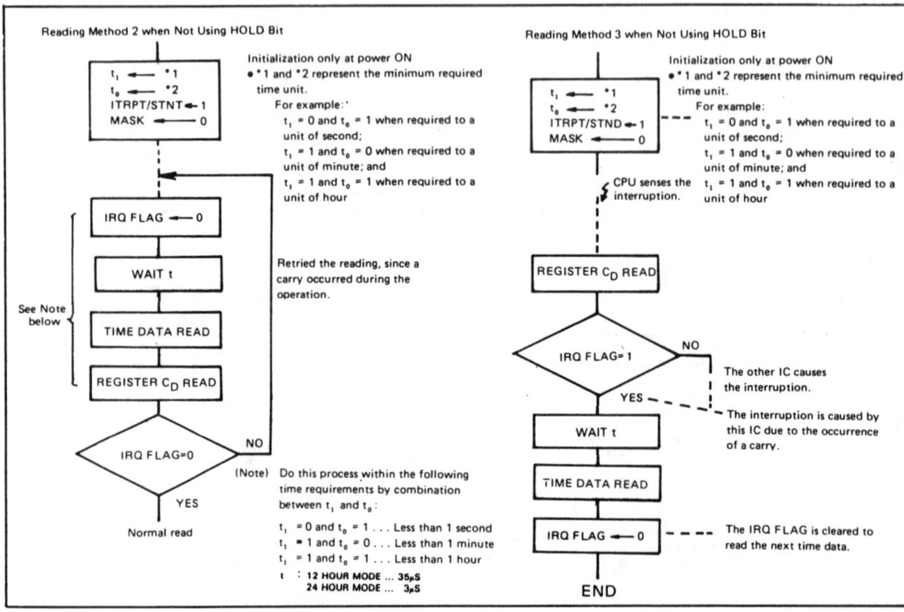

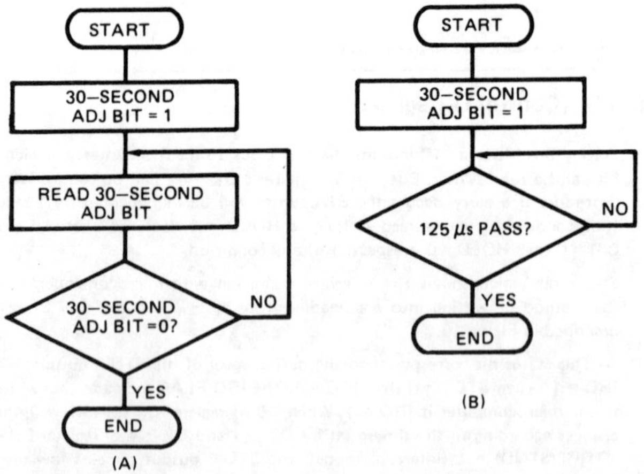

Figure 11. Writing 30-Second Adj. bit (Two Ways A, B)

■ CE REGISTER (Control E Register)

a) MASK (D0) – This bit controls the STD.P output. When MASK = 1, then STD.P = 1 (open); when MASK = 0, then STD.P = output mode. The relationship between the MASK bit and STD.P output is shown Figure 12.

b) INTRPT/STND (D1) – The INTRPT/STND input is used to switch the STD.P output between its two modes of operation, interrupt and Standard timing waveforms. When INTRPT/STND 0 a fixed cycle waveform with a low-level pulse width of 7.8125 ms is present at the STD.P output. At this time the MASK bit must equal 0, while the period in either mode is determined by T0(D2) and T1(D3) of Register E.

c) T0 (D2), T1 (D3) – These two bits determine the period of the STD.P output in both Interrupt and Fixed timing waveform modes. The tables below show the timing associated with the T0, T1 inputs as well as their relationship to INTRPT/STND and STD.P.

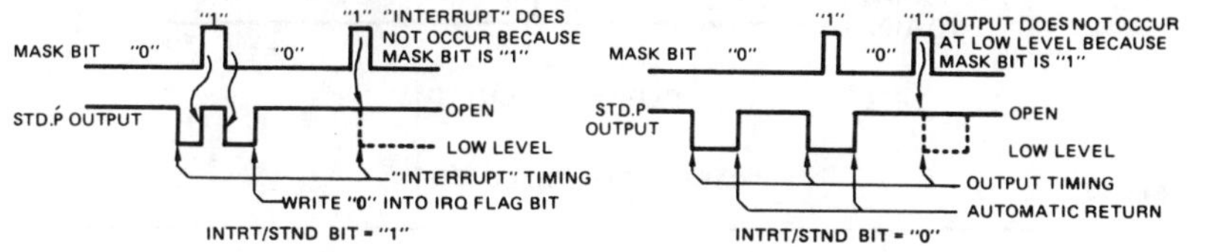

Figure 12.

t_1	t_0	Period	Duty CYCLE of "0" level when ITRPT/STND bit is "0".
0	0	1/64 second	1/2
0	1	1 second	1/128
1	0	1 minute	1/7680
1	1	1 hour	1/460800

TABLE 2

The timing of the STD.P output designated by T1 and T0 occurs the moment that a carry occurs to a clock digit.

(EXAMPLE) WHEN t_1 = 1, t_0 = 1 and MASK = 0.

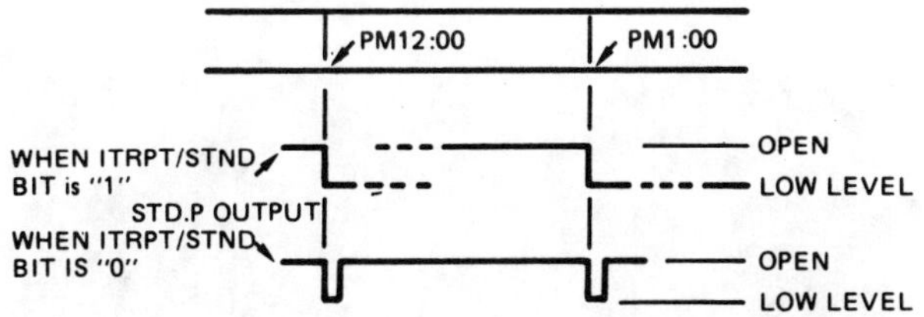

d) The low-level pulse width of the fixed cycle waveform (ITRPT/STND = 0) is 7.8125 ms independent of T0/T1 inputs.

e) The fixed cycle waveform mode can be used for adjustment of the oscillator frequency time base. (See Figure 14).

f) During ±30 second adjustment a carry can occur that will cause the STD.P output to go low when T0/T1 = 1,0 or 1,1. However, when T1/T0 = 0, 0 and ITRPT/STND = 0, carry does not occur and the STD.P output resumes normal operation.

g) The STD.P output is held (frozen) at the point at which STOP = 1 while ITRPT/STND = 0.

h) No STD.P output change occurs as a result of writing data to registers S1 ~ H1.

▪ CF REGISTER (Control F Register)

a) REST (D0) – "RESET" — This bit is used to clear the clock's internal divider/counter of less than a second. When REST = 1, the counter is Reset for the duration of REST. In order to release this counter from Reset, a "0" must be written to the REST bit. If CSI = 0 then REST = 0 automatically.

b) STOP (D1) – The STOP FLAG Only inhibits carries into the 8192Hz divider stage. There may be up to 122μs delay before timing starts or stops after changing this flag; 1 = STOP/0 = RUN.

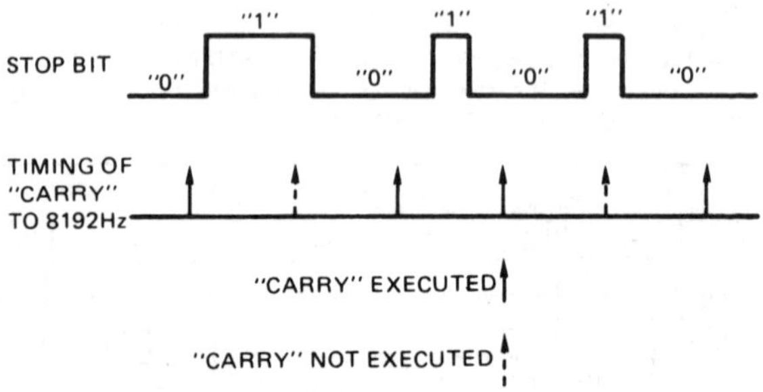

Figure 13

c) 24/12 (D2) – This bit is for selection of 24/12 hour time modes. If D2 = 1–24 hour mode is selected and the PM/AM bit is invalid. If D2 = 0–12 hour mode is selected and the PM/AM bit is valid.

"24 HOUR/ 12 HOUR" — Setting of the 24/12 hour bit is as follows:

1) REST bit = 1
2) 24/12 hour bit = 0 or 1
3) REST bit = 0

* REST bit must = 1 to write to the 24/12 hour bit.

d) TEST (d3) – When the TEST flag is a "1", the input to the SECONDS counter comes from the counter/divider stage instead of the 15th divider stage. This makes the SECONDS counter count at 5.4163KHz instead of 1Hz. When TEST = 1 (Test Mode) the STOP & REST (Reset) flags do not inhibit internal counting. When Hold = 1 during Test (Test = 1) internal counting is inhibited; however, when the HOLD FLAG goes inactive (Hold = 0) counter updating is not guaranteed.

TYPICAL APPLICATION INTERFACE WITH MSM6242B AND MICROCONTROLLERS

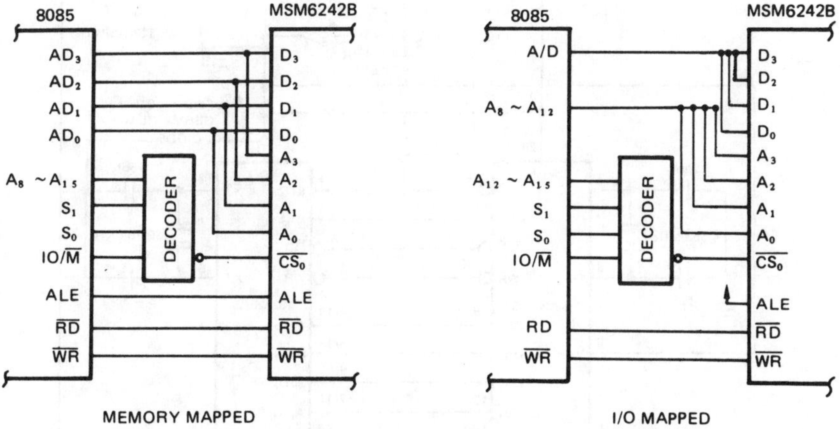

Figure 15.

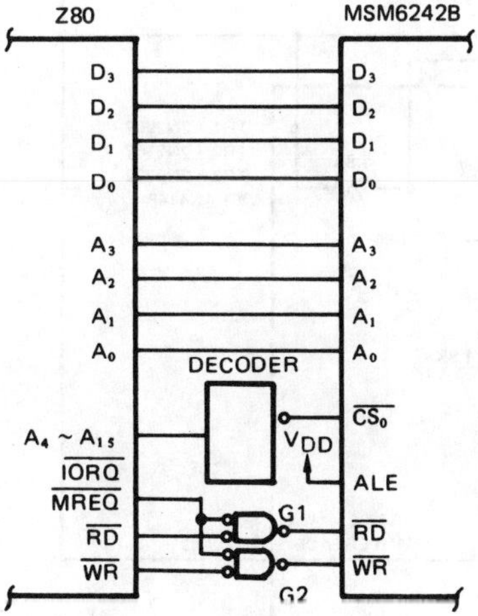

Figure 16.

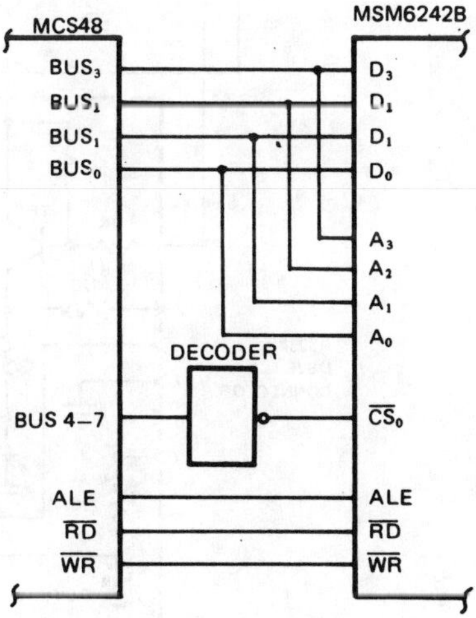

Figure 17.

TYPICAL APPLICATIONS – INTERFACE WITH MSM80C49

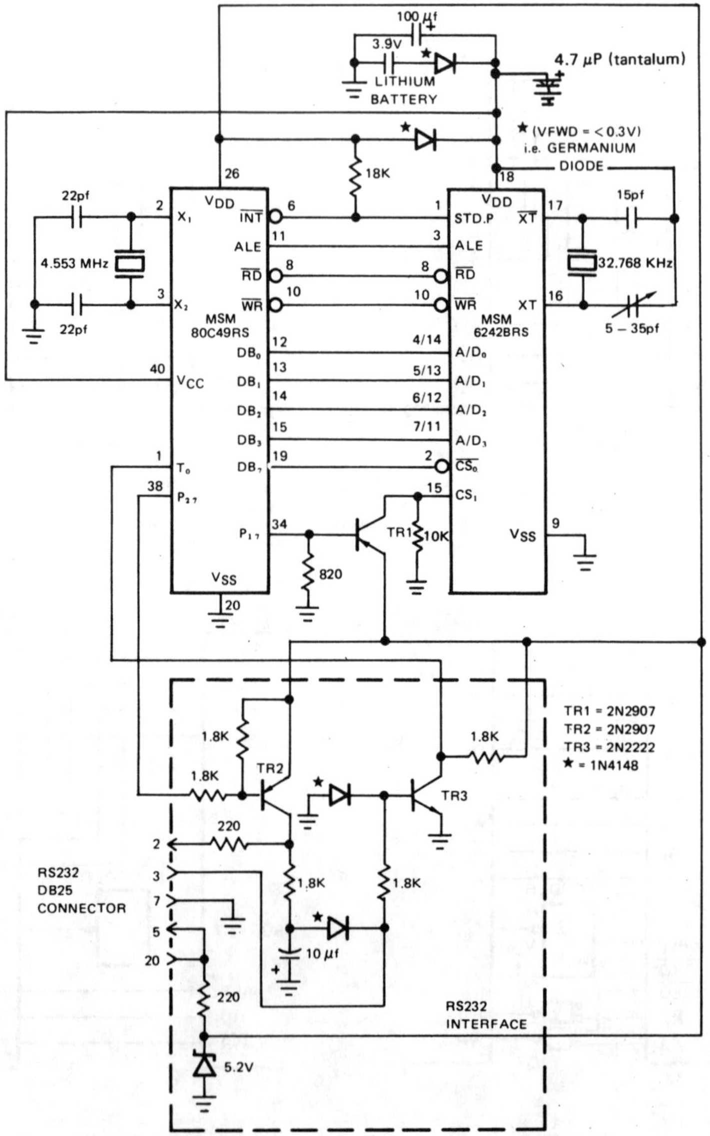

Figure 18.

APPLICATION NOTE

1. Power Supply

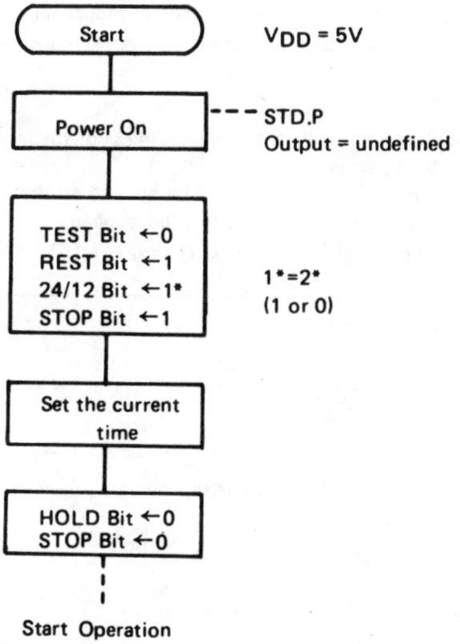

2. Adjustment of Frequency

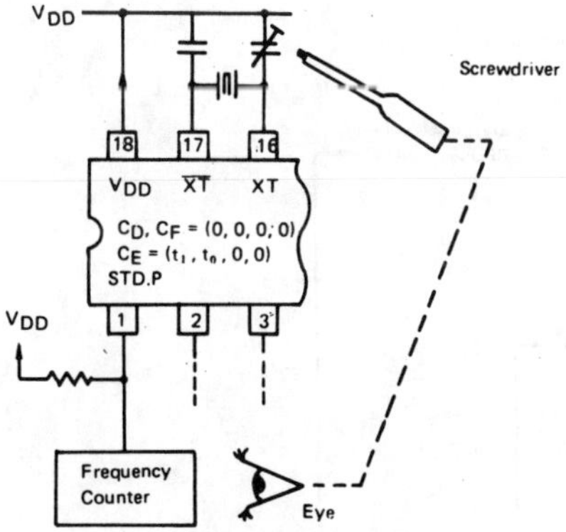

$C_D \sim C_F$ are to be set at as described in the figure and the capacitor is to be adjusted to meet the settle frequency of t_0 and t_1.
If the right oscillation can not be obtained,

1. Check the waveform of $\overline{XT}$
2. Check $C_D \sim C_F$ content
3. Check the noise.

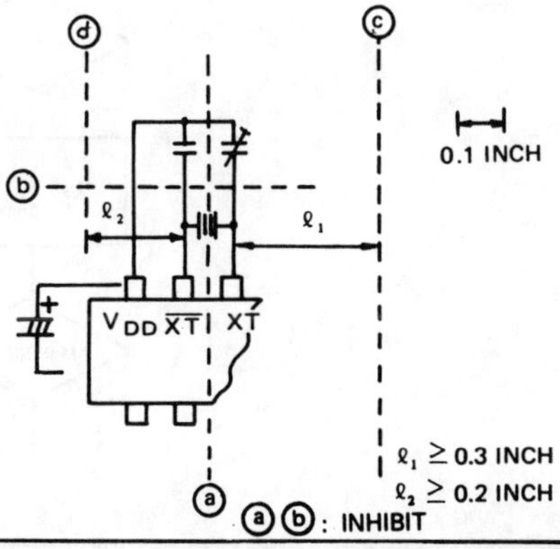

3. CH_1 (Chip Select)

V_{IH} and V_{IL} of CH_1 has 3 functions.

a) To accomplish the interface with a microcontroller/microprocessor.
b) To inhibit the control bus, data bus and address bus and to reduce input gate pass current in the stand-by mode.
c) To protect internal data when the mode is moved to and from standby mode.

To realize the above functions:

a) More than 4/5 V_{DD} should be applied to the MSM6242B for the interface with a microcontroller/microprocessor in 5V operation.
b) In moving to the standby mode, 1/5 V_{DD} should be applied so that all data buses should be disabled. In the standby mode, approx. 0V should be applied.
c) To and from the standby mode, obey following Timing chart.

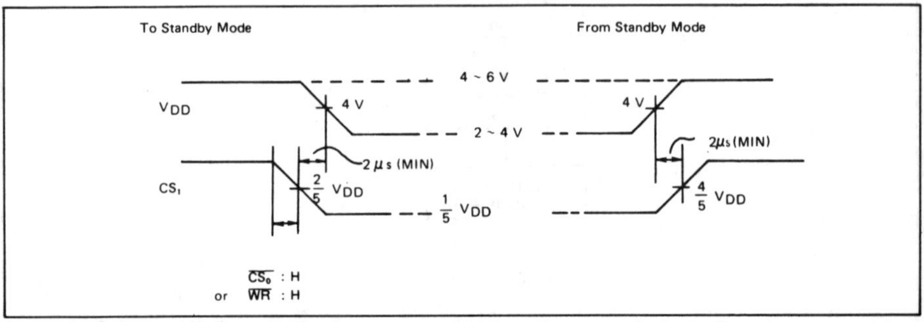

4. Set STD.P at arlarm mode

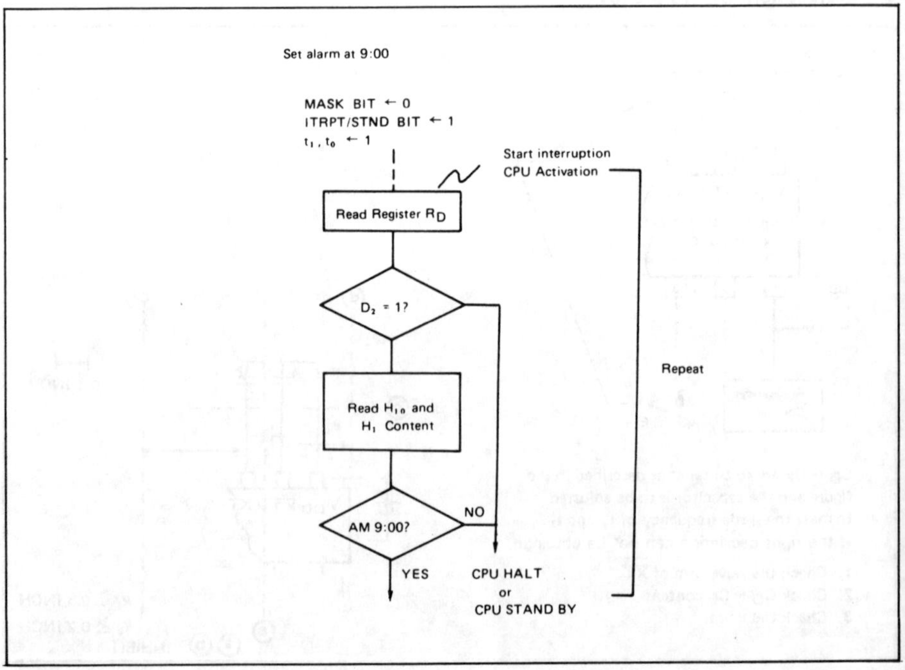

TYPICAL APPLICATION – POWER SUPPLY CIRCUIT

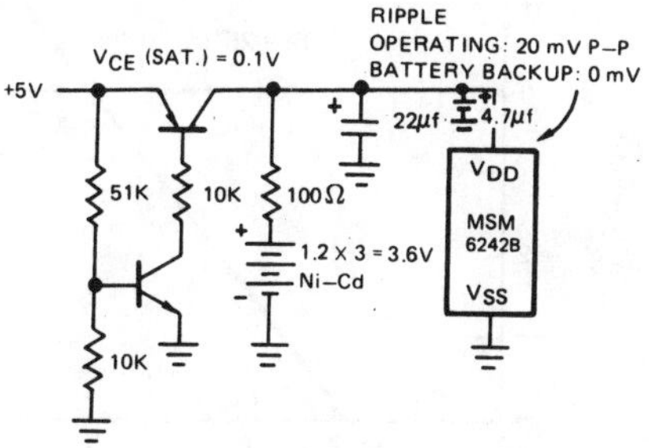

Figure 19.

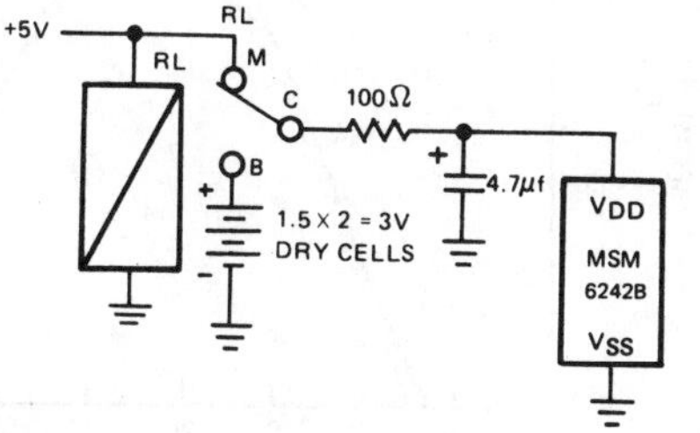

Figure 20.

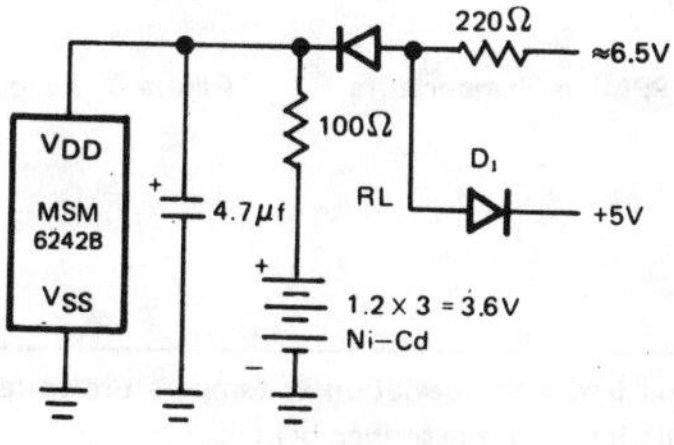

Figure 21.

4.7 µF: tantalum

SUPPLEMENTARY DESCRIPTION

- When "0" is written to the IRQ FLAG bit, the IRQ FLAG bit is cleared. However, if "0" is assigned to the IRQ FLAG bit when written to the other bits, the 30-sec ADJ bit and the HOLD bit, the IRQ FLAG = 1 and was generated before the writing and IRQ FLG = 1 generated in a moment then will be cleared. To avoid this, always set "1" to the IRQ FLAG unless "0" is written to it intentionally. By writing "1" to it, the IRQ FLAG bit does not become "1".
- Since the IRQ FLAG bit becomes "1" in some cases when rewriting either of the t_1, t_0, or ITRPT/STND bit of register C_E, be sure to write "0" to the IRQ FLAG bit after writing to make valid the IRQ FLAG = 1 to be generated after it.
- The relationship between SDT. P OUT and IRQ FLAG bit is shown below:

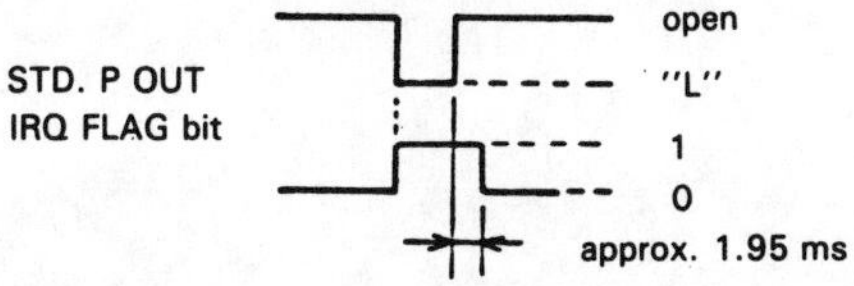

OSCILLATOR FREQUENCY DEVIATIONS

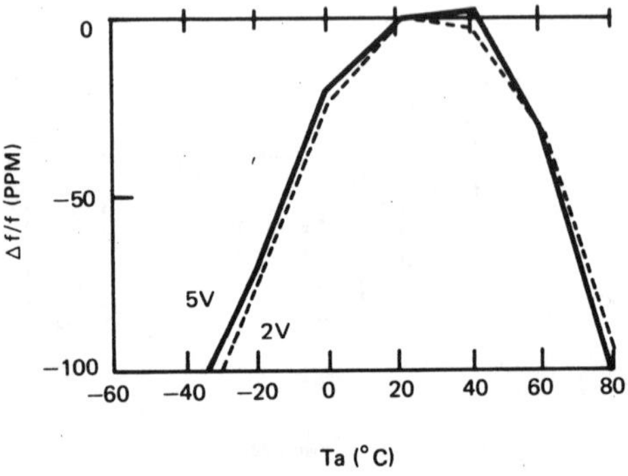

Figure 2. Frequency Deviation (PPM) vs Temperature

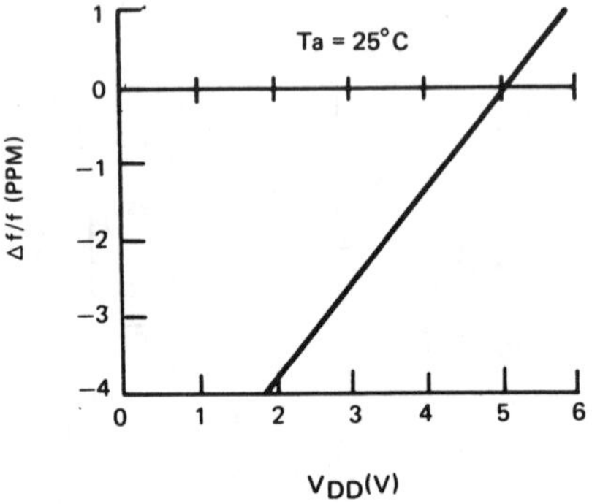

Figure 3. Frequency Deviation (PPM) vs Voltage

Note: 1. The graphs above showing frequency deviation vs temperature/voltage are primarily characteristic of the MSM6242B with the oscillation circuit described below.

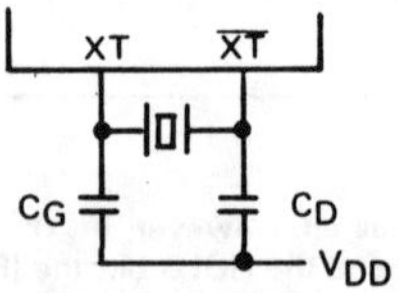

Crystal: Type N_0, P_3 by kinseki (32.768 KHz)

C_G, C_D: 22pF (Temperature Characteristics: 0)

FEATURES

- Real Time clock counts seconds, minutes, hours, date of the month, day of the week and year with Leap Year compensation
- 24 x 8 RAM for scratch pad data storage
- Serial I/O for minimum pin count
- 3 volt clock operation
- Uses less than1 uA at 3 volts
- Single byte or multiple byte (burst mode) data transfer for read or write of clock or RAM data
- 8-pin DIP or optional 16-pin SOIC for surface mount
- Simple 3-wire interface
- TTL compatible (V_{CC} = 5V)

PIN CONNECTIONS

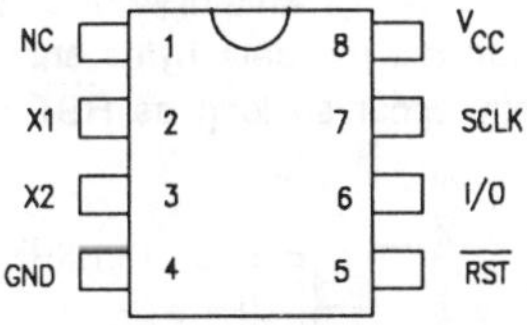

8-Pin DIP

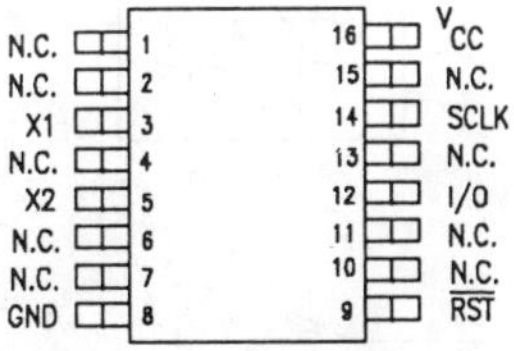

16-Pin SOIC

PIN NAMES

N.C.	-No Connection
X1, X2	-32.768 KHz Crystal Input
GND	-Ground
$\overline{\text{RST}}$	- Reset
I/O	-Data Input/Output
SCLK	-Serial Clock
V_{cc}	-Power Supply Pin

DESCRIPTION

The DS1202 contains a RealTime Clock/Calendar, 24 bytes of static RAM, and communicates with a microprocessor via a simple serial interface. The RealTime Clock/Calendar provides seconds, minutes, hours, day, date, month, and year information. The end of the month date is automatically adjusted for months with less than 31 days, including corrections for Leap Year. The clock operates in either the 24-hour or 12-hourformat with an AM/PM indicator. Interfacing the DS1202 with a microprocessor is simplified using synchronous serial communication. Only three wires are required to communicate with the Clock /RAM: (1) $\overline{\text{RST}}$ (Reset), (2) I/O (Data line), and (3) SCLK (Serial Clock). Data can be transferred to and from the Clock/RAM one byte at a time or in a burst of up to 24 bytes. The DS1202 is designed to operate on very low power and retain data and clock information on less than 1 uA with voltage input, (V_{cc}) as low as three volts.

OPERATION

The main elements of the serial Timekeeper are shown in Figure 1, namely, shift register, control logic, oscillator, RealTime Clock and RAM. To initiate any transfer of data, $\overline{\text{RST}}$ is taken high and eight bits are loaded into the shift register providing both addrocc and command information. Each bit is serially input on the rising edge of the clock input. The first eight bits specify which of 32 bytes will be accessed, whether a read or write cycle will take place, and whether a byte or burst mode transfer is to occur. After the first eight clock cycles have occurred which load the command word into the shift register, additional clocks will output data for a read, or input data for a write. The number of clock pulses equals eight plus eight for byte mode or eight plus up to 192 for burst mode.

ADDRESS/COMMAND BYTE

The address/command byte is shown in Figure 2. Each data transfer is initiated by a one byte input called the address/command byte. As defined, the MSB (Bit 7) must be a logical one. If zero, further action will be terminated. Bit 6 specifies a clock/calendar register if logic zero or a RAM location if Logical One. Bits one through five specify the designated registers to be input or output and the LSB (Bit 0) specifies a write operation (input) if logical zero or read operation output if logical one.

BURST MODE

Burst mode may be specified for either the clock/calendar or the RAM registers by addressing location 31 decimal (address/command bits one through five = logical one). As before, bit six specifies clock or RAM and bit 0 specifies read or write. There is no data storage capacity at location 8 through 31 in the Clock/Calendar Registers or locations 24 through 31 in the RAM Registers.

RESET AND CLOCK CONTROL

All data transfers are initiated by driving the $\overline{RST}$ input high. The $\overline{RST}$ input serves two functions. First, $\overline{RST}$ turns on the control logic which allows access to the shift register for the address/command sequence. Second, the $\overline{RST}$ signal provides a method of terminating either single byte or multiple byte data transfer. A clock cycle is a sequence of a falling edge followed by a rising edge. For data inputs, data must be valid during the rising edge of the clock and data bits are output on the falling edge of clock. All data transfer terminates if the $\overline{RST}$ input is low and the I/O pin goes to a high impedance state. When data transfer is terminated to the Real-Time Clock or to RAM using $\overline{RST}$, the transition of $\overline{RST}$ must occur while the clock is at high level to avoid disturbing the last bit of data and write cycle transfer must occur in 8-bit groups. Data transfer is illustrated in Figure 3

DATA INPUT

Following the eight SCLK cycles that input the write mode address/command byte (Bit 0 = Logical 0), a data byte is input on the rising edge of the next eight SCLK cycles (per byte, if burst mode is specified). Additional SCLK cycles are ignored should they inadvertently occur.

DATA OUTPUT

Following the eight SCLK cycles that input the read mode address/command byte (Bit 0 = Logical 1), a data byte is output on the falling edge of the next eight SCLK cycles (per byte, if the burst mode is specified). Note that the first data bit to be transmitted from the clock/RAM occurs on the first falling edge after the last bit of the command byte is written. Additional SCLK cycles retransmit the data bytes should they inadvertently occur so long as $\overline{RST}$ remains

DS1202 BLOCK DIAGRAM Figure 1

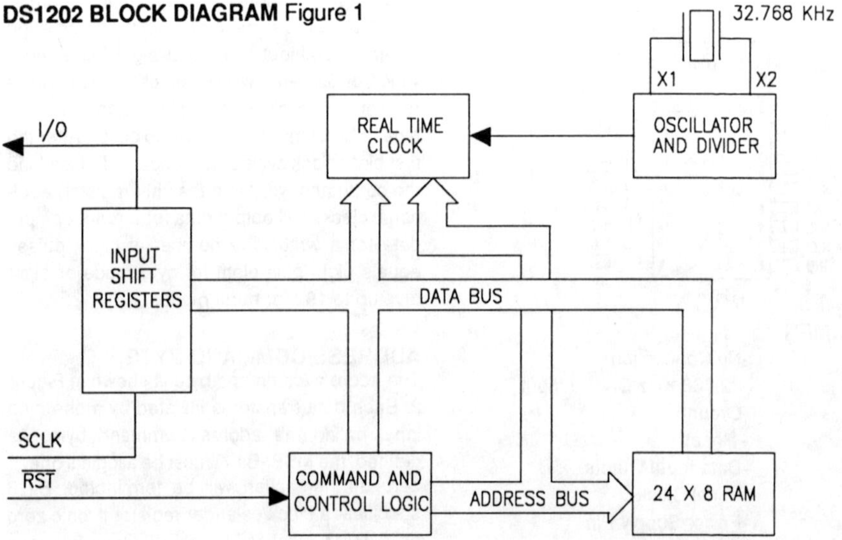

high. This operaton permits continuous burst read mode capability.

ADDRESS/COMMAND BYTE Figure 2

7	6	5	4	3	2	1	0
1	RAM / $\overline{CK}$	A4	A3	A2	A1	A0	RD / $\overline{W}$

DATA TRANSFER SUMMARY Figure 3

SINGLE BYTE TRANSFER

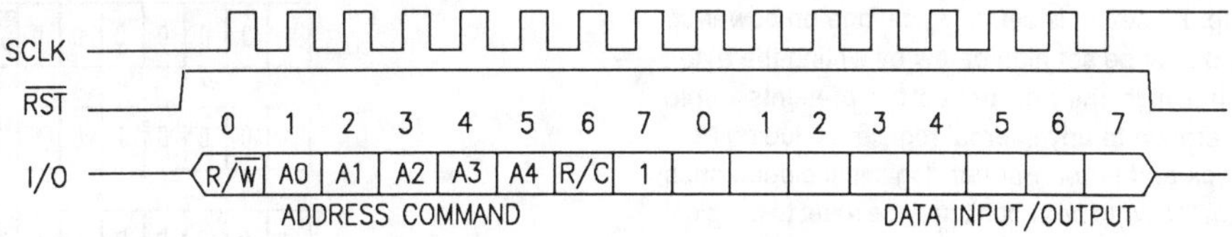

BURST MODE TRANSFER

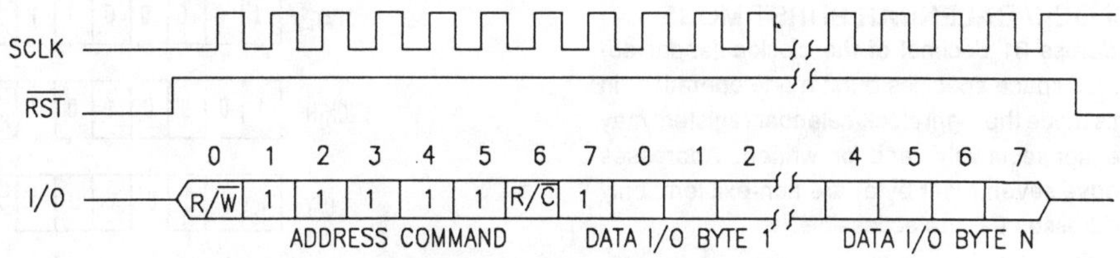

FUNCTION	BYTE N	SCLK n
CLOCK	8	72
RAM	24	200

CLOCK/CALENDAR

The Clock/Calendar is contained in eight writeable/readable registers as shown in Figure 4. Data contained in the clock/calendar registers is in binary coded decimal format (BCD) except the control byte which is binary.

CLOCK HALT FLAG

Bit 7 of the seconds register is defined as the clock halt flag. When this bit is set to logic one, the clock oscillator is stopped and the DS1202 is placed into a low power standby mode with a current drain of less than .1 microamp. When this bit is written to logical zero, the clocks oscillator will run and keep time count from the entered value.

AM-PM/12-24 MODE

Bit 7 of the hours register is defined as the 12- or 24-hour mode select bit. When high, the 12-hour mode is selected. In the 12-hour mode, bit 5 is the AM/PM bit with logic high being PM. In the 24-hour mode, bit 5 is the second 10 hour bit (20-23 hours).

TEST MODE BITS

Bit 7 of the date register and bit 7 of the day register are test mode bits. These bits are forced to zero under normal operation and will always read logical zero when read.

CONTROL BYTE AND WRITE PROTECT BIT

Byte 7 of the clock/calendar registers is the write protect byte. The first seven bits (bits 0-6) are forced to zero and will always read a zero when read. Bit 7 of the user byte is the write protect flag. Bit seven is set to logical one on power up and may be set high or low by writing the byte . When high, the write protect flag prevents a write operation to any internal register including both clock and RAM. Further, logic is included such that the write protect bit may be reset to a logical zero by a write operation.

CLOCK/ CALENDAR BURST MODE

Address 31 decimal of the clock/calendar address space specifies burst mode operation. In this mode the eight clock/calendar registers may be consecutively read or written. Addresses above seven (user byte) are non-existent; only addresses 0-7 are accessible.

RAM

The static RAM is contained in 24 writeable/ readable registers, addressed consecutively in the RAM address space beginning at location zero.

RAM BURST MODE

Addresses 31 decimal of the RAM address space specifies burst mode operation. In this mode, the 24 RAM registers may be consecutively read or written. Addresses above the maximum RAM address location are non-existent and are not accessible.

REGISTER SUMMARY

A register data format summary is shown in Figure 4.

CRYSTAL SELECTION

A 32.768 KHZ crystal, Daiwa Part No. DT26S, Seiko Part No. DS-VT-200 or equivalent, can be directly connected to the DS1202 via pins 2 and 3 (x1, x2). The crystal selected for use should have a specified load capacitance (C_L) of 6 pF.

REGISTER ADDRESS/DEFINITION Figure 4

REGISTER ADDRESS

A. CLOCK

	7	6	5	4	3	2	1	0
SEC	1	0	0	0	0	0	0	RD/$\overline{W}$
MIN	1	0	0	0	0	0	1	RD/$\overline{W}$
HR	1	0	0	0	0	1	0	RD/$\overline{W}$
DATE	1	0	0	0	0	1	1	RD/$\overline{W}$
MONTH	1	0	0	0	1	0	0	RD/$\overline{W}$
DAY	1	0	0	0	1	0	1	RD/$\overline{W}$
YEAR	1	0	0	0	1	1	0	RD/$\overline{W}$
CONTROL	1	0	0	0	1	1	1	RD/$\overline{W}$
CLOCK BURST	1	0	1	1	1	1	1	RD/$\overline{W}$

B. RAM

	7	6	5	4	3	2	1	0
RAM 0	1	1	0	0	0	0	0	RD/$\overline{W}$
⋮								
RAM 23	1	1	1	0	1	1	1	RD/$\overline{W}$
RAM BURST	1	1	1	1	1	1	1	RD/$\overline{W}$

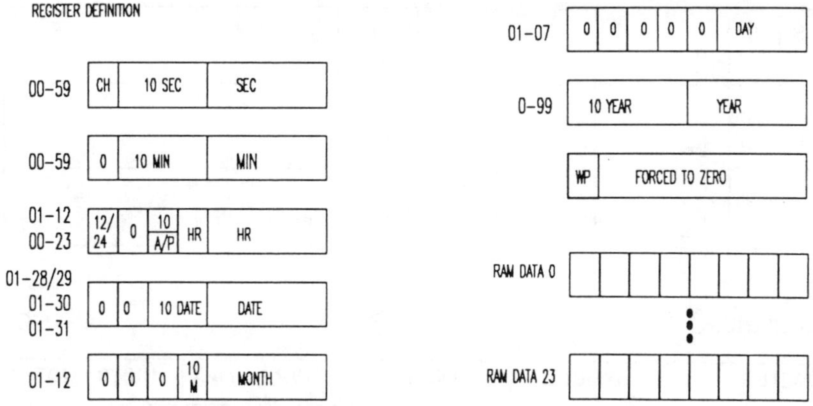

ABSOLUTE MAXIMUM RATINGS

VOLTAGE ON ANY PIN RELATIVE TO GROUND -0.5V TO +7.0V
OPERATING TEMPERATURE 0°C TO +70°C
STORAGE TEMPERATURE -55°C TO +125°C
SOLDERING TEMPERATURE -260°C FOR 10 SEC

RECOMMENDED D.C. OPERATING CONDITIONS

(0° to +70°C)

PARAMETER	SYMBOL	MIN	TYP	MAX	UNITS	NOTES
Supply voltage	V_{CC}	4.5	5.0	5.5	VOLTS	1
Standby Supply Voltage	V_{CC1}	3.0		5.5	VOLTS	1
Logic 1 Input	V_{IH}	2.0		V_{CC}	VOLTS	1
Logic 0 Input	V_{IL}	-0.5		0.8	VOLTS	1

D.C. ELECTRICAL CHARACTERISTICS

(0° to +70°C, V_{CC} = 5V ±10%)

PARAMETER	SYMBOL	MIN	TYP	MAX	UNITS	NOTES
Input Leakage	I_{LI}			+500	uA	6
I/O Leakage	I_{LO}			+500	uA	6
Logic 1 Output	V_{OH}	2.4			VOLTS	2
Logic 0 Output	V_{OL}			0.4	VOLTS	3

Active Supply Current	I_{CC}			4	mA	4
Standby Supply Current	I_{CC1}			1	uA	5
StandbySupply Current	I_{CC2}			100	nA	10

CAPACITANCE

(TA =25°C)

PARAMETER	SYMBOL	CONDITION	TYP	MAX	UNITS	NOTES
Input Capacitance	C_I		5		pF	
I/O Capacitance	$C_{I/O}$		10		pF	
Crystal Capacitance	C_X		6		pF	

A.C. ELECTRICAL CHARACTERISTICS

(V_{CC}=+5V ±10% 0°C TO 70°C)

PARAMETER	SYMBOL	MIIN	TYP	MAX	UNITS	NOTES
Data To CLK Setup	t_{DC}	50			ns	7
CLK To Data Hold	t_{CDH}	70			ns	7
CLK To Data Delay	t_{CDD}			200	ns	7,8,9
CLK Low Time	t_{CC}	250			ns	7
CLK High Time	t_{CH}	250			ns	7
CLK Frequency	f_{CLK}	D.C.		2.0	MHz	7
CLK Rise &Fall	t_F			500	ns	
RST To CLK Setup	t_{CC}	1			us	7
CLK To RST Hold	t_{CCH}	60			ns	7
RST Inactive Time	t_{CWH}	1			us	7
RST To I/O High Z	t_{CDZ}			70	us	7

TIMING DIAGRAM - READ/WRITE DATA TRANSFER Figure 5

WRITE DATA TRANSFER

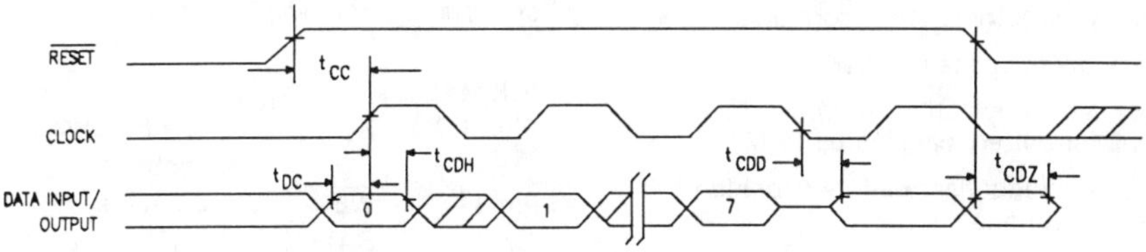

READ DATA TRANSFER

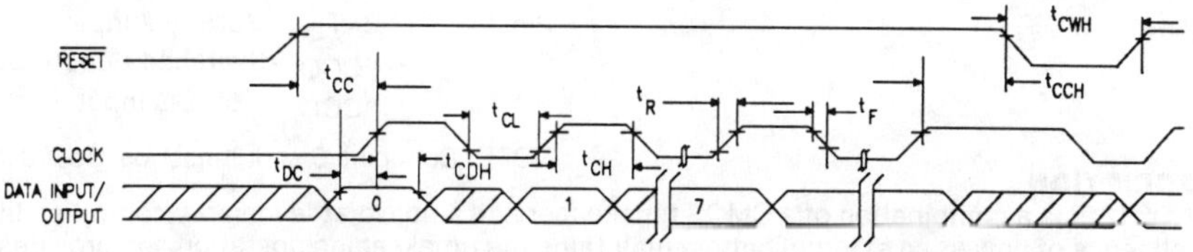

NOTES

1. All voltages are referenced to ground.
2. Logic one voltages are specified at a source current of 1 MA.
3. Logic zero voltages are specified at a sink current of 4 MA.
4. I_{CC} is specified with the I/O pin open.
5. I_{CC1} is specified with V_{CC} at 3.0 volts and $\overline{RST}$, I/O, and SCLK are open.
6. $\overline{RST}$, SCLK and I/O all have 40 K ohm pull down resistors to ground.
7. Measured at V_{IH} = 2.0V or V_{IL} = 0.8V and 10 ms maximum rise and fall time.
8. Measured at V_{OH} = 2.4V or V_{OL} = 0.4V.
9. Load capacitance = 50 pF.
10. I_{CC2} is specified with V_{CC} at 3.0 volts and $\overline{RST}$, I/O, and SCLK are open. The clock halt flag must also be set to logic one.

DS1215 Real Time Clock

FEATURES

- TimeChip keeps track of hundredths of seconds, seconds, minutes, hours, days, date of the month, months, and years
- Adjusts for months with fewer than 31 days
- Leap year automatically corrected
- No address space required
- Provides nonvolatile controller functions for battery backing up RAM
- Supports redundant batteries for high-rel applications
- Uses a 32.768 KHz watch crystal
- Full 10% operating range
- Operating temperature range 0°C to 70°C
- Space saving 16-pin DIP package

PIN CONNECTIONS

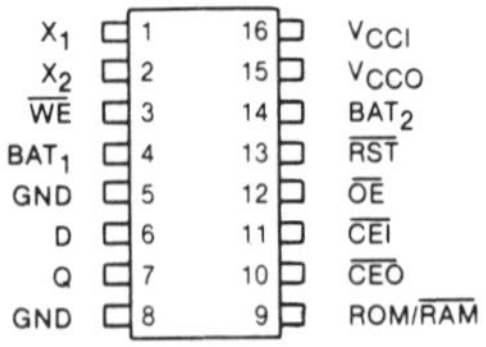

PIN NAMES

Pins 1 & 2	- X_1, X_2	- 32.768 KHz Crystal Connections
Pin 3	- $\overline{WE}$	- Write Enable
Pin 4	- BAT_1	- Battery 1 Input
Pins 5 & 8	- GND	- Ground
Pin 6	- D	- Data In
Pin 7	- Q	- Data Out
Pin 9	- ROM/$\overline{RAM}$	- ROM-RAM Select
Pin 10	- $\overline{CEO}$	- Chip Enable Out
Pin 11	- $\overline{CEI}$	- Chip Enable Input
Pin 12	- $\overline{OE}$	- Output Enable
Pin 13	- $\overline{RST}$	- Reset
Pin 14	- BAT_2	- Battery 2 Input
Pin 15	- V_{CCO}	- Switched Supply Output
Pin 16	- V_{CCI}	- +5V DC Input

NOTE: Both pins 5 and 8 must be grounded.

DESCRIPTION

The DS1215 is a combination of a CMOS timekeeper and a nonvolatile memory controller. In the absence of power, an external battery maintains the timekeeping operation and provides power for a CMOS static RAM. The watch provides hundredths of seconds, seconds, minutes, hours, day, date, month, and year information, while the nonvolatile controller supplies all the necessary support circuitry to convert a CMOS RAM to a nonvolatile memory. The DS1215 can be interfaced with either RAM or ROM without leaving gaps in memory.

The last date of the month is automatically adjusted for months with less than 31 days, including correction for leap year every four years. The watch operates in one of two formats: a 12-hour mode with an AM/PM indicator, or a 24-hour mode.

The nonvolatile memory controller portion of the circuit is designed to handle power fail detection, memory write protection, and battery redundancy. In short, the controller changes standard CMOS memories into nonvolatile memories, and provides continuous power to the TimeChip. Alternatively the TimeChip can be used with ROM memory by controlling the Chip Enable Output signal ($\overline{CEO}$) while the TimeChip is being accessed.

OPERATION

The block diagram of Figure 3 illustrates the main elements of the TimeChip. Communication with the TimeChip is established by pattern recognition of a serial bit stream of 64 bits which must be matched by executing 64 consecutive write cycles containing the proper data on Data In (D). All accesses which occur prior to recognition of the 64-bit pattern are directed to memory via the Chip Enable Output pin ($\overline{CEO}$).

After recognition is established, the next 64 read or write cycles either extract or update data in the TimeChip and Chip Enable Output remains high during this time, disabling the connected memory.

Data transfer to and from the timekeeping function is accomplished with a serial bit stream under control of chip enable ($\overline{CEI}$), output enable ($\overline{OE}$), and write enable ($\overline{WE}$). Initially, a read cycle using the $\overline{CEI}$ and $\overline{OE}$ control of the TimeChip starts the pattern recognition sequence by moving a pointer to the first bit of the 64-bit comparison register. Next, 64 consecutive write cycles are executed using the $\overline{CEI}$ and $\overline{WE}$ control of the TimeChip. These 64 write cycles are used only to gain access to the TimeChip.

When the first write cycle is executed, it is compared to bit 1 of the 64-bit comparison register. If a match is found, the pointer increments to the next location of the comparison register and awaits the next write cycle. If a match is *not* found, the pointer does not advance and all subsequent write cycles are ignored. If a read cycle occurs at any time during pattern recognition, the present sequence is aborted and the comparison register pointer is reset. Pattern recognition continues for a total of 64 write cycles as described above until all the bits in the comparison register have been matched. (This bit pattern is shown in Figure 1). With a correct match for 64 bits, the TimeChip is enabled and data transfer to or from the timekeeping registers may proceed. The next 64 cycles will cause the TimeChip to either receive data on D, or transmit data on Q, depending on the level of $\overline{OE}$ pin or the $\overline{WE}$ pin. Cycles to other locations outside the memory block can be interleaved with $\overline{CEI}$ cycles without interrupting the pattern recognition sequence or data transfer sequence to the TimeChip.

A 32,768 Hz quartz crystal, Daiwa part no. DT-26S or equivalent, can be directly connected to the DS1215 via pins 1 and 2 (X_1, X_2). The crystal selected for use should have a specified load capacitance of 6 pF.

NONVOLATILE CONTROLLER OPERATION

The operation of the nonvolatile controller circuits within the TimeChip is determined by the level of the ROM/$\overline{RAM}$ select pin. When ROM/$\overline{RAM}$ is connected to ground, the controller is set in the RAM mode and performs the circuit functions required to make static CMOS RAM and the timekeeping function nonvolatile. First a switch is provided to direct power from the battery inputs or V_{CCI} to V_{CCO} with a maximum voltage drop of 0.2 volts. The V_{CCO} output pin is used to supply uninterrupted power to CMOS static RAM. The DS1215 also performs redundant battery control for high reliability. On power fail the battery with the highest voltage is automatically switched to V_{CCO}. If only one battery is used in the system, the unused battery input should be connected to ground. The DS1215 provides the function of safeguarding the TimeChip and RAM data by power fail detection and write protection. Power fail detection occurs when V_{CCI} falls below VTP which is equal to $1.26 \times V_{BAT}$. The DS1215 constantly monitors the V_{CCI} supply pin. When V_{CCI} is less than VTP, a comparator outputs a power fail signal to the control logic. The power fail signal forces the chip enable output ($\overline{CEO}$) to V_{CCI} or $V_{BAT} - 0.2$ volts for external RAM write protection. During nominal supply conditions, $\overline{CEO}$ will track $\overline{CEI}$ with a maximum propagation delay of 20 ns. Internally, the DS1215 aborts any data transfer in progress without changing any of the TimeChip registers and prevents future access until V_{CCI} exceeds VTP. A typical RAM/TimeChip interface is illustrated in Figure 4.

When the ROM/$\overline{RAM}$ pin is connected to V_{CCO}, the controller is set in the ROM mode. Since ROM is a read-only device which retains data in the absence of power, battery backup and write protection is not required. As a result, the chip enable logic will not force $\overline{CEO}$ high when power fails. However, the TimeChip does retain the same internal nonvolatility and write protection as described in the RAM mode. In addition, the chip enable output is set at a low level on power fail as V_{CCI} falls below the level of V_{BAT}. A typical ROM/TimeChip interface is illustrated in Figure 5.

TIMECHIP COMPARISON REGISTER DEFINITION Figure 1

	7	6	5	4	3	2	1	0	
Byte 0	1	1	0	0	0	1	0	1	C5
Byte 1	0	0	1	1	1	0	1	0	3A
Byte 2	1	0	1	0	0	0	1	1	A3
Byte 3	0	1	0	1	1	1	0	0	5C
Byte 4	1	1	0	0	0	1	0	1	C5
Byte 5	0	0	1	1	1	0	1	0	3A
Byte 6	1	0	1	0	0	0	1	1	A3
Byte 7	0	1	0	1	1	1	0	0	5C

Note:
The pattern recognition in Hex is C5, 3A, A3, 5C, C5, 3A, A3, 5C. The odds of this pattern being accidentally duplicated and causing inadvertent entry to the TimeChip is less than 1 in 10^{19}.

TIMECHIP REGISTER INFORMATION
The TimeChip information is contained in 8 registers of 8 bits each which are sequentially accessed one bit at a time after the 64-bit pattern recognition sequence has been completed. When updating the TimeChip registers, each must be handled in groups of 8 bits. Writing and reading individual bits within a register could produce erroneous results. These read/write registers are defined in Figure 2.

Data contained in the TimeChip registers are not binary coded decimal format (BCD) in 12-hour mode. Reading and writing the registers is always accomplished by stepping through all 8 registers, starting with bit 0 of register 0 and ending with bit 7 of register 7.

TIMECHIP REGISTER DEFINITION Figure 2

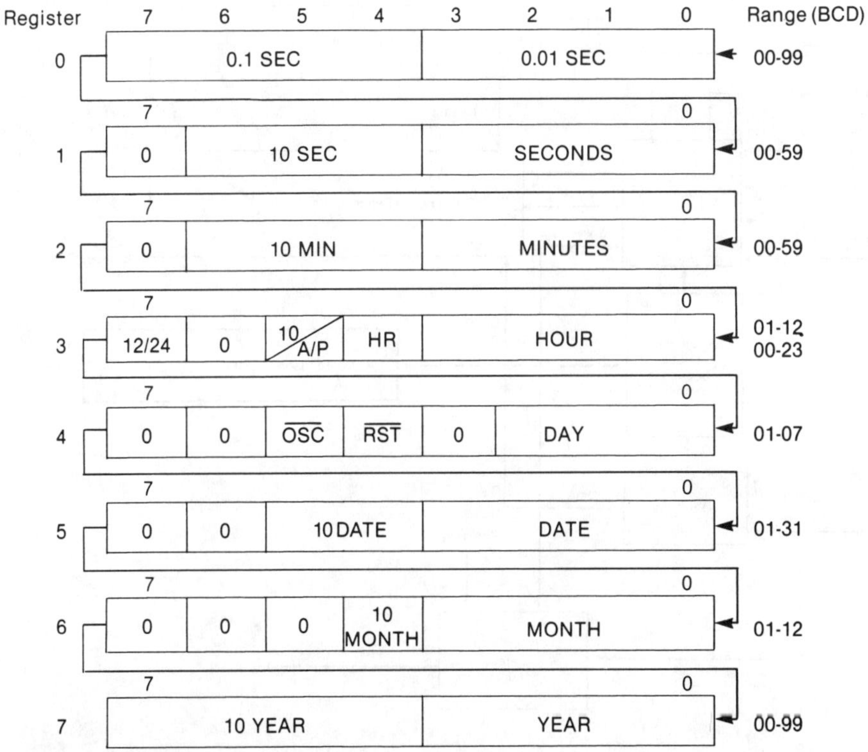

AM-PM/12/24 MODE
Bit 7 of the hours register is defined as the 12- or 24-hour mode select bit. When high, the 12-hour mode is selected. In the 12-hour mode, bit 5 is the AM/PM bit with logic high being PM. In the 24-hour mode, bit 5 is the second 10-hour bit (20-23 hours).

OSCILLATOR AND RESET BITS
Bits 4 and 5 of the day register are used to control the reset and oscillator functions. Bit 4 controls the reset pin (Pin 13). When the reset bit is set to logical 1, the reset input pin is ignored. When the reset bit is set to logical 0, a low input on the reset pin will cause the TimeChip to abort data transfer without changing data in the timekeeping registers. Reset operates independently of all other inputs. Bit 5 controls the oscillator. When set to Logic 0 the oscillator turns on and the watch becomes operational.

ZERO BITS
Registers 1, 2, 3, 4, 5, and 6 contain one or more bits which will always read logical 0. When writing these locations, either a logical 1 or 0 is acceptable.

TIMECHIP BLOCK DIAGRAM Figure 3

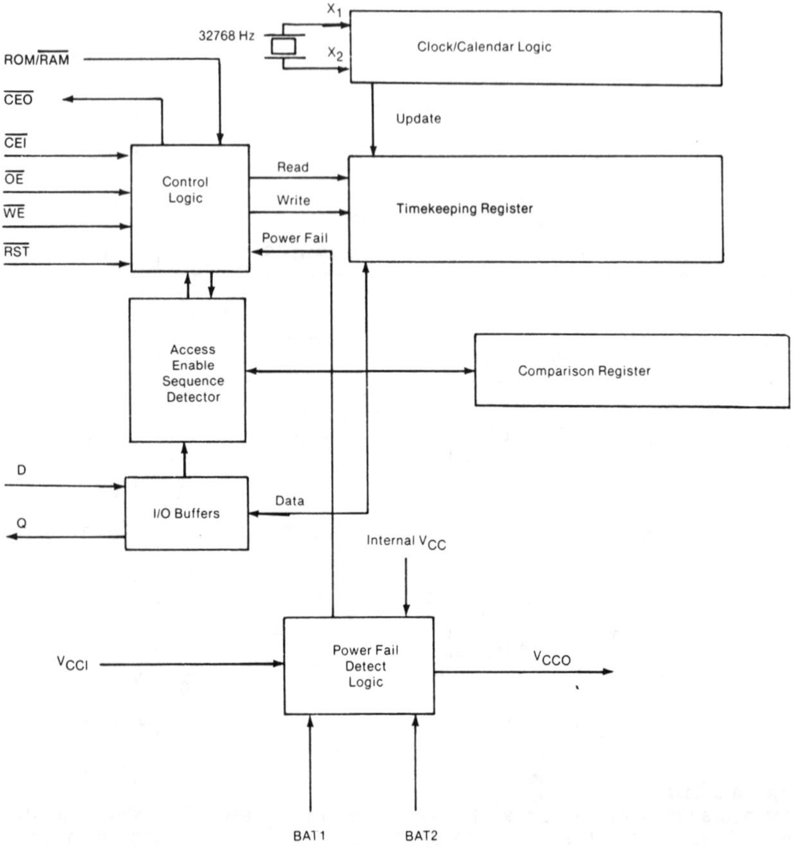

RAM/TIMECHIP INTERFACE Figure 4

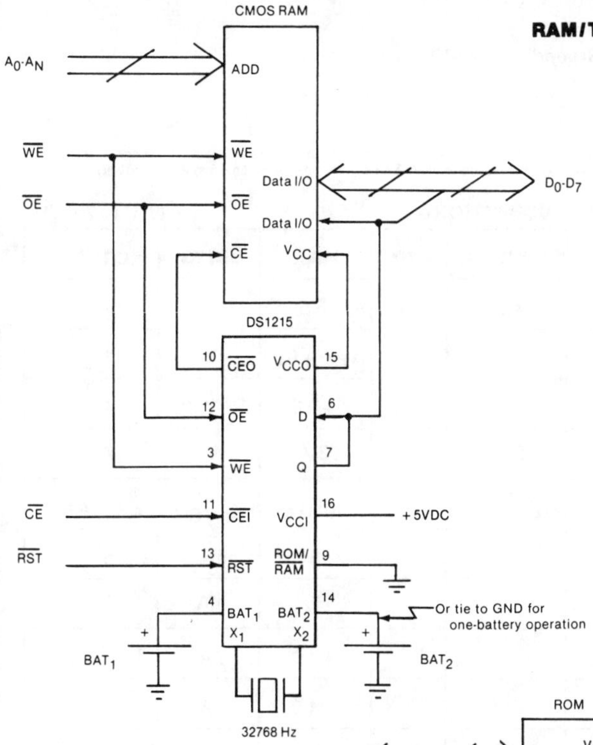

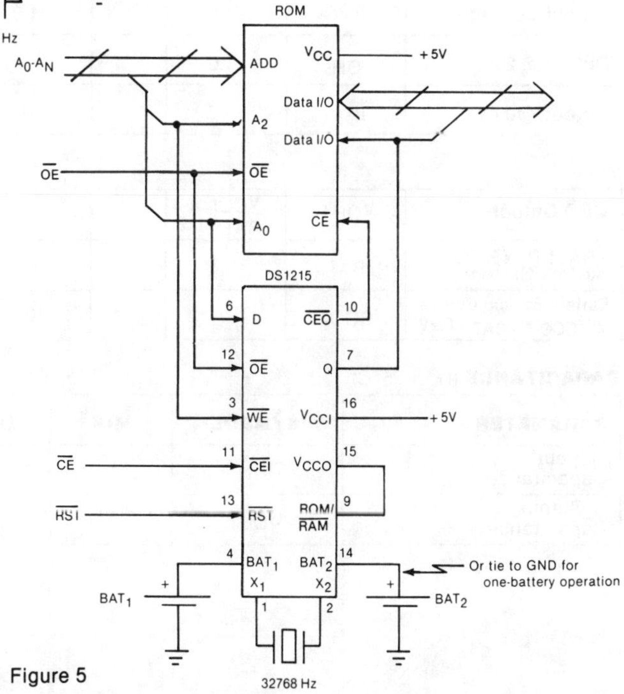

ROM/TIMECHIP INTERFACE Figure 5

ABSOLUTE MAXIMUM RATINGS*

Voltage on any Pin Relative to Ground -1.0V to +7.0V
Operating Temperature 0°C to 70°C
Storage Temperature -55°C to 125°C
Soldering Temperature 260°C for 10 Sec

*This is a stress rating only and functional operation of the device at these or any other conditions above those indicated in the operation sections of this specification is not implied. Exposure to absolute maximum rating conditions for extended periods of time may affect reliability.

RECOMMENDED D.C. OPERATING CONDITIONS (0°C to 70°C)

PARAMETER	SYMBOL	MIN	TYP	MAX	UNITS	NOTES
Supply Voltage	V_{CC}	4.5	5.0	5.5	V	1
Logic 1	V_{IH}	2.2		$V_{CC}+0.3$	V	1
Logic 0	V_{IL}	−0.3		+0.8	V	1
V_{BAT1} or V_{BAT2} Battery Voltage	V_{BAT}	2.5		3.7	V	7

D.C. ELECTRICAL CHARACTERISTICS (0°C to 70°C, V_{CC} = 4.5 to 5.5V)

Supply Current	I_{CCI}			5	mA	6
Supply Current $V_{CCO}=V_{CCI}-0.2$	I_{CCO1}			80	mA	8
Input Leakage	I_{IL}	−1.0		+1.0	μA	
Output Leakage	I_{LO}	−1.0		+1.0	μA	
Output @2.4V	I_{OH}	−1.0			mA	2
Output @0.4V	I_{OL}			4.0	mA	2

(0°C to 70°C, $V_{CC} < 4.5V$)

$\overline{CEO}$ Output	V_{OH1}	V_{CCI} or $V_{BAT}-0.2$			V	9
V_{BAT1} or V_{BAT2} Battery Current	I_{BAT}			1	μA	6
Battery Backup Current @$V_{CCO}=V_{BAT}-0.2V$	I_{CCO2}			10	μA	10

CAPACITANCE (t_A = 25°C)

PARAMETER	SYMBOL	MIN	UNITS	NOTES
Input Capacitance	C_{IN}	5	pF	
Output Capacitance	C_{OUT}	7	pF	

A.C. ELECTRICAL CHARACTERISTICS ROM/$\overline{RAM}$ = GND (0°C to 70°C, V_{CC} = 4.5 to 5.5V)

PARAMETER	SYMBOL	MIN	TYP	MAX	UNITS	NOTES
Read Cycle Time	t_{RC}	250			ns	
$\overline{CEI}$ Access Time	t_{CO}			200	ns	
$\overline{OE}$ Access Time	t_{OE}			100	ns	
$\overline{CEI}$ To Output Low Z	t_{COE}	10			ns	
$\overline{OE}$ To Output Low Z	t_{OEE}	10			ns	
$\overline{CEI}$ To Output High Z	t_{OD}			100	ns	
$\overline{OE}$ To Output High Z	t_{ODO}			100	ns	
Read Recovery	t_{RR}	50			ns	
Write Cycle	t_{WC}	250			ns	
Write Pulse Width	t_{WP}	170			ns	
Write Recovery	t_{WR}	50			ns	4
Data Set Up	t_{DS}	100			ns	5
Data Hold Time	t_{DH}	10			ns	5
$\overline{CEI}$ Pulse Width	t_{CW}	170			ns	
$\overline{RST}$ Pulse Width	t_{RST}	200			ns	
$\overline{CEI}$ Propagation Delay	t_{PD}	5	10	20	ns	2, 3
$\overline{CEI}$ High to Power Fail	t_{PF}			0	ns	

(0°C to 70°C, $V_{CC} < 4.5V$)

Recovery at Power Up	t_{REC}			2	ms	
V_{CC} Slew Rate 4.5 - 3.0V	t_F	0			ms	

TIMING DIAGRAM—READ CYCLE TO TIMECHIP ROM/$\overline{RAM}$ = GND

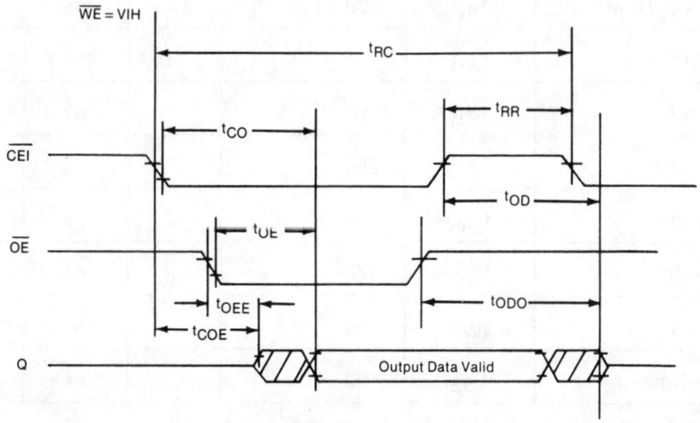

TIMING DIAGRAM—WRITE CYCLE TO TIMECHIP ROM/$\overline{RAM}$ = GND

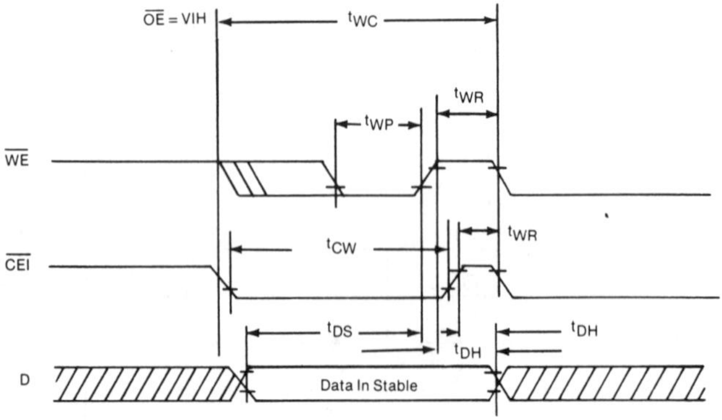

A.C. ELECTRICAL CHARACTERISTICS ROM/$\overline{RAM}$ = V_{CCO} (0 °C to 70 °C, V_{CC} = 5V ± 10%)

PARAMETER	SYMBOL	MIN	TYP	MAX	UNITS	NOTES
Read Cycle Time	t_{RC}	250			ns	
$\overline{CEI}$ Access Time	t_{CO}			200	ns	
$\overline{OE}$ Access Time	t_{OE}			200	ns	
$\overline{CEI}$ to Output in Low Z	t_{COE}	10			ns	
$\overline{OE}$ to Output in Low Z	t_{OEE}	10			ns	
$\overline{CEI}$ to Output in High Z	t_{OD}			100	ns	
$\overline{OE}$ to Output in High Z	t_{ODO}			100	ns	
Address Set Up Time	t_{AS}	20			ns	
Address Hold Time	t_{AH}			10	ns	
Read Recovery	t_{RR}	50			ns	
Write Cycle Time	t_{WC}	250			ns	
$\overline{CEI}$ Pulse Width	t_{CW}	170			ns	
$\overline{OE}$ Pulse Width	t_{OW}	170			ns	
Write Recovery	t_{WR}	50			ns	4
Data Set Up Time	t_{DS}	100			ns	5

Data Hold Time	t_{DH}	10			ns	5
$\overline{RST}$ Pulse Width	t_{RST}	200			ns	
$\overline{CEI}$ Propagation Delay	t_{PD}	5	10	20	ns	2,3
$\overline{CEI}$ High to Power Fail	t_{PF}			0	ns	

(0 °C to 70 °C, $V_{CC} < 4.5V$)

Recovery at Power Up	t_{REC}			2	ms	
V_{CC} Slew Rate 4.5 -3V	t_F	0			ms	

TIMING DIAGRAM—READ CYCLE ROM/$\overline{RAM}$ = V_{CCO}

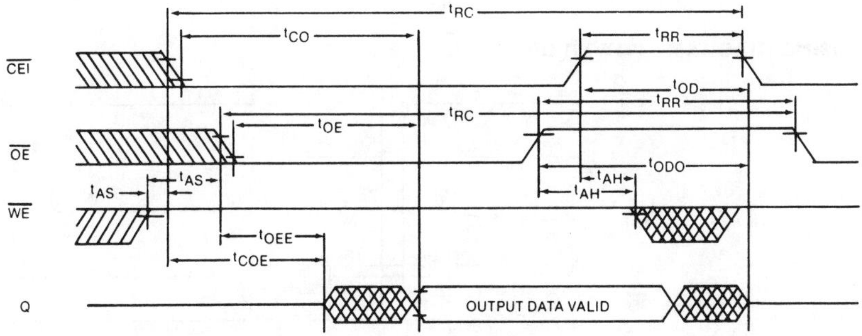

TIMING DIAGRAM—WRITE CYCLE ROM/$\overline{RAM}$ = V_{CCO}

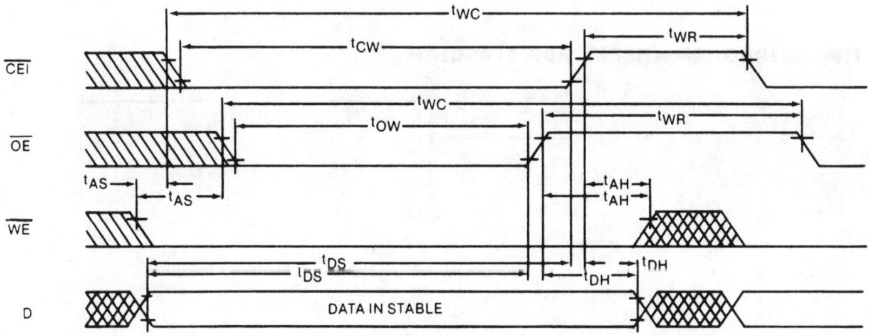

TIMING DIAGRAM—POWER DOWN

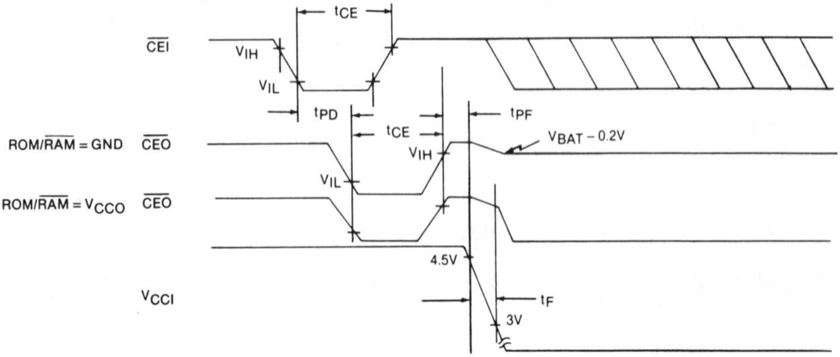

TIMING DIAGRAM—POWER UP

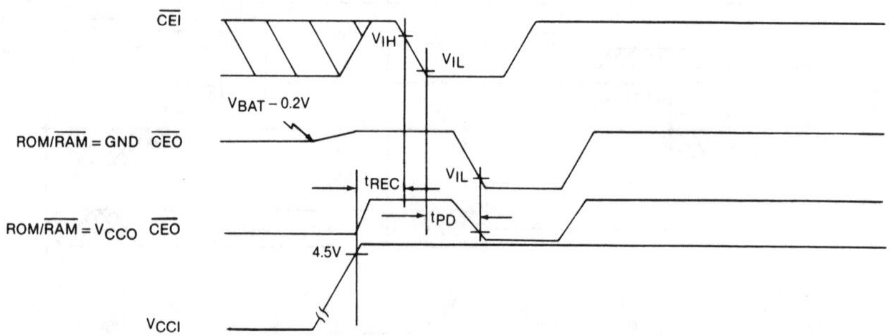

TIMING DIAGRAM—RESET FOR TIMECHIP

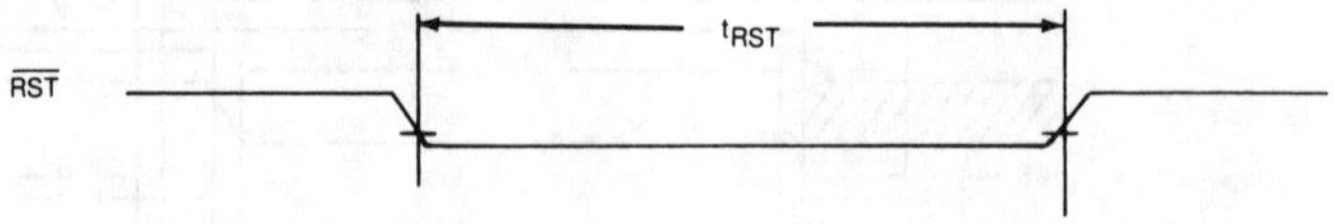

NOTES

1. All voltages are referenced to ground.
2. Measured with load shown in Figure 6.
3. Input pulse rise and fall times equal 10 ns.
4. t_{WR} is a function of the latter occurring edge of $\overline{WE}$ or $\overline{CE}$ in RAM mode or $\overline{OE}$ or $\overline{CE}$ in ROM mode.
5. t_{DH} and t_{DS} are functions of the first occurring edge of $\overline{WE}$ or $\overline{CE}$ in RAM mode or $\overline{OE}$ or $\overline{CE}$ in ROM mode.
6. Measured without RAM connected.
7. Trip point voltage for power fail detect. $V_{TP} = 1.26 \times V_{BAT}$ For 10% operation $V_{BAT} = 3.5V$ max.; for 5% operation $V_{BAT} = 3.7V$ max.
8. I_{CCO1} is the maximum average load current the DS1215 can supply to memory.
9. Applies to $\overline{CEO}$ with the ROM/$\overline{RAM}$ pin grounded. When the ROM/$\overline{RAM}$ pin is connected to V_{CCO}, $\overline{CEO}$ will go to a low level as V_{CCI} falls below V_{BAT}.
10. I_{CCO2} is the maximum average load current which the DS1215 can supply to memory in the battery backup mode.
11. Applies to all input pins except $\overline{RST}$. $\overline{RST}$ is pulled internally to V_{CCI}.

OUTPUT LOAD Figure 6

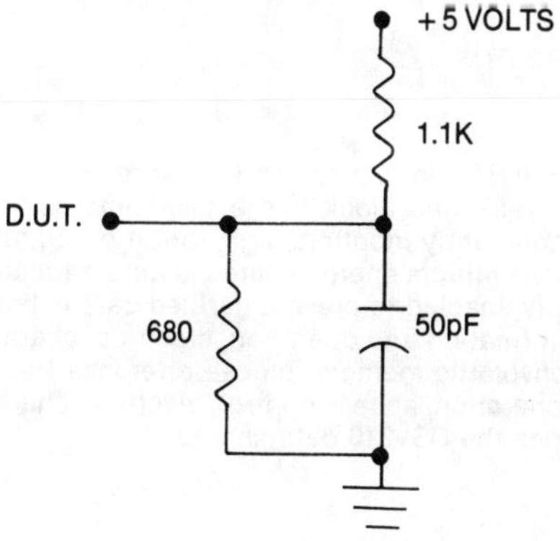

DS1243Y Real Time Clock

FEATURES

- Real Time Clock keeps track of hundredths of seconds, seconds, minutes, hours, days, date of the month, months, and years
- 8K × 8 NV SRAM directly replaces volatile static RAM or EEPROM
- Embedded lithium energy cell maintains watch information and retains RAM data
- Watch function is transparent to RAM operation
- Month and year determine the number of days in each month
- Standard 28-pin JEDEC pinout
- Full 10% operating range
- Operating temperature range 0 °C to 70 °C
- Accuracy is better than ± 1 min/month @ 25 °C
- Over 5 years of data retention in the absence of power
- Unlimited write cycles

PIN CONNECTIONS

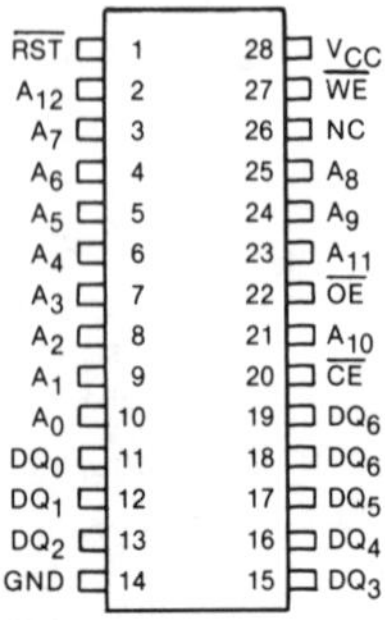

PIN NAMES

A_0-A_{12}	- Address Inputs
$\overline{CE}$	- Chip Enable
GND	- Ground
DQ_0-DQ_7	- Data In/Data Out
V_{CC}	- Power (+ 5V)
$\overline{WE}$	- Write Enable
$\overline{OE}$	- Output Enable
NC	- No Connect
$\overline{RST}$	- Reset

DESCRIPTION

The DS1243Y is a fully static nonvolatile RAM (organized as 8192 words by 8 bits) with built-in Real Time Clock. This memory and real time clock has a self-contained lithium energy source and control circuitry which constantly monitors V_{CC} for an out-of-tolerance condition. When such a condition occurs, the lithium energy source is automatically switched on and write protection is unconditionally enabled to prevent garbled data in both the memory and real time clock. For complete information and operation, electrical characteristics, and timing as it relates to the 8K × 8 nonvolatile memory, please reference the DS1225Y data sheet. For complete information on operation, access control, electrical characteristics and timing of the real time clock, reference the DS1216 data sheet.

FEATURES

- Watchdog Timekeeper keeps track of hundredths of seconds, seconds, minutes, hours, days, date of the month, months and years
- Watchdog Timer restarts an out of control processor
- Alarm function schedules real time related activities
- Embedded lithium energy cell maintains time, Watchdog, user RAM and alarm information
- Programmable interrupts and square wave outputs maintain 28-pin JEDEC footprint
- All registers are individually addressable via the address and data bus
- Accuracy is better than 1 minute/month at 25° C
- Greater than 10 years of timekeeping in the absence of Vcc
- 50 bytes of user NV RAM

DESCRIPTION

The DS1286 Watchdog Timekeeper is a self contained real time clock, alarm, watchdog timer, and interval timer in a 28-pin JEDEC DIP package. The DS1286 contains an embedded lithium energy source and a quartz crystal which eliminates need for any external circuitry. Data contained within 64 eight bit registers can be read or written in the same manner as bytewide static RAM. Data is maintained in the Watchdog Timekeeper by intelligent control circuitry which detects the status of Vcc and write protects memory when Vcc is out of tolerance. The lithium energy source can maintain data and real time for over ten years in the absence of Vcc. The Watchdog Timekeeper information includes hundredths of seconds, seconds, minutes, hours, day, date, month, and year information. The date at the end of the month is automatically adjusted for months with less than 31 days, including correction for leap years. The Watchdog Timekeeper operates in either 24 hour or 12 hour format with an AM/PM indicator. The Watchdog timer provides alarm windows and interval timing between 0.01 seconds and 99.99 seconds. The real time alarm provides for preset times of up to one week.

PIN DESCRIPTION

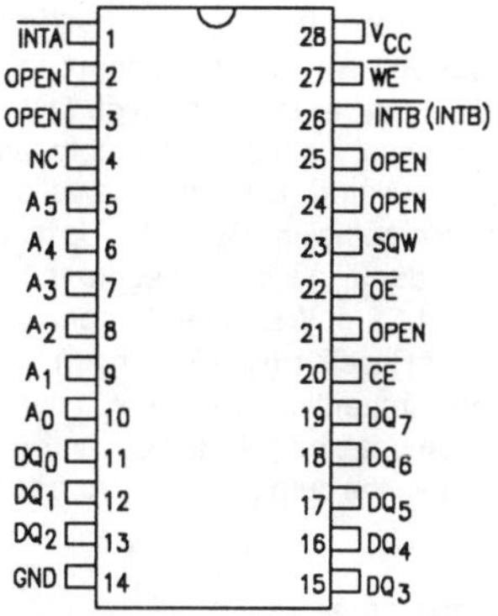

PIN NAMES

INTA	- Interrupt Output A
INTB(INTB)	- Interrupt Output B
A0-A5	- Address Inputs
DQ0-DQ7	- Data Input/Output
CE	- Chip Enable
OE	- Output Enable
WE	- Write Enable
Vcc	- +5 Volts
GND	- Ground
N.C.	- No Connection
OPEN	- Pin Missing
SQW	- Square Wave Output

OPERATION - READ REGISTERS

The DS1286 executes a read cycle whenever WE (Write Enable) is inactive (High) and CE and OE are active (LOW). The unique address specified by the six address inputs (A0-A5) defines which of the 64 registers is to be accessed. Valid data will be available to the eight data output drivers within t_{Acc} (Access Time) after the last address input signal is stable, providing that CE (Chip Enable) and OE (Output Enable) access times are also satisfied. If OE and CE access times are not satisfied, then data access must be measured from the latter occurring signal (CE or OE) and the limiting parameter is either t_{CO} for CE or t_{OE} for OE rather than address access.

OPERATION - WRITE REGISTERS

The DS1286 is in the write mode whenever the WE (Write Enable) and CE (Chip Enable) signals are in the active (Low) state after the address inputs are stable. The latter occurring falling edge of $\overline{CE}$ or $\overline{WE}$ will determine the start of the write cycle. The write cycle is terminated by the earlier rising edge of $\overline{CE}$ or $\overline{WE}$. All address inputs must be kept valid throughout the write cycle. WE must return to the high state for a minimum recovery state (t_{WR}) before another cycle can be initiated. Data must be valid on the data bus with sufficient Data Set Up (t_{DS}) and Data Hold Time (t_{DH}) with respect to the earlier rising edge of $\overline{CE}$ or $\overline{WE}$. The $\overline{OE}$ control signal should be kept inactive (High) during write cycles to avoid bus contention. However, if the output bus has been enabled ($\overline{CE}$ and $\overline{OE}$ active), then $\overline{WE}$ will disable the outputs in t_{ODW} from its falling edge.

DATA RETENTION

The Watchdog Timekeeper provides full functional capability when Vcc is greater than 4.5 volts and write protects the register contents at 4.25 volts typical. Data is maintained in the absence of Vcc without any additional support circuitry. The DS1286 constantly monitors Vcc. Should the supply voltage decay, the Watchdog TimeKeeper will automatically write protect itself and all inputs to the registers become Don't Care. The two interrupts $\overline{INTA}$ and $\overline{INTB}$ (INTB) and the internal clock and timers continue to run regardless of the level of Vcc. As Vcc falls below approximately 3.0 volts, a power switching circuit turns the internal lithium energy source on to maintain the clock and timer data and functionality. During power up, when Vcc rises above approximately 3.0 volts, the power switching circuit connects external Vcc and disconnects the internal lithium energy source. Normal operation can resume after Vcc exceeds 4.5 volts for a period of 150 ms.

WATCHDOG TIMEKEEPER REGISTERS

The Watchdog Timekeeper has 64 registers which are eight bits wide that contain all of the Timekeeping, Alarm, Watchdog, Control, and Data information. The Clock, Calendar, Alarm and Watchdog Registers are memory locations which contain external (user accessible) and internal copies of the data. The external copies are independent of internal functions except that they are updated periodically by the simultane-

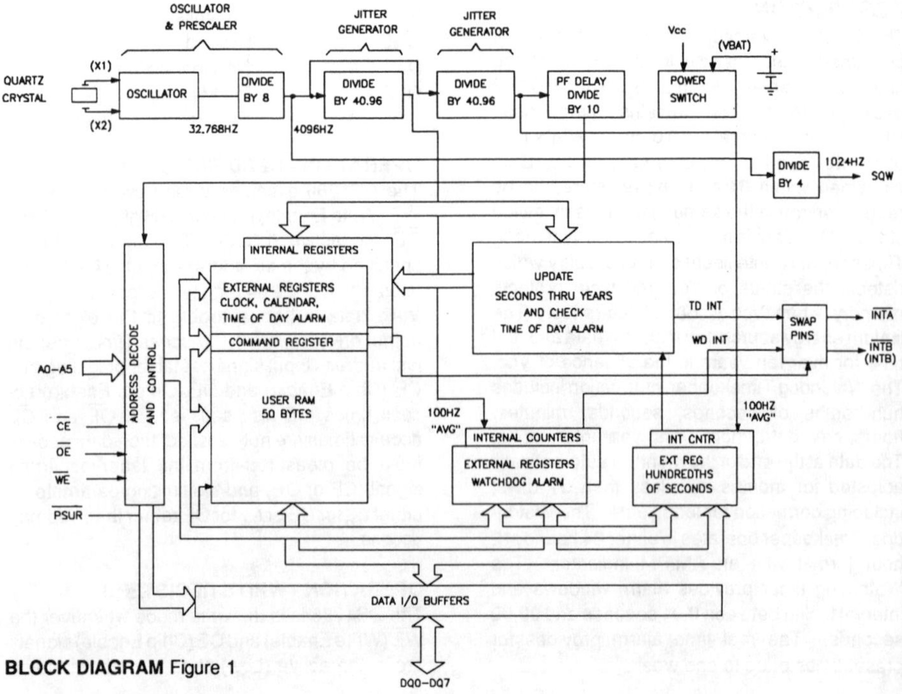

BLOCK DIAGRAM Figure 1

ous transfer of the incremented internal copy (see Figure 1). The Command Register bits are affected by both internal and external functions. This register will be discussed later. The 50 bytes of RAM registers can only be accessed from the external address and data bus. Register 0, 1, 2, 4, 6, 8, 9 and A contain time of day and date information (see Figure 2). Time of Day information is stored in BCD. Registers 3, 5, and 7 contain the Time of Day Alarm information. Time of Day Alarm information is stored in BCD. Register B is the Command Register and information in this register is binary. Register C and D are the Watchdog Alarm Registers and information which is stored in these two registers is in BCD. Register E through Register 3F are user bytes and can be used to contain data at the user's discretion.

TIME OF DAY REGISTERS

Registers 0, 1, 2, 4, 6, 8, 9 and A contain Time of Day data in BCD. Ten bits within these eight registers are not used and will always read zero regardless of how they are written. Bits 6 and 7 in the Months Register (9) are binary bits. When set to logical zero, $\overline{\text{EOSC}}$ (Bit 7) enables the Real Time Clock oscillator. This bit is set to logical one as shipped from Dallas Semiconductor to prevent lithium energy consumption during storage and shipment. This bit will normally be turned on by the user during device initialization. However, the oscillator can be turned on and off as necessary by setting this bit to the appropriate level. Bit 6 of this same byte controls the Square Wave Output (pin 24). When set to logical zero, the Square Wave Output Pin will output a 1024 HZ Square Wave Signal. When set to logic one the Square Wave Output Pin is in a high impedance state. Bit 6 of the Hours Register is defined as the 12 or 24 Hour Select Bit. When set to logic one, the 12 Hour Format is selected. In the 12 Hour Format, Bit 5 is the AM/PM Bit with logical one being PM. In the 24 Hour Mode, Bit 5 is the Second 10 Hour bit (20-23 hours). The Time of Day Registers are updated every .01 seconds from the Real Time Clock, except when the TE bit (Bit 7 of Register B) is set low or the clock oscillator is not running.

The preferred method of synchronizing data access to and from the Watchdog Timekeeper is to access the Command Register by doing a write cycle to address location 0B and setting the TE bit (Transfer Enable bit) to a logic zero. This will freeze the External Time of Day Registers at the present recorded time allowing access to occur without danger of simultaneous update. When the watch registers have been read or written a second write cycle to location 0B, setting the TE bit to a logic one, will put the Time of Day Registers back to being updated every .01 second. No time is lost in the Real Time Clock because the internal copy of the Time of Day Register buffers are continually incremented while the external memory registers are frozen. An alternate method of reading and writing the Time of Day Registers is to ignore synchronization. However, any single read may give erroneous data as the Real Time Clock may be in the process of updating the external memory registers as data is being read. The internal copies of seconds through years are incremented and Time of Day Alarm is checked during the period that hundreds of seconds reads 99 and are transferred to the external register when hundredths of seconds roll from 99 to 00. A way of making sure data is valid is to do multiple reads and compare. Writing the registers can also produce erroneous results for the same reasons. A way of making sure that the write cycle has caused proper update is to do read verifies and re-execute the write cycle if data is not correct. While the possibility of erroneous results from reads and write cycles has been stated, it is worth noting that the probability of an incorrect result is kept to a minimum due to the redundant structure of the Watchdog Timekeeper.

TIME OF DAY ALARM REGISTERS

Registers 3, 5, and 7 contain the Time of Day Alarm Registers. Bits 3, 4, 5, and 6 of Register 7 will always read zero regardless of how they are written. Bit 7 of Registers 3, 5, and 7 are mask bits (Figure 3). When all of the mask bits are logical zero, a Time of Day Alarm will only occur when Registers 2, 4, and 6 match the values stored in Registers 3, 5, and 7. An alarm will be generated every day when Bit 7 of Register 7 is set to a logical one. Similarly, an alarm is generated every hour when Bit 7 of Registers 7 and 5 is set to a logical 1. When Bit 7 of Registers 7, 5, and 3 is set to a logical 1, an alarm will occur every minute when Register 1 (seconds) rolls from 59 to 00.

Time of Day Alarm Registers are written and read in the same format as the Time of Day Registers. The Time of Day Alarm Flag and Interrupt is always cleared when Alarm Registers are read or written.

DS1286 WATCHDOG TIMEKEEPER REGISTERS Figure 2

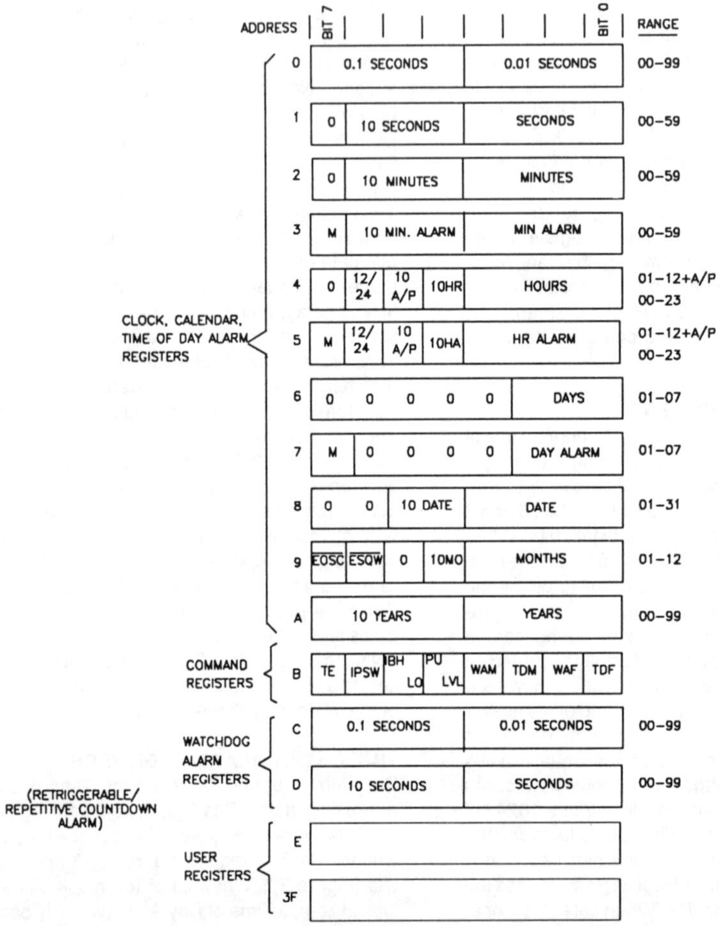

TIME OF DAY ALARM MASK BITS Figure 3

MINUTES	HOURS	DAYS	
1	1	1	ALARM ONCE PER MINUTE
0	1	1	ALARM WHEN MINUTES MATCH
0	0	1	ALARM WHEN HOURS AND MINUTES MATCH
0	0	0	ALARM WHEN HOURS, MINUTES, AND DAYS MATCH

NOTE: ANY OTHER COMBINATIONS OF MASK BIT SETTINGS PRODUCE ILLOGICAL OPERATION.

WATCHDOG ALARM REGISTERS

Registers C and D contain the time for the Watchdog Alarm. The two registers contain a time count from 00.01 to 99.99 seconds in BCD. The value written into the Watchdog Alarm Registers can be written or read in any order. Any access to Register C or D will cause the Watchdog Alarm to reinitialize and clears the Watchdog Flag Bit and the Watchdog Interrupt Output. When a new value is entered or the Watchdog Registers are read, the Watchdog Timer will start counting down from the entered value to zero. When zero is reached, the Watchdog Interrupt Output will go to the active state. The Watchdog Timer Countdown is interrupted and reinitialized back to the entered value every time either of the registers are accessed. In this manner, controlled periodic accesses to the Watchdog Timer can prevent the Watchdog Alarm from ever going to an active level. If access does not occur, countdown alarm will be repetitive. The Watchdog Alarm Registers always read the entered value. The actual count down register is internal and is not readable. Writing registers C and D to zero will disable the Watchdog Alarm feature.

COMMAND REGISTER

Address location 0B is the Command Register where mask bits, control bits, and flag bits reside. Bit 0 is the Time of Day Alarm Flag (TDF). When this bit is set internally to a logical one, an alarm has occurred. The time of the alarm can be determined by reading the Time of Day Alarm Registers. However, if the transfer enable bit is set to logical zero the Time of Day registers may not reflect the exact time that the alarm occurred. This bit is read only and writing this register has no effect on the bit. The bit is reset when any of the Time of Day Alarm Registers are read. Bit 1 is the Watchdog Alarm Flag (WAF). When this bit is set internally to a logical one, a Watchdog Alarm has occurred. This bit is read only and writing this register has no effect on the bit. The bit is reset when any of the Time of Day Alarm Registers are accessed. Bit 2 of the Command Register contains the Time of Day Alarm Mask Bit (TDM). When this bit is written to a logical one, the Time of Day Alarm Interrupt Output is deactivated regardless of the value of the Time of Day Alarm Flag. When TDM is set to logical zero, the Time of Day Interrupt Output will go to the active state which is determined by bits 0, 4, 5, and 6 of the Command Register. Bit 3 of the Command Register contains the Watchdog Alarm Mask Bit (WAM). When this bit is written to a logical one, the Watchdog Interrupt Output is deactivated regardless of the value in the Watchdog Alarm Registers. When WAM is set to logic zero, the Watchdog Interrupt Output will go to the active state which is determined by bits 1, 4, 5, and 6 of the Command Register. These four bits define how Interrupt Output Pins $\overline{INTA}$ and INTB ($\overline{INTB}$) will be operated. Bit 4 of the Command Register determines whether both interrupts will output a pulse or level when activated. If Bit 4 is set to logic one, the pulse mode is selected and $\overline{INTA}$ will sink current for a minimum of 3 ms and then release. Output INTB ($\overline{INTB}$) will either sink or source current for a minimum of 3 ms depending on the level of Bit 5. When Bit 5 is set to logic one, the B interrupt will source current. When Bit 5 is set to logical zero, the B interrupt will sink current. Bit 6 of the Command Register directs which type of interrupt will be present on interrupt pins $\overline{INTA}$ or INTB ($\overline{INTB}$). When set to logical one, $\overline{INTA}$ becomes the Time of Day Alarm Interrupt Pin and INTB ($\overline{INTB}$) becomes the Watchdog Interrupt Pin. When Bit 6 is set to logical zero, the interrupt functions are reversed such that the Time of Day Alarm will be output on INTB ($\overline{INTB}$) and the Watchdog Interrupt will be output on $\overline{INTA}$. Caution should be exercised when dynamically setting this bit as the interrupts will be reversed even if in an active state. Bit 7 of the Command Register is for Transfer Enable (TE). The function of this bit is described in the Time of Day Registers.

ABSOLUTE MAXIMUM RATINGS
VOLTAGE ON ANY PIN RELATIVE TO GROUND -0.3V TO +7.0V
OPERATING TEMPERATURE 0°C TO 70°C
STORAGE TEMPERATURE -40°C TO +70°C
SOLDERING TEMPERATURE 260°C FOR 10 SEC.

RECOMMENDED D.C. OPERATING CONDITIONS (0° C to 70° C)

PARAMETER	SYMBOL	MIN	TYP.	MAX	UNITS	NOTES
SUPPLY VOLTAGE	V_{cc}	4.5	5.0	5.5	V	10
INPUT LOGIC 1	V_{IH}	2.2		V_{cc} + 0.3	V	10
INPUT LOGIC 0	V_{IL}	-0.3		+0.8	V	10

D.C. ELECTRICAL CHARACTERISTICS (0° C to 70° C, Vcc =5V ± 10%)

PARAMETER	SYMBOL	MIN	TYP.	MAX	UNITS	NOTES
INPUT LEAKAGE CURRENT	I_{IL}	-1.0		+1.0	uA	
OUTPUT LEAKAGE CURRENT	I_{LO}	-1.0		+1.0	uA	
I/O LEAKAGE CURRENT	I_{LIO}	-1.0		+1.0	uA	
OUTPUT CURRENT @ 2.4V	I_{OH}	-1.0			mA	
OUTPUT CURRENT @ 0.4V	I_{OL}	2.0			mA	13
STANDBY CURRENT $\overline{CE}$= 2.2V	I_{CCS1}		3.0	7.0	mA	
STANDBY CURRENT $\overline{CE}$ ≥ Vcc -0.5	I_{CCS2}			4.0	mA	
ACTIVE CURRENT	I_{CC}			15	mA	
WRITE PROTECTION VOLTAGE	V_{TP}		4.25		V	

CAPACITANCE

(T_A=25° C)

PARAMETER	SYMBOL	TYP.	MAX	UNITS	NOTES
INPUT CAPACITANCE	C_{IN}	7	10	pF	
OUTPUT CAPACITANCE	C_{OUT}	7	10	pF	
INPUT/OUTPUT CAPACITANCE	$C_{I/O}$	7	10	pF	

A.C. ELECTRICAL CHARACTERISTICS

(0° C to 70° C, Vcc = 4.5v to 5.5v)

PARAMETER	SYMBOL	MIN	TYP.	MAX	UNITS	NOTES
READ CYCLE TIME	t_{RC}	150			ns	1
ADDRESS ACCESS TIME	t_{ACC}			150	ns	
$\overline{CE}$ ACCESS TIME	t_{CO}			150	ns	
$\overline{OE}$ ACCESS TIME	t_{OE}			75	ns	
$\overline{OE}$ OR $\overline{CE}$ TO OUTPUT ACTIVE	t_{COE}	10			ns	
OUTPUT HIGH Z FROM DESELECT	t_{OD}			75	ns	
OUTPUT HOLD FROM ADDRESS CHANGE	t_{OH}	10			ns	
WRITE CYCLE TIME	t_{WC}	150			ns	
WRITE PULSE WIDTH	t_{WP}	140			ns	3
ADDRESS SETUP TIME	t_{AW}	0			ns	
WRITE RECOVERY TIME	t_{WR}	10			ns	
OUTPUT HIGH Z FROM $\overline{WE}$	t_{ODW}			50	ns	
OUTPUT ACTIVE FROM $\overline{WE}$	t_{OEW}	10			ns	
DATA SETUP TIME	t_{DS}	60			ns	4
DATA HOLD TIME	t_{DH}	0			ns	4,5
$\overline{INTA}$, $\overline{INTB}$ PULSE WIDTH	t_{IPW}	3			ms	11,12

READ CYCLE (1)

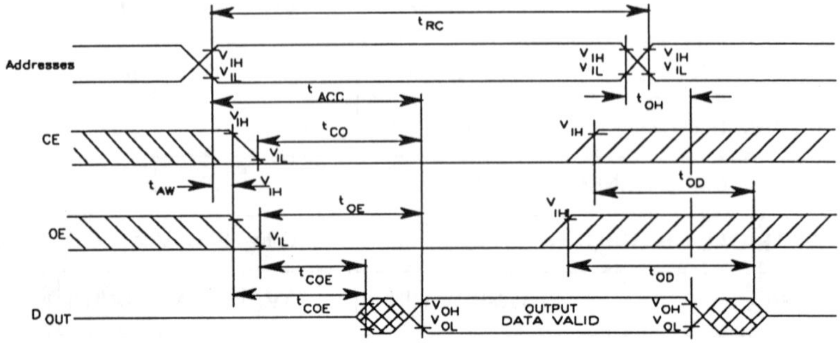

WRITE CYCLE 1 (2), (6), (7)

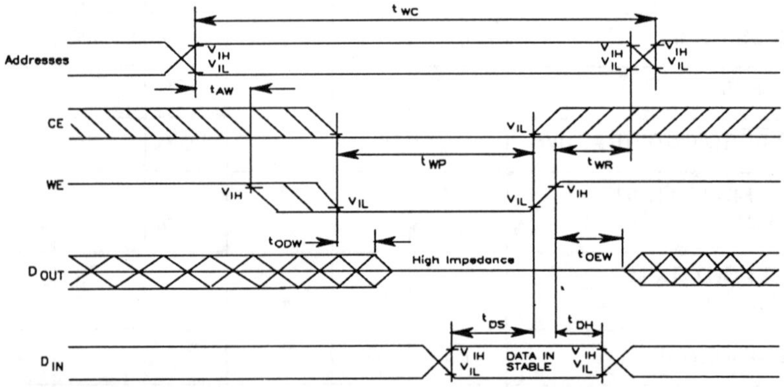

WRITE CYCLE 2 (2), (8)

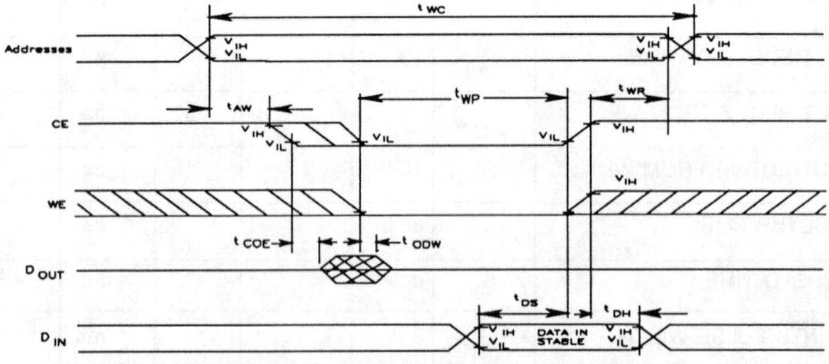

TIMING DIAGRAM - INTERRUPT OUTPUTS PULSE MODE (SEE NOTES 11,12)

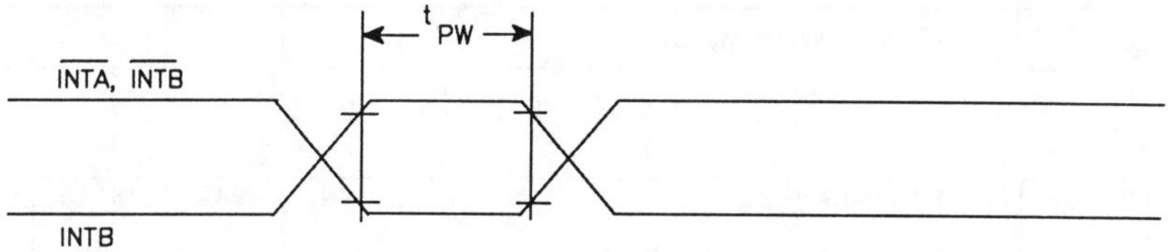

POWER-DOWN/POWER-UP CONDITION

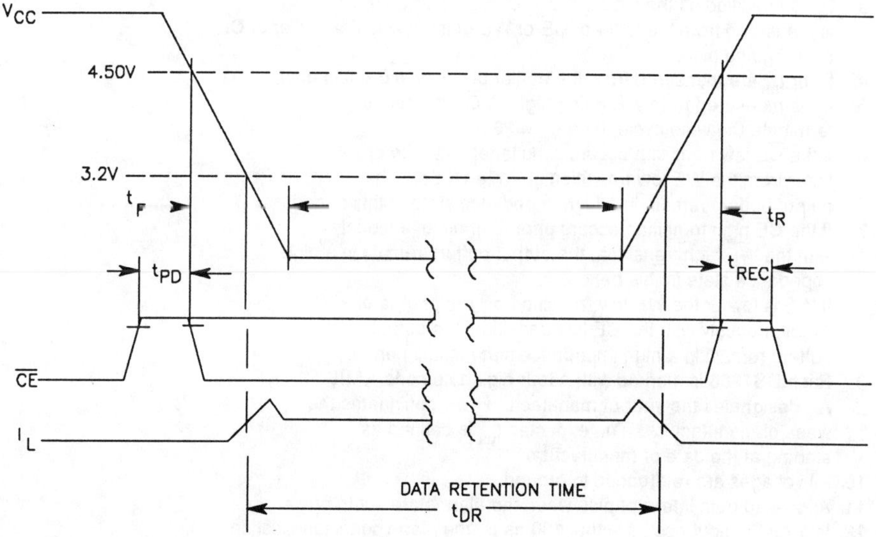

LEAKAGE CURRENT I_L SUPPLIED FROM LITHIUM CELL

POWER-UP/POWER-DOWN CONDITION

SYM	PARAMETER	MIN	MAX	UNITS	NOTES
t_{PD}	$\overline{CE}$ at VIH before Power Down	0		us	
t_F	VCC slew from 4.5V to 0V ($\overline{CE}$ at VIH)	350		us	
t_R	VCC slew from 0V to 4.5V ($\overline{CE}$ at VIH	100		us	
t_{REC}	$\overline{CE}$ at VIH after Power Up		150	ms	

(t_A=25°C)

SYM	PARAMETER	MIN	MAX	UNITS	NOTES
t_{DR}	Expected Data Retention Time	10		years	9

WARNING:
Under no circumstances are negative undershoots, of any amplitude, allowed when device is in battery backup mode.

NOTES

1. $\overline{WE}$ is high for a read cycle.
2. $\overline{OE}$ = V_{IH} or V_{IL}. If $\overline{OE}$ = V_{IH} during write cycle, the Output Buffers remain in a high impedance state.
3. t_{WP} is specified as the logical "and" of the $\overline{CE}$ and $\overline{WE}$. t_{WP} is measured from the latter of $\overline{CE}$ or $\overline{WE}$ going low to the earlier of $\overline{CE}$ or $\overline{WE}$ going high.
4. t_{DS} or t_{DH} are measured from the earlier of $\overline{CE}$ or $\overline{WE}$ going high.
5. t_{DH} is measured from $\overline{WE}$ going high. If $\overline{CE}$ is used to terminate the write cycle, then t_{DH} = 20 ns.
6. If the $\overline{CE}$ low transition occurs simultaneously with or latter from the $\overline{WE}$ low transition in Write Cycle 1, the output buffers remain in a high impedance state in this period.
7. If the $\overline{CE}$ high transition occurs prior to or simultaneously with the $\overline{WE}$ high transition, the output buffers remain in a high impedance state in this period.
8. If WE is low or the $\overline{WE}$ low transition occurs prior to or simultaneously with the $\overline{CE}$ low transition, the output buffers remain in a high impedance state in this period.
9. Each DS1286 is marked with a four digit date code AABB. AA designates the year of manufacture. BB designates the week of manufacture. The expected t_{DR} is defined as starting at the date of manufacture.
10. All voltages are referenced to ground.
11. Applies to both interrupt pins when the alarms are set to pulse.
12. Interrupt Output occurs within 100 ns on the alarm condition existing.
13. Both $\overline{INTA}$ and $\overline{INTB}$ (INTB) are open drain outputs.

A.C. TEST CONDITIONS

Output Load: 100pF + 1TTL Gate
Input Pulse Levels: 0-3.0V
Timing Measurement Reference Levels
Input: 1.5V
Output: 1.5V
Input Pulse Rise and Fall Times: 5 ns.

The MC1488 is a monolithic quad line driver designed to interface data terminal equipment with data communications equipment in conformance with the specifications of EIA Standard No. RS-232C.

Features:

- Current Limited Output
  ±10 mA typ
- Power-Off Source Impedance
  300 Ohms min
- Simple Slew Rate Control with External Capacitor
- Flexible Operating Supply Range
- Compatible with All Motorola MDTL and MTTL Logic Families

TYPICAL APPLICATION

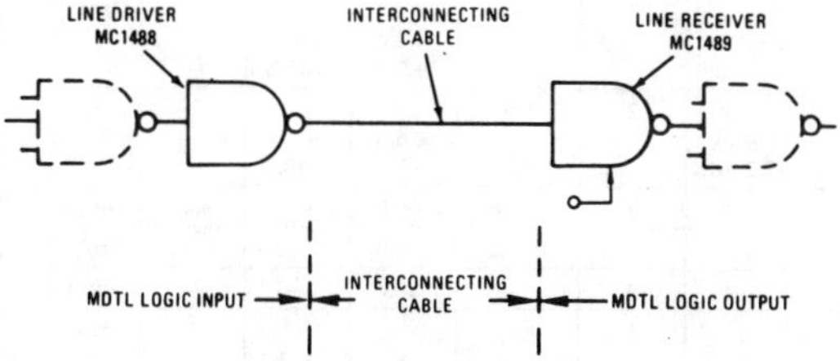

PIN CONNECTIONS

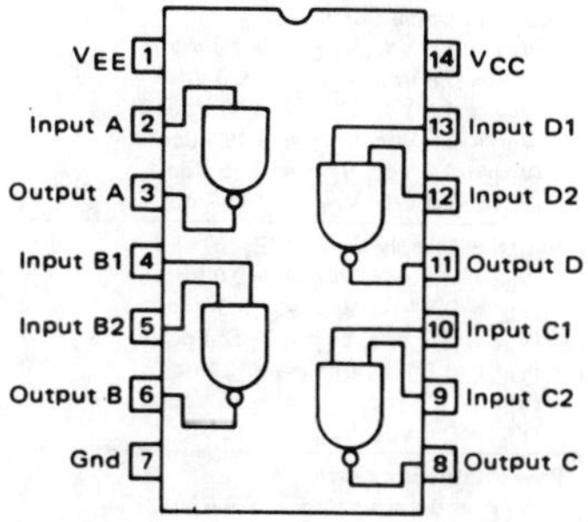

CIRCUIT SCHEMATIC

(1/4 OF CIRCUIT SHOWN)

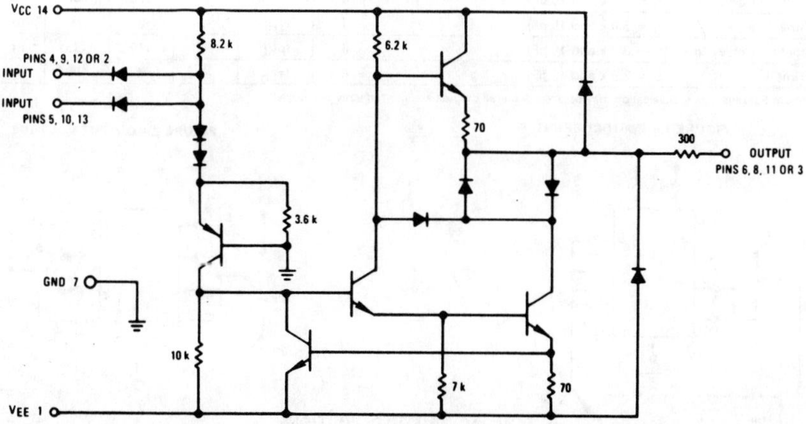

MAXIMUM RATINGS (T_A = +25°C unless otherwise noted.)

Rating	Symbol	Value	Unit
Power Supply Voltage	V_{CC} V_{EE}	+15 −15	Vdc
Input Voltage Range	V_{IR}	$-15 \leq V_{IR} \leq 7.0$	Vdc
Output Signal Voltage	V_O	±15	Vdc
Power Derating (Package Limitation, Ceramic and Plastic Dual-In-Line Package) Derate above T_A = +25°C	P_D $1/R_{\theta JA}$	1000 6.7	mW mW/°C
Operating Ambient Temperature Range	T_A	0 to +75	°C
Storage Temperature Range	T_{stg}	−65 to +175	°C

ELECTRICAL CHARACTERISTICS (V_{CC} = +9.0 ±1% Vdc, V_{EE} = −9.0 ±1% Vdc, T_A = 0 to 75°C unless otherwise noted.)

Characteristic	Figure	Symbol	Min	Typ	Max	Unit
Input Current — Low Logic State (V_{IL} = 0)	1	I_{IL}	—	1.0	1.6	mA
Input Current — High Logic State (V_{IH} = 5.0 V)	1	I_{IH}	—	—	10	µA
Output Voltage — High Logic State	2	V_{OH}				Vdc
(V_{IL} = 0.8 Vdc, R_L = 3.0 kΩ, V_{CC} = +9.0 Vdc, V_{EE} = −9.0 Vdc)			+6.0	+7.0	—	
(V_{IL} = 0.8 Vdc, R_L = 3.0 kΩ, V_{CC} = +13.2 Vdc, V_{EE} = −13.2 Vdc)			+9.0	+10.5	—	
Output Voltage — Low Logic State	2	V_{OL}				Vdc
(V_{IH} = 1.9 Vdc, R_L = 3.0 kΩ, V_{CC} = +9.0 Vdc, V_{EE} = −9.0 Vdc)			−6.0	−7.0	—	
(V_{IH} = 1.9 Vdc, R_L = 3.0 kΩ, V_{CC} = +13.2 Vdc, V_{EE} = −13.2 Vdc)			−9.0	−10.5	—	
Positive Output Short-Circuit Current (1)	3	I_{OS+}	+6.0	+10	+12	mA
Negative Output Short-Circuit Current (1)	3	I_{OS-}	−6.0	−10	−12	mA
Output Resistance (V_{CC} = V_{EE} = 0, $\lvert V_O \rvert$ = ±2.0 V)	4	r_o	300	—	—	Ohms
Positive Supply Current (R_l = ∞)	5	I_{CC}				mA
(V_{IH} = 1.9 Vdc, V_{CC} = +9.0 Vdc)			—	+15	+20	
(V_{IL} = 0.8 Vdc, V_{CC} = +9.0 Vdc)			—	+4.5	+6.0	
(V_{IH} = 1.9 Vdc, V_{CC} = +12 Vdc)			—	+19	+25	
(V_{IL} = 0.8 Vdc, V_{CC} = +12 Vdc)			—	+5.5	+7.0	
(V_{IH} = 1.9 Vdc, V_{CC} = +15 Vdc)			—	—	+34	
(V_{IL} = 0.8 Vdc, V_{CC} = +15 Vdc)			—	—	+12	
Negative Supply Current (R_L = ∞)	5	I_{EE}				
(V_{IH} = 1.9 Vdc, V_{EE} = −9.0 Vdc)			—	−13	−17	mA
(V_{IL} = 0.8 Vdc, V_{EE} = −9.0 Vdc)			—	—	−500	µA
(V_{IH} = 1.9 Vdc, V_{EE} = −12 Vdc)			—	−18	−23	mA
(V_{IL} = 0.8 Vdc, V_{EE} = −12 Vdc)			—	—	−500	µA
(V_{IH} = 1.9 Vdc, V_{EE} = −15 Vdc)			—	—	−34	mA
(V_{IL} = 0.8 Vdc, V_{EE} = −15 Vdc)			—	—	−2.5	mA
Power Consumption		P_C				mW
(V_{CC} = 9.0 Vdc, V_{EE} = −9.0 Vdc)			—	—	333	
(V_{CC} = 12 Vdc, V_{EE} = −12 Vdc)			—	—	576	

SWITCHING CHARACTERISTICS (V_{CC} = +9.0 ±1% Vdc, V_{EE} = −9.0 ±1% Vdc, T_A = +25°C.)

Propagation Delay Time (z_l = 3.0 k and 15 pF)	6	t_{PLH}	—	275	350	ns
Fall Time (z_l = 3.0 k and 15 pF)	6	t_{THL}	—	45	75	ns
Propagation Delay Time (z_l = 3.0 k and 15 pF)	6	t_{PHL}	—	110	175	ns
Rise Time (z_l = 3.0 k and 15 pF)	6	t_{TLH}	—	55	100	ns

(1) Maximum Package Power Dissipation may be exceeded if all outputs are shorted simultaneously.

FIGURE 1 – INPUT CURRENT

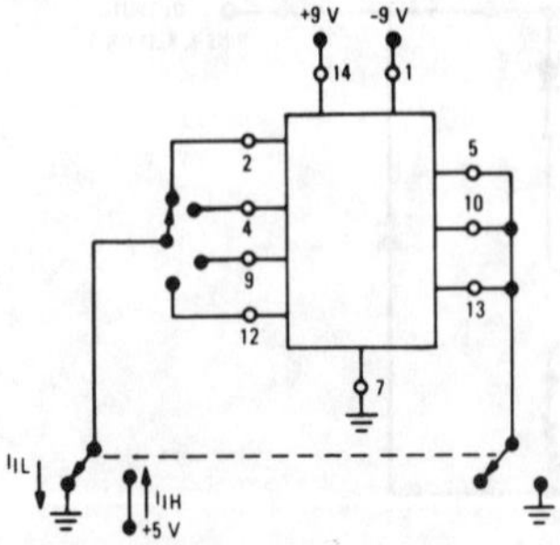

FIGURE 2 – OUTPUT VOLTAGE

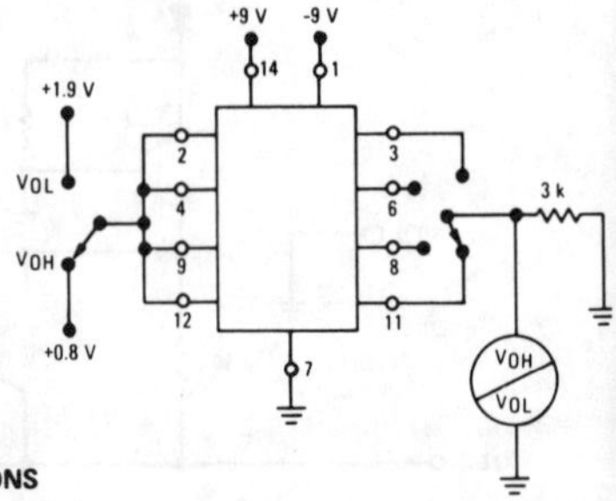

CHARACTERISTIC DEFINITIONS

FIGURE 3 – OUTPUT SHORT-CIRCUIT CURRENT

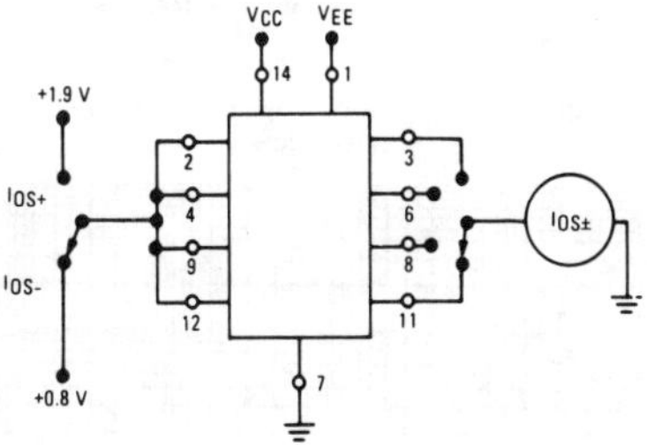

FIGURE 4 – OUTPUT RESISTANCE (POWER-OFF)

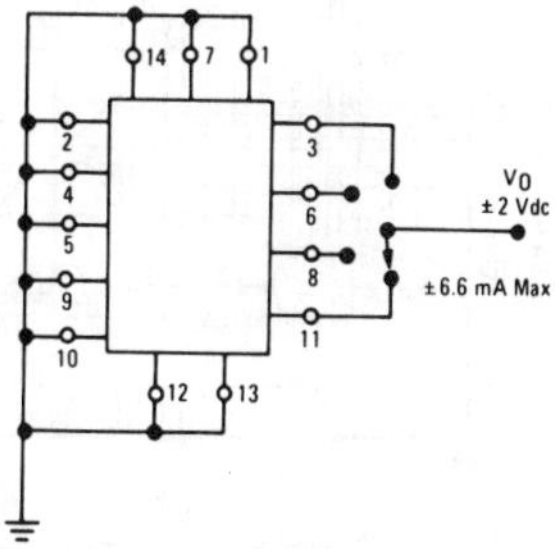

FIGURE 5 – POWER-SUPPLY CURRENTS

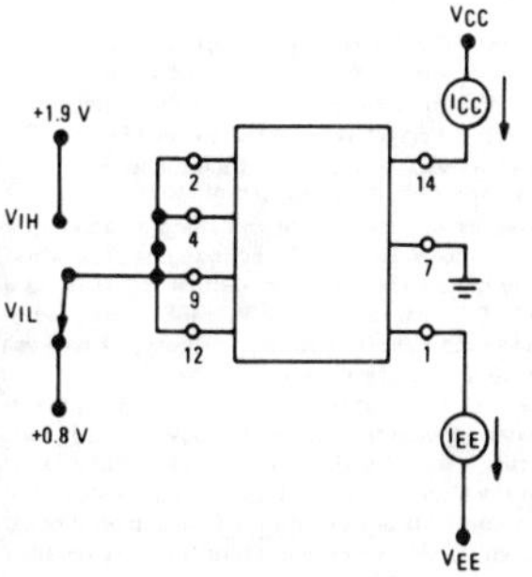

FIGURE 6 – SWITCHING RESPONSE

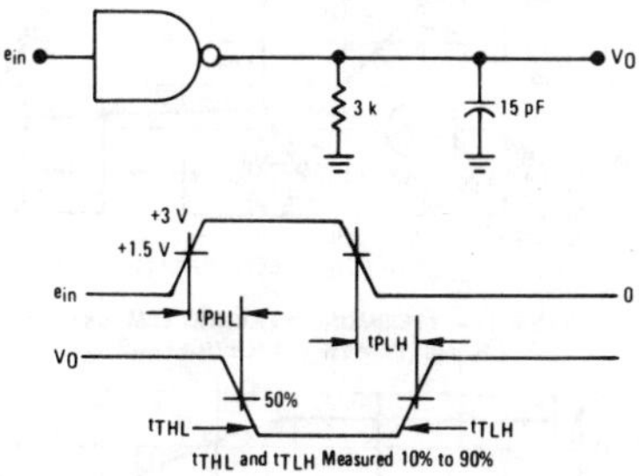

TYPICAL CHARACTERISTICS

(T_A = +25°C unless otherwise noted.)

FIGURE 7 — TRANSFER CHARACTERISTICS versus POWER-SUPPLY VOLTAGE

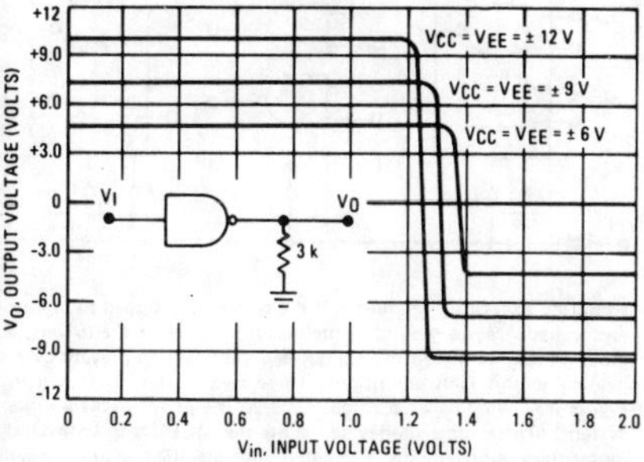

FIGURE 8 — SHORT-CIRCUIT OUTPUT CURRENT versus TEMPERATURE

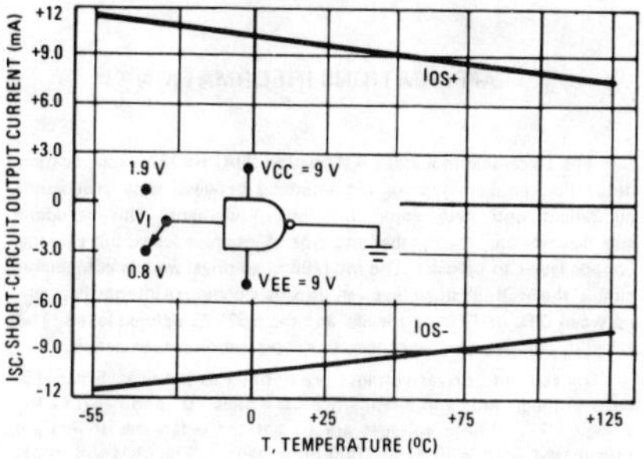

FIGURE 9 — OUTPUT SLEW RATE versus LOAD CAPACITANCE

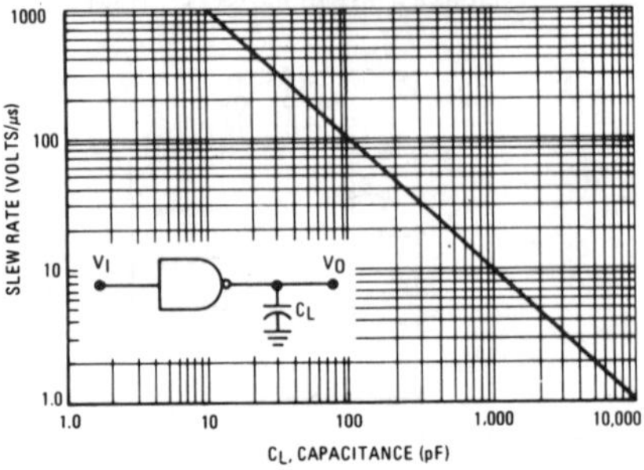

FIGURE 10 — OUTPUT VOLTAGE AND CURRENT-LIMITING CHARACTERISTICS

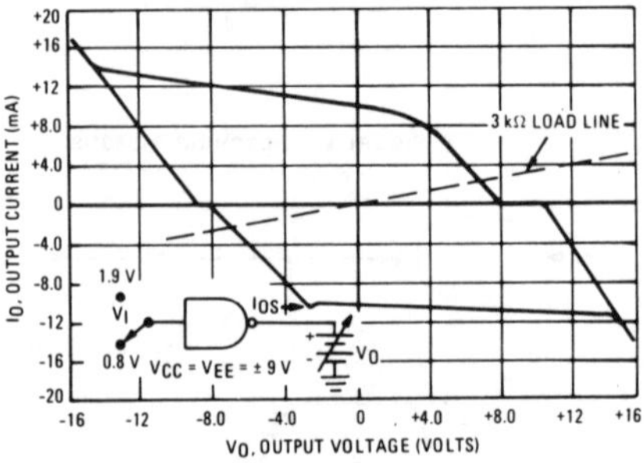

FIGURE 11 — MAXIMUM OPERATING TEMPERATURE versus POWER-SUPPLY VOLTAGE

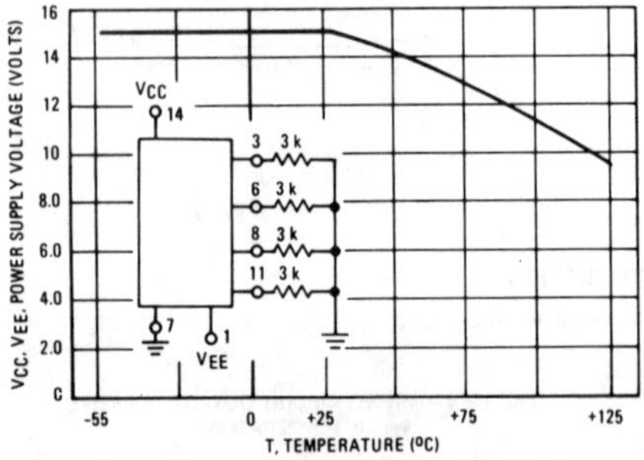

APPLICATIONS INFORMATION

The Electronic Industries Association (EIA) RS232C specification detail the requirements for the interface between data processing equipment and data communications equipment. This standard specifies not only the number and type of interface leads, but also the voltage levels to be used. The MC1488 quad driver and its companion circuit, the MC1489 quad receiver, provide a complete interface system between DTL or TTL logic levels and the RS232C defined levels. The RS232C requirements as applied to drivers are discussed herein.

The required driver voltages are defined as between 5 and 15-volts in magnitude and are positive for a logic "0" and negative for a logic "1". These voltages are so defined when the drivers are terminated with a 3000 to 7000-ohm resistor. The MC1488 meets this voltage requirement by converting a DTL/TTL logic level into RS232C levels with one stage of inversion.

The RS232C specification further requires that during transitions, the driver output slew rate must not exceed 30 volts per microsecond. The inherent slew rate of the MC1488 is much too

FIGURE 12 – SLEW RATE versus CAPACITANCE FOR I_{SC} = 10 mA

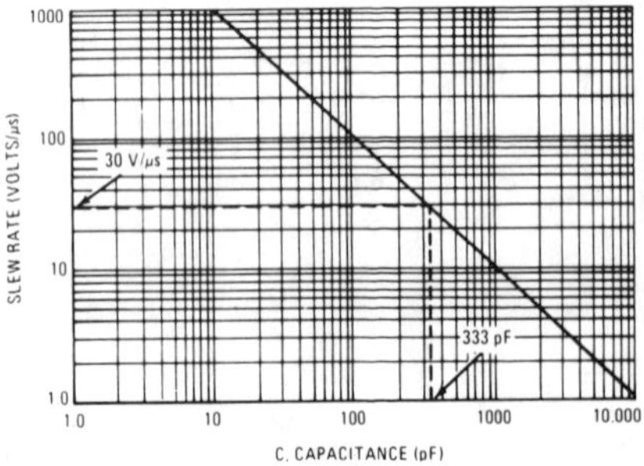

fast for this requirement. The current limited output of the device can be used to control this slew rate by connecting a capacitor to each driver output. The required capacitor can be easily determined by using the relationship $C = I_{OS} \times \Delta T / \Delta V$ from which Figure 12 is derived. Accordingly, a 330-pF capacitor on each output will guarantee a worst case slew rate of 30 volts per microsecond.

The interface driver is also required to withstand an accidental short to any other conductor in an interconnecting cable. The worst possible signal on any conductor would be another driver using a plus or minus 15-volt, 500-mA source. The MC1488 is designed to indefinitely withstand such a short to all four outputs in a package as long as the power-supply voltages are greater than 9.0 volts (i.e., $V_{CC} \geqslant 9.0$ V; $V_{EE} \leqslant -9.0$ V). In some power-supply designs, a loss of system power causes a low impedance on the power-supply outputs. When this occurs, a low impedance to ground would exist at the power inputs to the MC1488 effectively shorting the 300-ohm output resistors to ground. If all four outputs were then shorted to plus or minus 15 volts, the power dissipation in these resistors

FIGURE 13 – POWER-SUPPLY PROTECTION TO MEET POWER-OFF FAULT CONDITIONS

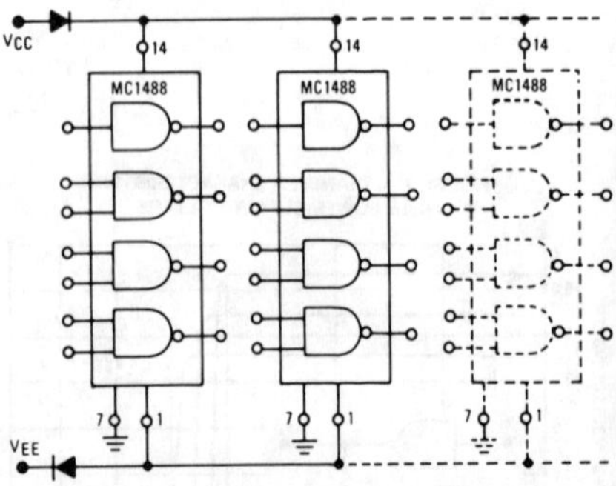

would be excessive. Therefore, if the system is designed to permit low impedances to ground at the power-supplies of the drivers, a diode should be placed in each power-supply lead to prevent overheating in this fault condition. These two diodes, as shown in Figure 13, could be used to decouple all the driver packages in a system. (These same diodes will allow the MC1488 to withstand momentary shorts to the ±25-volt limits specified in the earlier

Standard RS232B.) The addition of the diodes also permits the MC1488 to withstand faults with power-supplies of less than the 9.0 volts stated above.

The maximum short-circuit current allowable under fault conditions is more than guaranteed by the previously mentioned 10 mA output current limiting.

Other Applications

The MC1488 is an extremely versatile line driver with a myriad of possible applications. Several features of the drivers enhance this versatility:

1. Output Current Limiting – this enables the circuit designer to define the output voltage levels independent of power-supplies and can be accomplished by diode clamping of the output pins. Figure 14 shows the MC1488 used as a DTL to MOS translator where the high-level voltage output is clamped one diode above ground. The resistor divider shown is used to reduce the output voltage below the 300 mV above ground MOS input level limit.

2. Power-Supply Range – as can be seen from the schematic drawing of the drivers, the positive and negative driving elements of the device are essentially independent and do not require matching power-supplies. In fact, the positive supply can vary from a minimum seven volts (required for driving the negative pulldown section) to the maximum specified 15 volts. The negative supply can vary from approximately -2.5 volts to the minimum specified -15 volts. The MC1488 will drive the output to within 2 volts of the positive or negative supplies as long as the current output limits are not exceeded. The combination of the current-limiting and supply-voltage features allow a wide combination of possible outputs within the same quad package. Thus if only a portion of the four drivers are used for driving RS232C lines, the remainder could be used for DTL to MOS or even DTL to DTL translation. Figure 15 shows one such combination.

FIGURE 14 – MDTL/MTTL-TO-MOS TRANSLATOR

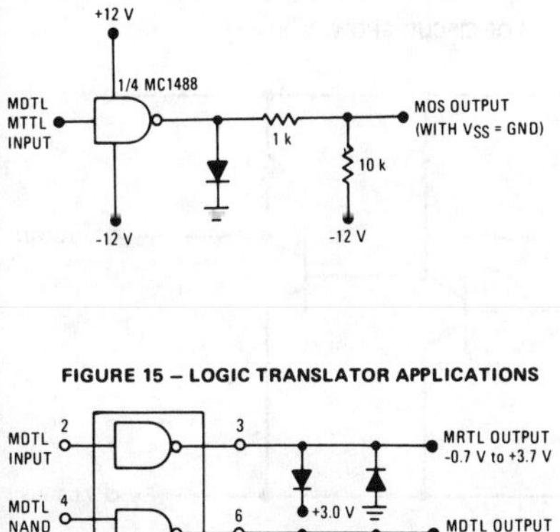

FIGURE 15 – LOGIC TRANSLATOR APPLICATIONS

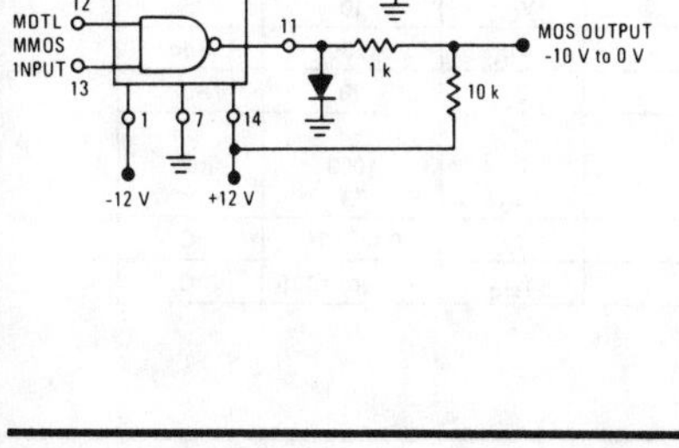

MC1489 serial data driver/receiver

The MC1489 monolithic quad line receivers are designed to interface data terminal equipment with data communications equipment in conformance with the specifications of EIA Standard No. RS-232C.

- Input Resistance – 3.0 k to 7.0 kilohms
- Input Signal Range – ±30 Volts
- Input Threshold Hysteresis Built In
- Response Control
  - a) Logic Threshold Shifting
  - b) Input Noise Filtering

TYPICAL APPLICATION

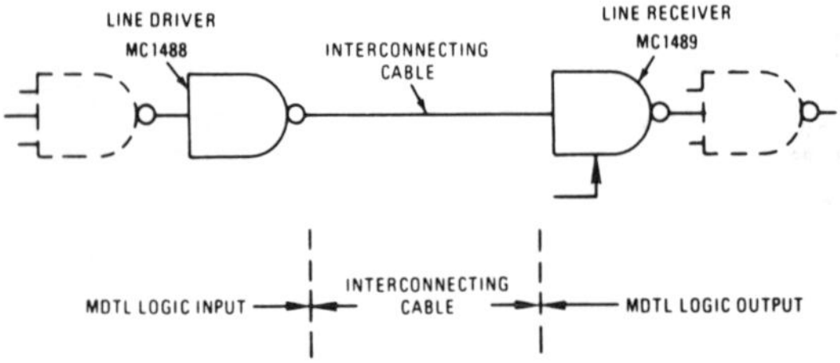

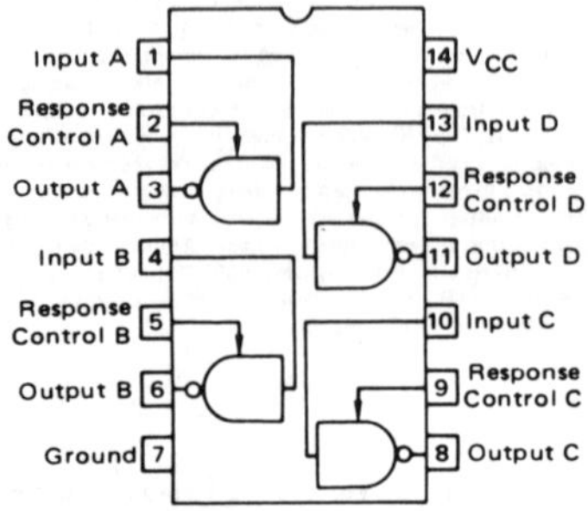

EQUIVALENT CIRCUIT SCHEMATIC (1/4 OF CIRCUIT SHOWN)

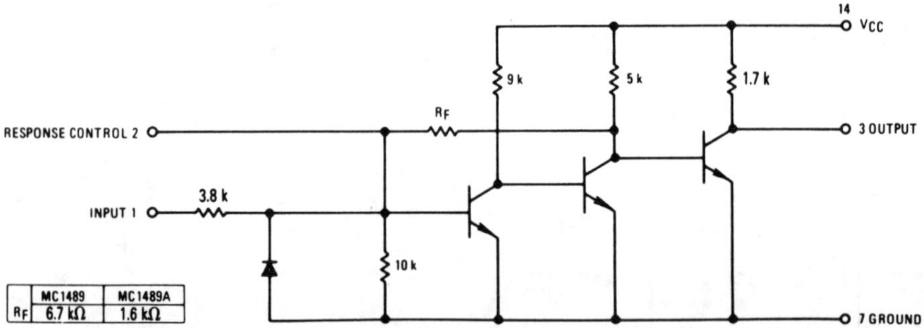

	MC1489	MC1489A
R_F	6.7 kΩ	1.6 kΩ

MAXIMUM RATINGS (T_A = +25°C unless otherwise noted)

Rating	Symbol	Value	Unit
Power Supply Voltage	V_{CC}	10	Vdc
Input Voltage Range	V_{IR}	±30	Vdc
Output Load Current	I_L	20	mA
Power Dissipation (Package Limitation, Ceramic and Plastic Dual In-Line Package) Derate above T_A = +25°C	P_D $1/\theta_{JA}$	1000 6.7	mW mW/°C
Operating Ambient Temperature Range	T_A	0 to +75	°C
Storage Temperature Range	T_{stg}	−65 to +175	°C

ELECTRICAL CHARACTERISTICS (Response control pin is open.) (V_{CC} = +5.0 Vdc ±10%, T_A = 0 to +75°C unless otherwise noted)

Characteristics		Symbol	Min	Typ	Max	Unit
Positive Input Current	(V_{IH} = +25 Vdc) (V_{IH} = +3.0 Vdc)	I_{IH}	3.6 0.43	— —	8.3 —	mA
Negative Input Current	(V_{IL} = −25 Vdc) (V_{IL} = −3.0 Vdc)	I_{IL}	−3.6 −0.43	— —	−8.3 —	mA
Input Turn-On Threshold Voltage (T_A = +25°C, V_{OL} ≤ 0.45 V)	MC1489 MC1489A	V_{IH}	1.0 1.75	— 1.95	1.5 2.25	Vdc
Input Turn-Off Threshold Voltage (T_A = +25°C, V_{OH} ≥ 2.5 V, I_L = −0.5 mA)	MC1489 MC1489A	V_{IL}	0.75 0.75	— 0.8	1.25 1.25	Vdc
Output Voltage High	(V_{IH} = 0.75 V, I_L = −0.5 mA) (Input Open Circuit, I_L = −0.5 mA)	V_{OH}	2.5 2.5	4.0 4.0	5.0 5.0	Vdc
Output Voltage Low	(V_{IL} = 3.0 V, I_L = 10 mA)	V_{OL}	—	0.2	0.45	Vdc
Output Short-Circuit Current		I_{OS}	—	−3.0	−4.0	mA
Power Supply Current (All Gates "on," I_{out} = 0 mA, V_{IH} = +5.0 Vdc)		I_{CC}	—	16	26	mA
Power Consumption	(V_{IH} = +5.0 Vdc)	P_C	—	80	130	mW

SWITCHING CHARACTERISTICS (V_{CC} = 5.0 Vdc ±1%, T_A = +25°C, See Figure 1.)

Characteristics		Symbol	Min	Typ	Max	Unit
Propagation Delay Time	(R_L = 3.9 kΩ)	t_{PLH}	—	25	85	ns
Rise Time	(R_L = 3.9 kΩ)	t_{TLH}	—	120	175	ns
Propagation Delay Time	(R_L = 390 kΩ)	t_{PHL}	—	25	50	ns
Fall Time	(R_L = 390 kΩ)	t_{THL}	—	10	20	ns

TEST CIRCUITS

FIGURE 1 — SWITCHING RESPONSE

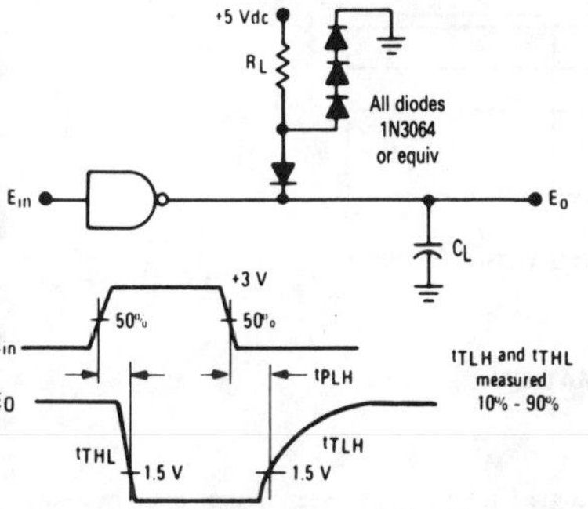

C_L = 15 pF = total parasitic capacitance, which includes probe and wiring capacitances

FIGURE 2 — RESPONSE CONTROL NODE

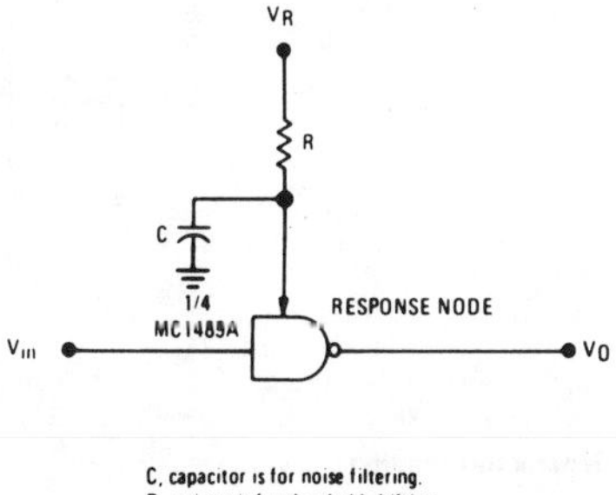

C, capacitor is for noise filtering.
R, resistor is for threshold shifting.

TYPICAL CHARACTERISTICS

(V_{CC} = 5.0 Vdc, T_A = +25°C unless otherwise noted)

FIGURE 3 — INPUT CURRENT

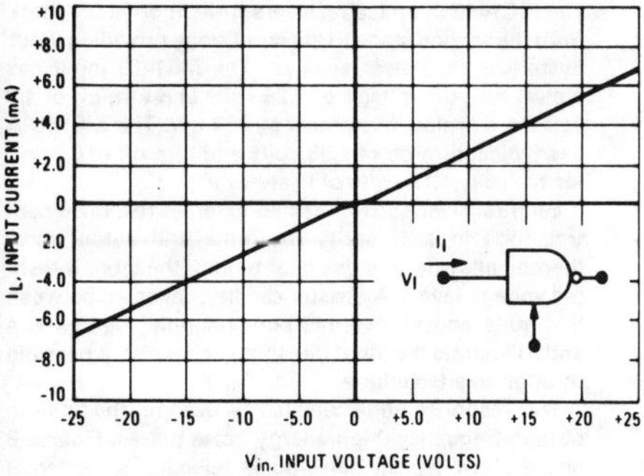

FIGURE 4 — MC1489 INPUT THRESHOLD VOLTAGE ADJUSTMENT

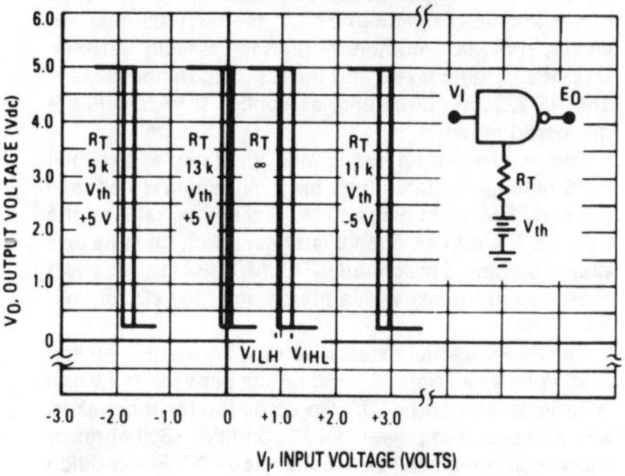

FIGURE 5 — MC1489A INPUT THRESHOLD VOLTAGE ADJUSTMENT

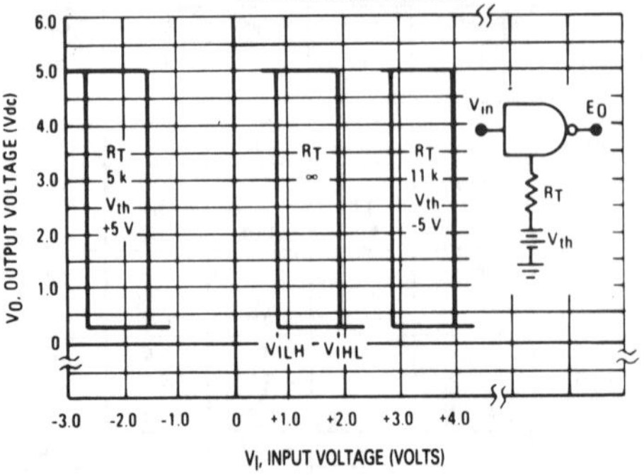

FIGURE 6 — INPUT THRESHOLD VOLTAGE versus TEMPERATURE

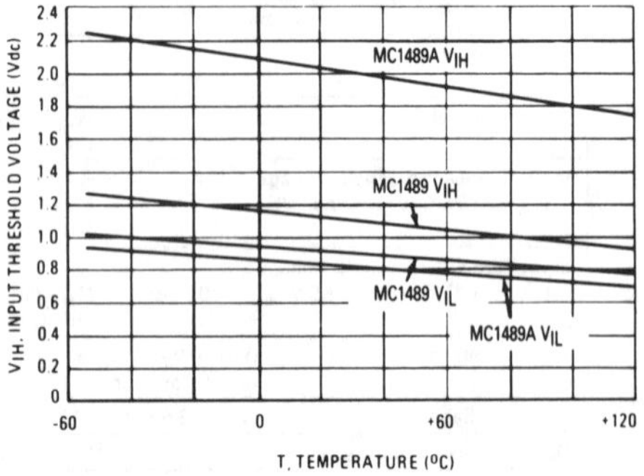

FIGURE 7 — INPUT THRESHOLD versus POWER-SUPPLY VOLTAGE

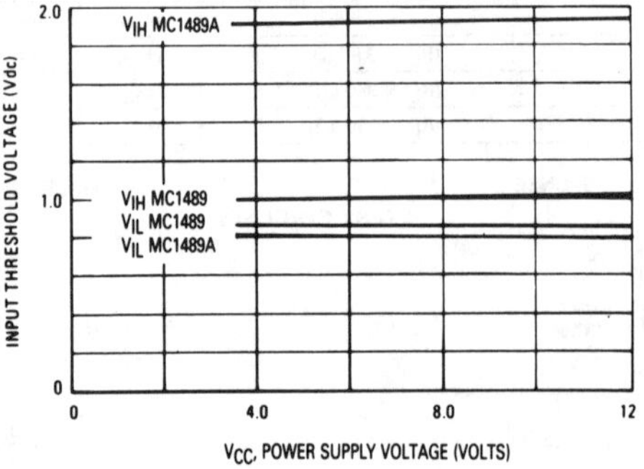

APPLICATIONS INFORMATION

General Information

The Electronic Industries Association (EIA) has released the RS-232C specification detailing the requirements for the interface between data processing equipment and data communications equipment. This standard specifies not only the number and type of interface leads, but also the voltage levels to be used. The MC1488 quad driver and its companion circuit, the MC1489 quad receiver, provide a complete interface system between DTL or TTL logic levels and the RS-232C defined levels. The RS-232C requirements as applied to receivers are discussed herein.

The required input impedance is defined as between 3000 ohms and 7000 ohms for input voltages between 3.0 and 25 volts in magnitude; and any voltage on the receiver input in an open circuit condition must be less than 2.0 volts in magnitude. The MC1489 circuits meet these requirements with a maximum open circuit voltage of one V_{BE}.

The receiver shall detect a voltage between −3.0 and −25 volts as a Logic "1" and inputs between +3.0 and +25 volts as a Logic "0." On some interchange leads, an open circuit of power "OFF" condition (300 ohms or more to ground) shall be decoded as an "OFF" condition or Logic "1." For this reason, the input hysteresis thresholds of the MC1489 circuits are all above ground. Thus an open or grounded input will cause the same output as a negative or Logic "1" input.

Device Characteristics

The MC1489 interface receivers have internal feedback from the second stage to the input stage providing input hysteresis for noise rejection. The MC1489 input has typical turn-on voltage of 1.25 volts and turn-off of 1.0 volt for a typical hysteresis of 250 mV. The MC1489A has typical turn-on of 1.95 volts and turn-off of 0.8 volt for typically 1.15 volts of hysteresis.

Each receiver section has an external response control node in addition to the input and output pins, thereby allowing the designer to vary the input threshold voltage levels. A resistor can be connected between this node and an external power-supply. Figures 2, 4 and 5 illustrate the input threshold voltage shift possible through this technique.

This response node can also be used for the filtering of high-frequency, high-energy noise pulses. Figures 8 and 9 show typical noise-pulse rejection for external capacitors of various sizes.

These two operations on the response node can be combined or used individually for many combinations of interfacing applications. The MC1489 circuits are particularly useful for interfacing between MOS circuits and MDTL/MTTL logic systems. In this application, the input threshold voltages are adjusted (with the appropriate supply and resistor values) to fall in the center of the MOS voltage logic levels. (See Figure 10)

The response node may also be used as the receiver input as long as the designer realizes that he may not drive this node with a low impedance source to a voltage greater than one diode above ground or less than one diode below ground. This feature is demonstrated in Figure 11 where two receivers are slaved to the same line that must still meet the RS-232C impedance requirement.

APPLICATIONS INFORMATION (continued)

FIGURE 8 — TYPICAL TURN-ON THRESHOLD versus CAPACITANCE FROM RESPONSE CONTROL PIN TO GND

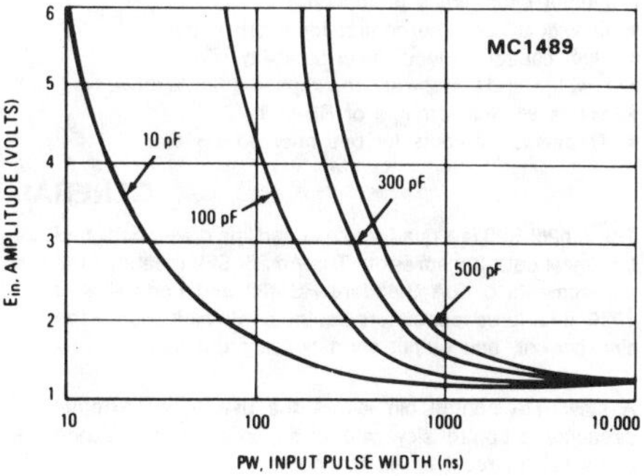

FIGURE 9 — TYPICAL TURN-ON THRESHOLD versus CAPACITANCE FROM RESPONSE CONTROL PIN TO GND

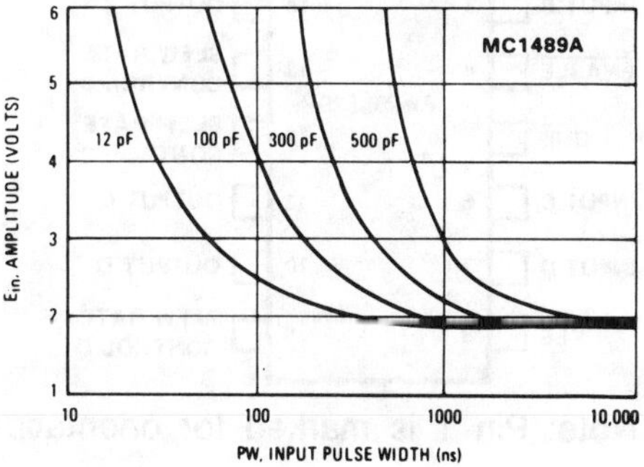

FIGURE 10 — TYPICAL TRANSLATOR APPLICATION — MOS TO DTL OR TTL

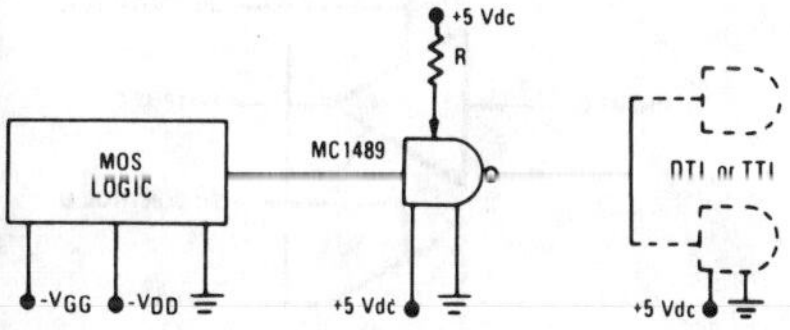

FIGURE 11 — TYPICAL PARALLELING OF TWO MC1489,A RECEIVERS TO MEET RS-232C

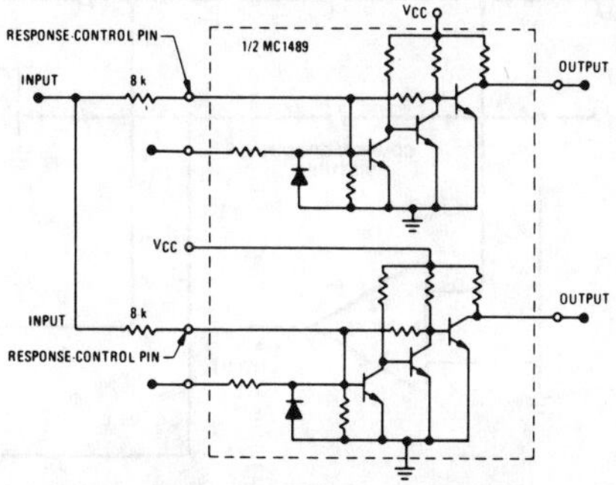

Am26LS29 serial data driver/receiver

DISTINCTIVE CHARACTERISTICS

- Four single ended line drivers in one package for maximum package density
- Output short-circuit protection
- Individual rise time control for each output
- High capacitive load drive capability
- Low I_{CC} and I_{EE} power consumption (26mW/driver typ.)
- Meets all requirements of RS-423
- Three-state outputs for bus oriented systems
- Outputs do not clamp line with power off or in hi-impedance state over entire transmission line voltage range of RS-423
- Low current PNP inputs compatible with TTL, MOS and CMOS
- Available in military and commercial temperature range
- Advanced low power Schottky processing

GENERAL DESCRIPTION

The Am26LS29 is a quad single ended line driver, designed for digital data transmission. The Am26LS29 meets all the requirements of EIA Standard RS-423 and Federal STD 1030. It features four buffered outputs with high source and sink current, and output short circuit protection.

A slew rate control pin allows the use of an external capacitor to control slew rate for suppression of near end cross talk to receivers in the cable.

The Am26LS29 has three-state outputs for bus oriented systems. The outputs in the hi-impedance state will not clamp the line over the transmission line voltage of RS-423. A typical full duplex system would use the Am26LS29 line driver and up to twelve Am26LS32 line receivers or an Am26LS32 line receiver and up to thirty-two Am26LS29 line drivers with only one enabled at a time and all others in the three-state mode.

The Am26LS29 is constructed using advanced low-power Schottky processing.

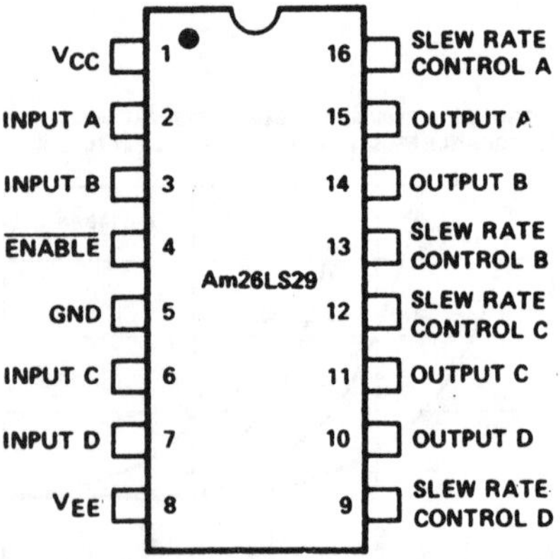

Note: Pin 1 is marked for orientation

BLOCK DIAGRAM

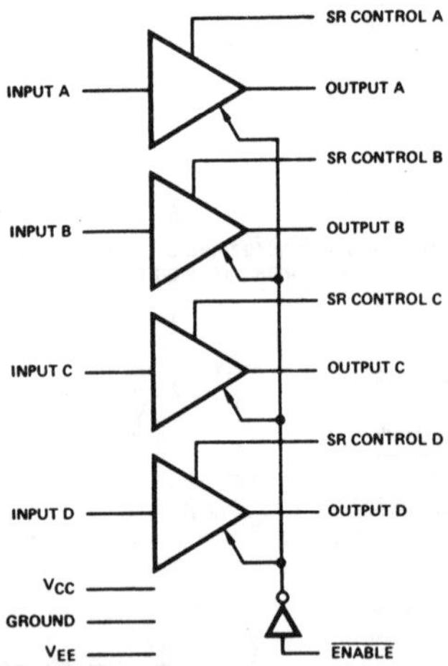

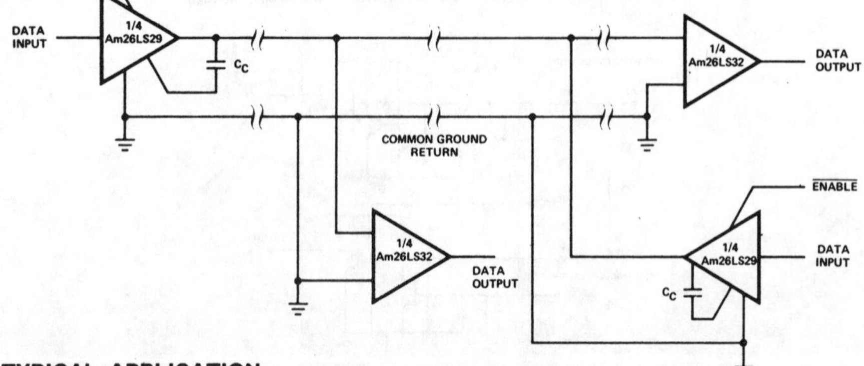

TYPICAL APPLICATION

ABSOLUTE MAXIMUM RATINGS

Storage Temperature .... −65°C to +150°C
Supply Voltage
V+ 7.0V
V− .... −7.0V
Power Dissipation 600mW
Input Voltage .... −0.5 to +15.0V
Output Voltage (Power Off) .... ±15V
Lead Soldering Temperature (10) seconds) .... 300°C

Stresses above those listed under ABSOLUTE MAXIMUM RATINGS may cause permanent device failure. Functionality at or above these limits is not implied. Exposure to absolute maximum ratings for extended periods may affect device reliability.

OPERATING RANGES

Commercial (C) Devices
Temperature .... 0°C to +70°C
Supply Voltage (V_{CC}) .... +4.75V to +5.25V
(V_{EE}) .... −4.75V to −5.25V

Military (M) Devices
Temperature .... −55°C to +125°C
Supply Voltage (V_{CC}) .... +4.5V to +5.5V
(V_{EE}) .... −4.75 to −5.5V

Operating ranges define those limits over which the functionality of the device is guaranteed.

DC CHARACTERISTICS over operating range unless otherwise specified

Parameters	Description	Test Conditions		Min	Typ (Note 1)	Max	Units
V_O	Output Voltage	$R_L = \infty$(Note 3)	$V_{IN} = 2.4V$	4.0	4.4	6.0	Volts
$\overline{V_O}$			$V_{IN} = 0.4V$	−4.0	−4.4	−6.0	Volts
V_T	Output Voltage	$R_L = 450\Omega$	$V_{IN} = 2.4V$	3.6	4.1		Volts
$\overline{V_T}$			$V_{IN} = 0.4V$	−3.6	−4.1		Volts
$\|V_T\|-\|\overline{V_T}\|$	Output Unbalance	$\|V_{CC}\| = \|V_{EE}\|$, $R_L = 450\Omega$			0.02	0.4	Volts
I_X+	Output Leakage Power Off	$V_{CC} = V_{EE} = 0V$	$V_O = 10V$		2.0	100	μA
I_X-			$V_O = -10V$		−2.0	−100	μA
I_S+	Output Short Circuit Current	$V_O = 0V$	$V_{IN} = 2.4V$		−70	−150	mA
I_S-			$V_{IN} = 0.4V$		60	150	mA
I_{SLEW}	Slew Control Current	$V_{SLEW} = V_{EE} + 0.9V$			±110		μA
I_{CC}	Positive Supply Current	$V_{IN} = 0.4V$, $R_L = I\infty$			18	30	mA
I_{EE}	Negative Supply Current	$V_{IN} = 0.4V$, $R_L = \infty$			−10	−22	mA
I_O	Off State (High Impedance) Output Current	V_{CC} = MAX	$V_O = 10V$		2.0	100	μA
			$V_O = -10V$		−2.0	−100	μA
V_{IH}	High Level Input Voltage			2.0			Volts
V_{IL}	Low Level Input Voltage					0.8	Volts
I_{IH}	High Level Input Current	$V_{IN} = 2.4V$			1.0	40	μA
		$V_{IN} \leq 15V$			10	100	μA
I_{IL}	Low Level Input Current	$V_{IN} = 0.4V$			−30	−200	μA
V_I	Input Clamp Voltage	$I_{IN} = -12mA$				−1.5	Volts

Notes: 1. Typical limits are at $V_{CC} = 5.0V$, $V_{EE} = -5.0V$, 25°C ambient and maximum loading.
2. Symbols and definitions correspond to EIA RS-423 where applicable.
3. Output voltage is +3.9V minimum and −3.9V minimum at −55°C.

TYPICAL PERFORMANCE CURVES

Slew Rate (Rise or Fall Time) Versus External Capacitor

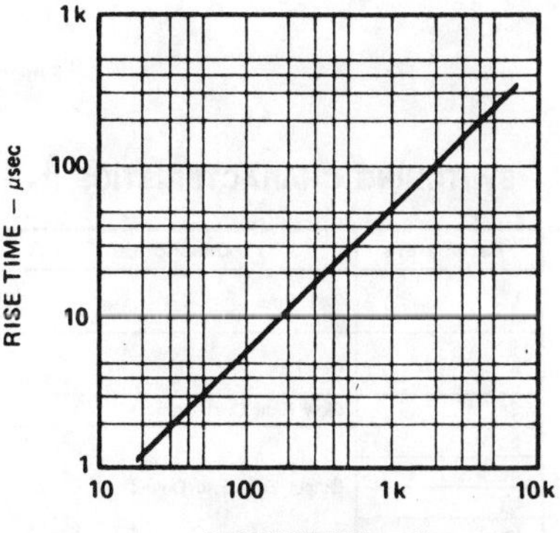

SWITCHING TEST CIRCUIT / SWITCHING TEST WAVEFORM

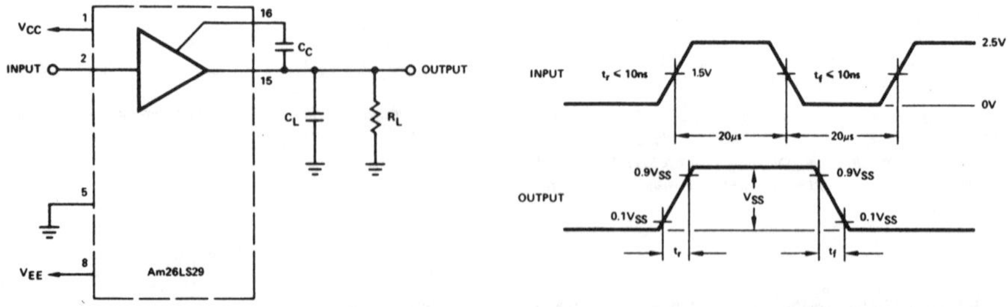

Figure 1. Rise Time Control.

SWITCHING TEST CIRCUIT / SWITCHING TEST WAVEFORM

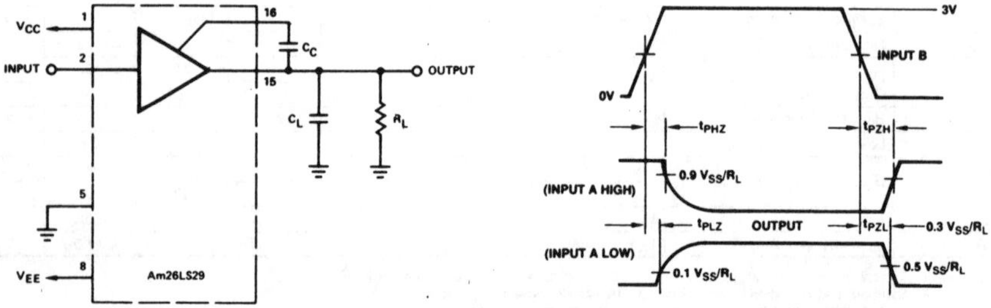

Figure 2. Three State Delays

SWITCHING CHARACTERISTICS ($T_A = +25°C$, $V_{CC} = 5.0V$, $V_{EE} = -5.0V$)

Parameters	Description	Test Conditions		Min	Typ	Max	Units
t_r	Rise Time	$R_L = 450\ \Omega$, $C_L = 500$ pF, Fig. 1	$C_C = 50$ pF		3.0		μs
			$C_C = 0$ pF		120	300	ns
t_f	Fall Time	$R_L = 450\ \Omega$, $C_L = 500$ pF, Fig. 1	$C_C = 50$ pF		3.0		μs
			$C_C = 0$ pF		120	300	ns
Src	Slow Rate Coefficient	$R_L = 450\ \Omega$, $C_L = 500$ pF, Fig. 1			.06		μs/pF
t_{LZ}	Output Enable to Output	$R_L = 450\ \Omega$, $C_L = 500$ pF, $C_C = 0$ pF, Fig. 2			180	300	ns
t_{HZ}					250	350	
t_{ZL}		$R_L = 450\ \Omega$, $C_L = 500$ pF, $C_C = 0$ pF, Fig. 2.			250	350	
t_{ZH}					180	300	

Am26LS29EQUIVALENT CIRCUIT

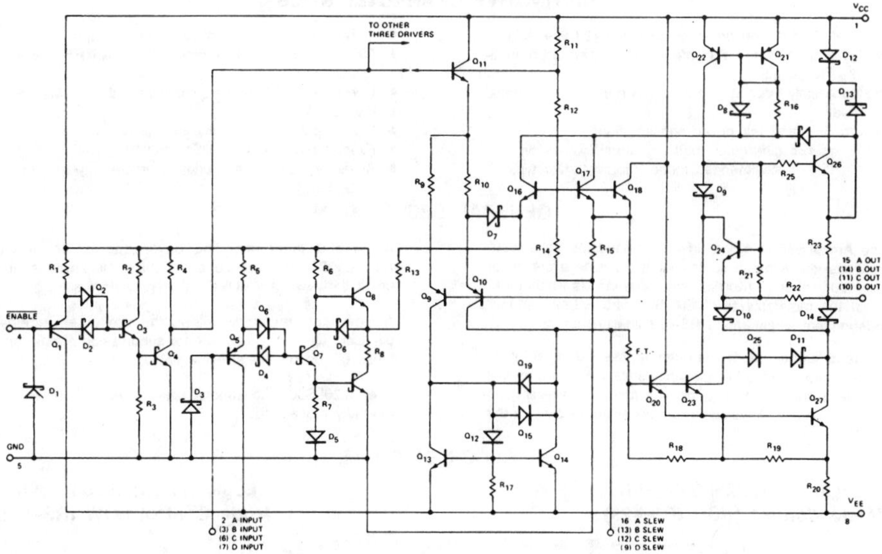

Am26LS30 serial data driver/receiver

DISTINCTIVE CHARACTERISTICS

- Dual RS-422 line driver or quad RS-423 line driver
- Driver outputs do not clamp line with power off or in hi-impedance state
- Individually three-state drivers when used in differential mode
- Low I_{CC} and I_{EE} power consumption
  - RS-422 differential mode 35mW/driver typ.
  - RS-423 single-ended mode 26mW/driver typ.
- Individual slew rate control for each output
- 50Ω transmission line drive capability (RS-422 into virtual ground)
- Low current PNP inputs compatible with TTL, MOS and CMOS
- High capacitive load drive capability
- Exact replacement for DS16/3691
- Advanced low power Schottky processing

GENERAL DESCRIPTION

The Am26LS30 is a line driver designed for digital data transmission. A mode control input provides a choice of operation either as two differential line drivers which meet all of the requirements of EIA Standard RS-422 or four independent single-ended RS-423 line drivers.

In the differential mode the outputs have individual three-state controls. In the hi-impedance state these outputs will not clamp the line over a common mode transmissin line voltage of ±10V. A typical full duplex system would be the Am26LS30 differential line driver and up to twelve Am26LS32 line receivers or an Am26LS32 line receiver and up to thirty-two Am26LS30 differential drivers.

A slew rate control pin allows the use of an external capacitor to control slew rate for suppression of near end cross talk to receivers in the cable.

The Am26LS30 is constructed using Advanced Low Power Schottky processing.

BLOCK DIAGRAM

Logic for Am26LS30 with Mode Control HIGH (RS-423)

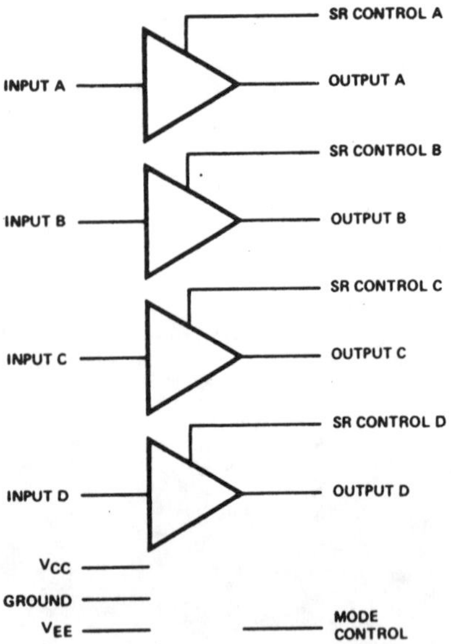

Logic for Am26LS30 with Mode Control LOW (RS-422)

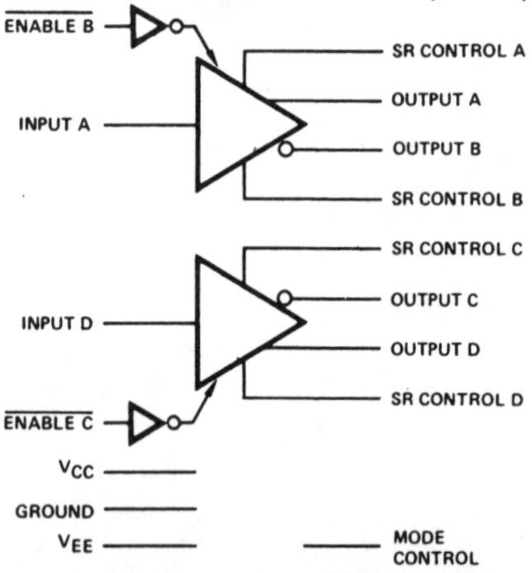

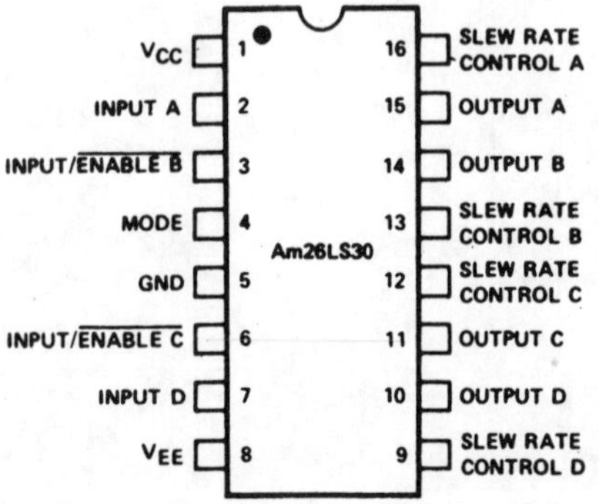

Note: Pin 1 is marked for orientation

TYPICAL APPLICATION

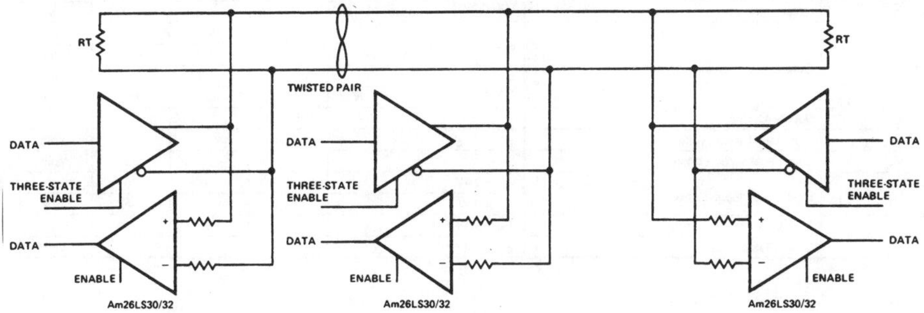

Am26LS30 FUNCTION TABLE

MODE	INPUTS A(D)	INPUTS B(C)	OUTPUTS A(D)	OUTPUTS B(C)
0	0	0	0	1
0	0	1	Z	Z
0	1	0	1	0
0	1	1	Z	Z
1	0	0	0	0
1	0	1	0	1
1	1	0	1	0
1	1	1	1	1

OPERATING RANGES

Commercial (C) Devices
- Temperature .... 0°C to +70°C
- Supply Voltage (V_{CC}) .... +4.75V to +5.25V
- (V_{EE}) .... GND

Military (M) Devices
- Temperature .... −55°C to +125°C
- Supply Voltage (V_{CC}) .... +4.5V to +5.5V
- (V_{EE}) .... GND

Operating ranges define those limits over which the functionality of the device is guaranteed.

ABSOLUTE MAXIMUM RATINGS

Storage Temperature .... −65°C to +150°C
Supply Voltage
- V+ 7.0V
- V− .... −7.0V

Power Dissipation 600mW
Input Voltage .... −0.5 to +15.0V
Output Voltage (Power Off) .... ±15V
Lead Soldering Temperature (10 seconds) .... 300°C

Stresses above those listed under ABSOLUTE MAXIMUM RATINGS may cause permanent device failure. Functionality at or above these limits is not implied. Exposure to absolute maximum ratings for extended periods may affect device reliability.

DC CHARACTERISTICS over operating range unless otherwise specified

EIA RS-422 Connection, Mode Voltage ⩽0.8V

Parameters	Description	Test Conditions (Note 3)		Min	Typ (Note 1)	Max	Units
V_O	Differential Output Voltage, $V_{A,B}$	$R_L = \infty$	$V_{IN} = 2.0V$		3.6	6.0	Volts
$\overline{V_O}$			$V_{IN} = 0.8V$		−3.6	−6.0	Volts
V_T	Differential Output Voltage, $V_{A,B}$	$R_L = 100\Omega$	$V_{IN} = 2.0V$	2.0	2.4		Volts
$\overline{V_T}$			$V_{IN} = 0.8V$	−2.0	−2.1		Volts
V_{OS}, $\overline{V_{OS}}$	Common Mode Offset Voltage	$R_L = 100\Omega$			2.5	3.0	Volts
$\lvert V_T \rvert - \lvert \overline{V_T} \rvert$	Difference in Differential Output Voltage	$R_L = 100\Omega$			0.005	0.4	Volts
$\lvert V_{OS} \rvert - \lvert \overline{V_{OS}} \rvert$	Difference in Common Mode Offset Voltage	$R_L = 100\Omega$			0.005	0.4	Volts
V_{SS}	$\lvert V_T - \overline{V_T} \rvert$	$R_L = 100\Omega$		4.0	4.8		Volts
V_{CMR}	Output Voltage Common Mode Range	$\overline{V_{ENABLE}} = 2.4V$		±10			Volts
I_{XA}	Output Leakage Current	$V_{CC} = 0V$	$V_{CMR} = 10V$			100	μA
I_{XB}			$V_{CMR} = -10V$			−100	μA

I_{OX}	Off State (High Impedance) Output Current	V_{CC} = MAX	$V_{CMR} \leq 10V$			100	μA
			$V_{CMR} \geq -10V$			−100	μA
I_{SA}, I_{SB}	Output Short Circuit Current	V_{IN} = 2.4V	V_{OA} = 6.0V		80	150	mA
			V_{OB} = 0V		−80	−150	mA
		V_{IN} = 0.4V	V_{OA} = 0V		−80	−150	mA
			V_{OB} = 6.0V		80	150	mA
I_{CC}	Supply Current				18	30	mA
V_{IH}	High Level Input Voltage			2.0			Volts
V_{IL}	Low Level Input Voltage					0.8	Volts
I_{IH}	High Level Input Current	V_{IN} = 2.4V			1.0	40	μA
		$V_{IN} \leq 15V$			10	100	μA
I_{IL}	Low Level Input Current	V_{IN} = 0.4V			−30	−200	μA
V_I	Input Clamp Voltage	I_{IN} = −12mA				−1.5	Volts

TYPICAL PERFORMANCE CURVES

Slew Rate (Rise or Fall Time) Versus External Capacitor

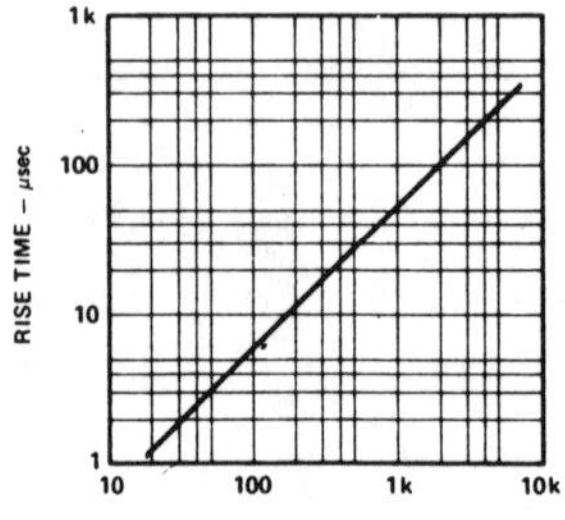

EIA RS-423 CONNECTION

SWITCHING TEST CIRCUIT

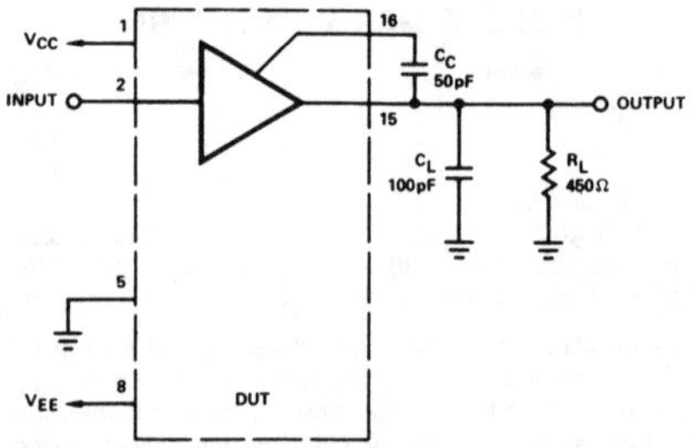

SWITCHING TEST WAVEFORM

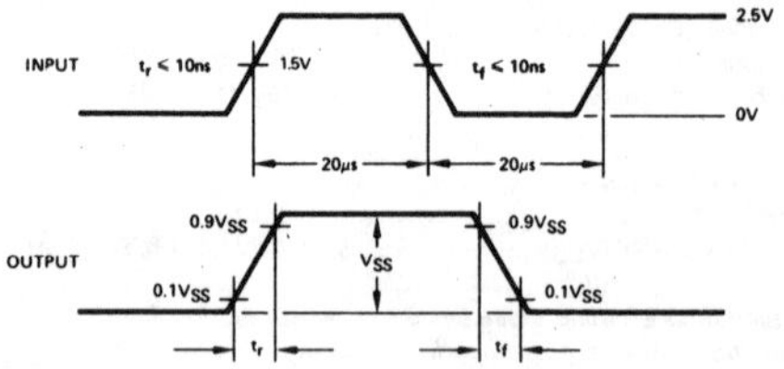

Figure 1. Rise Time Control for RS-423.

RS-422 CONNECTION

SWITCHING TEST CIRCUIT

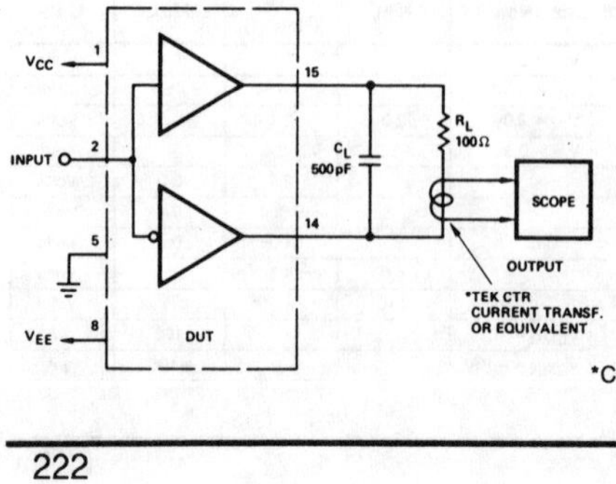

SWITCHING TEST WAVEFORM

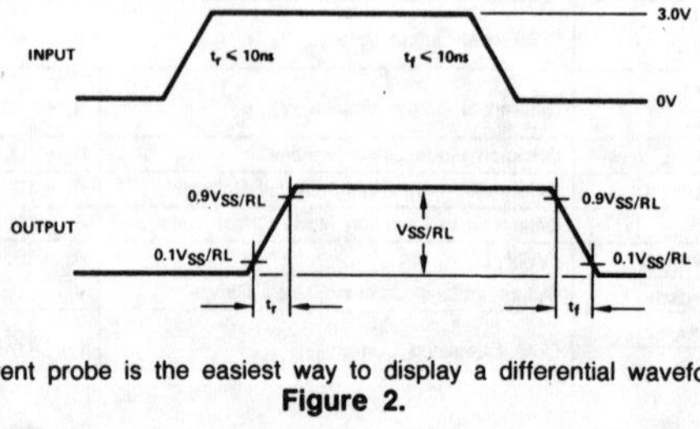

*Current probe is the easiest way to display a differential waveform.

Figure 2.

SWITCHING TEST CIRCUIT

SWITCHING TEST WAVEFORM

Figure 3. Three State Delays.

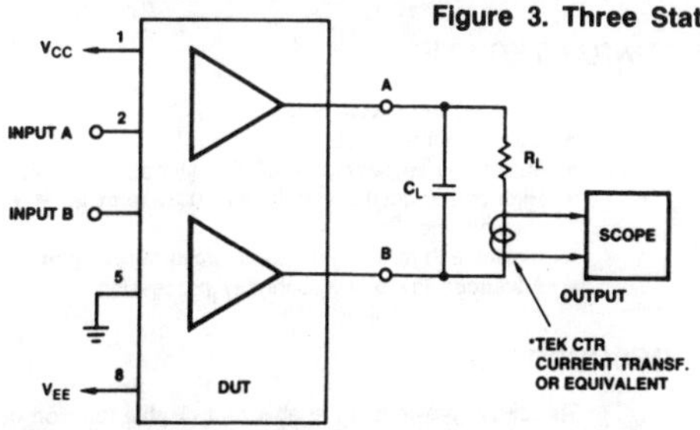

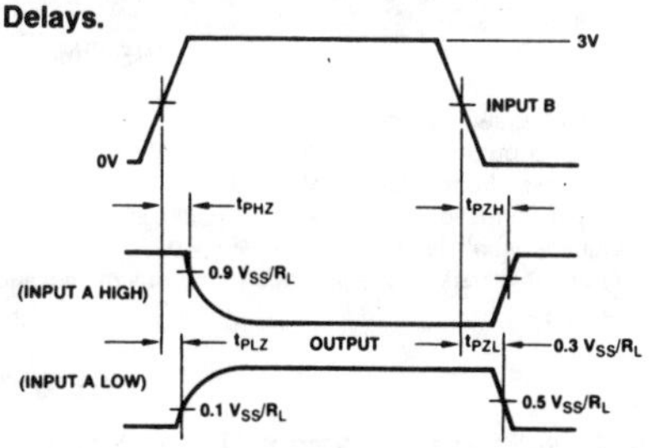

SWITCHING CHARACTERISTICS

EIA RS-422 Connection, $V_{CC} = 5.0V$, $V_{EE} = GND$, Mode = 0.4V, $T_A = 25°C$

Parameters	Description	Test Conditions	Min	Typ	Max	Units
t_r	Differential Output Rise Time	Fig. 2, $R_L = 100\ \Omega$, $C_L = 500$ pF		120	200	ns
t_f	Differential Output Fall Time	Fig. 2, $R_L = 100\ \Omega$, $C_L = 500$ pF		120	200	ns
t_{PDH}	Output Propagation Delay	Fig. 2, $R_L = 100\ \Omega$, $C_L = 500$ pF		120	200	ns
t_{PDL}	Output Propagation Delay	Fig. 2, $R_L = 100\ \Omega$, $C_L = 500$ pF		120	200	ns
t_{LZ}	Output Enable to Output	$R_L = 450\ \Omega$, $C_L = 500$ pF, $C_C = 0$ pF, Fig. 3		180	300	ns
t_{HZ}				250	350	
t_{ZL}		$R_L = 450\ \Omega$, $C_L = 500$ pF, $C_C = 0$ pF, Fig. 3		250	350	
t_{ZH}				180	300	

Notes:
1. Typical limits are at $V_{CC} = 5.0$ V, $V_{EE} = GND$, 25°C ambient and maximum loading.
2. Symbols and definitions correspond to EIA RS-422 where applicable.
3. R_L connected between each output and its complement.

SWITCHING CHARACTERISTICS

RS-423 Connection, $V_{CC} = 5.0V$, $V_{EE} = -5.0V$, Mode = 2.4V, $T_A = 25°C$

Parameters	Description	Test Conditions		Min	Typ	Max	Units
t_r	Rise Time	Fig. 1, $R_L = 450\ \Omega$, $C_L = 500$ pF	$C_C = 50$ pF		3.0		μs
			$C_C = 0$		120	300	ns
t_f	Fall Time	Fig. 1, $R_L = 450\ \Omega$, $C_L = 500$ pF	$C_C = 50$ pF		3.0		μs
			$C_C = 0$		120	300	ns
Src	Slow Rate Coefficient	Fig 1, $R_L = 450\ \Omega$, $C_L = 500$ pF			.06		μs/pF
t_{PDH}	Output Propagation Delay	Fig. 1, $R_L = 450\ \Omega$, $C_L = 500$ pF, $C_C = 0$			180	300	ns
t_{PDL}	Output Propagation Delay	Fig. 1, $R_L = 450\ \Omega$, $C_L = 500$ pF, $C_C = 0$			180	300	ns

Am26LS30 EQUIVALENT CIRCUIT

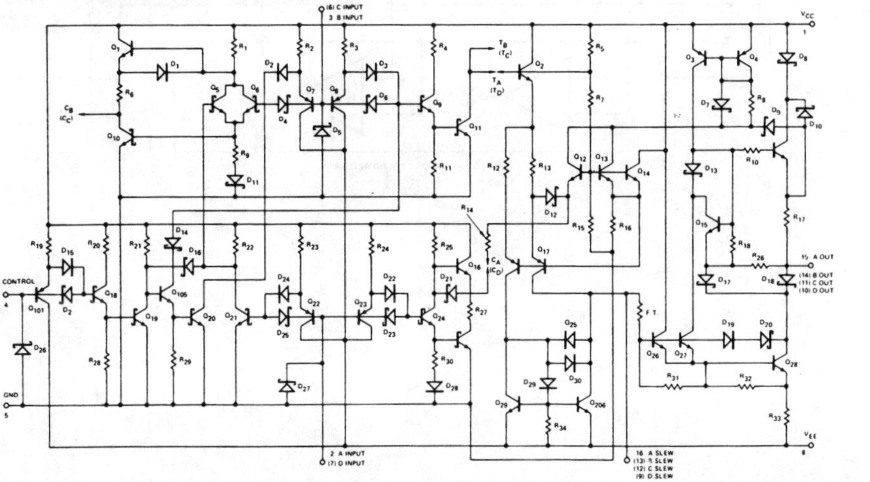

Am26LS31 serial data driver/receiver

DISTINCTIVE CHARACTERISTICS

- Output skew – 2.0ns typical
- Input to output delay – 12ns
- Operation from single +5V supply
- 16-pin hermetic and molded DIP package
- Outputs won't load line when $V_{CC} = 0$
- Four line drivers in one package for maximum package density
- Output short-circuit protection
- Complementary outputs
- Meets the requirements of EIA standard RS-422
- High output drive capability for 100Ω terminated transmission lines
- Available in military and commercial temperature range
- Advanced low-power Schottky processing

GENERAL DESCRIPTION

The Am26LS31 is a quad-differential line driver, designed for digital data transmission over balanced lines. The Am26LS31 meets all the requirements of EIA standard RS-422 and federal standard 1020. It is designed to provide unipolar differential drive to twisted-pair or parallel-wire transmission lines.

The circuit provides an enable and disable function common to all four drivers. The Am26LS31 features 3-state outputs and logical OR-ed complementary enable inputs. The inputs are all LS compatible and are all one unit load.

The Am26LS31 is constructed using advanced low-power Schottky processing.

BLOCK DIAGRAM

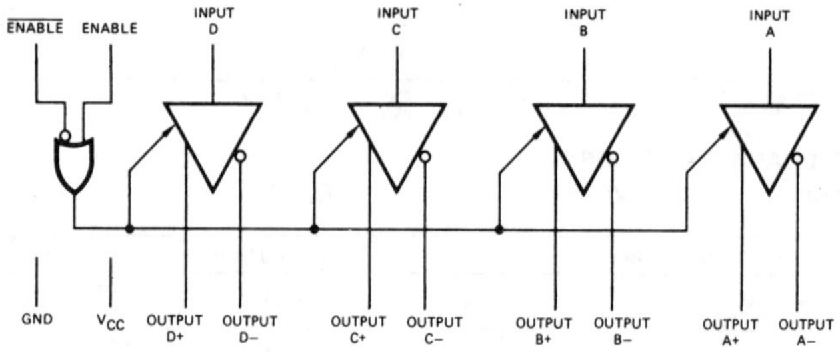

TYPICAL APPLICATION

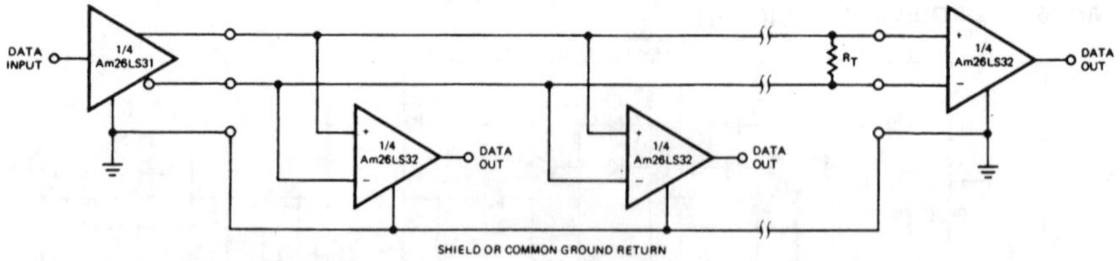

DC CHARACTERISTICS over operating range unless otherwise specified

Parameters	Description	Test Conditions (Note 2)		Min	Typ (Note 1)	Max	Units
V_{OH}	Output HIGH Voltage	V_{CC} = Min, I_{OH} = –20mA		2.5	3.2		Volts
V_{OL}	Output LOW Voltage	V_{CC} = Min, I_{OL} = 20mA			0.32	0.5	Volts
V_{IH}	Input HIGH Voltage	V_{CC} = Min		2.0			Volts
V_{IL}	Input LOW Voltage	V_{CC} = Max				0.8	Volts
I_{IL}	Input LOW Current	V_{CC} = Max, V_{IN} = 0.4V			–0.20	–0.36	mA
I_{IH}	Input HIGH Current	V_{CC} = Max, V_{IN} = 2.7V			0.5	20	μA
I_I	Input Reverse Current	V_{CC} = Max, V_{IN} = 7.0V			0.001	0.1	mA
I_O	Off-State (High Impedance) Output Current	V_{CC} = MAX	V_O = 2.5V		0.5	20	μA
			V_O = 0.5V		0.5	–20	
V_I	Input Clamp Voltage	V_{CC} = Min, I_{IN} = 18mA			–0.8	–1.5	Volts
I_{SC}	Output Short Circuit Current	V_{CC} = Max		–30	–60	–150	mA
I_{CC}	Power Supply Current	V_{CC} = Max, all outputs disabled			60	80	mA
t_{PLH}	Input to Output	V_{CC} = 5.0V, T_A = 25°C, Load = Note 2			12	20	ns
t_{PHL}	Input to Output	V_{CC} = 5.0V, T_A = 25°C, Load = Note 2			12	20	ns
SKEW	Output to Output	V_{CC} = 5.0V, T_A = 25°C, Load = Note 2			2.0	6.0	ns
t_{LZ}	Enable to Output	V_{CC} = 5.0V, T_A = 25°C, C_L = 10pF			23	35	ns
t_{HZ}	Enable to Output	V_{CC} = 5.0V, T_A = 25°C, C_L = 10pF			17	30	ns
t_{ZL}	Enable to Output	V_{CC} = 5.0V, T_A = 25°C, Load = Note 2			35	45	ns
t_{ZH}	Enable to Output	V_{CC} = 5.0V, T_A = 25°C, Load = Note 2			30	40	ns

Notes: 1. All typical values are V_{CC} = 5.0V, T_A = 25°C.
2. C_L = 30pF, V_{IN} = 1.3V to V_{OUT} = 1.3V, V_{PULSE} = 0V to +3.0V, See Below.

PERFORMANCE CURVES

Guaranteed V_{OH} and V_{OL} (T_A = –55°C to +125°C)

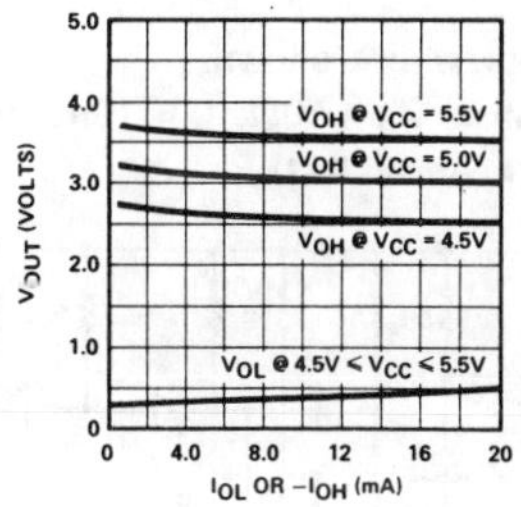

V_{OUT} Versus V_{CC}

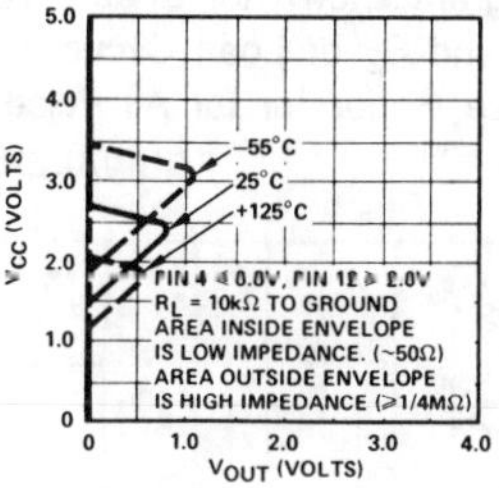

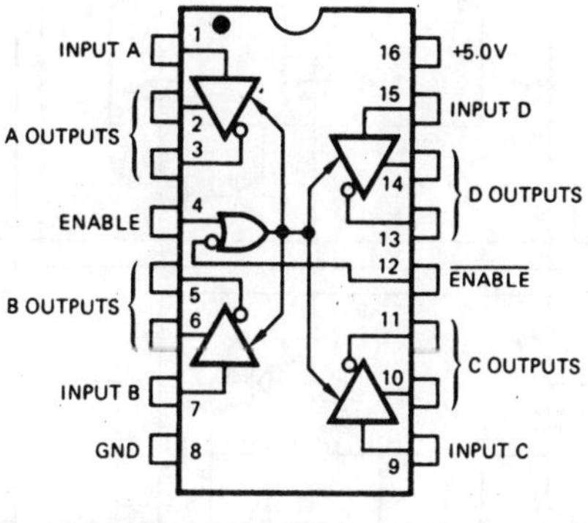

Note: Pin 1 is marked for orientation

SWITCHING TEST CIRCUIT FOR THREE-STATE OUTPUTS

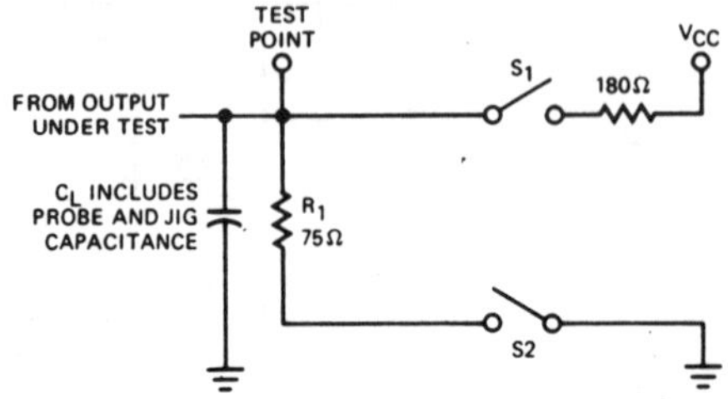

PROPAGATION DELAY (Notes 1 and 3)

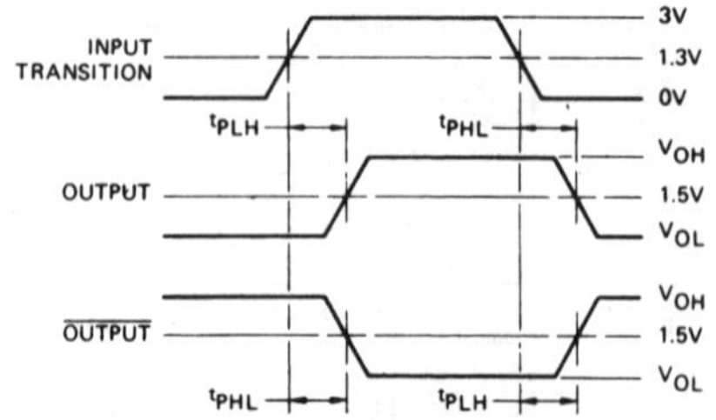

ENABLE AND DISABLE TIMES (Notes 2 and 3)

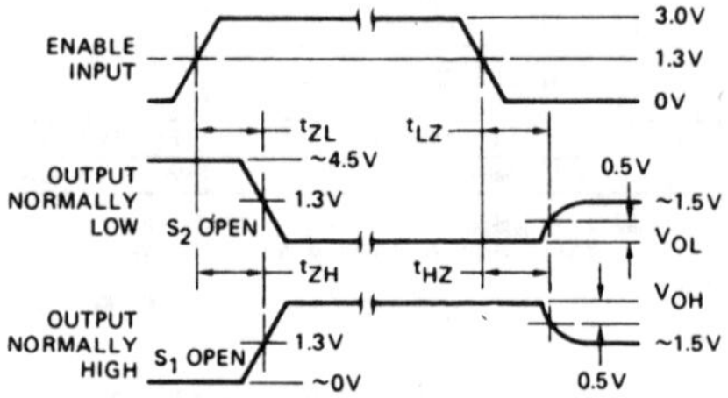

Notes: 1. Diagram shown for $\overline{\text{Enable}}$ LOW.
2. S_1 and S_2 of Load Circuit are closed except where shown.
3. Pulse Generator for All Pulses: Rate ≤ 1.0MHz; $Z_o = 50\Omega$; $t_r \leq 15ns$; $t_f \leq 6.0ns$.

EQUIVALENT CIRCUIT (1/4 Am26LS31)

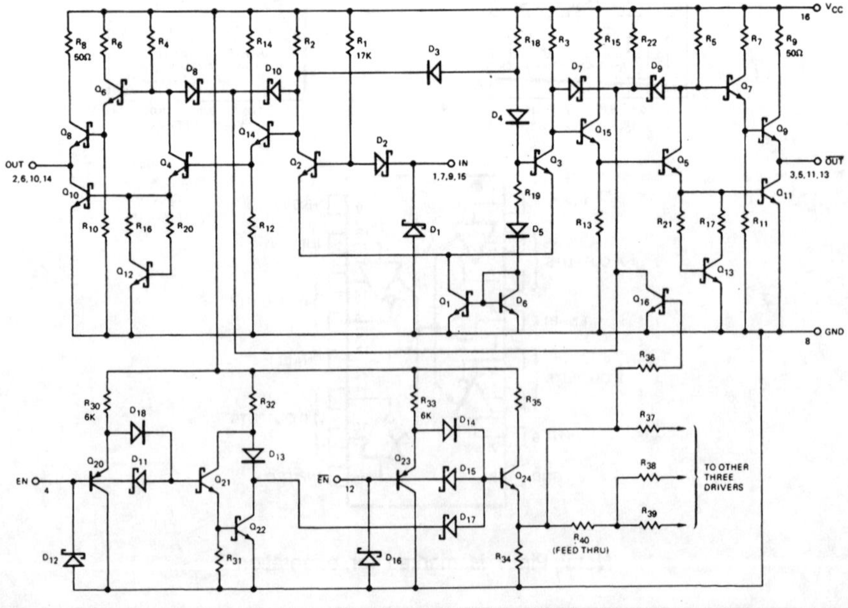

serial data driver/receiver Am26LS32/33

DISTINCTIVE CHARACTERISTICS

- Input voltage range of 15V (differential or common mode) on Am26LS33; 7V (differential or common mode) on Am26LS32
  - ±0.2V sensitivity over the input voltage range on Am26LS32;
  - ±0.5V sensitivity on Am26LS33
- 6k minimum input impedance with 30mV input hysteresis
- The Am26LS32 meets all the requirements of RS-422 and RS-423
- Operation from single +5V supply
- Fail safe input-output relationship. Output always high when inputs are open
- Three-state drive, with choice of complementary output enables, for receiving directly onto a data bus.

GENERAL DESCRIPTION

The Am26LS32 is a quad line receiver designed to meet the requirements of RS-422 and RS-423, and Federal Standards 1020 and 1030 for balanced and unbalanced digital data transmission.

The Am26LS32 features an input sensitivity of 200mV over the input voltage range of ±7V.

The Am26LS33 features an input sensitivity of 500mV over the input voltage range of ±15V.

The Am26LS32 and Am26LS33 provide an enable and disable function common to all four receivers. Both parts feature 3-state outputs with 8mA sink capability and incorporate a fail safe input-output relationship which keeps the outputs high when the inputs are open.

The Am26LS32 and Am26LS33 are constructed using Advanced Low-Power Schottky processing.

BLOCK DIAGRAM

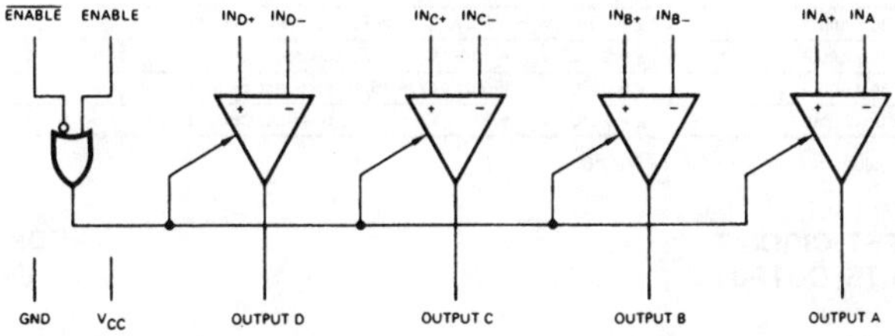

ABSOLUTE MAXIMUM RATINGS

Supply Voltage	7.0V
Commom Mode Range	±25V
Differential Input Voltage	±25V
Enable Voltage	7.0V
Output Sink Current	50mA
Storage Temperature Range	−65°C to +165°C

Stresses above those listed under ABSOLUTE MAXIMUM RATINGS may cause permanent device failure. Functionality at or above these limits is not implied. Exposure to absolute maximum ratings for extended periods may affect device reliability.

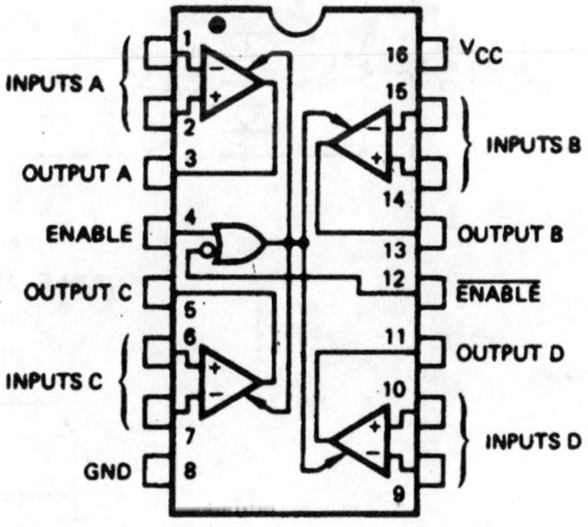

OPERATING RANGES

Commercial (C) Devices

Temperature	0°C to +70°C
Supply Voltage	+4.75V to +5.25V

Military (M) Devices

Temperature	−55°C to +125°C
Supply Voltage	+4.5V to +5.5V

Operating ranges define those limits over which the functionality of the device is guaranteed.

DC CHARACTERISTICS over operating range unless otherwise specified

Parameters	Description	Test Conditions		Min	Typ (Note 1)	Max	Units
V_{TH}	Differential Input Voltage	$V_{OUT} = V_{OL}$ or V_{OH}	Am26LS32, $-7V \leqslant V_{CM} \leqslant +7V$	−0.2	±0.06	+0.2	Volts
			Am26LS33, $-15V \leqslant V_{CM} \leqslant +15V$	−0.5	±0.12	+0.5	
R_{IN}	Input Resistance	$-15V \leqslant V_{CM} \leqslant +15V$ (One input AC ground)		6.0	9.8		kΩ
I_{IN}	Input Current (Under Test)	$V_{IN} = +15V$, Other Input $-15V \leqslant V_{IN} \leqslant +15V$				2.3	mA
I_{IN}	Input Current (Under Test)	$V_{IN} = -15V$, Other Input $-15V \leqslant V_{IN} \leqslant +15V$				−2.8	mA
V_{OH}	Output HIGH Voltage	V_{CC} = Min, $\Delta V_{IN} = +1.0V$	COM'L	2.7	3.4		Volts
		$V_{\overline{ENABLE}} = 0.8V$, $I_{OH} = -440\mu A$	MIL	2.5	3.4		
V_{OL}	Output LOW Voltage	V_{CC} = Min, $\Delta V_{IN} = -1.0V$	$I_{OL} = 4.0mA$			0.4	Volts
		$V_{\overline{ENABLE}} = 0.8V$	$I_{OL} = 8.0mA$			0.45	
V_{IL}	Enable LOW Voltage					0.8	Volts
V_{IH}	Enable HIGH Voltage			2.0			Volts
V_I	Enable Clamp Voltage	V_{CC} = Min, $I_{IN} = -18mA$				−1.5	Volts
I_O	Off-State (High Impedance) Output Current	V_{CC} = Max	$V_O = 2.4V$			20	μA
			$V_O = 0.4V$			−20	
I_{IL}	Enable LOW Current	$V_{IN} = 0.4V$			−0.2	−0.36	mA
I_{IH}	Enable HIGH Current	$V_{IN} = 2.7V$			0.5	20	μA
I_I	Enable Input High Current	$V_{IN} = 5.5V$			1	100	μA
I_{SC}	Output Short Circuit Current	$V_O = 0V$, V_{CC} = Max, $\Delta V_{IN} = +1.0V$		−15	−50	−85	mA
I_{CC}	Power Supply Current	V_{CC} = Max, All V_{IN} = GND, Outputs Disabled			52	70	mA
V_{HYST}	Input Hysteresis	$T_A = 25°C$, $V_{CC} = 5.0V$, $V_{CM} = 0V$			30		mV
t_{PLH}	Input to Output	$T_A = 25°C$, $V_{CC} = 5.0V$, $C_L = 15pF$, see test cond. below			17	25	ns
t_{PHL}	Input to Output	$T_A = 25°C$, $V_{CC} = 5.0V$, $C_L = 15pF$, see test cond. below			17	25	ns
t_{LZ}	Enable to Output	$T_A = 25°C$, $V_{CC} = 5.0V$, $C_L = 5pF$, see test cond. below			20	30	ns
t_{HZ}	Enable to Output	$T_A = 25°C$, $V_{CC} = 5.0V$, $C_L = 5pF$, see test cond. below			15	22	ns
t_{ZL}	Enable to Output	$T_A = 25°C$, $V_{CC} = 5.0V$, $C_L = 15pF$, see test cond. below			15	22	ns
t_{ZH}	Enable to Output	$T_A = 25°C$, $V_{CC} = 5.0V$, $C_L = 15pF$, see test cond. below			15	22	ns

Note: 1. All typical values are $V_{CC} = 5.0V$, $T_A = 25°C$.

SWITCHING TEST CIRCUIT FOR THREE-STATE OUTPUTS

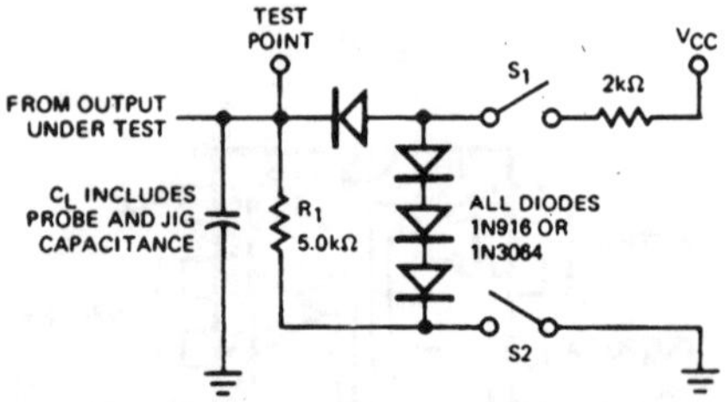

PROPAGATION DELAY
(Notes 1 and 3)

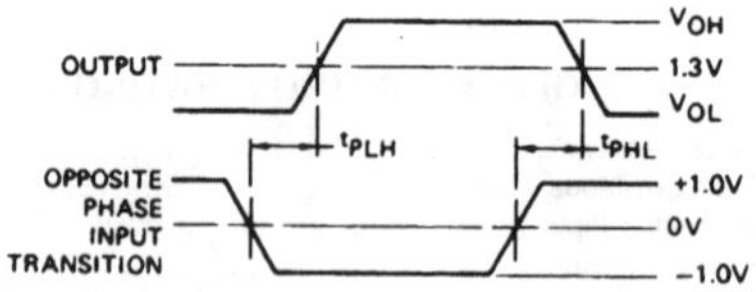

ENABLE AND DISABLE TIMES
(Notes 2 and 3)

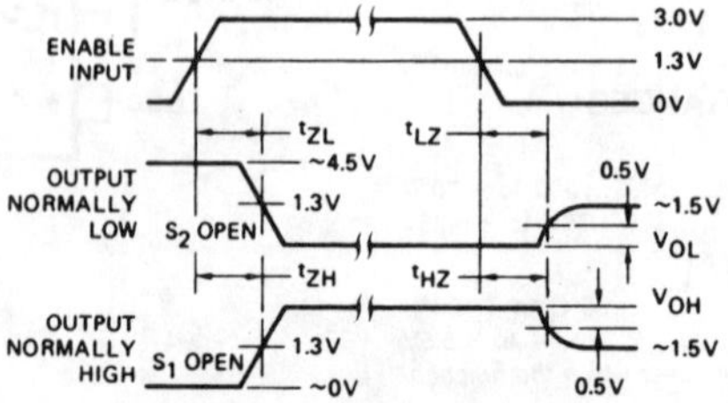

serial data driver/receiver Am26LS32B

DISTINCTIVE CHARACTERISTICS

- ±100mV sensitivity over V_{IN} range of 0V to 5V
- ±200mV sensitivity over V_{CM} range
- −7V to +12V input voltage range – differential or common mode
- Guaranteed input voltage hysteresis limits
  - 80mV minimum
  - 200mV maximum
- 3V maximum open circuit input voltage
- Three-state outputs disabled during power-up and power down
- Maximum guarantees for t_{PD} skew
- All AC and DC parameters guaranteed over COM'L and MIL operating temperature ranges
- Single +5V supply
- Advanced low-power Schottky processing

GENERAL DESCRIPTION

The Am26LS32B is a quad line receiver designed to meet the requirements of RS-422 and RS-423, CCITT V.10 and V.11, and Federal Standards 1020 and 1030 for balanced and unbalanced digital data transmission.

The Am26LS32B features an input sensitivity of 200mV over the common mode input voltage range of −7V to +12V.

The Am26LS32B is the first device in the Am26LS32 configuration to guarantee minimum hysteresis and propagation delay skew while maintaining better propagation delay guarantees than the Am26LS32. This allows a more critical analysis of performance in high noise environments and better performance in terms of signal quality, resulting in better system performance.

The Am26LS32B provides an enable and disable function common to all four receivers. It features three-state outputs with 24mA sink capability and incorporates a fail safe input-output relationship which keeps the outputs high when the inputs are open.

The Am26LS32B is constructed using Advanced Low-Power Schottky processing.

BLOCK DIAGRAM

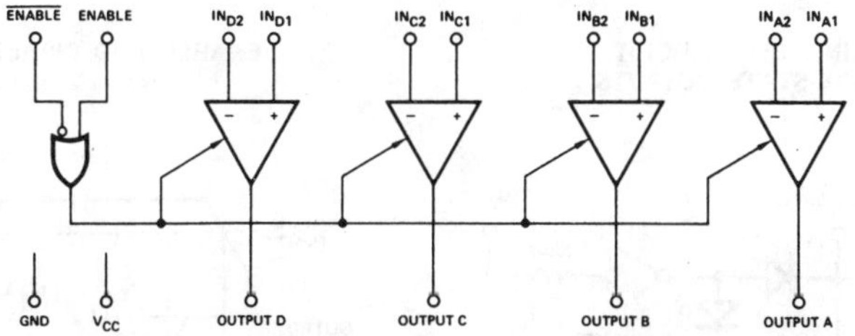

ABSOLUTE MAXIMUM RATINGS

Supply Voltage	7.0V
Commom Mode Range	±25V
Differential Input Voltage	±25V
Enable Voltage	7.0V
Output Sink Current	50mA
Storage Temperature Range	−65°C to +165°C

Stresses above those listed under ABSOLUTE MAXIMUM RATINGS may cause permanent device failure. Functionality at or above these limits is not implied. Exposure to absolute maximum ratings for extended periods may affect device reliability.

OPERATING RANGES

Commercial (C) Devices

Temperature	0°C to +70°C
Supply Voltage	+4.75V to +5.25V

Military (M) Devices

Temperature	−55°C to +125°C
Supply Voltage	+4.5V to +5.5V

Operating ranges define those limits over which the functionality of the device is guaranteed.

CONNECTION DIAGRAM
Top View

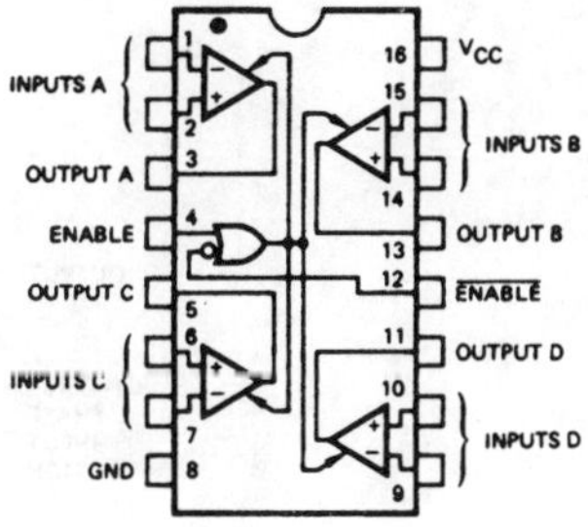

DC CHARACTERISTICS over operating range unless otherwise specified

Parameters	Description	Test Conditions		Min	Typ (Note 1)	Max	Units
V_{TH}	Differential Input Voltage	$V_{OUT} = V_{OL}$ or V_{OH}	$0 \leqslant V_{CM} \leqslant +5V$	−100	±60	100	mV
			$-7V \leqslant V_{CM} \leqslant +12V$	−200		200	
V_{HYST}	Input Hysteresis			80	120	200	mV
V_{IOC}	Open Circuit Input Voltage			2.0		3.0	Volts
R_{IN}	Input Resistance	$-15V \leqslant V_{CM} \leqslant +15V$ (One input AC ground)		6.0	10		kΩ
I_{IN}	Input Current (Under Test)	$V_{IN} = +15V$, Other Input $-15V \leqslant V_{IN} \leqslant +15V$				2.3	mA
I_{IN}	Input Current (Under Test)	$V_{IN} = -15V$, Other Input $-15V \leqslant V_{IN} \leqslant +15V$				−2.8	mA
V_{OH}	Output HIGH Voltage	V_{CC} = Min, $\Delta V_{IN} = +1.0V$	$I_{OH} = -12mA$	2.0			Volts
		$V_{\overline{ENABLE}} = 0.8V$,	$I_{OH} = -1mA$	2.4			
V_{OL}	Output LOW Voltage	V_{CC} = Min, $\Delta V_{IN} = -1.0V$	$I_{OL} = 16mA$			0.4	Volts
		$V_{\overline{ENABLE}} = 0.8V$	$I_{OL} = 24mA$			0.5	
V_{IL}	Enable LOW Voltage					0.8	Volts
V_{IH}	Enable HIGH Voltage			2.0			Volts
V_I	Enable Clamp Voltage	V_{CC} = Min, $I_{IN} = -18mA$				−1.5	Volts
I_O	Off-State (High Impedance) Output Current	V_{CC} = Max	$V_O = 2.4V$			50	μA
			$V_O = 0.4V$			−50	
I_{IL}	Enable LOW Current	$V_{IN} = 0.4V$				−0.36	mA
I_{IH}	Enable HIGH Current	$V_{IH} = 2.7V$				20	μA
I_I	Enable HIGH Current	$V_{IN} = 5.5V$				100	μA
I_{SC}	Output Short Circuit Current	$V_O = 0V$, V_{CC} = Max, $\Delta V_{IN} = +1.0V$		−30	−65	−120	mA
I_{CC}	Power Supply Current	V_{CC} = Max, All V_{IN} = GND, Outputs Disabled			52	70	mA

Note: 1. All typical values are $V_{CC} = 5.0V$, $T_A = 25°C$.

SWITCHING TEST CIRCUIT FOR THREE-STATE OUTPUTS

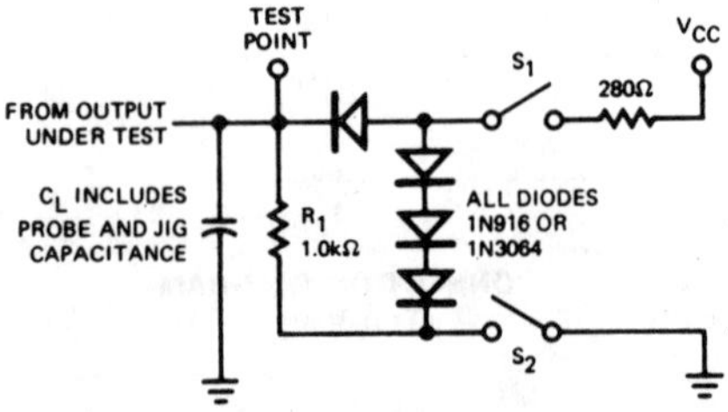

ENABLE AND DISABLE TIMES
(Notes 2 and 3)

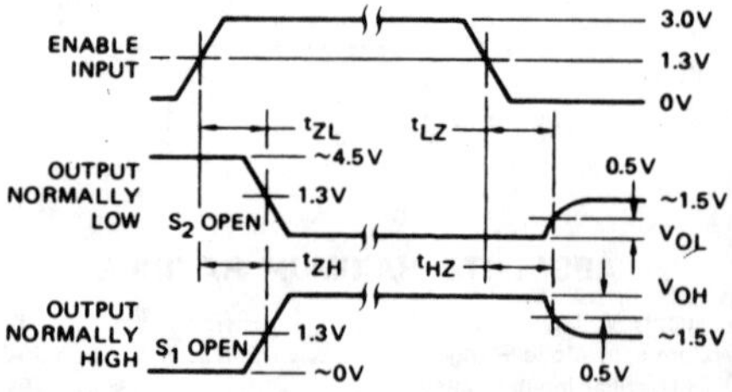

PROPAGATION DELAY
(Notes 1 and 3)

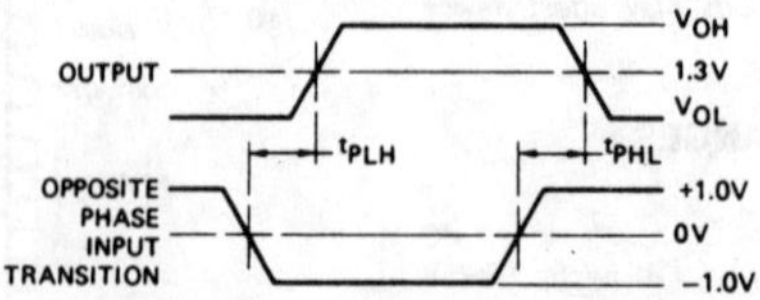

Notes: 1. Diagram shown for Enable LOW.
2. S_1 and S_2 of Load Circuit are closed except where shown.
3. Pulse Generator for All Pulses: Rate $\leqslant$ 1.0MHz; $Z_O = 50\Omega$; $t_r \leqslant 2.5ns$; $t_f \leqslant 2.5ns$.

DISTINCTIVE CHARACTERISTICS

- Meets all requirements of EIA Standards RS-422, RS-423, CCITT V.10 and V.11, and the new party line standard in development under EIA Project Number 1360.
- ±200mV sensitivity over input voltage range
- ±150mV sensitivity for $V_{CM} = 0$
- −7V to +12V common mode input voltage range
- 12kΩ minimum input impedance
- Maximum guarantees for t_{PD} skew
- All AC and DC parameters guaranteed over MIL and COM'L temperature ranges
- Guaranteed input voltages hysteresis limits
  - 120mV minimum
  - 300mV maximum
- No internal failsafe
- Pin compatible with Am26LS32/32B/33

GENERAL DESCRIPTION

The Am26LS34 is a high performance, quad, differential line receiver. It has higher impedance and higher input voltage hysteresis than the similar Am26LS32B. The Am26LS34 also does not have internal fail-safe to allow greater user flexibility.

Input threshold sensitivty is specified for three different V_{CM} ranges. The improved sensitivity, guaranteed hysteresis and skew limits allow a more critical analysis of system performance in high noise environments and better system performance capability.

All performance parameters are guaranted over ±10% supplies and over the operating temperature range. In addition; I_{OL} is specified to 24mA for easy system bus interfacing.

BLOCK DIAGRAM

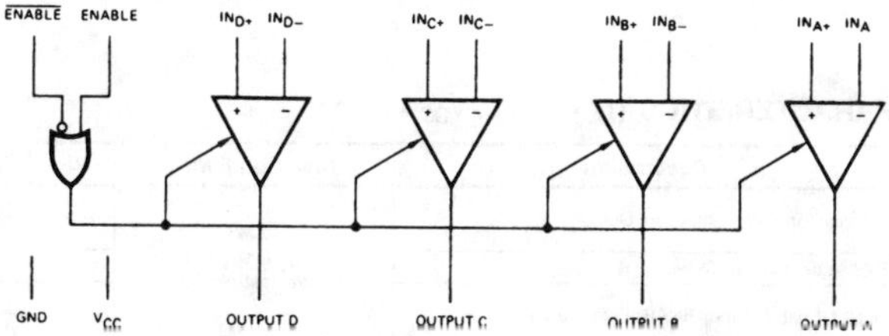

ABSOLUTE MAXIMUM RATINGS

Supply Voltage	7.0V
Commom Mode Voltage	±25V
Differential Input Voltage	30V
Enable Voltage	7.0V
Output Sink Current	50mA
Storage Temperature Range	−65°C to +165°C

Stresses above those listed under ABSOLUTE MAXIMUM RATINGS may cause permanent device failure. Functionality at or above these limits is not implied. Exposure to absolute maximum ratings for extended periods may affect device reliability.

OPERATING RANGES

Commercial (C) Devices	
Temperature	0°C to +70°C
Supply Voltage	+4.75V to +5.25V
Military (M) Devices	
Temperature	−55°C to +125°C
Supply Voltage	+4.5V to +5.5V

Operating ranges define those limits over which the functionality of the device is guaranteed.

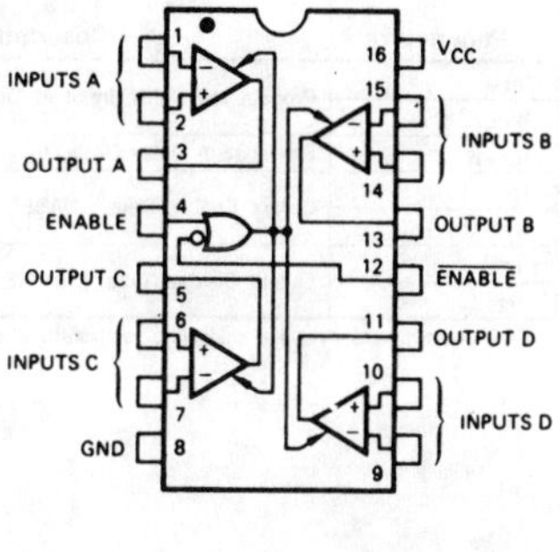

DC CHARACTERISTICS over operating range unless otherwise specified

Parameters	Description	Test Conditions		Min	Typ (Note 1)	Max	Units
V_{TH}	Differential Input Voltage	$V_{OUT} = V_{OL}$ or V_{OH}	$V_{CM} = 0V$	−150	±90	+150	mV
			$-7V \leq V_{CM} \leq +12V$	−200		+200	
			$-15V \leq V_{CM} \leq +15V$	−400		+400	
V_{HYST}	Input Hysteresis			120	180	300	mV
R_{IN}	Input Resistance	$-15V \leq V_{CM} \leq +15V$ (One input AC ground)		12k	20k	40k	Ω
I_{IN}	Input Current (Under Test)	$V_{IN} = +12V$			0.7	1.0	mA
I_{IN}	Input Current (Under Test)	$V_{IN} = -7V$			−0.5	−0.8	mA
V_{OH}	Output HIGH Voltage	V_{CC} = Min, $\Delta V_{IN} = +1.0V$ $V_{\overline{ENABLE}} = 0.8V$	−12mA	2.0			Volts
			−1mA	2.4	3.4		
V_{OL}	Output LOW Voltage	V_{CC} = Min, V_{CC} = Min, $\Delta V_{IN} = -1.0V$ $V_{\overline{ENABLE}} = 0.8V$	$I_{OH} = 16mA$			0.4	Volts
			$I_{OL} = 24mA$			0.5	
V_{IL}	Enable LOW Voltage					0.8	Volts
V_{IH}	Enable HIGH Voltage			2.0			Volts
V_I	Enable Clamp Voltage	V_{CC} = Min, $I_{IN} = -18mA$				−1.5	Volts
V_{IOC}	Open Circuit Input Voltage			2.0		3.0	Volts
I_O	Off-State (High Impedance) Output Current	V_{CC} = Max	$V_O = 2.4V$			50	μA
			$V_O = 0.4V$			−50	
I_{IL}	Enable LOW Current	$V_{IN} = 0.4V$			−0.03	−0.2	mA
I_{IH}	Enable HIGH Current	$V_{IH} = 2.7V$			0.5	20	μA
I_I	Enable Input High Current	$V_{IN} = 5.5V$			1	100	μA
I_{SC}	Output Short Circuit Current	$V_O = 0V$, V_{CC} = Max, $\Delta V_{IN} = +1.0V$		−30	−65	−120	mA
I_{CC}	Power Supply Current	V_{CC} = Max, All V_{IN} = GND, Outputs Disabled			52	70	mA

Note: 1. All typical values are $V_{CC} = 5.0V$, $T_A = 25°C$.

SWITCHING CHARACTERISTICS ($T_A = +25°C$, $V_{CC} = 5.0V$)

Parameters	Description	Test Conditions	Min	Typ	Max	Units
t_{PLH}	Propagation Delay, Input to Output	$C_L = 50$ pF See test circuit		18	24	ns
t_{PHL}				20	24	ns
t_{SKEW}	Propagation Delay Skew, $t_{PLH} - t_{PHL}$			2	4	ns
t_{ZL}	Output Enable Time, ENABLE to Output			16	22	ns
t_{ZH}				10	16	ns
t_{LZ}	Output Disable Time, ENABLE to Output	$C_L = 5$ pF See test circuit		11	18	ns
t_{HZ}				13	18	ns

SWITHCING CHARACTERISTICS* over operating range unless otherwise specified

Parameters	Description	Test Conditions	COMMERCIAL Am26LS34		MILITARY Am26LS34		Units
			Min	Max	Min	Max	
t_{PLH}	Propagation Delay, Input to Output	$C_L = 50$ pF See test circuit		30		30	ns
t_{PHL}				30		30	ns
t_{SKEW}	Propagation Delay Skew, $t_{PLH} - t_{PHL}$			±5		±5	ns
t_{ZL}	Output Enable Time, ENABLE to Output			33		33	ns
t_{ZH}				22		22	ns
t_{LZ}	Output Disable Time, ENABLE to Output	$C_L = 5$ pF See test circuit		27		27	ns
t_{HZ}				27		27	ns

*AC performance over the operating temperature range is guaranteed by testing defined in Group A, Subgroup 9.

SWITCHING TEST CIRCUIT FOR THREE-STATE OUTPUTS

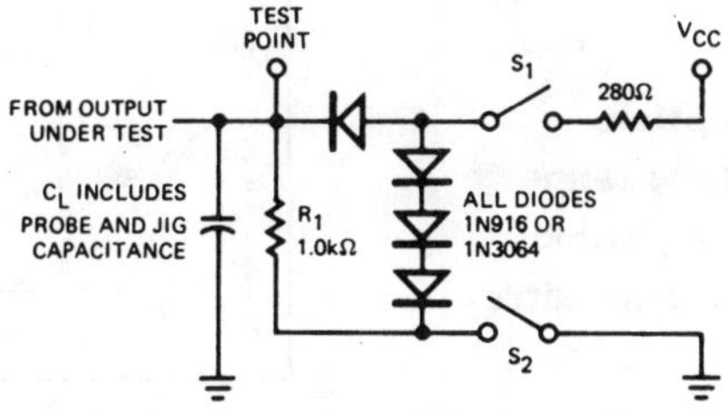

PROPAGATION DELAY
(Notes 1 and 3)

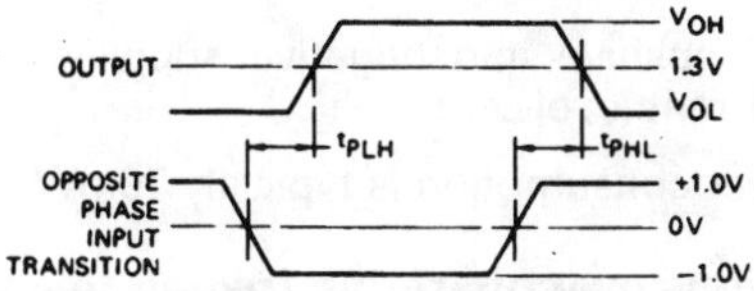

ENABLE AND DISABLE TIMES
(Notes 2 and 3)

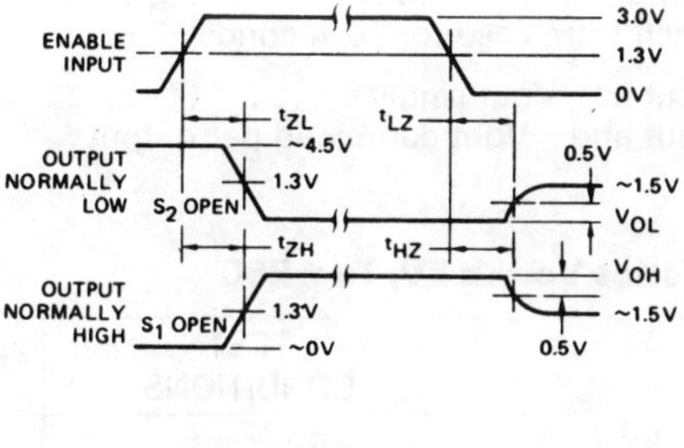

Notes: 1. Diagram shown for $\overline{\text{Enable}}$ LOW.
2. S_1 and S_2 of Load Circuit are closed except where shown.
3. Pulse Generator Rate $\leqslant$ 1.0MHz; $Z_O = 50\Omega$; t_r, $t_f \leqslant$ 2.5ns.

NM232C serial data driver/receiver

- ★ **5 Volt only operation**
- ★ **EIA — RS232C compatible**
- ★ **DIL 0.5″ package**
- ★ **Low profile**
- ★ **Low power consumption**
- ★ **Flexible supply voltage range**
- ★ **TTL/CMOS logic compatible**
- ★ **High reliability hybrid circuitry**

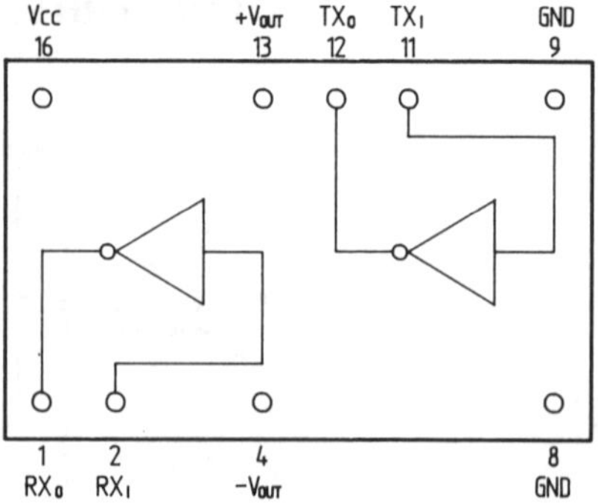

description

The NM232C is designed to interface data terminal equipment with data communications equipment in conformance with the specifications of EIA Standard RS232C. The operating temperature range is 0C to 70C. The device provides one data receive channel and one data transmit channel. Each channel is completely RS232C compatible at the interface boundary and TTL/CMOS compatible at the logic connections.

The internally generated positive and negative supplies are made available for external use at limited current levels.

Total device no-load power consumption is typically 70mW.

absolute maximum ratings over operating free-air temperature range

Supply voltage Vcc+ . . . . 4V to 7V
Input voltage at receiver . . . . ±30V
Output current from receiver 30mA
Output voltage at transmitter . . . . ±15V
Input voltage to transmitter . . . . −0.3V to 30V

Operating free-air temperature range . . . . 0C to 70C
Storage temperature range . . . . −55C to 125C
Lead temperature 1/16 inch from case for 10 seconds 300C

Current supplied by Vout or −Vout singly 15mA
Current supplied by Vout and −Vout combined per output 10mA

Transmitter

switching characteristics Vcc+ = 5V, Ta = 25C

PARAMETER	TEST CONDITIONS	MIN	TYP	MAX	UNIT
t_{PLH} Propagation delay time L to H	R_L = 3KΩ C_L = 30pF		650	800	ns
t_{PHL} Propagation delay time H to L			1.0	1.2	μs
t_{TLH} Transition time L to H level			0.9	1.0	μs
t_{THL} Transition time H to L level			0.9	1.0	μs
t_{TLH} Transition time L to H level	R_L = 3KΩ to 7KΩ C_L = 2500pF		2.0	2.5	μs
t_{THL} Transition time H to L level			2.0	2.5	μs

electrical characteristics over operating free-air temperature range Vcc+ = 5V

PARAMETER	TEST CONDITIONS		MIN	TYP	MAX	UNIT
V_{IH} High-level input voltage			1.9			V
V_{IL} Low-level input voltage					0.8	V
V_{OH} High-level output voltage	V_{IL} = 0.8V	Vcc = 5V	8.0	9.0		V
	R_L = 3KΩ	Vcc = 4.5V	8.0	8.5		
V_{OL} Low-level output voltage	V_{IH} = 1.9V	Vcc = 5V	−7.5	−8.0		V
	R_L = 3KΩ	Vcc = 4.5V	−6.5	−7.0		
I_{IH} High-level input current	V_{IN} = 5V				0.25	μA
I_{IL} Low-level input current	V_{IN} = 0V				0.25	μA
$I_{OS(H)}$ Short-circuit output current	V_{IN} = 0.8V		15	20		mA
$I_{OS(L)}$ Short-circuit output current	V_{IN} = 1.9V		−10	−15		mA
Ro Output resistance power off	Vcc = 0V		300			Ω

all typical values are at Ta = 25C

Receiver

electrical characteristics over operating free-air temperature range Vcc+ = 5V

PARAMETER	TEST CONDITIONS		MIN	TYP	MAX	UNIT
V_{T+} Positive going threshold		TA = 25C		2.0	2.4	V
V_{T-} Negative going threshold		TA = 25C	1.0	1.6		V
V_{OH} High-Level output voltage	V_{IN} = 0.75V	I_{OH} = −0.5mA	4.4		5.0	V
	Input open,	I_{OH} = −0.5mA	4.4		5.0	
V_{OL} Low-Level output voltage	V_{IN} = 3V	I_{OL} = 10mA	0.05	0.1	0.2	V
I_{IH} High-Level input current	V_{IN} = 25V		5.5		6.3	mA
	V_{IN} = 3V			0.6	0.65	
I_{IL} Low-Level input current	V_{IN} = −25V		−6.0		−6.8	mA
	V_{IN} = −3V			−0.6	−0.65	
I_{OS} Short-circuit output current	V_{IN} = 0V			−5.0		mA

all typical values are at Ta = 25C

switching characteristics Vcc+ = 5V, Ta = 25C, Vin = ±6V

PARAMETER	TEST CONDITIONS (1)	MIN	TYP	MAX	UNIT
t_{PLH} Propagation delay time L to H	C_L = 30pF, R_L = 3.9K		1.3		μs
t_{PHL} Propagation delay time H to L	C_L = 30pF, R_L = 390		350	450	ns
t_{TLH} Transition time L to H level	C_L = 30pF, R_L = 3.9K		500		ns
t_{THL} Transition time H to L level	C_L = 30pF, R_L = 390		250		ns

(1) Test load is simulated TTL and STTL

Transmitter and Receiver

electrical characteristics over operating temperature range Vcc+ = 5V

PARAMETER	TEST CONDITIONS		MIN	TYP	MAX	UNIT
Icc Supply current	R_L = 3KΩ at TX_O	Input at 0.8V		27		mA
		Input at 1.9V		20		
P_D Total power dissipation	No load	Vcc = 5V		70	100	mW
		Vcc = 4.5V		65	95	
V_{OUT+} Positive output voltage	No external load			10.5	12	V
	10 mA external load			10		
V_{OUT-} Negative output voltage	No external load			−10	−11.5	V
	10 mA external load			−9.5		

all typical values are at Ta = 25C

★ **5 Volt only operation**
★ **EIA — RS232C compatible**
★ **DIL 0.5″ package**
★ **Low profile**
★ **Low power consumption**
★ **Flexible supply voltage range**
★ **TTL/CMOS logic compatible**
★ **Downward pin compatible with NM232C**

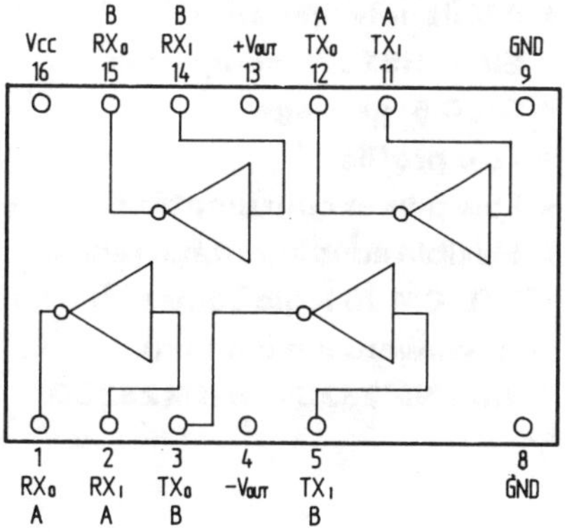

description

The NM232CD is a dual transmitter and receiver designed to interface data terminal equipment with data communications equipment. Each circuit conforms with the specifications of the EIA Standard RS232C. The device provides two data receive channels and two data transmit channels. Each channel is completely RS232C compatible at the interface boundary and TTL/CMOS compatible at the logic connections. The operating temperature range is from 0C to 70C.

The internally generated positive and negative supplies are made available for external use at limited current levels.

Total device no-load power consumption is typically 110mW.

Transmitter and Receiver

electrical characteristics over operating temperature range Vcc+ = 5V

PARAMETER	TEST CONDITIONS		MIN	TYP	MAX	UNIT
Icc Supply current	R_L = 3KΩ at both TX_0's	Inputs at 0.8V		45	50	mA
		Inputs at 1.9V		26	30	
P_D Total power dissipation	No load	Vcc = 5V		110	150	mW
		Vcc = 4.5V		100	145	
V_{OUT+} Positive output voltage	No external load			10.5	12	V
	10 mA external load			10		
V_{OUT-} Negative output voltage	No external load			−10	−11.5	V
	10 mA external load			−9.5		

all typical values are at Ta = 25C

NM232CQ serial data driver/receiver

- ★ **5 Volt only operation**
- ★ **EIA – RS232C compatible**
- ★ **DIL 0.5″ package**
- ★ **Low profile**
- ★ **Low power consumption**
- ★ **Flexible supply voltage range**
- ★ **TTL/CMOS logic compatible**
- ★ **Downward pin compatible with NM232C and NM232CD**

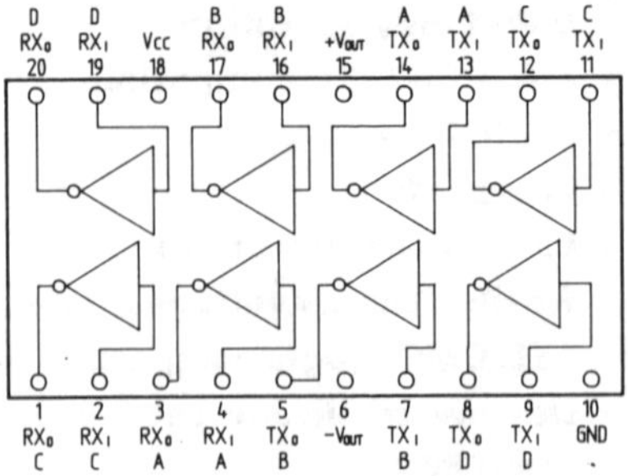

description

The NM232CQ is a quad transmitter and receiver designed to interface data terminal equipment with data communications equipment. Each circuit conforms with the specifications of the EIA Standard RS232C. The device provides four data receive channels and four data transmit channels. Each channel is completely compatible at the interface boundary and TTL/CMOS compatible at the logic connections. The operating temperature range is from 0C to 70C.

The internally generated positive and negative supplies are made available for external use at limited current levels.

Total device power consumption is typically 125mW.

Transmitter and Receiver

electrical characteristics over operating range, Vcc = 5V

PARAMETER	TEST CONDITIONS		MIN	TYP	MAX	UNIT
Icc Supply current	R_L – 3KΩ at all TX_0's	Inputs at 0.8V		60	80	mA
		Inputs at 1.9V		50	70	
P_D Total power dissipation	No load	Vcc – 5V		125	150	mW
		Vcc – 4.5V		100	145	
V_{OUT+} Positive output voltage	No external load			10.5	12	V
	10 mA external load			10		
V_{OUT-} Negative output voltage	No external load			–10	–11.5	V
	10 mA external load			–9.5		

all typical values are at Ta = 25C

- ★ **Bidirectional Transceiver**
- ★ **5 Volt only operation**
- ★ **Meets EIA — RS232C and RS422A Standards**
- ★ **DIL 0.5″ package**
- ★ **Low profile**
- ★ **Low power consumption**
- ★ **3-State Driver Output**
- ★ **Individual Driver and Receiver Enables**

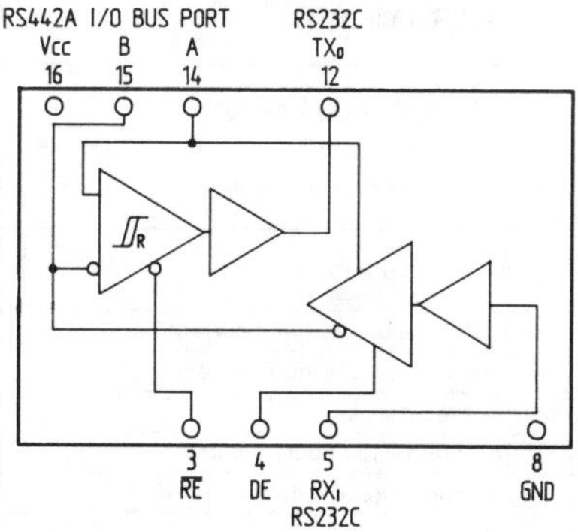

description

The NM422A Transceiver is designed for balanced transmission lines and meets EIA Standard RS422A for the bus port connection and at the RX IN and TX OUT connection it conforms with the specifications of EIA Standard RS232C. The device operates from a single 5 Volt power supply yet provides full RS232C transmitter voltage levels.

The bus port driver and receiver have active enable lines that can be connected externally to function as a direction control. The driver differential output and the receiver differential input are internally connected forming a differential input/output bus port. The loading on the bus is minimised whenever the bus driver is disabled (three-state) or Vcc = 0. The bus receiver has a minimum input impedance of 12K ohm and input sensitivity of ±200mV. The bus driver can handle loads up to 60mA of sink or source current.

The RX IN and TX OUT lines provide a data receive channel and data transmit channel both RS232C compatible connected as input and output to the RS422A compatible driver and receiver.

The operating temperature range is 0C to 70C and the total power demand is typically 200mW.

absolute maximum ratings over operating free-air temperature range

Supply voltage Vcc+ 7V
Voltage at any bus terminal . . . . −10V to 15V
Enable input voltage 5.5V
Input voltage RS232C Receiver . . . . ±30V
Output voltage RS232C Transmitter . . . . ±15V
Continuous total dissipation at or below 25C free-air temperature 750mW
Operating free-air temperature range . . . . 0C to 70C
Storage temperature range . . . . −55C to 125C
Lead temperature 1/16 inch from case for 10 seconds 300C

RS422A Receiver to RS232C Transmitter

electrical characteristics over operating free-air temperature range Vcc+ = 5V

PARAMETER	TEST CONDITIONS	MIN	TYP	MAX	UNIT
V_{TH} Differential input H threshold				0.2	V
V_{TL} Differential input L threshold		−0.2			V
V_{T+} to V_{T-} Hysteresis			50		mV
V_{IH} High-level enable input voltage		2			V
V_{IL} Low-level enable input voltage				0.8	V

PARAMETER	TEST CONDITIONS		MIN	TYP	MAX	UNIT
V_{OH} High-level output voltage	V_{IH} = 0.2V, R_L = 3KΩ	Vcc = 5V	8.0	9.0		V
V_{OL} Low-level output voltage	V_{IL} = −0.2V, R_L = 3KΩ	Vcc = 5V	−7.5	−8.0		V
I_I Line input current	Other input = 0	V_I = 12V			1	mA
		V_I = −7V			−0.8	mA
I_{IH} High-level enable input current	V_{IH} = 2.7V				20	µA
I_{IL} Low-level enable input current	V_{IL} = 0.4V				−100	µA
ri Input resistance			12			KΩ
$I_{OS(H)}$ Short-circuit output current	V_{IH} = 0.2V		15	20		mA
$I_{OS(L)}$ Short-circuit output current	V_{IL} = −0.2V		−10	−15		mA
Ro	Vcc = 0		300			Ω

all typical values are at Ta = 25C

switching characteristics Vcc+ = 5V, Ta = 25C

PARAMETER	TEST CONDITIONS	MIN	TYP	MAX	UNIT
t_{PLH} Propagation delay time L to H	R_L = 3KΩ, C_L = 30pF		1.3		µs
t_{PHL} Propagation delay time H to L	R_L = 3KΩ, C_L = 30pF		1.2		µs
t_{TLH} Transition time L to H level	R_L = 3KΩ, C_L = 30pF		1.0	1.6	µs
t_{THL} Transition time H to L level	R_L = 3KΩ, C_L = 30pF		1.0	1.6	µs
t_{TLH} Transition time L to H level	R_L = 3KΩ to 7KΩ, C_L = 2500pF		2.0	2.5	µs
t_{THL} Transition time H to L level	R_L = 3KΩ to 7KΩ, C_L = 2500pF		2.0	2.5	µs

RS232C Receiver to RS422A Driver

electrical characteristics over operating free-air temperature range Vcc+ = 5V

PARAMETER		TEST CONDITIONS	MIN	TYP	MAX	UNIT
V_{T+} Positive going threshold				2.0	2.4	V
V_{T-} Negative going threshold			1.0	1.6		V
V_{OH} High-level output voltage		V_{IH} = 3V, I_{OH} = −33mA		3.7		V
V_{OL} Low-level output voltage		V_{IL} = −3V, I_{OL} = 33mA		1.1		V
$[V_{OD1}]$ Differential output voltage		I_O = 0			$2V_{OD2}$	V
$[V_{OD2}]$ Differential output voltage		R_L = 100Ω	2	2.7		V
		R_L = 54Ω	1.5	2.4		V
$\Delta [V_{OD}]$	Change in magnitude of differential output voltage	R_L = 54Ω or 100Ω			±0.2	V
V_{OC} Common-mode output voltage		R_L = 54Ω or 100Ω			3	V
$\Delta [V_{OC}]$	Change in magnitude of differential output voltage	R_L = 54Ω or 100Ω			±0.2	V

PARAMETER	TEST CONDITIONS		MIN	TYP	MAX	UNIT
I_O Output current	Output disabled	$V_O = 12V$			1	mA
		$V_O = -7V$			−0.8	
I_{IH} High-level input current	$V_{IN} = 25V$		5.5		6.3	mA
	$V_{IN} = 3V$			0.6	0.65	
I_{IL} Low-level input current	$V_{IN} = -25V$		−6.0		−6.8	mA
	$V_{IN} = -3V$			−0.6	−0.65	
I_{OS} Short-circuit output current	$V_O = -7V$				−180	mA
	$V_O = V_{CC}$				180	
	$V_O = 12V$				500	

all typical values are at Ta = 25C

switching characteristics Vcc+ = 5V, Ta = 25C

PARAMETER	TEST CONDITIONS	MIN	TYP	MAX	UNIT
t_{DD} Differential output delay time	$R_L = 60\Omega$		35	50	ns
t_{TD} Differential output transition time			50	75	
t_{PLH} Propagation delay time L to H	$R_L = 27\Omega$		16	25	ns
t_{PHL} Propagation delay time H to L			44	65	
t_{PZH} Output enable time to H level	$R_L = 110\Omega$		60	80	ns
t_{PZL} Output enable time to L level	$R_L = 110\Omega$		30	45	ns
t_{PHZ} Output disable time from H level	$R_L = 110\Omega$		51	75	ns
t_{PLZ} Output disable time from L level	$R_L = 110\Omega$		18	30	ns

Transmitter and Receiver

electrical characteristics over operating temperature range Vcc+ = 5V

PARAMETER	TEST CONDITIONS		MIN	TYP	MAX	UNIT
I_{CC} Supply current	No loads	Inputs high		30		mA
		Inputs low		40		
P_D Total power dissipation	RS232C $R_L = 3K\Omega$ RS422A $R_L = 60\Omega$			385		mW

all typical values are at Ta = 25C

RS422A connection techniques

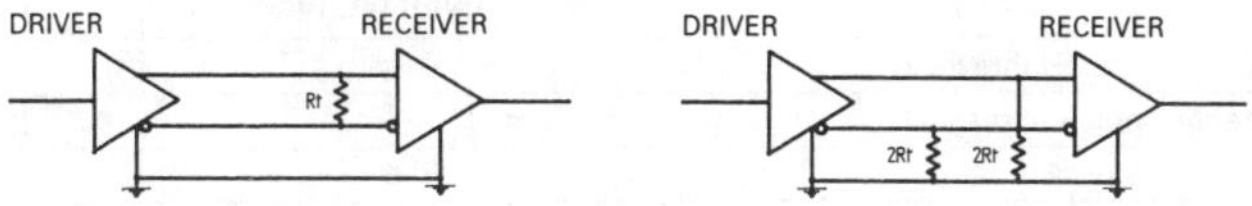

NM422AD serial data driver/receiver

★ **5 Volt only operation**
★ **Meets EIA — RS232C and RS422A Standards**
★ **Two full-duplex links**
★ **DIL 0.5″ package**
★ **Low profile**
★ **Low power consumption**

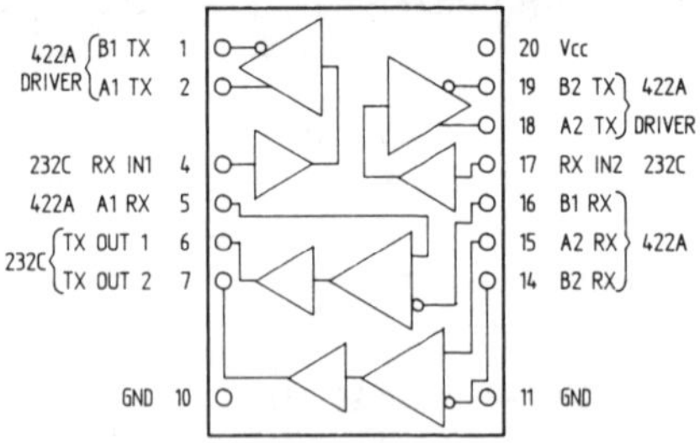

description

The NM422AD is a device for connecting and converting data levels between the RS422A standard and the RS232C standard. RS422A uses balanced transmission lines and RS232C uses single signal lines. Two full-duplex links can be constructed between the two standards with a pair of modules. The transceiver operates from a single 5 Volt supply yet all inputs and outputs meet the EIA Standards for RS422A and RS232C.

The RS422A receivers utilise Schottky circuitry and have differential line inputs which are compatible with either a single ended or a differential line system. The RS422A drivers provide complementary output signals with high-current capability for driving balanced lines. Driver output stages are TTL totem-pole type having a high-impedance state when in the power-off condition.

The operating temperature range is 0C to 70C and the total power demand is typically 450mW with no load.

absolute maximum ratings over operating free-air temperature range

Supply voltage Vcc+ 7V
Voltage at RS422A Receiver . . . . ±15V
Input voltage RS232C Receiver . . . . ±30V
Output voltage RS232C Transmitter . . . . ±15V
Continuous total dissipation at or below 25C free-air temperature 1.0W
Operating free air temperature range . . . . 0C to 70C
Storage temperature range . . . . −55C to +125C
Lead temperature 1/16 inch from case for 10 seconds 300C

RS422A Receiver to RS232C Transmitter

electrical characteristics over operating free-air temperature range Vcc+ = 5V

PARAMETER	TEST CONDITIONS		MIN	TYP	MAX	UNIT
V_{TH} Differential input H threshold					0.2	V
V_{TL} Differential input L threshold			−0.2			V
V_{T+} to V_{T-} Hysteresis				70		mV
V_{OH} High-level output voltage	V_{IH} = 0.2V	Vcc = 5V	8.0	9.0		V
	R_L = 3KΩ					

PARAMETER	TEST CONDITIONS (1)		MIN	TYP	MAX	UNIT
V_{OL} Low-level output voltage	$V_{IL} = -0.2V$, $R_L = 3K\Omega$	Vcc = 5V	−7.5	−8.0		V
I_I Line input current	Other input = 0	$V_I = 10V$			3.25	mA
		$V_I = -10V$			−3.25	
ri Input resistance				8		KΩ
$I_{OS(H)}$ Short-circuit output current	$V_{IH} = 0.2V$		15	20		mA
$I_{OS(L)}$ Short-circuit output current	$V_{IL} = -0.2V$		−10	−15		mA
Ro	Vcc = 0		300			Ω

all typical values at Ta = 25C

switching characteristics Vcc+ = 5V, Ta = 25C

PARAMETER	TEST CONDITIONS	MIN	TYP	MAX	UNIT
t_{PLH} Propagation delay time L to H	$R_L = 3K\Omega$, $C_L = 30pF$		1.3		μs
t_{PHL} Propagation delay time H to L			1.2		μs
t_{TLH} Transition time L to H level			1.0	1.6	μs
t_{THL} Transition time H to L level			1.0	1.6	μs
t_{TLH} Transition time L to H level	$R_L = 3K\Omega$ to $7K\Omega$, $C_L = 2500pF$		2.0	2.5	μs
t_{THL} Transition time H to L level			2.0	2.5	μs

RS232C Receiver to RS422A Driver

electrical characteristics over operating free-air temperature range Vcc+ = 5V

PARAMETER		TEST CONDITIONS		MIN	TYP	MAX	UNIT
V_{T+} Positive going threshold					2.0	2.4	V
V_{T-} Negative going threshold				1.0	1.6		V
V_{OH} High-level output voltage		$V_{IH} = 3V$, $I_{OH} = -40mA$		2.4	3.0		V
V_{OL} Low-level output voltage		$V_{IL} = -3V$, $I_{OL} = 40mA$			0.2	0.4	V
$[V_{OD1}]$ Differential output voltage		$I_O = 0$			3.5	$2V_{OD2}$	V
$[V_{OD2}]$ Differential output voltage		$R_L = 100\Omega$		2	3.0		V
$\Delta [V_{OD}]$	Change in magnitude of differential output voltage	Vcc = Min			±0.02	±0.4	V
V_{OC} Common-mode output voltage		$R_L = 100\Omega$				3	V
$\Delta [V_{OC}]$	Change in magnitude of differential output voltage	$R_C = 100\Omega$, Vcc = Min or Max				±0.4	V
I_O Output current with power off		Vcc = 0	$V_O = 6V$			100	μA
			$V_O = -0.25$			−100	
I_{IH} High-level input current		$V_{IN} = 25V$		5.5		6.3	mA
		$V_{IN} = 3V$			0.6	0.65	
I_{IL} Low-level input current		$V_{IN} = -25V$		−6.0		−6.8	mA
		$V_{IN} = -3V$			−0.6	−0.65	
I_{OS} Short-circuit output current (Only one output at a time max. 1 second.)		Vcc = Max				−150	mA

all typical values at Ta = 25C

switching characteristics Vcc+ = 5V, Ta = 25C

PARAMETER	TEST CONDITIONS	MIN	TYP	MAX	UNIT
t_{PLH} Propagation delay time L to H	$R_L = 100\Omega$		25	35	ns
t_{PHL} Propagation delay time H to L			44	65	ns
t_{TLH} Transition time L to H level	$R_L = 100\Omega$		4	20	ns
t_{THL} Transition time H to L level			4	20	ns

electrical characteristics over operating temperature range Vcc+ = 5V

PARAMETER	TEST CONDITIONS		MIN	TYP	MAX	UNIT
I_{CC} Supply current	No loads	Inputs high		180		mA
		Inputs low		90		
P_D Total power dissipation	RS232C $R_L = 3K\Omega$ RS422A $R_L = 100\Omega$			800		mW

all typical values at Ta = 25C

RS422A connection techniques

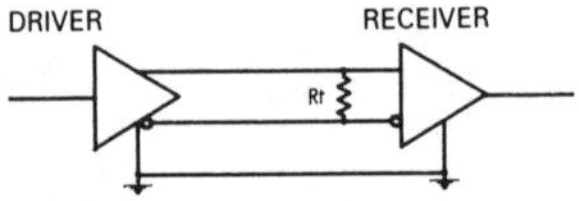

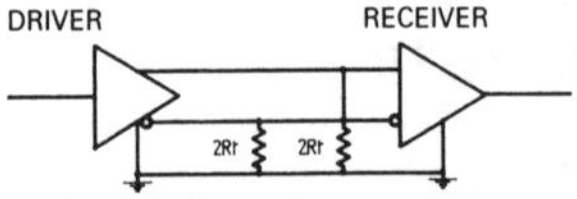

General Description

Maxim's family of line drivers/receivers are intended for all RS-232 and V.28/V.24 communications interfaces, and in particular, for those applications where ±12V is not available. The MAX230, MAX236, MAX240 and MAX241 are particularly useful in battery powered systems since their low power shutdown mode reduces power dissipation to less than 5μW. The MAX233 and MAX235 use no external components and are recommended for applications where printed circuit board space is critical.

All members of the family except the MAX231 and MAX239 need only a single +5V supply for operation. The RS-232 drivers/receivers have on-board charge pump voltage converters which convert the +5V input power to the ±10V needed to generate the RS-232 output levels. The MAX231 and MAX239, designed to operate from +5V and +12V, contain a +12V to -12V charge pump voltage converter.

Since nearly all RS-232 applications need both line drivers and receivers, the family includes both receivers and drivers in one package. The wide variety of RS-232 applications require differing numbers of drivers and receivers. Maxim offers a wide selection of RS-232 driver/receiver combinations in order to minimize the package count (see table below).

Both the receivers and the line drivers (transmitters) meet all EIA RS-232C and CCITT V.28 specifications.

Features

- **Operates from Single 5V Power Supply (+5V and +12V — MAX231 and MAX239)**
- **Meets All RS-232C and V.28 Specifications**
- **Multiple Drivers and Receivers**
- **Onboard DC-DC Converters**
- **±9V Output Swing with +5V Supply**
- **Low Power Shutdown — <1μA (typ)**
- **3-State TTL/CMOS Receiver Outputs**
- **±30V Receiver Input Levels**

Applications

Computers
Peripherals
Modems
Printers
Instruments

Selection Table

Part Number	Power Supply Voltage	No. of RS-232 Drivers	No. of RS-232 Receivers	External Components	Low Power Shutdown /TTL 3-State	No. of Pins
MAX230	+5V	5	0	4 capacitors	Yes/No	20
MAX231	+5V and +7.5V to 13.2V	2	2	2 capacitors	No/No	14
MAX232	+5V	2	2	4 capacitors	No/No	16
MAX233	+5V	2	2	None	No/No	20
MAX234	+5V	4	0	4 capacitors	No/No	16
MAX235	+5V	5	5	None	Yes/Yes	24
MAX236	+5V	4	3	4 capacitors	Yes/Yes	24
MAX237	+5V	5	3	4 capacitors	No/No	24
MAX238	+5V	4	4	4 capacitors	No/No	24
MAX239	+5V and +7.5V to 13.2V	3	5	2 capacitors	No/Yes	24
MAX240	+5V	5	5	4 capacitors	Yes/Yes	44 (Flatpak)
MAX241	+5V	4	5	4 capacitors	Yes/Yes	28 (Small Outline)

*Patent Pending

ABSOLUTE MAXIMUM RATINGS

V_{CC} .... -0.3V to +6V
V^+ .... (V_{CC} - 0.3V) to +15V
V^- .... +0.3V to -15V
Input Voltages
T_{IN} .... -0.3 to (V_{CC} + 0.3V)
R_{IN} .... ±30V
Output Voltages
T_{OUT} .... (V^+ + 0.3V) to (V^- - 0.3V)
R_{OUT} .... -0.3V to (V_{CC} + 0.3V)
Short Circuit Duration
T_{OUT} .... continuous
Power Dissipation
CERDIP 675mW
(derate 9.5mW/°C above +70°C)
Plastic DIP 375mW
(derate 7mW/°C above +70°C)
Small Outline (SO) 375mW
(derate 7mW/°C above +70°C)
Lead Temperature (soldering 10 seconds) .... +300°C
Storage Temperature .... -65°C to +160°C

Stresses above those listed under "Absolute Maximum Ratings" may cause permanent damage to the device. These are stress ratings only, and functional operation of the device at these or any other conditions above those indicated in the operational sections of the specifications is not implied. Exposure to absolute maximum rating conditions for extended periods may affect device reliability.

ELECTRICAL CHARACTERISTICS

(MAX232, 234, 236, 237, 238, 240, 241 V_{CC} = 5V ± 10%; MAX233, 235 V_{CC} = 5V ± 5%; MAX231, 239 V_{CC} = 5V ± 10%, V^+ = 7.5V to 13.2V; T_A = Operating Temperature Range, Figures 3-14, unless otherwise noted.)

PARAMETER	CONDITIONS	MIN.	TYP.	MAX.	UNITS
Output Voltage Swing	All Transmitter Outputs loaded with 3kΩ to Ground	±5	±9		V

V_{CC} Power Supply Current	No load, T_A = +25°C			5	10	mA
	MAX231, MAX239			0.4	1	
V^+ Power Supply Current	No load, MAX231 and MAX239 only	MAX231		1.8	5	mA
		MAX239		5	15	
Shutdown Supply Current	Figure 1, T_A = +25°C			1	10	μA
Input Logic Threshold Low	T_{IN}, $\overline{EN}$, Shutdown				0.8	V
Input Logic Threshold High	T_{IN}		2.0			V
	$\overline{EN}$, Shutdown		2.4			
Logic Pullup Current	T_{IN} = 0V			15	200	μA
RS-232 Input Voltage Operating Range			-30		+30	V
RS-232 Input Threshold Low	V_{CC} = 5V, T_A = +25°C		0.8	1.2		V
RS-232 Input Threshold High	V_{CC} = 5V, T_A = +25°C			1.7	2.4	V
RS-232 Input Hysteresis	V_{CC} = 5V		0.2	0.5	1.0	V
RS-232 Input Resistance	T_A = +25°C, V_{CC} = 5V		3	5	7	kΩ
TTL/CMOS Output Voltage Low	I_{OUT} = 1.6mA (MAX231-233, I_{OUT} = 3.2mA)				0.4	V
TTL/CMOS Output Voltage High	I_{OUT} = -1.0mA		3.5			V
TTL/CMOS Output Leakage Current	$\overline{EN}$ = V_{CC}, 0V ≤ R_{OUT} ≤ V_{CC}			0.05	±10	μA
Output Enable Time (Figure 2)	MAX235, MAX236, MAX239, MAX240, 241			400		ns
Output Disable Time (Figure 2)	MAX235, MAX236, MAX239, MAX240, 241			250		ns
Propagation Delay	RS-232 to TTL			0.5		μs
Instantaneous Slew Rate	C_L = 10pF, R_L = 3-7kΩ T_A = +25°C (Note 1)				30	V/μs
Transition Region Slew Rate	R_L = 3kΩ, C_L = 2500pF Measured from +3V to -3V or -3V to +3V			3		V/μs
Output Resistance	V_{CC} = V^+ = V^- = 0V, V_{OUT} = ±2V		300			Ω
RS-232 Output Short Circuit Current				±10		mA

Note 1: Sample tested.

Typical Operating Characteristics

TRANSMITTER SLEW RATE vs. LOAD CAPACITANCE

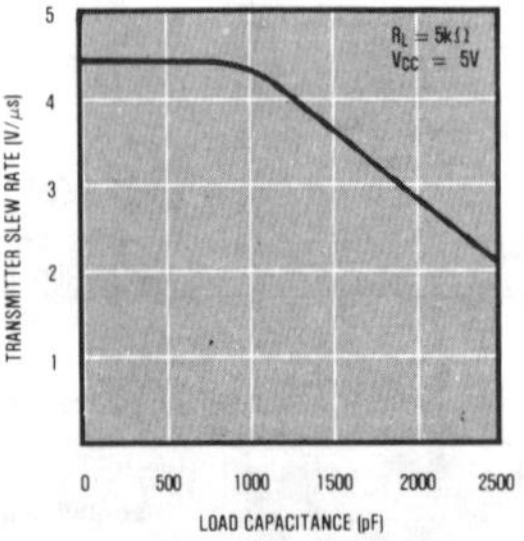

MAX239 TRANSMITTER OUTPUT VOLTAGE vs. V^+ VOLTAGE

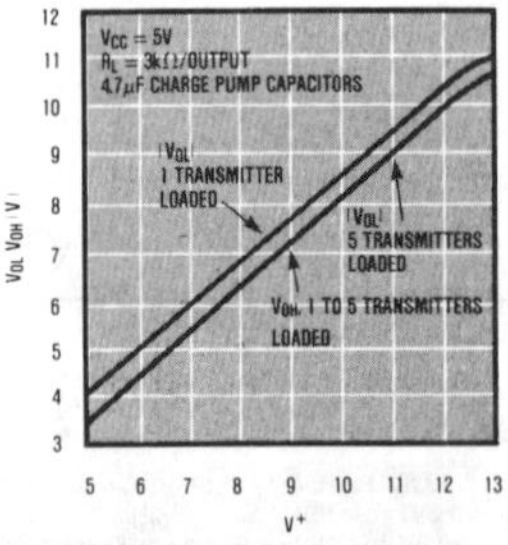

TRANSMITTER OUTPUT VOLTAGE vs. V_{CC} VOLTAGE

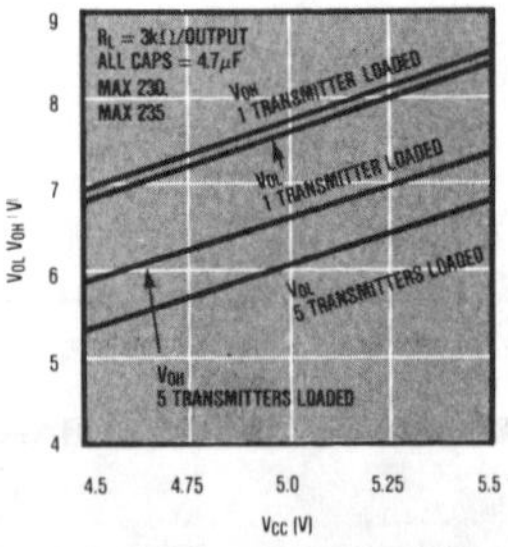

V^+ SUPPLY VOLTAGE vs. LOAD CURRENT (MAX230, 234-238, 240, 241)

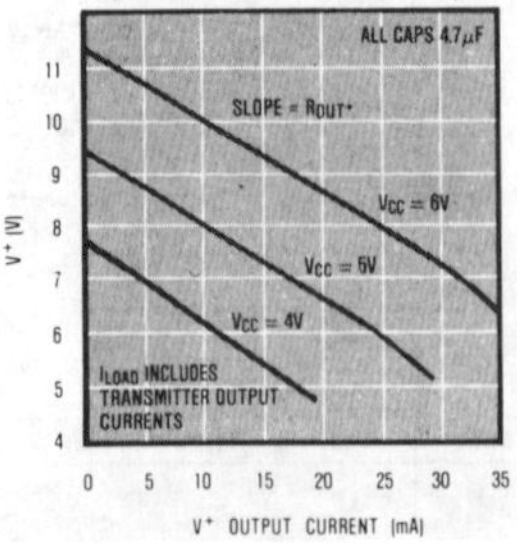

V^- SUPPLY VOLTAGE vs. LOAD CURRENT (MAX230, 234-238, 240, 241)

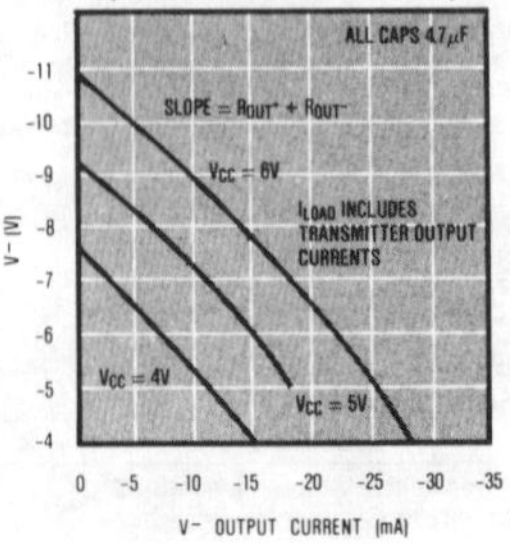

CHARGE PUMP OUTPUT IMPEDANCE vs. V_{CC} (MAX230, 234-238, 240, 241)

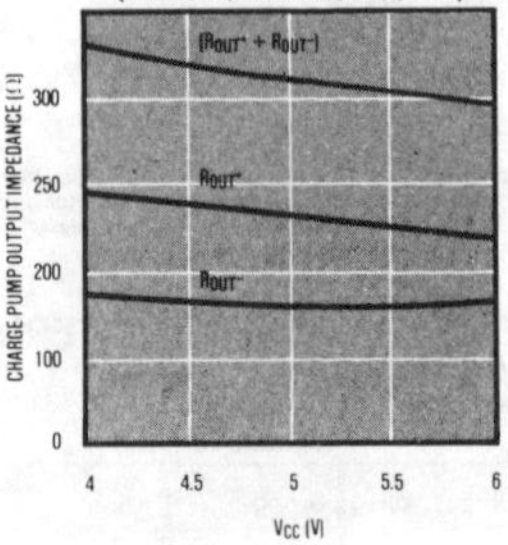

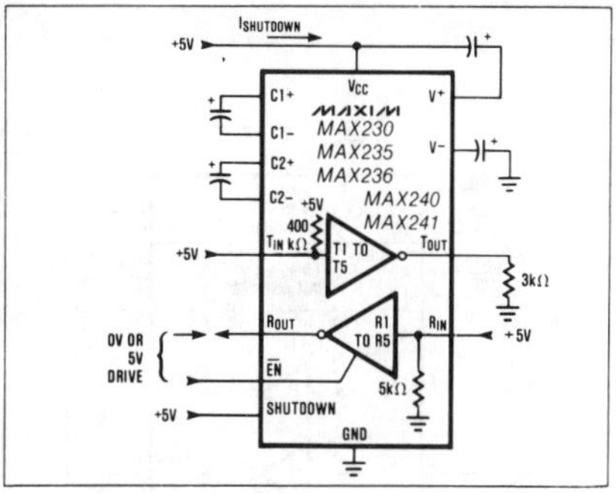

Figure 1. Shutdown Current Test Circuit

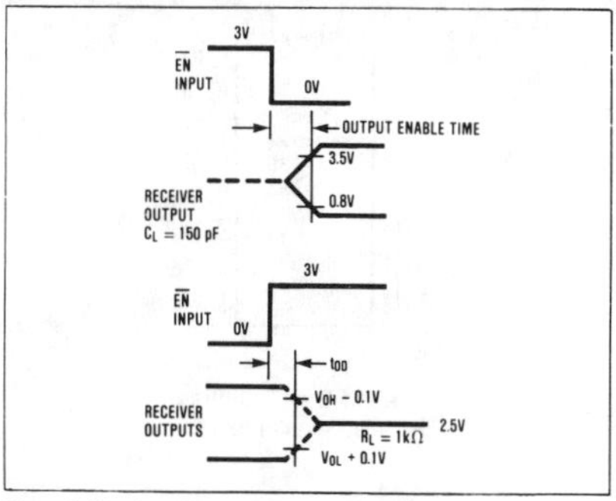

Figure 2. Receiver Output Enable and Disable Timing

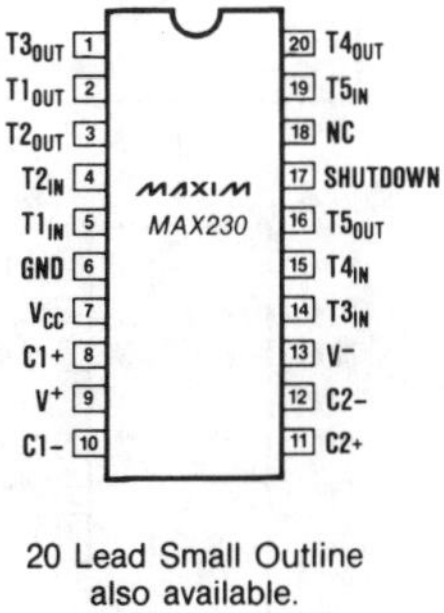

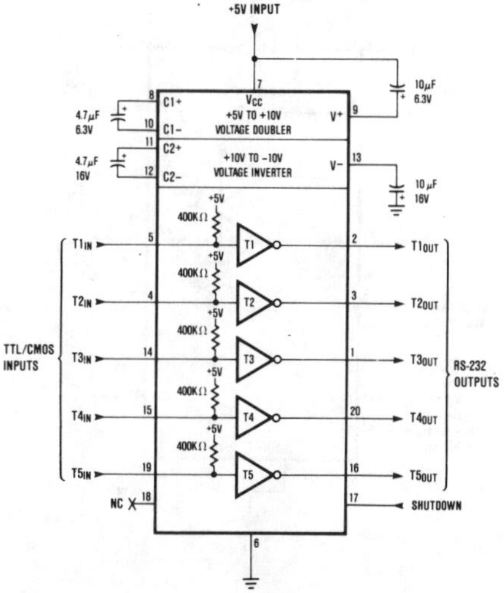

Figure 3. MAX230 Typical Operating Circuit

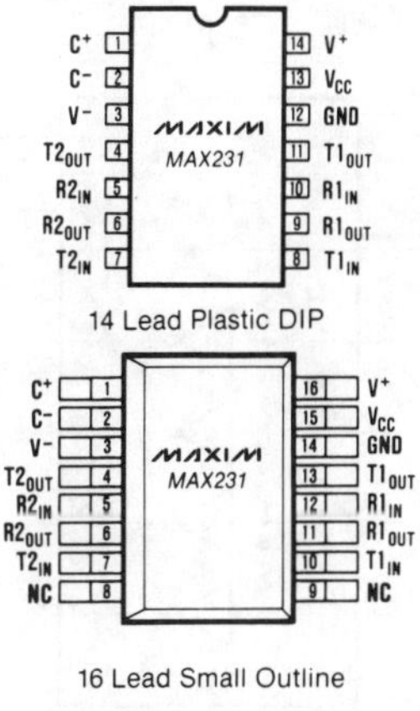

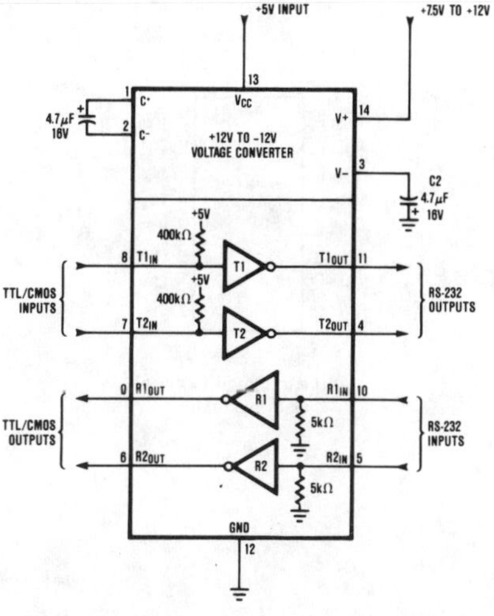

Figure 4. MAX231 Typical Operating Circuit

Figure 5. MAX232 Typical Operating Circuit

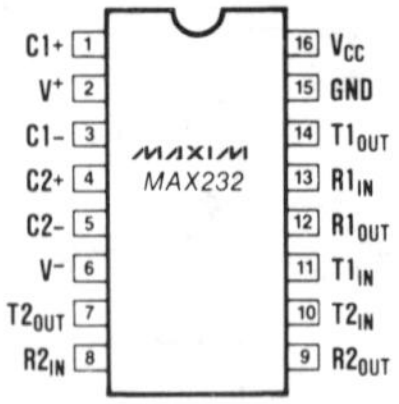

16 Lead Small Outline also available.

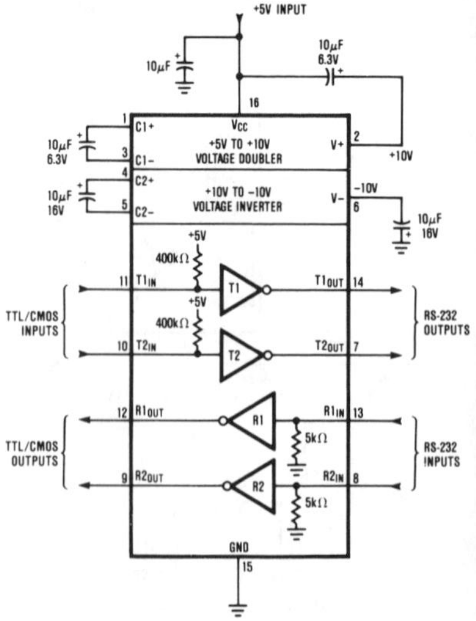

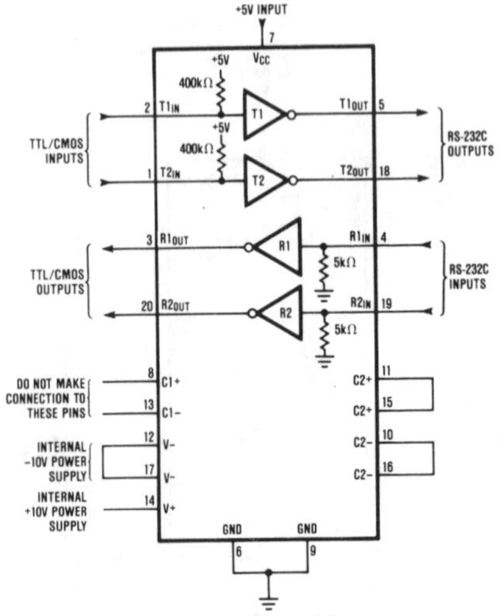

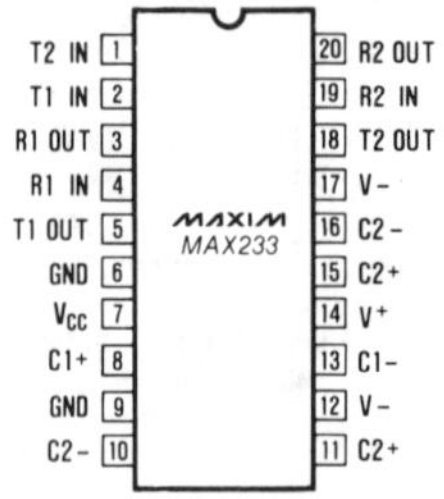

Small Outline Not Available

Figure 6. MAX233 Typical Operating Circuit

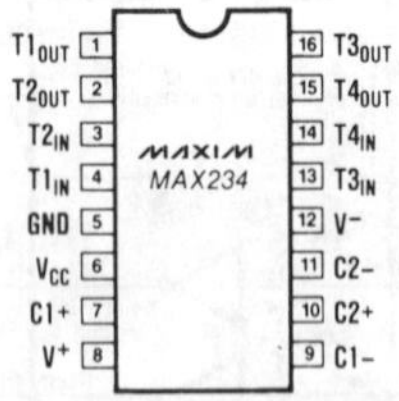

16 Lead Small Outline also available.

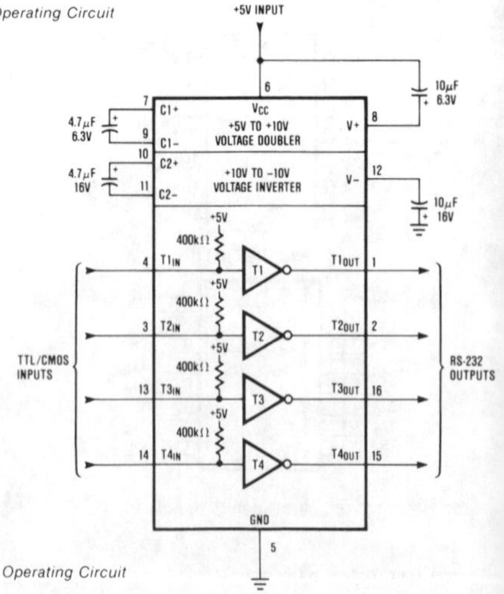

Figure 7. MAX234 Typical Operating Circuit

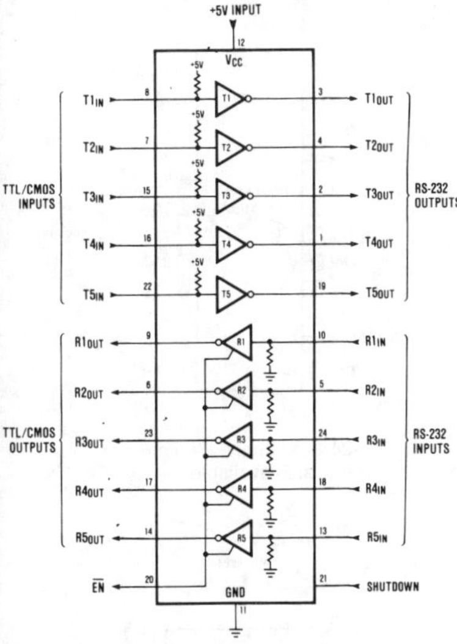

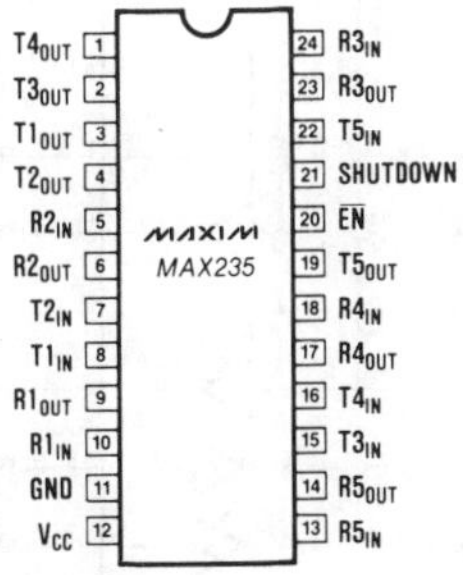

Small Outline Not Available

Figure 8. MAX235 Typical Operating Circuit

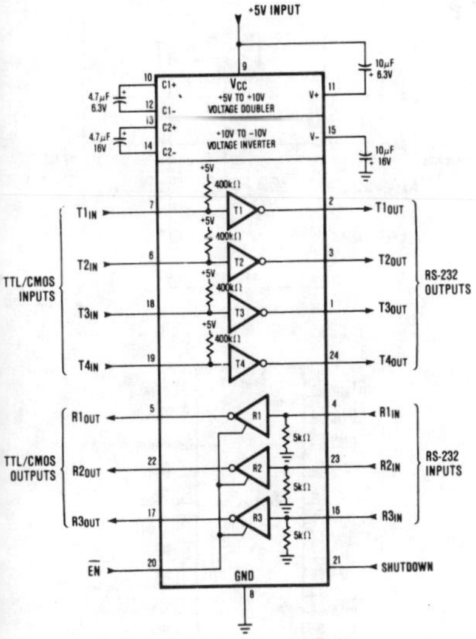

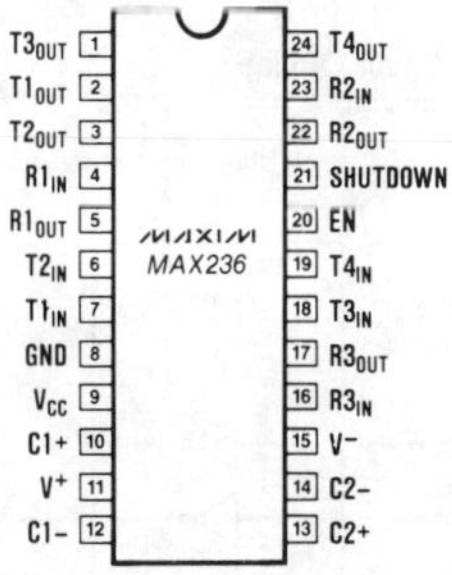

24 Lead Small Outline
also available.

Figure 9. MAX236 Typical Operating Circuit

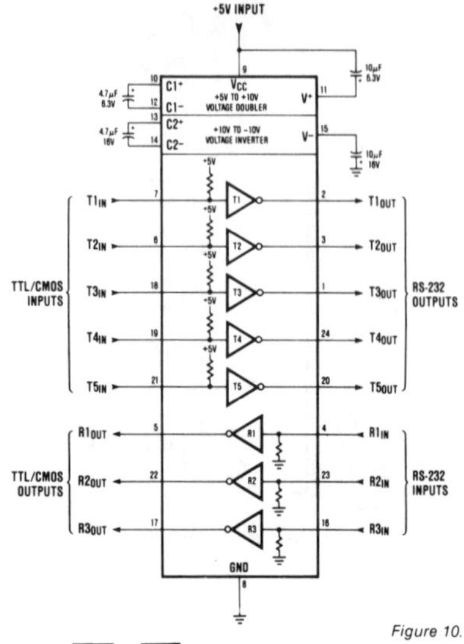

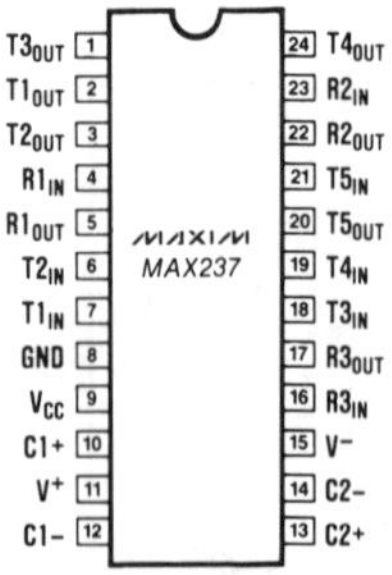

24 Lead Small Outline also available.

Figure 10. MAX237 Typical Operating Circuit

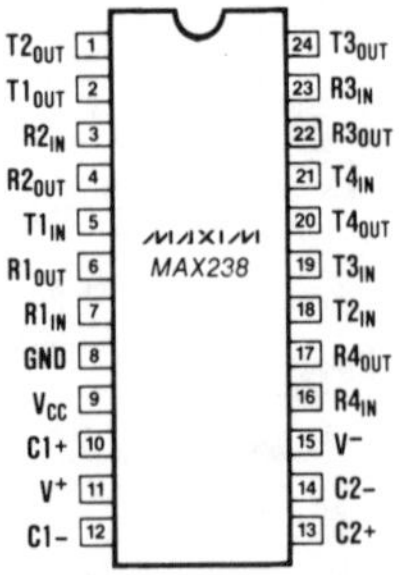

24 Lead Small Outline also available.

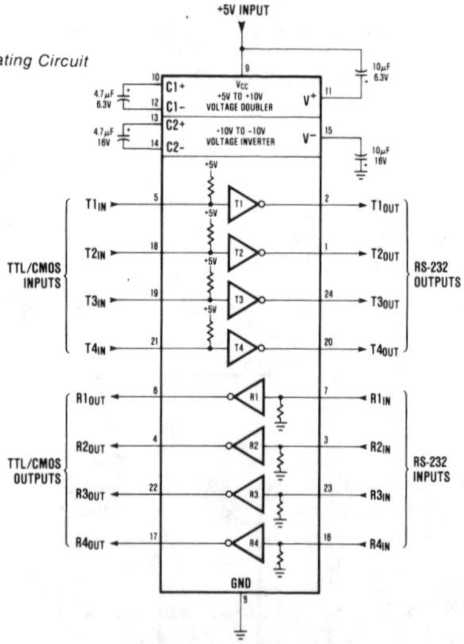

Figure 11. MAX238 Typical Operating Circuit

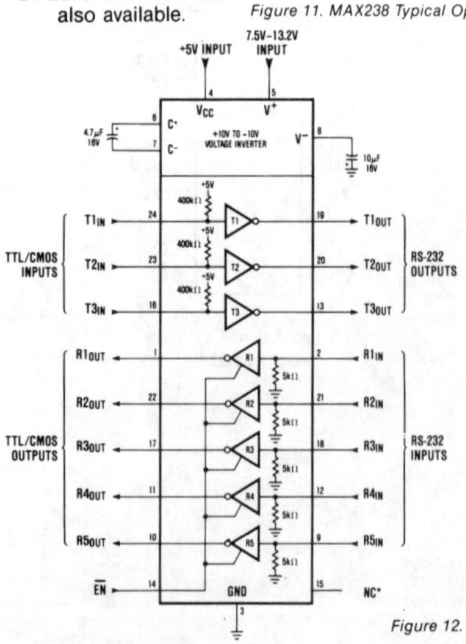

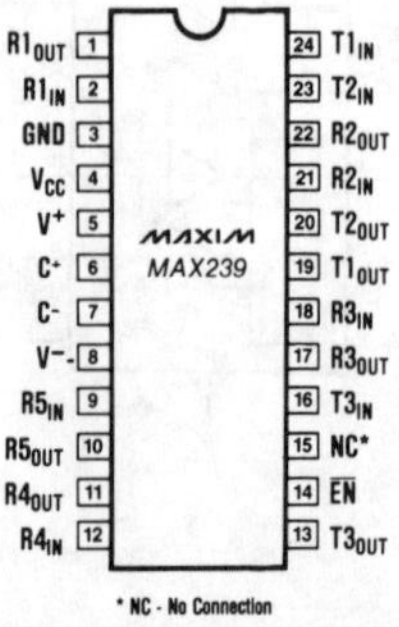

24 Lead Small Outline also available.

Figure 12. MAX239 Typical Operating Circuit

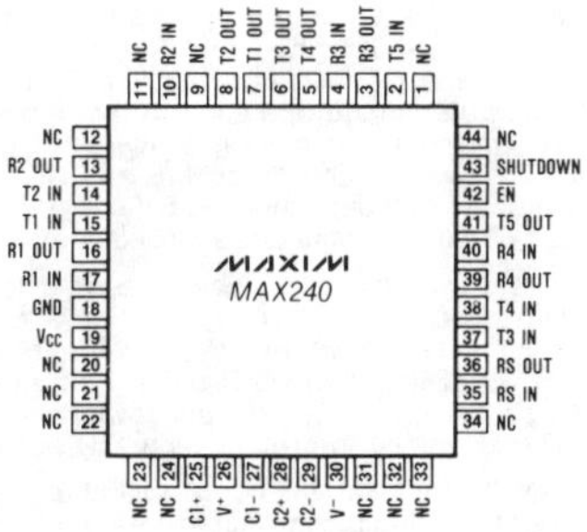

44 Lead Plastic Flatpak Only

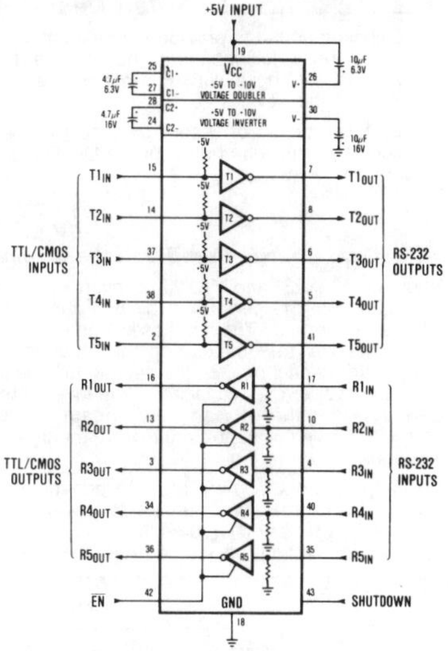

Figure 13. MAX240 Typical Operating Circuit.

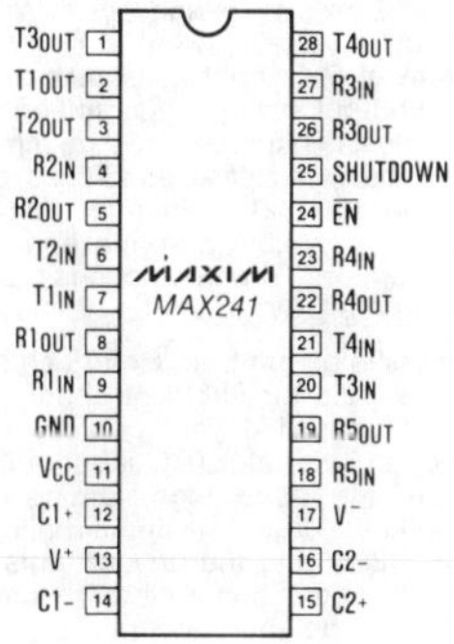

28 Lead Wide Small Outline Only

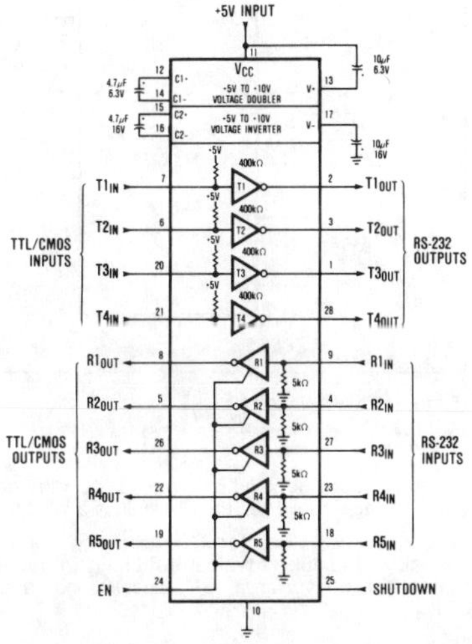

Figure 14. MAX241 Typical Operating Circuit.

Typical Applications

Figures 3 through 14 show typical applications. The capacitor values are non-critical. Reducing the capacitors C1 and C2 to 1μF will slightly increase the impedance of the charge pump, lowering the RS 232 driver output voltages by about 100mV. Lower values of C3 and C4 increase the ripple on the V^+ and V^- outputs.

If the power supply input to the device has a very fast rate-of-rise (as would occur if a PCB were to be plugged into a card cage with power already on), use the simple RC filter shown in Figure 15. This bypass network is not needed if the V_{CC} rate-of-rise is below 1V/μs.

All receivers and drivers are inverting. The $\overline{EN}$able control of the MAX235, MAX236, MAX239, MAX240 and MAX241 enables the receiver TTL/CMOS outputs when it is at a low level, and places the TTL/CMOS outputs of the receivers into a high impedance state when it is a high level.

When the Shutdown control of the MAX230, MAX235, MAX236, MAX240 and MAX241 is at a logic 1 the charge pump is turned off, the receiver outputs are put into the high impedance state, V^+ is pulled down to V_{CC}, V^- is pulled up to ground, and the transmitter outputs are disabled. The supply current drops to less than 10μA.

Detailed Description

The following sections provide supplementary information for those designers with non-standard applications and for those with interest in the internal operation of the devices.

The devices consist of 3 sections: the transmitters, the receivers, and the charge pump DC-DC voltage converter.

+5V to ±10V Dual Charge Pump Voltage Converter

All but the MAX231 and MAX239 convert +5V to ±10V. This conversion is performed by two charge pump voltage converters. The first uses capacitor C1 to double the +5V to +10V, storing the +10V on the V^+ output filter capacitor, C3. The second charge pump voltage converter uses capacitor C2 to invert the +10V to -10V, storing the -10V on the V^- output filter capacitor, C4. The equivalent circuit of the charge pump section is shown in Figure 16.

A small amount of power may be drawn from the +10V (V^+) and -10V (V^-) outputs to power external circuitry. The typical characteristics graphs show the typical output voltage vs. load current characteristics.

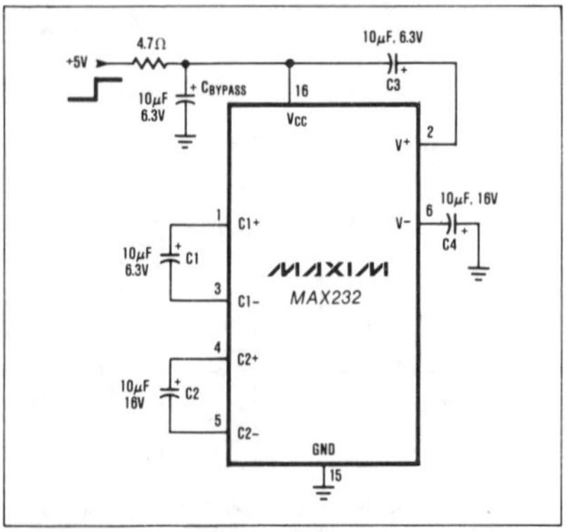

Figure 15. Protection from High $\frac{dV}{dT}$

For applications needing only the +5V to ±10V charge pump voltage converter, the MAX680 is available.

The capacitor values for C1 through C4 are non-critical. At the 15kHz typical switching frequency of the voltage converter, a 1µF capacitor has approximately 10Ω impedance, and replacing the 4.7µF and 10µF capacitors shown in the typical applications with 1µF for C1 and C2 will increase the output impedance of the V^+ output by about 10Ω and the output impedance of V^- by about 20Ω. Lowering the value of C3 and C4 increases the ripple on the V^+ and V^- outputs. Where operation to the upper temperature limit is not required, or V_{CC} will not go below 4.75V, C1 and C2 can be 1µF, and C3 and C4 can be 1µF per output channel (1µF if one transmitter is used, 5µF if five transmitters are used).

There are parasitic diodes which become forward biased if V^+ goes below V_{CC} or V^- goes above ground. When in the shutdown mode (MAX230, MAX235, MAX236, MAX240 and MAX241 only), V^+ is internally connected to V_{CC} by a 1kΩ pulldown, and V^- is internally connected to ground via a 1kΩ pullup.

The MAX233 and MAX235 contain all charge pump components, including the capacitors, and operate with NO external components.

The MAX231 and MAX239 include only the V^+ to V^- charge pump, and are intended for applications which have a +5V supply and either a +12V ± 10% supply or a 7.5V to 13.2V battery voltage. When operating with V^+ greater than 8.0V, both capacitors can be 1µF.

Driver (Transmitter) Section

The transmitters or line drivers are inverting level translators which convert the CMOS or TTL input levels to RS-232 or V.28 voltage levels. With +5V V_{CC}, the typical output voltage swing is ±9V when loaded with the nominal 5kΩ input resistance of an RS-232 receiver. The output swing is guaranteed to meet the RS-232/V.28 specification of ±5V minimum output swing under the worst case conditions of all transmitters driving the 3kΩ minimum allowable load impedance, V_{CC} = 4.5V, and maximum operating ambient temperature. The open circuit output voltage swing is from (V^+ - 0.6V) to V^-.

The input thresholds are both CMOS and TTL compatible, with a logic threshold of about 25% of V_{CC}. The inputs of unused drivers sections can be left unconnected; an internal 400kΩ input pullup resistor to V_{CC} will pull the inputs high, forcing the unused transmitter outputs low. The input pullup resistors source about 12µA, and the driver inputs should be driven high or open circuited to minimize power supply current in the shutdown mode.

When in the low power shutdown mode, the driver outputs are turned off and their leakage current is less than 1µA with the driver output pulled to ground. The driver output leakage remains less than 1µA, even if the transmitter output is backdriven between 0V and (V_{CC} + 6V). Below -0.5V the transmitter is diode

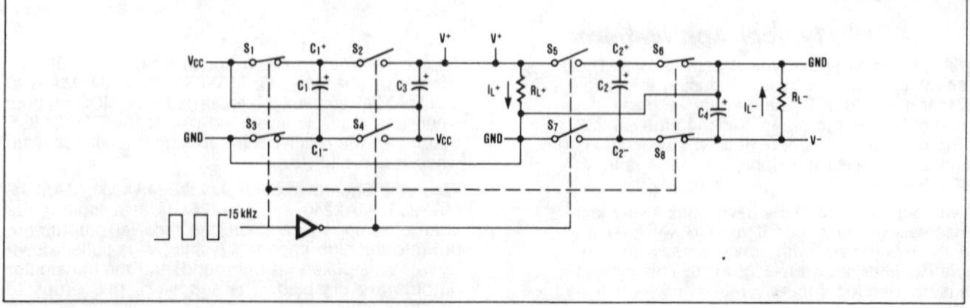

Figure 16. Charge Pump Diagram.

clamped to ground with 1kΩ series impedance. The transmitter is also zener clamped to approximately V_{CC} + 6V, with a series impedance of 1kΩ. As required by the RS232 and V.28, the slew rate is limited to less than 30V/μs. This limits the maximum usable baud rate to 19,200 baud.

Receiver Section

All but the MAX230 and MAX234 contain RS-232/V.28 receivers. These receivers convert the ±5V to ±15V RS-232 signals to 5V TTL/CMOS outputs. Since the RS-232C/V.28 specifications define a voltage level greater than +3V as a 0, the receivers are inverting. Maxim has set the guaranteed input thresholds of the receivers to 0.8V minimum and 2.4V maximum, which are significantly tighter than the -3.0V minimum and +3.0V maximum required by the RS-232 and V.28 specifications. This allows the receivers to respond both to RS-232/V.28 levels and TTL level inputs. The receivers are protected against input overvoltage up to ±30V.

The 0.8V guaranteed lower threshold is important to ensure that the receivers will have a logic 1 output if the receiver is not being driven because the equipment containing the line driver is turned off or disconnected, or if the connecting cable has an open circuit or short circuit. In other words, the receiver implements Type 1 interpretation of fault conditions (§7 of V.28, §2.5 of RS-232C). While a 0V or even a -3V receiver threshold would be acceptable for the data lines, these lower thresholds would not give proper indication on the control lines such as DTR and DSR. The receivers, on the other hand, have a full 0.8V noise margin for detecting the power-down or cable-disconnected states.

The receivers have a hysteresis of approximately 0.5V, with a minimum guaranteed hysteresis of 200mV. This aids in obtaining clean output transitions, even with slow rise and fall time input signals with moderate amounts of noise and ringing. The propagation delays of the receivers are 350ns for negative-going input signals, and 650ns for positive-going input signals (see Typical Characteristics graphs).

The MAX239 has a receiver 3-state control line, and the MAX235, MAX236, MAX240 and MAX241 have both a receiver 3-state control line and a low power shutdown control. The receiver TTL/CMOS outputs are in a high impedance 3-state mode whenever the 3-state $\overline{\text{EN}}$able line is high, and are also high impedance whenever the Shutdown control line is high.

Review of EIA Standard RS-232-C and CCITT Recommendations V.28 and V.24

The most common serial interface between electronic equipment is the "RS232" interface. This serial interface has been found to be particularly useful for the interface between units made by different manufacturers since the voltage levels are defined by the EIA Standard RS-232-C and CCITT Recommendation V.28. The RS-232 specification also contains signal circuit definitions and connector pin assignments, while CCITT circuit definitions are contained in a separate document, Recommendation V.24. Originally intended to interface modems to computers and terminals, these standards have many signals which are not used for computer-to-computer or computer-to-peripheral communication.

Serial interfaces can be used with a variety of transmission formats. The most popular by far is the asynchronous format, generally at one of the standard baud rates of 300, 600, 1200, etc. The maximum recommended baud rate for RS-232 and V.28 is 20,000 baud, and the fastest commonly used baud rate is 19,200 baud. Asynchronous serial links use a variety of combinations of the number of data bits, what type (if any) of parity bit, and the number of stop bits. A typical combination is 7 data bits, even parity, and 1 stop bit.

RS232/V.28 physical links are also suitable for synchronous transmission protocols. These higher level protocols often use the standard RS-232C/V.28 voltage levels. Note that one type of physical link (such as RS-232/V.28 voltage levels) can be used for a variety of higher level protocols. Table 2 summarizes the voltage levels and other requirements of V.28 and RS-232.

Comparison of RS-232C/V.28 with other Standards

The other two most common serial interface specifications are the EIA RS423 and RS422/RS485 (CCITT recommendations V.10 and V.11). While the RS-232 or V.28/V.24 interface is the most common interface for communication between equipment made by different manufacturers, the RS423/V.10 interface and RS422/V.11 interfaces can operate at higher baud rates. In addition, the RS485 interface can be used for low cost local area networks.

The RS423 and V.10 interfaces are unbalanced or "single-ended" interfaces which use a differential receiver. This standard is intended for data signaling rates up to 100 kbit/s (100 kilobaud). It achieves this higher baud rate through more precise requirements on the waveshape of the transmitters and through the use of differential receivers to compensate for ground potential variations beween the transmitting and receiving equipment. With certain limitations, this interface is compatible with RS-232 and V.28. The limitations are:

1) less than 20,000 baud rate,
2) maximum cable lengths determined by RS-232 performance,
3) RS423/V.10 DTE and DCE signal return paths must be connected to the the RS232/V.28 signal ground,
4) the RS-232 transmitter output voltages must be limited to ±12V, or additional protection must be provided for the RS423/V.10 receivers, and
5) not all RS232/V.28 receivers will show proper power-off detection of V.10 transmitter outputs.

Maxim's MAX230 and MAX232-MAX238, MAX240 and MAX241 meet restrictions 4 and 5 over the entire range of recommended operating conditions. The MAX231 and MAX239 meet restrictions 4 and 5 provided that the V^+ voltage is 12.5V or less.

The RS422, RS485, and V.11 interfaces are balanced double-current interchanges suitable for baud rates up to 10 Mbit/s. These interfaces are not compatible with RS-232 or V.28 voltage levels.

Application Hints

Operation at High Baud Rates

V.28 states that "the time required for the signal to pass through the transition region during a change in state shall not exceed 1 millisecond or 3 percent of the nominal element period on the interchange circuit, whichever is less." RS-232C allows the transition time to be 4 percent of the duration of a signal element. At 19,200 baud, the "nominal element period" is approximately 50μs, of which 3 percent is 1.5μs. Since the transition region is from -3V to +3V, this means the V.28 slew rate would ideally be faster than 6V/1.5μs = 4V/μs at 19.2 kbaud and 2V/μs at 9600 baud.

The RS-232 requirement is equivalent to 3V/μs at 19.2 kbaud, 1.5V/μs at 9600 baud, etc. The slew rate of the MAX230 series devices is about 3V/μs with the maximum recommended load of 2500pF. In practice, the effect of less than optimum slew rate is a distortion of the recovered data, where the 1's and 0's no longer have equal width. This distortion generally has negligible effect and the devices can be reliably used for 19.2 kbaud serial links when the cable capacitance is kept below 2500pF. With very low capacitance loading, the MAX230 and MAX234-239, MAX240 and MAX241 may even be used at 38.4 kbaud, since the typical slew rate is 5V/μs when loaded with 500pF in parallel with 5kΩ. Under no circumstance will the slew rate exceed the RS-232/V.28 maximum spec of 30V/μs and, unlike the 1488 driver, no external compensation capacitors are needed under any load condition.

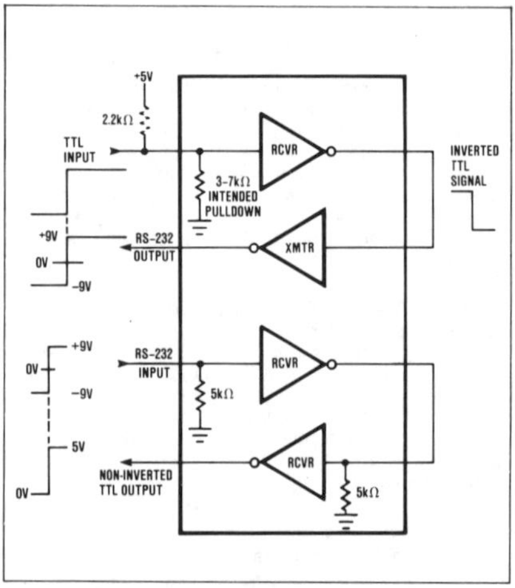

Figure 17. Non-inverting RS-232 Transmitters and Receivers.

Driving Long Cables

The RS-232 standard states that "The use of short cables (each less than approximately 50 feet or 15 meters) is recommended; however, longer cables are permissible, provided that the load capacitance . . . does not exceed 2500pF."

Baud rate and cable length can be traded off: use lower baud rates for long cables, use short cables if high baud rates are desired. For both long cables and high baud rates, use RS422/V.11. The maximum cable length for a given baud rate is determined by several factors, including the capacitance per meter of cable, the slew rate of the driver under high capacitive loading, the receiver threshold and hysteresis, and the acceptable bit error rate. The receivers have 0.5V of hysteresis, and the drivers are designed such that the slew rate reduction caused by capacitive loading is minimized (see Typical Characteristics).

Non-Inverting Drivers and Receivers

Occasionally a non-inverting driver or receiver is needed instead of the inverting drivers and receivers of the family. Simply use one of the receivers as a TTL/CMOS inverter to get the desired operation (Figure 17). If the logic output driving the receiver input has less than 1mA of output source capability, then add the 2.2kΩ pullup resistor.

The receiver TTL outputs can directly drive the input of another receiver to form a non-inverting RS-232 receiver.

Protection for Shorts to ±15V Supplies

All driver outputs except on the MAX231, MAX232 and MAX233 are protected against short circuits to ±15V, which is the maximum allowable loaded output voltage of an RS-232/V.28 transmitter. The MAX231, MAX232, and MAX233 can be protected against short circuits to ±15V power supplies by the addition of a series 220Ω resistor in each output. This protection is not needed to protect against short circuits to most RS-232 transmitters such as the 1488, since they have an internal short circuit current limit of 12mA.

The power dissipation of the MAX230 and MAX234-MAX239, MAX240 and MAX241 is about 200mW with all transmitters shorted to ±15V.

Isolated RS-232 Interfaces

RS-232 and V.28 specifications require a common ground connection between the two units communicating via the RS-232/V.28 interface. In some cases, there may be large differences in ground potential between the two units, and in other cases it may be desired to avoid ground loop currents by isolating the two grounds. In other cases, a computer or control system must be protected against accidental connection of the RS-232/V.28 signal lines to 110/220VAC power lines. Figure 18 shows a circuit with this isolation. The power for the MAX233 is generated by a MAX635 DC-DC converter. When the MAX635 regulates point "A" to -5V, the isolated output at point "B" will be semi-regulated to +5V. The two optocouplers maintain isolation between the system ground and the RS-232 ground while transferring the data across the isolation barrier. While this circuit will not withstand 110VAC between the RS-232 ground and either the receiver or transmitter lines, the voltage difference between the two grounds is only limited by the optocoupler and DC-DC converter transformer breakdown ratings.

Table 1. Circuits Commonly Used for RS-232C and V.24 Asynchronous Interfaces

PIN	CIRCUIT	
1	Protective Ground	Connect to Earth Ground
2	Transmit Data (TD)	Data from DTE
3	Receive Data (RD)	Data from DCE
4	Request To Send (RTS)	Handshake from DTE
5	Clear to Send (CTS)	Handshake from DCE
6	Data Set ready (DSR)	Handshake from DCE
7	Signal Ground	Reference Point for Signals
8	Received Line Signal Detector (sometimes called Carrier Detect, DCD)	Handshake from DCE
11	Printer Busy Signal	Handshake from Printer
20	Data Terminal Ready	Handshake from DTE
22	Ring Indicator	Handshake from DCE

Table 2. Summary of RS-232C and V.28 Electrical Specifications

PARAMETER	SPECIFICATION	COMMENTS
Driver Output Voltage		
0 level	+5V to +15V	With 3-7kΩ load
1 level	-5V to -15V	With 3-7kΩ load
Max. output	±25V Max.	No Load
Receiver Input Thresholds (data and clock signals)		
0 level	+3V to +25V	
1 level	-3V to -25V	
Receiver Thresholds RTS, DSR, DTR		
On level	+3V to +25V	
Off level	Open Circuit or -3V to -25V	Detects Power Off Condition at Driver
Receiver Input Resistance	3kΩ to 7kΩ	
Driver Output Resistance, power off condition	300Ω Min.	$V_{OUT} < \pm 2V$
Driver Slew Rate	30V/μs Max.	$3k\Omega < R_L < 7k\Omega$; $0pF < C_L < 2500pF$
Signalling Rate	Up to 20kbits/sec.	
Cable Length	50'/15 m. Recommended Max. Length	Longer cables permissible, if $C_{LOAD} \leq 2500pF$

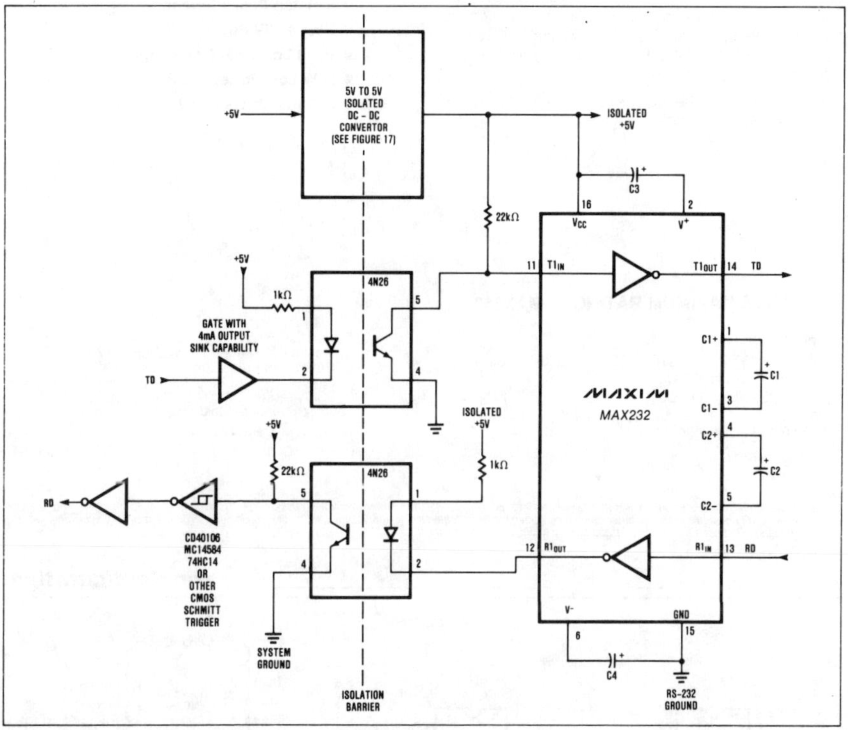

Figure 18. Optically isolated RS-232 Interface.

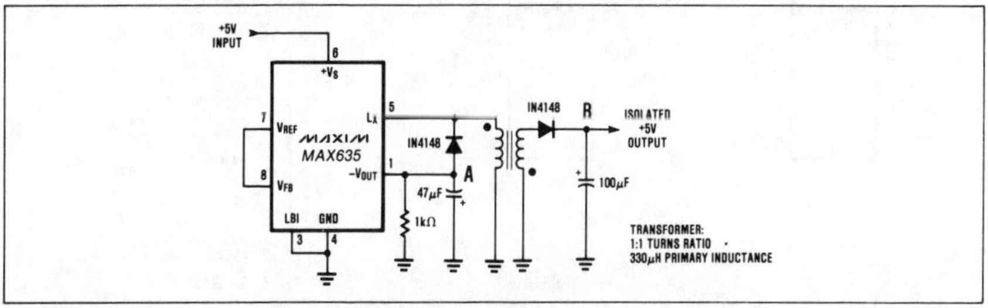

Figure 19. +5V Isolated Power Supply For Optically Isolated RS-232 Interface.

MAX250/251 serial data driver/receiver

General Description

The MAX250 and MAX251 chip set form the heart of a complete, electrically isolated, RS-232 dual transmitter/receiver. By combining many functions on two chips, the cost and complexity required for an isolated digital interface is greatly reduced. Four low cost optocouplers, four capacitors, a diode and a small pot-core type transformer are all that are required to complete a 19.2k baud transceiver. Faster data rates are possible by using high speed optocouplers. In addition to the driving and receiving circuitry for the optocouplers, the chip set includes a push-pull transformer driver to supply power to the interface's isolated side.

Other convenient features include single +5V operation, a low power shutdown mode, and output enable control for three-state operation. The MAX250 and MAX251 are supplied in 14 lead DIP, 14 lead small outline and 20 leadless chip carrier packages.

The MAX252 has all the required components for RS-232 communication in a single package.

Applications

High Noise Data Communications
Industrial Communications
Data Links To Analog Circuits
Bridge Ground Differentials

Features

- **Isolated Data Interface**
- **Single +5V Supply**
- **Uses Low Cost Optocouplers**
- **5μW Low Power Shutdown**
- **2 Transmitters and 2 Receivers**

ABSOLUTE MAXIMUM RATINGS: MAX250

Supply Voltage, V_{CC}	6V
Input Voltages	-0.3V to (V_{CC} +0.3V)
Output Drive Current, D1, D2	240mA
Output Drive Voltage, D1, D2	V_{CC} + 6V

Opto Driver pins $T1_{LDR}$, $T2_{LDR}$, $R1_{OUT}$ and $R2_{OUT}$ may be shorted one at a time indefinitely to V_{CC} or GND

Power Dissipation	
Plastic DIP (derate 7mW/°C above 70°C)	375mW
CERDIP (derate 9.5mW/°C above 70°C)	675mW
Small Outline (derate 7mW/°C above 70°C)	375mW
LCC (derate 7mW/°C above 70°C)	375mW
Lead Temperature (Soldering, 10 seconds)	+300°C
Storage Temperature	-65°C to +160°C

Stresses above those listed under "Absolute Maximum Ratings" may cause permanent damage to the device. These are stress ratings only and functional operation of the device at these or any other conditions above those indicated in the operational section of the specification is not implied. Exposure to absolute maximum rating conditions for extended periods may affect device reliability.

Pin Configurations

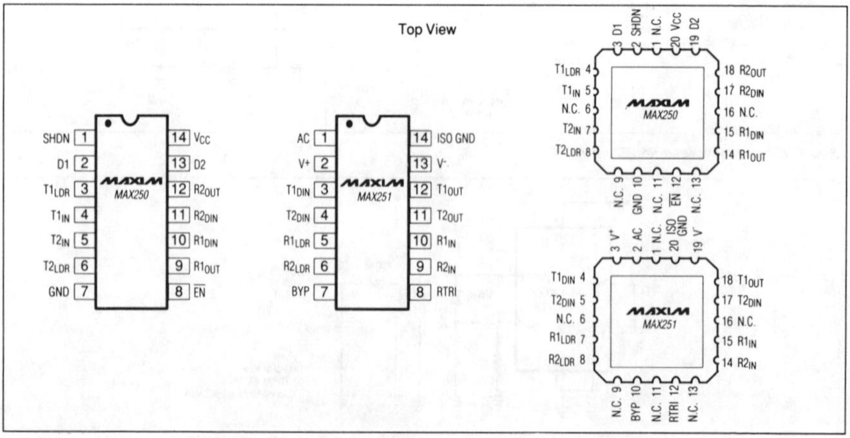

ELECTRICAL CHARACTERISTICS: MAX250

(V_{CC} = 5V ±10%, T_A = Full Temperature Range unless otherwise noted.)

PARAMETER	SYMBOL	CONDITIONS	MIN	TYP	MAX	UNITS
Supply Voltage Range	V_{CC}	Over Temp.	4.5		5.5	V
Operating Supply Current	I_{CC}	D1, D2 Open		0.1	0.5	mA
Shutdown Supply Current	I_{CS}	Shutdown T_A = -40°C to +85°C T_A = -55°C to +125°C		1	10 100	μA
Input Currents	$I_{\overline{EN}}$, I_{SHDN}	Input = GND to V_{CC}		0.001	1	μA
POWER DRIVER D1, D2						
Switch Frequency	$f_{D1, D2}$	V_{CC} = 5V, T_A = 25°C	100	200	275	kHz
ON Resistance Power Driver	$r_{DS(ON)}$	At 25 mA		25	50	Ω
Leakage Current					10	μA
Zener Clamp Voltage	V_{CL}	w. r. t. V_{CC}	6	8	10	V
DRIVER SECTION						
Pull-up Current Input source	I_P	V_{CC} = 5V, V_{IN} = 0V, T_A = 25°C	2	3	6	μA
Current Output Source	I_S	V_{OUT} = 1.4V, T_A = 25°C	-5	-8	-15	mA
TTL/CMOS Output Voltage Low	V_{OL}	I_{OUT} = 3.2mA			0.4	V
TTL/CMOS Output Voltage High	V_{OH}	I_{OUT} = -1.0mA	2.4			V
Input Logic Threshold High	V_{IH}	T_{IN}, R_{DIN}, $\overline{EN}$, Shutdown		1.8	2.4	V
Input Logic Threshold Low	V_{IL}	T_{IN}, R_{DIN}, $\overline{EN}$, Shutdown	0.8	1.3		V
Input Hysteresis	V_{IHYS}			0.5		V
Leakage Current Input and Output	I_L	($\overline{EN}$ or Shutdown) = V_{CC}			10	μA
Input Capacitance	C_{IN}			5		pF

ABSOLUTE MAXIMUM RATINGS: MAX251

Positive Input Voltage, AC terminal 15V
Positive Input Voltage, V^+ terminal 14V
Negative Input Voltage, V^- terminal .... -14V
RS-232 Input Voltage .... -30V to 30V
RS-232 Applied Output Voltage .... -15V to 15V
Tristate Input Voltage, V_{RTRI} .... -0.3V to (V^+ + 0.3V)
RS-232 Transmitters may be indefinitely shorted to GND
Opto Driver pins $R1_{LDR}$, $R2_{LDR}$ may be shorted one at a time indefinitely to GND

Diode Forward Current (AC to V^+) 250mA
Reverse Diode Voltage .... -28V
Power Dissipation
  Plastic DIP (derate 7mW/°C above 70°C) 375mW
  CERDIP (derate 9.5mW/°C above 70°C) 675mW
  Small Outline (derate 7mW/°C above 70°C) 375mW
  LCC (derate 7mW/°C above 70°C) 375mW
Lead Temperature (Soldering, 10 seconds) .... +300°C
Storage Temperature .... -65°C to +160°C

Stresses above those listed under "Absolute Maximum Ratings" may cause permanent damage to the device. These are stress ratings only and functional operation of the device at these or any other conditions above those indicated in the operational section of the specification is not implied. Exposure to absolute maximum rating conditions for extended periods may affect device reliability.

ELECTRICAL CHARACTERISTICS: MAX251

(Test Circuit 1, See Figure 3, T_A = Full Temperature Range unless otherwise noted.)

PARAMETER	SYMBOL	CONDITIONS	MIN	TYP	MAX	UNITS
Positive Supply Current	I^+	$R_L = \infty$		0.7	2.5	mA
Negative Supply Current	I^-	$R_L = \infty$		0.45	1.0	mA
RS-232 CHARACTERISTICS						
RS-232 Output Voltage Swing	T_{VS}	All Transmitter Outputs loaded with 3kΩ to Ground	±5	±7.2		V
RS-232 Output Leakage Current	T_{OL}	$V^+ = V^-$ = 0V T_{OUT} = ±15V	-10		+10	μA
RS-232 Input Threshold High	V_{IH}			1.8	3.0	V
RS-232 Input Threshold Low	V_{IL}		0.6	1.2		V

RS-232 Input Hysteresis	V_{IHYS}			0.6		V
RS-232 Input Resistance		T_A = 25°C	3		7	kΩ
3-State Enable	t_{EN}			3.5		μs
3-State Disable	t_{DS}			1.0		μs
Transmitter Slew Rate		R_L = 3kΩ, C_L = 2500pF	3			V/μs
OPTOINTERFACE CHARACTERISTICS						
Input Pull-up Current	I_P	T_A = 25°C	2.5	4	6	μA
Input Pull-up Voltage Clamp	V_{PCL}	w. r. t. ISO GND		3		V
Input Threshold Voltage High	V_{IH}			1.5	2	V
Input Threshold Voltage Low	V_{IL}		0.8	1.2		V
Input Hysteresis Voltage	V_{IHYS}			0.3		V

ELECTRICAL CHARACTERISTICS: MAX251 (continued)

(Test Circuit 1, See Figure 3, T_A = Full Temperature Range unless otherwise noted.)

PARAMETER	SYMBOL	CONDITIONS	MIN	TYP	MAX	UNITS
Output Source Current	I_{PH}	V_{OUT} = 1.4V, T_A = 25°C	-12	-7	-5	mA
Output Voltage Low	V_{OL}	I_{OUT} = 3.2mA			0.4	V
Output Leakage Current, $R1_{LDR}$, $R2_{LDR}$	I_L	(RTRI or Shutdown) = +5V			10	μA
3-STATE CONTROL						
Pulldown Current	I_{TPD}	V = GND	10	4	1	μA
Threshold Voltage	V_T		0.6	1.4	2	V

Typical Operating Characteristics

MAX251 V⁺ SUPPLY VOLTAGE vs. LOAD CURRENT

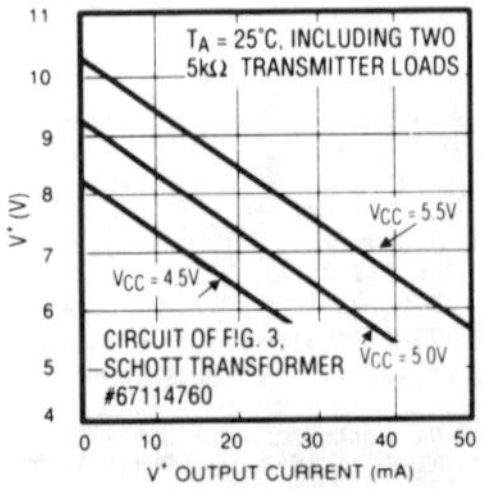

MAX251 V⁻ SUPPLY VOLTAGE vs. LOAD CURRENT

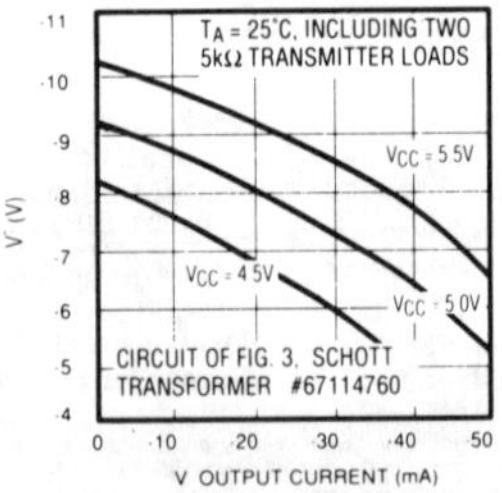

MAX251 V BYPASS vs. LOAD

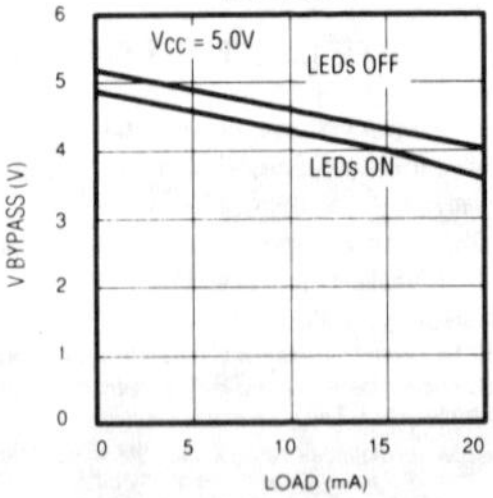

MAX251 TRANSMITTER SLEW RATE vs. LOAD CAPACITANCE

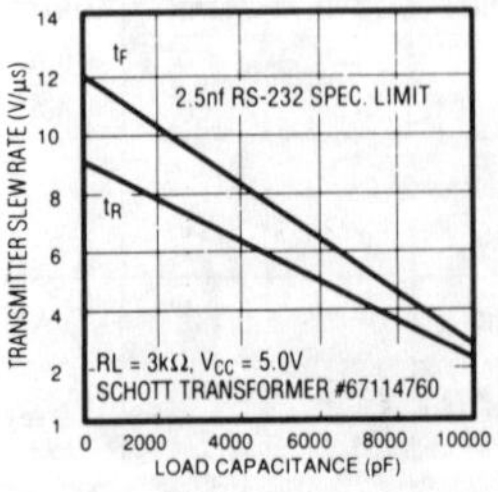

MAX250 PROPAGATION DELAY vs. TEMPERATURE

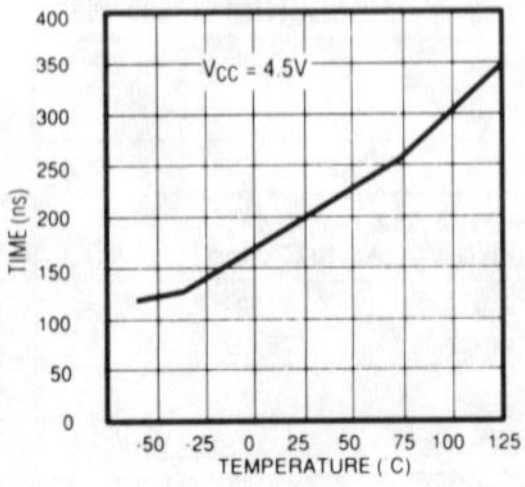

MAX251 PROPAGATION DELAY vs. TEMPERATURE

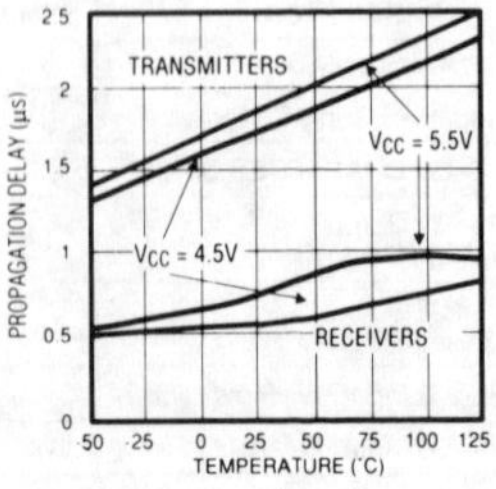

Typical Operating Characteristics (continued)

MAX251 TRANSMITTER SLEW RATE vs. TEMPERATURE

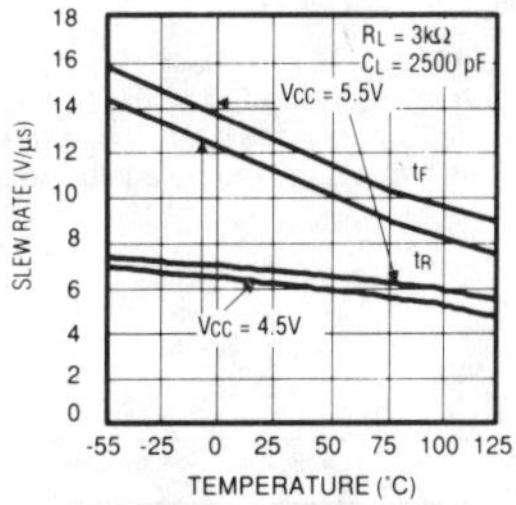

MAX250 D1, D2 SWITCH FREQUENCY vs. TEMPERATURE

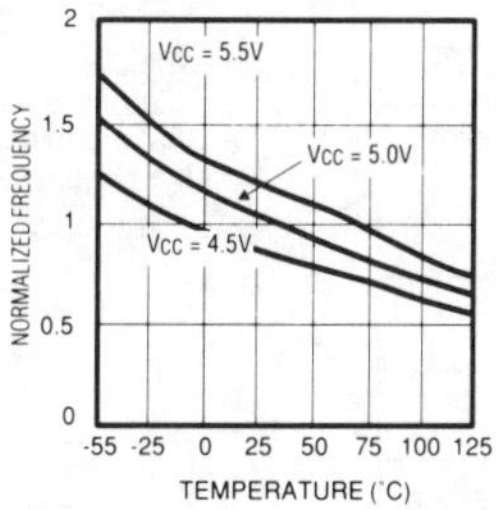

MAX250 ENABLE, DISABLE TIME vs. TEMPERATURE

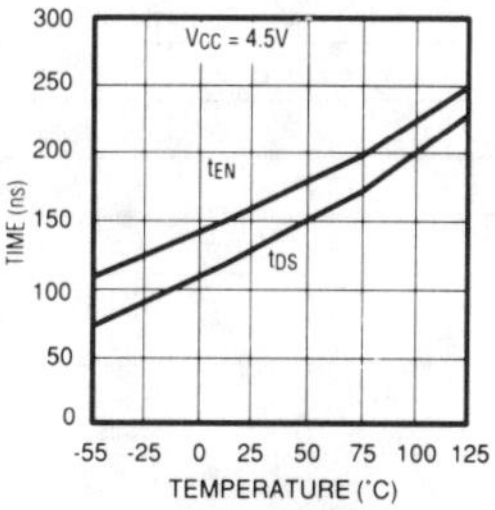

POWER UP DELAY FROM MAX250 V_{CC} TO MAX251 TRANSMITTER OUTPUTS

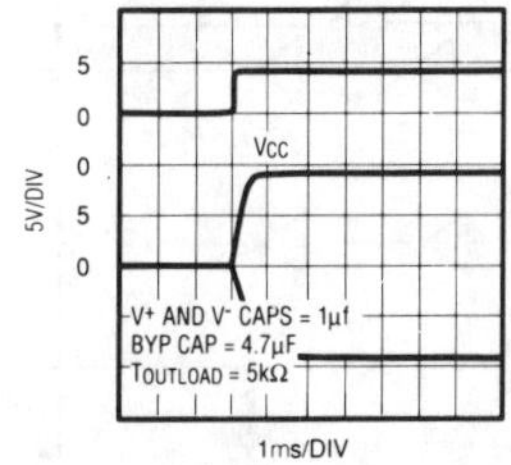

TIME FROM SHUTDOWN TO POWER UP

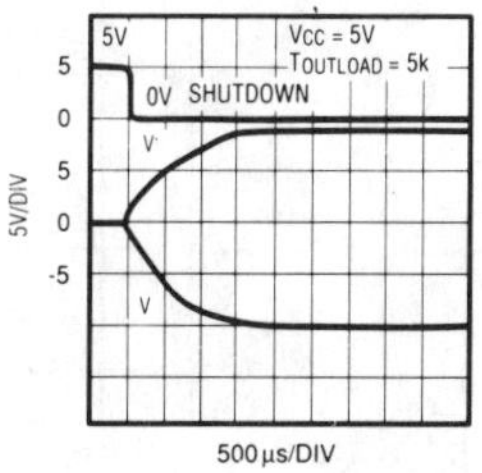

RTRI DELAY TIME TO RECEIVER OUTPUT ACTIVE

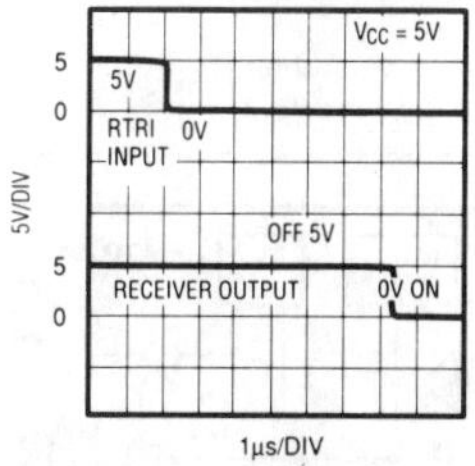

Pin Description

MAX250 LCC PIN#	MAX250 DIP & SO PIN#	SYMBOL	DESCRIPTION
1	-	N.C.	
2	1	SHDN	Shutdown: When+5V, turns off the oscillator, disconnects driver input pull-up resistors and opens D1, D2. For normal operation, ground shutdown.
3	2	D1	Open Drain of Transformer Driver MOSFET
4	3	$T1_{LDR}$	Transmitter #1 LED Driver
5	4	$T1_{IN}$	TTL/CMOS Transmitter #1 Input
6	-	N.C.	
7	5	$T2_{IN}$	TTL/CMOS Transmitter #2 Input
8	6	$T2_{LDR}$	Transmitter #2 LED Driver
9	-	N.C.	
10	7	GND	Ground
11	-	N.C.	
12	8	$\overline{EN}$	Output Enable: When +5V, Pins $T1_{LDR}$, $T2_{LDR}$, $R1_{OUT}$ and $R2_{OUT}$ go Hi impedance
13	-	N.C.	
14	9	$R1_{OUT}$	TTL/CMOS Receiver #1 Output
15	10	$R1_{DIN}$	Receiver #1 Detector Input
16	-	N.C.	
17	11	$R2_{DIN}$	Receiver #2 Detector Input
18	12	$R2_{OUT}$	TTL/CMOS Receiver #2 Output
19	13	D2	Open Drain of Transformer Driver MOSFET
20	14	V_{CC}	+5V Positive Supply Voltage

MAX251 LCC PIN#	MAX251 DIP & SO PIN#	SYMBOL	DESCRIPTION
1	-	N.C.	
2	1	AC	Anode of Input Power Supply Diode
3	2	V^+	Positive Supply Output Terminal
4	3	$T1_{DIN}$	Transmitter #1 Detector Input
5	4	$T2_{DIN}$	Transmitter #2 Detector Input
6	-	N.C.	
7	5	$R1_{LDR}$	Receiver #1 LED Driver
8	6	$R2_{LDR}$	Receiver #2 LED Driver
9	-	N.C.	

10	7	BYP	Internal V_{CC} Bypass Point
11	-	N.C.	
12	8	RTRI	Receiver Output 3-State: When +5V, Receiver Outputs go Hi impedance
13	-	N.C.	
14	9	$R2_{IN}$	RS-232 Receiver #2 Input
15	10	$R1_{IN}$	RS-232 Receiver #1 Input
16	-	N.C.	
17	11	$T2_{OUT}$	RS-232 Transmitter #2 Output
18	12	$T1_{OUT}$	RS-232 Transmitter #1 Output
19	13	V-	Negative Supply Output Voltage
20	14	ISO GND	Isolated Ground

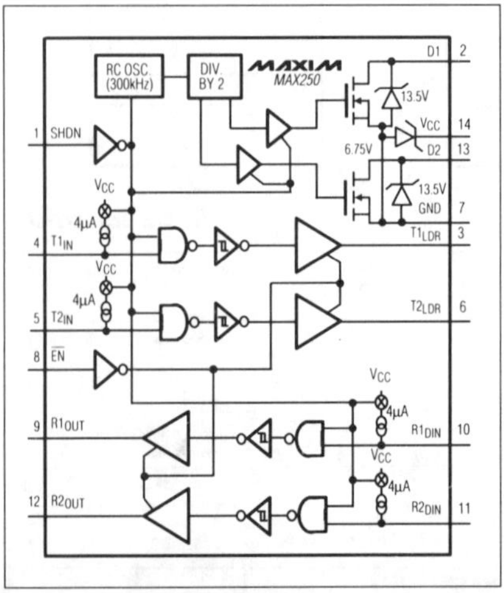

Figure 1. MAX250 Block Diagram

Typical Applications

Figure 3 shows the typical connection for a complete 19.2k baud isolated RS-232 circuit. Figure 3 also shows how 4N26 optocouplers can be replaced by 6N136 devices to achieve 90k baud rates.

A recommended printed circuit board layout is shown in Figure 4. This may be modified for individual designs but two important factors should be considered. 1.) To maximize isolation, the "isolation line" through the center of Figure 4 should not be breached. Connections and components from one side should not be located near those of the other side. 2.) Since the optocoupler outputs are relatively high impedance nodes, they should be located as close as possible to the MAX250 and MAX251. This minimizes stray capacitance and maximizes data rate.

When the MAX250's shutdown input (SHDN) is taken high, power is removed from the MAX251, and the RS-232 transmitter outputs ($T1_{OUT}$, $T2_{OUT}$) go to high impedance states. Timing plots in the Typical Operating Characteristics section show the turn-on and enable delays for various control functions.

The circuit in Figure 4 has been laid out so that it can be used for either a one or two sided PC board. The lines that are thick from one IC pad to the next IC pad are on the bottom side. Lines that are broken by a thin line can

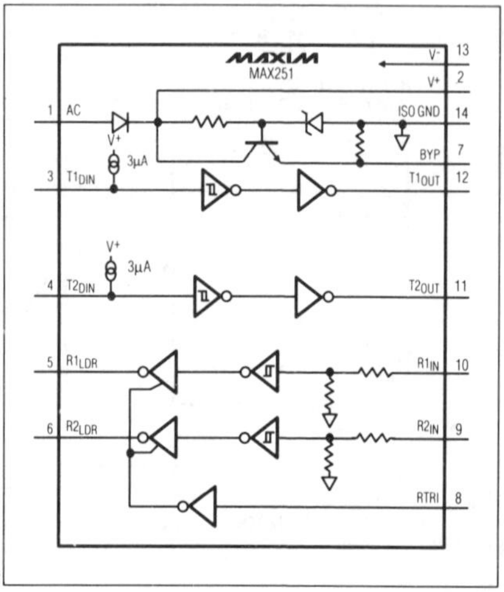

Figure 2. MAX251 Block Diagram

either go on the top side of the board or on the bottom side with jumpers where the thin lines appear. At no time should any lines cross the middle of the board at the isolation barrier.

The MAX250 and MAX251 have a logic inversion in the optocoupler when using the standard configuration. For applications where no inversion is required, or more LED drive current is needed, Figure 5 shows the output structure of the LDR output. The LDR output can typically source 7mA and sink 25mA. Because of the higher sinking capability, a current limiting resistor is required.

Detailed Description

The MAX250 and MAX251, together with four optocouplers and a transformer, form an isolated dual RS-232 transmitter and receiver (See Figure 3). The MAX250 connects to the non-isolated or "logic" side of the interface, translating logic signals to and from the optocouplers, while the MAX251 resides on the isolated or "cable" side, translating data between the optocouplers and RS-232 line drivers and receivers. In addition to the optocoupler drivers and receivers, the MAX250 also contains isolation transformer drive circuitry which supplies power to the isolated side of the interface, and the MAX251.

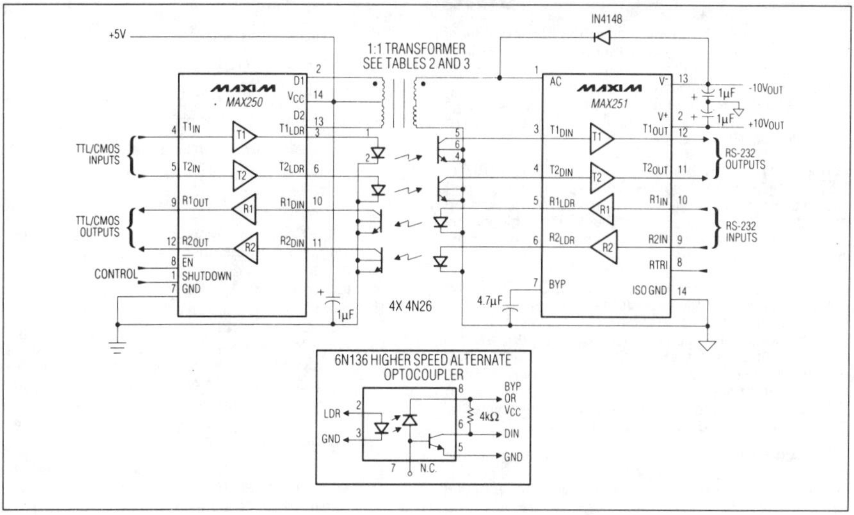

Figure 3. Isolated RS-232 Interface

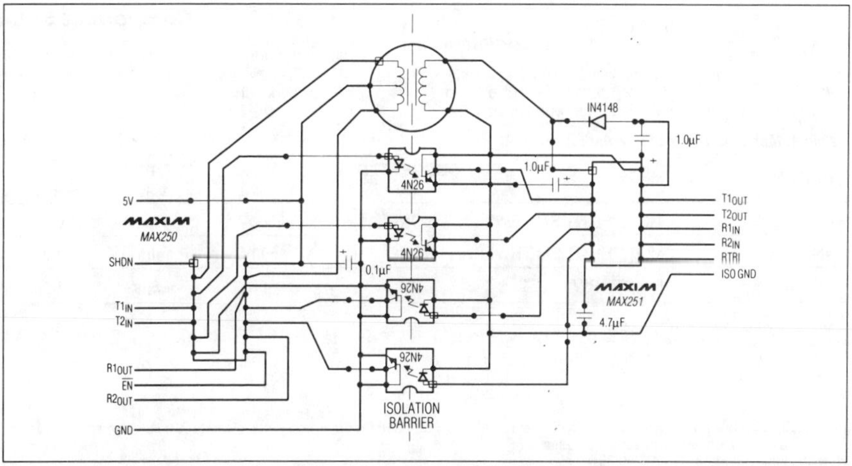

Figure 4. Recommended PC Board Layout for Dual Channel, Optoisolated, Self-Powered RS-232

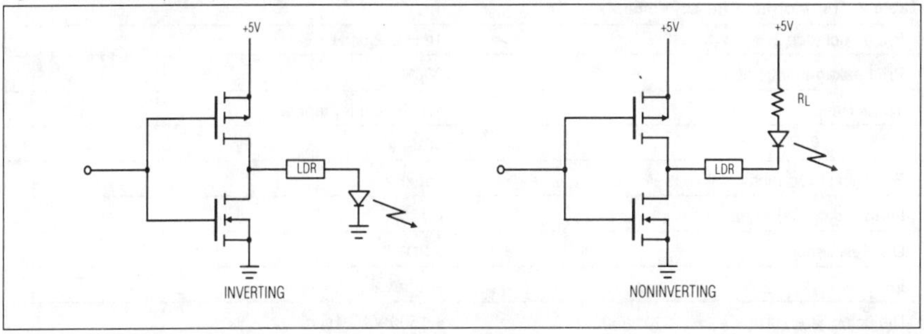

Figure 5. LDR Output Structure

MAX250

The MAX250 contains four identical noninverting drivers whose outputs may be used either as optocoupler LED drivers or as TTL/CMOS logic outputs. Each driver input ($T1_{IN}$, $T2_{IN}$, $R1_{DIN}$, $R2_{DIN}$) has a "weak" 4μA internal pull-up current source, and 0.5V of hysteresis to improve noise rejection. The input logic thresholds conform to standard TTL/CMOS specifications.

In normal operation, the MAX250 driver outputs ($T1_{LDR}$, $T2_{LDR}$, $R1_{OUT}$, $R2_{OUT}$) source 7mA via internal current sources and do not require limiting resistors when driving grounded optocoupler LEDs or CMOS/TTL logic inputs. The outputs can also sink up to 25mA when the current is limited by external resistors.

D1 and D2 are open-drain N-Channel MOSFETs which drive an external isolation transformer in push-pull fashion at 150kHz with a 50% duty cycle. A 1:1 transformer turns ratio provides a 10V peak-to-peak output at the secondary. Specifications and suitable manufacturer's part numbers for this transformer are listed in Tables 2 and 3. No transformer snubbers are required because D1 and D2 are protected against switching transients by internal 13.5V zener clamp diodes as shown in Figure 1.

The MAX250 functions also include an output enable control (EN) and a SHUTDOWN pin (SHDN). EN puts all driver outputs into a high impedance state when driven high. SHDN, when pulled high, disables the following MAX250 functions:

1.) Disables D1 and D2;

2.) Turns off the oscillator;

3.) Shuts off 4μA pull-up currents at driver inputs;

4.) Resets driver outputs to a low state;

5.) Lowers power consumption to 5μW.

MAX251

The MAX251 connects to the "cable" side of the RS-232 interface and includes two line drivers and receivers along with circuitry to translate these levels to optocoupler signals. The RS-232 inputs ($R1_{IN}$, $R2_{IN}$) and outputs ($T1_{OUT}$, $T2_{OUT}$) completely conform to all EIA RS-232C and CCITT V.28 specifications. The receiver outputs ($R1_{LDR}$, $R2_{LDR}$) source 7mA and can drive optocoupler inputs without external current limiting resistors. The MAX251 transmitter inputs ($T1_{DIN}$, $T2_{DIN}$) contain 4μA internal pull-ups which allow direct connection to optocoupler output transistors, again without external resistors.

When the MAX251's RTRI input is pulled high, the receiver outputs ($R1_{LDR}$, $R2_{LDR}$) are disabled and go to a high impedance state. In normal operation, this pin is left open or grounded.

Component Selection

Optoisolators

Optoisolator manufacturers are listed in Table 1 for easy selection. The MAX250/251 combination can be used with a 4N26 to obtain a 19.2k baud rate when used in the diode-to-diode mode (base tied to the emitter). When the MAX250/251 is used with the 6N136, a 90k baud rate can be achieved when a 4kΩ pull-up resistor to 5V is used on pin 6 of the 6N136.

Table 1. Manufacturers of Optoisolators

PART NO.	MFGS	SUGGESTED R_L	V_{IOS} (V_{PK})	TYP. PROP t_{pHL}	t_{pLH}
4N25	MOT,PHL,QT,SM,TRW*	NONE[2]	2500V	14μs	6.3μs
4N26	MOT,PHL,QT,SM,TRW	NONE[2]	1500V	14μs	4.3μs
6N136	HP,QT,TRW	4K	2500V	1.8μs	1.5μs

* MOT= Motorola Inc. (303) 337-3434
PHL= Phillips (401) 232-0500
QT = Quality Technologies (General Instrument) (415) 493-0400
SM = Siemens Components (408) 257-7910
TRW= TRW Electronic Components Group (214) 323-2200

Note 1: This list does not constitute an endorsement by Maxim Integrated Products and is not intended to be a comprehensive list of all manufacturers of these components.
Note 2: When used with a MAX250/251.

Transformers

Table 2. Transformer Characteristics

Pri. Inductance	1mH to 2.5mH
Pri. Leakage Inductance	30μH
Turns Ratio	1:1 Pri. center tapped
ET	50V-μs
Switching Frequency	150kHz
Interwinding Capacitance	< 100pF
DC Resistance	< 2Ω
Ipk	300mA
Dielectric Strength	> 1500 VAC/1sec.

General Description

The DS34C86 is a quad differential line receiver designed to meet the RS-422, RS-423, and Federal Standards 1020 and 1030 for balanced and unbalanced digital data transmission, while retaining the low power characteristics of CMOS.

The DS34C86 has an input sensitivity of 200 mV over the common mode input voltage range of ±7V. Hysteresis is provided to improve noise margin and discourage output instability for slowly changing input waveforms.

Separate enable pins allow independent control of receiver pairs. The TRI-STATE® outputs have 6 mA source and sink capability. The DS34C86 is pin compatible with the DS3486.

Features

- Low power CMOS design
- ±0.2V sensitivity over the entire common mode range
- Typical propagation delays: 20 ns
- Typical input hysteresis: 50 mV
- Inputs won't load line when V_{CC} = 0V
- Meets the requirements of EIA standard RS-422
- TRI-STATE outputs for connection to system buses

Logic Diagram

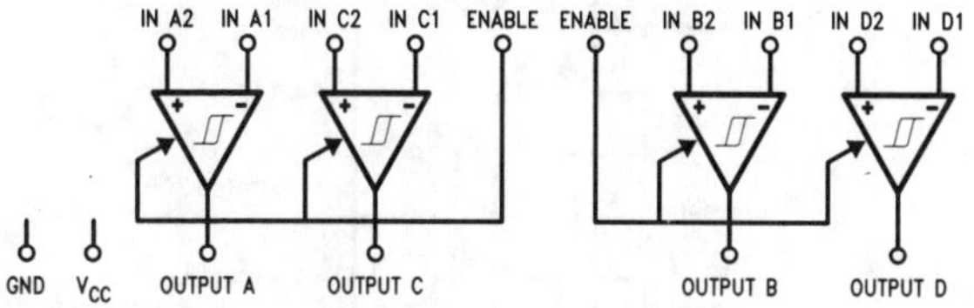

Connection Diagram

Dual-In-Line Package

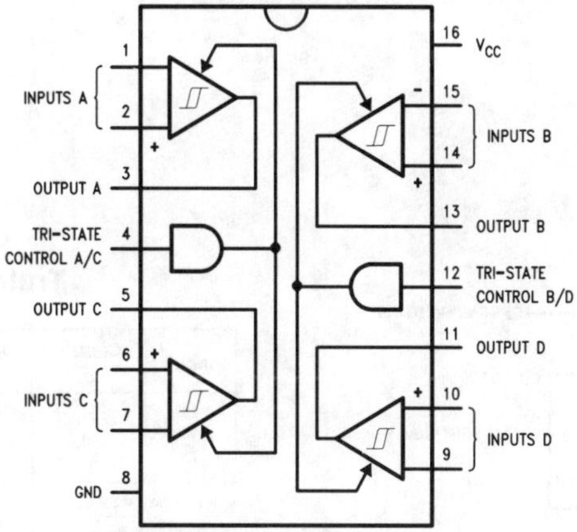

DS34C87 serial data driver/receiver

General Description

The DS34C87 is a quad differential line driver designed for digital data transmission over balanced lines. The DS34C87 meets all the requirements of EIA standard RS-422 while retaining the low power characteristics of CMOS. This enables the construction of serial and terminal interfaces while maintaining minimal power consumption.

The DS34C87 accepts TTL or CMOS input levels and translates these to RS-422 output levels. This part uses special output circuitry that enables the individual drivers to power down without loading down the bus. The DS34C87 also includes special power up and down circuitry which will TRI-STATE the outputs during power up or down, preventing spurious glitches on its outputs. This device has separate enable circuitry for each pair of the four drivers. The DS34C87 is pin compatible to the DS3487.

All inputs are protected against damage due to electrostatic discharge by diodes to V_{CC} and ground.

Features

- TTL input compatible
- Typical propagation delays: 8 ns
- Typical output skew: 0.5 ns
- Outputs won't load line when V_{CC} = 0V
- Meets the requirements of EIA standard RS-422
- Operation from single 5V supply
- TRI-STATE outputs for connection to system buses
- Low quiescent current

Connection and Logic Diagrams

Dual-In-Line Package

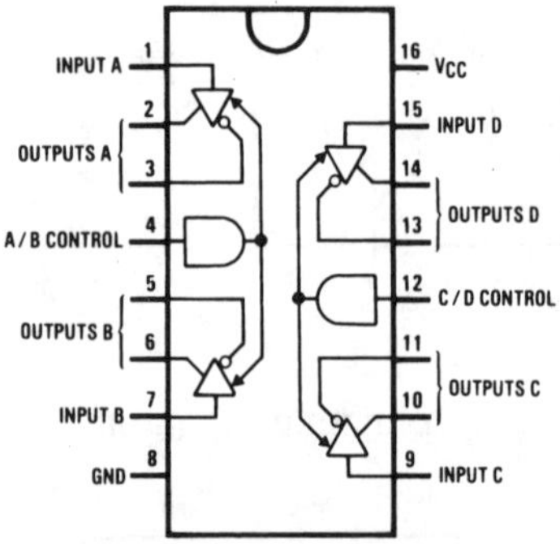

Top View

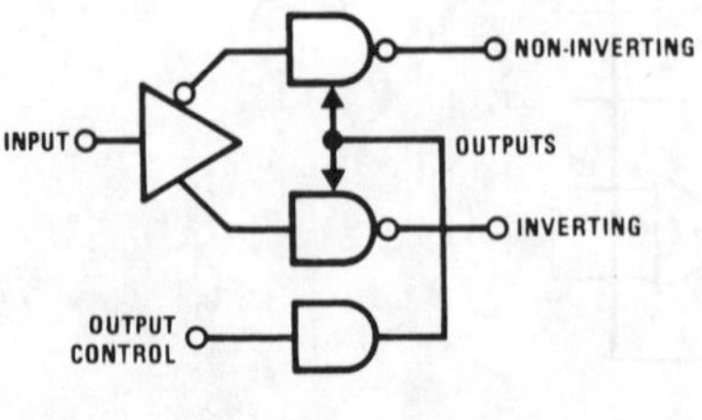

Truth Table

Input	Control Input	Non-Inverting Output	Inverting Output
H	H	H	L
L	H	L	H
X	L	Z	Z

L = Low logic state
H = High logic state
X = Irrelevant
Z = TRI-STATE (high impedance)

General Description

The DS3695, DS3696, DS3697 and DS3698 are high speed differential TRI-STATE® bus/line transceivers/repeaters designed to meet the requirements of EIA standard RS485 with extended common mode range (+12V to −7V), for multipoint data transmission. In addition they meet the requirements of RS422.

The driver and receiver outputs feature TRI-STATE capability. The driver outputs remain in TRI-STATE over the entire common mode range of +12V to −7V. Bus faults that cause excessive power dissipation within the device trigger a thermal shutdown circuit, which forces the driver outputs into the high impedance state. The DS3696 and DS3698 provide an output pin which reports the occurrence of a line fault causing thermal shutdown of the device. This is an "open collector" pin with an internal 10 kΩ pull-up resistor. This allows the line fault outputs of several devices to be wire OR-ed.

The receiver incorporates a fail safe feature which guarantees a high output state when the inputs are left open.

Both AC and DC specifications are guaranteed over the 0 to 70°C temperature and 4.75V to 5.25V supply voltage range.

Features

- Meets EIA standard RS485 for multipoint bus transmission and RS422
- 15 ns driver propagation delays with 2 ns skew (typical)
- Single +5V supply
- −7V to +12V bus common mode range permits ±7V ground difference between devices on the bus
- Thermal shutdown protection
- Power-up/down glitch-free driver outputs permit live insertion or removal of transceivers
- High impedance to bus with driver in TRI-STATE or with power off, over the entire common mode range allows the unused devices on the bus to be powered down
- Combined impedance of a driver output and receiver input is less than one RS485 unit load, allowing up to 32 transceivers on the bus
- 70 mV typical receiver hysteresis

Connection and Logic Diagrams

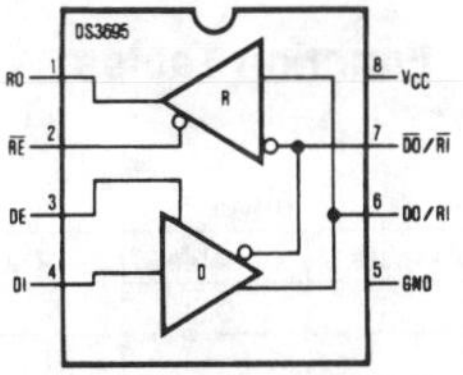

Top View

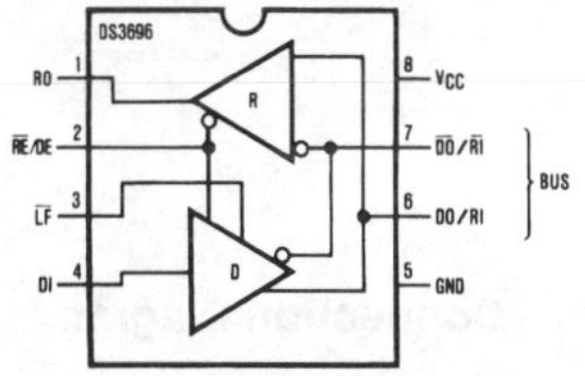

Top View

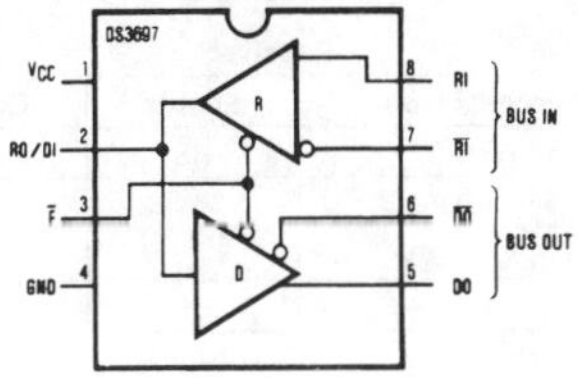

Top View

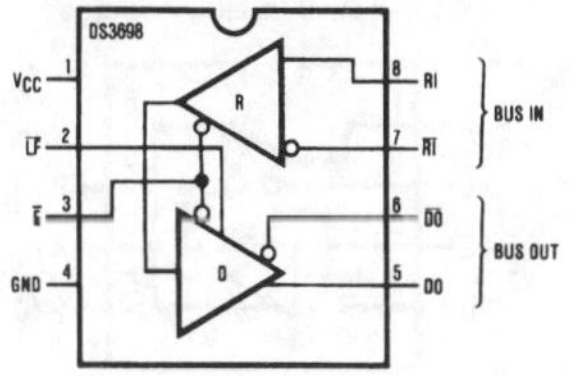

Top View

DS16F95/36F95 serial data driver/receiver

General Description

The DS16F95/DS36F95 Differential Bus Transceiver is a monolithic integrated circuit designed for bidirectional data communication on balanced multipoint bus transmission lines. The transceiver meets EIA Standard RS-485 as well as RS-422A.

The DS16F95/DS36F95 offers improved performance due to the use of state-of-the art L-FAST bipolar technology. The L-FAST technology allows for higher speeds and lower currents by utilizing extremely short gate delay times. Thus, the DS16F95/DS36F95 features lower power, extended temperature range, and improved specifications.

The DS16F95/DS36F95 combines a TRI-STATE® differential line driver and a differential input line receiver, both of which operate from a single 5.0V power supply. The driver and receiver have an active Enable that can be externally connected to function as a direction control. The driver differential outputs and the receiver differential inputs are internally connected to form differential input/output (I/O) bus ports that are designed to offer minimum loading to the bus whenever the driver is disabled or when V_{CC} = 0V. These ports feature wide positive and negative common mode voltage ranges, making the device suitable for multipoint applications in noisy environments.

The driver is designed to handle loads up to 60 mA of sink or source current. The driver features positive and negative current-limiting and thermal shutdown for protection from line fault conditions.

The DS16F95/DS36F95 can be used in transmission line applications employing the DS96F172 and the DS96F174 quad differential line drivers and the DS96F173 and DS96F175 quad differential line receivers.

Features

- Military temperature range
- Bidirectional transceiver
- Meets EIA Standard RS-422A and RS-485
- Meets SCSI specifications
- Designed for multipoint transmission
- TRI-STATE driver and receiver enables
- Individual driver and receiver enables
- Wide positive and negative input/output bus voltage ranges
- Driver output capability +60 mA maximum
- Thermal shutdown protection
- Driver positive and negative current-limiting
- High impedance receiver input
- Receiver input sensitivity of ±200 mV
- Receiver input hysteresis of 50 mV typical
- Operates from single 5.0V supply
- Low power version
- Pin compatible with DS3695 and SN75176A

Connection Diagram

8-Lead Dual-In-Line Package

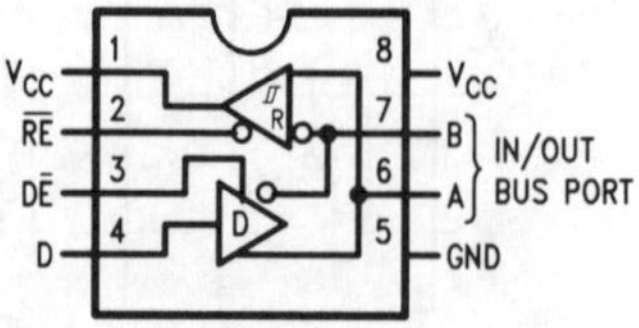

Top View

Function Tables

Driver

Differential Inputs	Enable	Outputs	
D	DE	A	B
H	H	H	L
L	H	L	H
X	L	Z	Z

Receiver

Differential Inputs	Enable	Output
A–B	$\overline{RE}$	R
$V_{ID} \geq 0.2V$	L	H
$V_{ID} \leq -0.2V$	L	L
X	H	Z

H = High Level
L = Low Level
X = Immaterial
Z = High Impedance (Off)

serial data driver/receiver SN75C1406

- **Meets EIA RS-232-D and CCITT-V.28 Specifications**
- **Functional Replacement for Motorola MC145406**
- **Very low Power Consumption . . . 5 mW (typ)**
- **BI-MOS Technology with CMOS and TTL Compatibility**
- **Meets MIL STD 883C Method 3015.4 class B ESD**

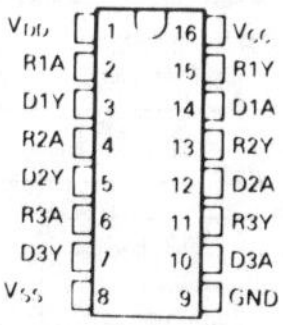

SN75C1406
D, J OR N PACKAGE
(TOP VIEW)

DRIVERS

- Wide Voltage Supply range . . . . ±4.5 V to ±15 V
- On-Chip Slew Rate Limit . . . . 30 V/us (Max)
- Output Current Limit . . . . ±10 mA (Typ)

RECEIVERS

- Input Resistance . . . . 3kΩ to 7kΩ
- Wide Input Signal range . . . . ±30 V
- Input Hysteresis
- Push-Pull outputs for fast transition times

description

SN75C1406 is a monolithic low power BI-MOS integrated circuit, containing three independent drivers and receivers. The package is designed to inferface data terminal equipment (DTE) with data circuit-terminating equipment (DCE) as defined by EIA RS-232-D and CCITT-V.28 standards. The inclusion of on chip slew rate limit eliminates the need for external capacitors. Each driver is similar to SN75C188 and each receiver is similar to SN75C189.

SN75C1406 is characterised for operation from −40 °C to 85 °C.

logic symbol†

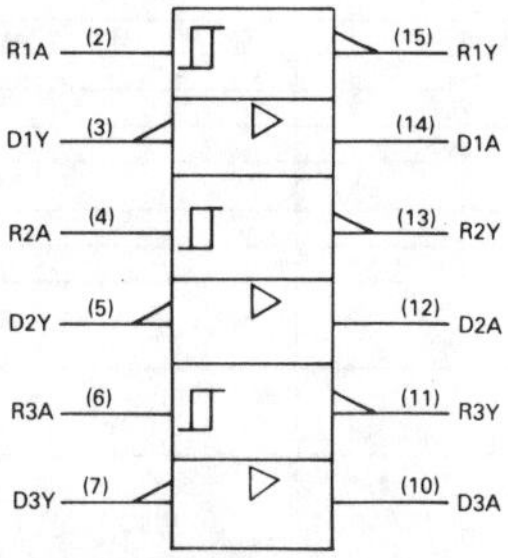

†This symbol is in accordance with IEEE Std 91-1984 and IEC Publication 617-12

logic diagram (positive logic)

Typical of each receiver

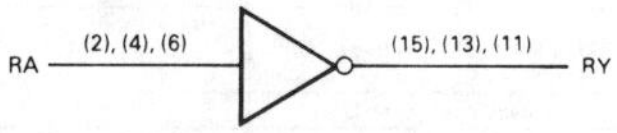

Typical of each driver

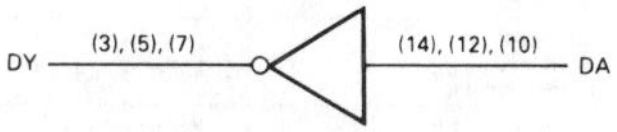

absolute maximum ratings over operating free-air temperature range (unless otherwise noted)

Supply voltage V_{DD} (see Note 1)	15 V
Supply voltage V_{SS} (see Note 1)	−15 V
Supply voltage V_{CC} (see Note 1)	7 V
Input voltage range: Driver	V_{SS} to V_{DD}
Receiver	−30 V to +30 V
Output voltage range: Driver	$(-6\text{ V} + V_{SS})$ to $(6\text{ V} + V_{DD})$
Receiver	(-0.3 V) to $V_{CC} + 0.3\text{ V})$
Continuous total dissipation at (or below) 25°C free air temperature (see Note 2):	
D package	950 mW
J package	1025 mW
N package	875 mW
Operating free-air temperature range	−40°C to 85°C
Storage temperature range	−60°C to 150°C
Lead temperature 1.6 mm (1/16 inch) form case for 60 seconds: J package	300°C
Lead temperature 1.6 mm (1/16 inch) form case for 10 seconds: D and N package	260°C

NOTES: 1. All voltages are with respect to the network ground terminal.
2. For operation above 25°C free-air temperature, refer to Dissipation Derating Table. In the J package, SN75C1406 chips are glass mounted.

DISSIPATION DERATING TABLE

PACKAGE	$T_A = 25°C$ POWER RATING	DERATING FACTOR	ABOVE T_A	$T_A = 85°C$ POWER RATING
D	950 mW	7.6 mW/°C	25°C	494 mW
J	1025 mW	8.2 mW/°C	25°C	533 mW
N	875 mW	7.0 mW/°C	25°C	455 mW

recommended operating conditions

		MIN	NOM	MAX	UNIT
Supply voltage, V_{DD}		4.5	12	15	V
Supply voltage, V_{SS}		−4.5	−12	−15	V
Supply voltage, V_{CC}		3	5	6	V
Input voltage, V_I (see Note 3)	Driver	$2+V_{SS}$		V_{DD}	V
	Receiver	−25		25	V
High-level input voltage, V_{IH}	Driver	2			V
Low-level input voltage, V_{IL}	Driver			0.8	V
High-level output current, I_{OH}	Receiver			−3.2	mA
Low-level output current, I_{OL}	Receiver			3.2	mA
Operating free-air temperature, T_A		−40		85	°C

electrical characteristics over recommended free-air temperature range, V_{DD} = 12 V, V_{SS} = −12 V, V_{CC} = 5 V ± 10% (unless otherwise noted)

total device

PARAMETER		TEST CONDITIONS		MIN	TYP	MAX	UNIT
I_{DD}	supply current from V_{DD}	all outputs open, all inputs at 2 V or 0.8 V	V_{DD} = 5 V, V_{SS} = −5 V		115	160	uA
			V_{DD} = 12 V, V_{SS} = −12 V		115	160	
I_{SS}	supply current from V_{SS}	all outputs open, all inputs at 2 V or 0.8 V	V_{DD} = 5 V, V_{SS} = −5 V		−115	−160	uA
			V_{DD} = 12 V, V_{SS} = −12 V		−115	−160	
I_{CC}	Supply current from V_{CC}	all outputs open, all inputs at 5 V or 0 V	V_{DD} = 5 V, V_{SS} = −5 V		350	450	uA
			V_{DD} = 12 V, V_{SS} = −12 V		350	450	

electrical characteristics over recommended free-air temperature range, V_{DD} = 12 V, V_{SS} = −12 V, V_{CC} = 5 V ± 10% (unless otherwise noted)

driver section only

PARAMETERS		TEST CONDITIONS		MIN	TYP*	MAX	UNIT
V_{OH}	High-level output voltage	V_{IL} = 0.8V, R_L = 3kΩ	V_{DD} = 5V, V_{SS} = −5V	4			V
			V_{DD} = 12V, V_{SS} = −12V	10			V
V_{OL}	Low-level output voltage (see Note 3)	V_{IH} = 2V, R_L = 3kΩ	V_{DD} = 5V, V_{SS} = −5V			−4	V
			V_{DD} = 12V, V_{SS} = −12V			−10	V
I_{IH}	High-level input current	V_I = 5V				1	uA
I_{IL}	Low-level input current	V_I = 0V				−1	uA
$I_{OS(H)}$	High-level short-circuit output current £	V_I = 0.8V, V_o = 0V or V_o = V_{SS}		−5.5	−10	−19.5	mA
$I_{OS(L)}$	Low-level short-circuit output current £	V_I = 2V, V_o = 0V or V_o = V_{DD}		5.5	10	19.5	mA
r_o	output resistance with power off	V_O = −2V to 2V, V_{DD} = V_{SS} = V_{CC} = 0V		300			ohms

* All typical values are at T_A = 25°C.

£ Not more than one output should be shorted at a time.

NOTE 3. The algebraic convention, where the more positive (less negative) limit is designated as maximum, is used in this data sheet for logic levels only, e.g., if −10 V is a maximum, the typical value is a more negative voltage.

electrical characteristics over recommended free-air temperatures range, V_{DD} = 12 V, V_{SS} = 12 V, V_{CC} = 5 V ± 10% (unless otherwise noted)

receiver section

PARAMETERS			TEST CONDITIONS		MIN	TYP*	MAX	UNIT
V_{T+}	Positive-going threshold level				1.75	1.9	2.25	V
V_{T-}	Negative-going threshold level				0.75	1	1.25	V
V_{OH}	High-level output voltage	HCMOS levels	V_I = 0.75 V, I_{OH} = −20 uA	V_{CC} = 3 V	2.9			V
				V_{CC} = 4.5 V	4.4			V
				V_{CC} = 6 V	5.9			V
		TTL levels	V_I = 0.75 V, I_{OH} = −3.2 mA	V_{CC} = 4.5 V to V_{CC} = 5.5 V	2.8			V
V_{OL}	Low-level output voltage	HCMOS levels	V_I = 3 V, I_{OL} = 20 uA	V_{CC} = 3 V to V_{CC} = 6 V			0.1	V
		TTL levels	V_I = 3 V, I_{OL} = 3.2 mA	V_{CC} = 4.5 V to V_{CC} = 5.5 V			0.4	V
I_{IH}	High-level input current			V_I = 25 V	3.6		8.3	mA
				V_I = 3 V	0.43			mA
I_{IL}	Low-level input current			V_I = −25 V	−3.6		−8.3	mA
				V_I = −3 V	−0.43			mA
$I_{OS(H)}$	High-level short-circuit output current		V_I = 0.75 V, V_O = 0 V				−25	mA
$I_{OS(L)}$	Low-level short-circuit output current		V_I = V_{CC}, V_O = V_{CC}				−25	mA

*All typical values are at T_A = 25°C.

switching characteristics over recommended free-air temperature range, V_{DD} = 12 V, V_{SS} = −12 V, V_{CC} = 5 V ± 10%

driver section only

PARAMETERS		TEST CONDITIONS	MIN	TYP*	MAX	UNIT
t_{PLH}	Propagation delay time, low-to-high-level output†	R_L = 3kΩ to 7kΩ, C_L = 15pF			3	us
t_{PHL}	Propagation delay time, high-to-low-level output†				3.5	us
t_{TLH}	Transition time, low-to-high-level output£		0.53	1	3.2	us
t_{THL}	Transition time, high-to-low-level output£		0.53	1	3.2	us
t_{TLH}	Transition time, low-to-high-level output@	R_L = 3kΩ to 7kΩ, C_L = 2500pF		1.5		us
t_{THL}	Transition time, high-to-low-level output@			1.5		us
S_R	Output Slew Rate@	R_L = 3kΩ to 7kΩ, C_L = 15pF	4	15	30	V/us

*All typical values are at T_A = 25°C.
†t_{PHL} and t_{PLH} include the additional time due to on-chip slew rate and is measured at the 50% points.
£Measured between 10% and 90% points of output waveform.
@Measured between +3V and −3V points of output waveform.

switching characteristics over recommended free-air temperature range, V_{DD} = 12 V, V_{SS} = −12 V, V_{CC} = 5 V ± 10%

receiver section only

PARAMETERS			TEST CONDITIONS	MIN	TYP*	MAX	UNIT
t_{PLH}	Propagation delay time, low-to-high-level output		C_L = 15 pF, R_L = 10 kΩ			3	us
t_{PHL}	Propagation delay time, high-to-low-level output		C_L = 15 pF, R_L = 1 kΩ			3	us
t_{TLH}	Transition time, low-to-high-level output†	HCMOS Load	C_L = 50 pF			400	ns
		TTL Load	C_L = 15 pF, R_L = 10 kΩ			120	ns
t_{THL}	Transition time, high-to-low level output†	HCMOS Loads	C_L = 50 pF			300	ns
		TTL Loads	C_L = 15 pF, R_L = 1 kΩ			100	ns

*All typical values are at T_A = 25°C.
†Measured between 10% and 90% points of output waveform.

schematics of inputs and outputs

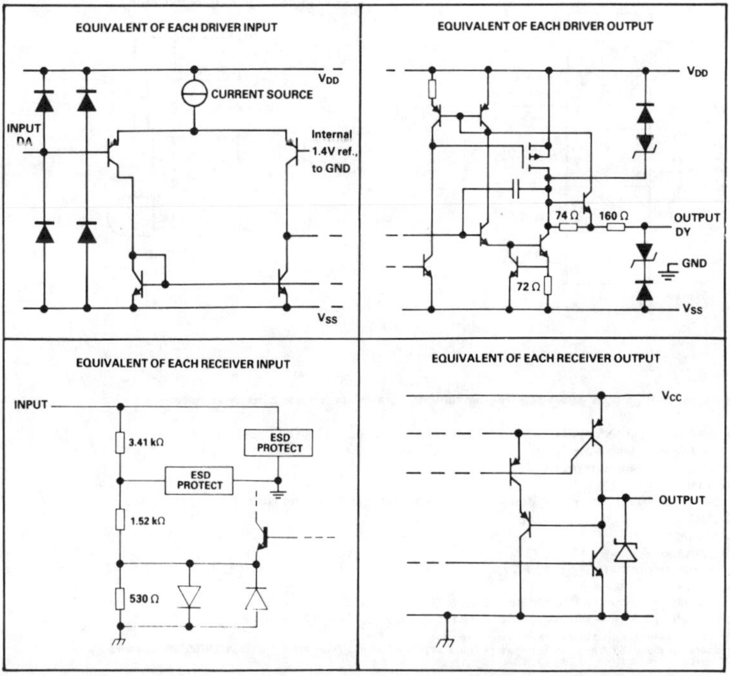

All resistor values shown are nominal.

- **Meets Specification of EIA RS-232-D**
- **Very Low Supply Current . . . 115 uA Typ**
- **Sleep Mode:**
  - **3-State Outputs in High Impedance State**
  - **Ultra Low Supply Current . . . 17 uA Typ**
- **Improved Functional Replacement for:**
  - **SN75188**
  - **Motorola MC1488**
  - **National Semiconductor DS14C88 and DS1488**
- **CMOS and TTL Compatible Data Inputs**
- **On Chip Slew Rate Limit . . . 30 V/us**
- **Output Current Limit . . . 10 mA Typ**
- **Wide Supply Voltage Range . . . ± 4.5 V to ± 15 V**
- **ESD Protection Circuitry Meeting MIL-STD-883C Method 3015.2 Class B**

D, J OR N PACKAGE
(TOP VIEW)

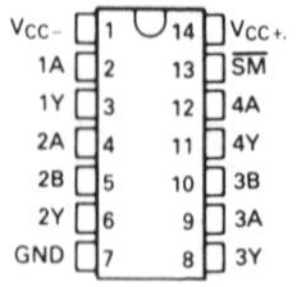

INPUT			OUTPUT
$\overline{SM}$	A	B	Y
H	H	H	L
H	L	X	H
H	X	L	H
L	X	X	Z

H = high level
L = low level
X = irrelevant
Z = high-impedance

description

The SN75C188 is a monolithic low power BI-MOS quadruple line driver designed to interface data terminal equipment (DTE) with data circuit-terminating equipment (DCE) in conformance with the specifications of EIA Standard RS-232-D.

The Sleep Mode pin can be used to switch the outputs to high impedance thus avoiding the transmission of corrupted data during power up and allowing significant system power savings during data 'off' periods.

The device is characterised for operation from −40°C to +85°C.

logic symbol†

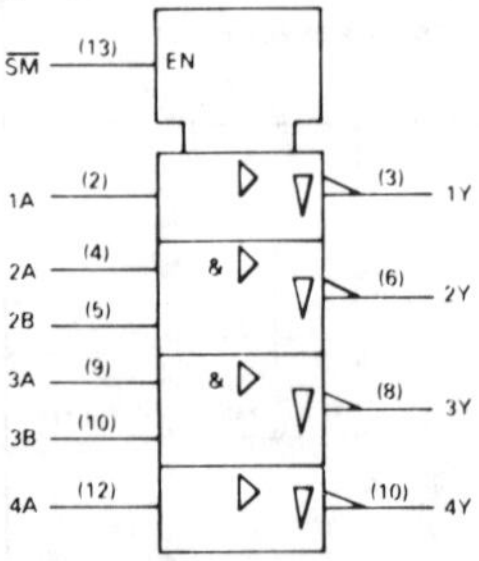

† This symbol is in accordance with IEEE Std 91 1984 and IEC Publication 617 12

logic diagram (positive logic)

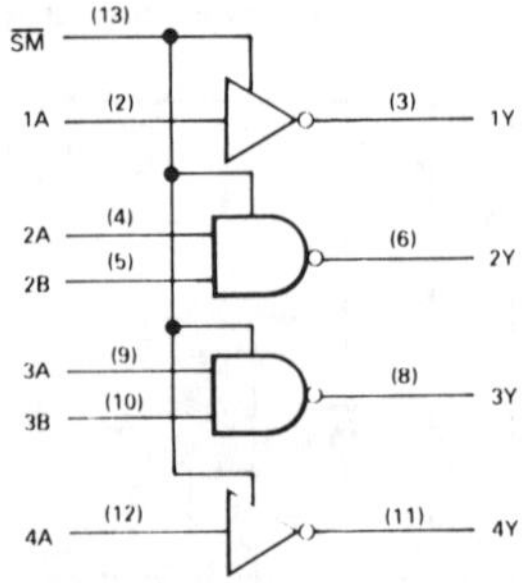

absolute maximum ratings over operating free-air temperature range (unless otherwise noted)

Supply voltage V_{CC+} (see Note 1)	15 V
Supply voltage V_{CC-} (see Note 1)	15 V
Voltage range at any input terminal	V_{CC-} to V_{CC+}
Output voltage range	(6 V + V_{CC-}) to (6 V + V_{CC+})
Continuous total dissipation at (or below) 25°C free air temperature (see Note 2):	
D package	950 mW
J package	1025 mW
N package	875 mW
Operating free-air temperature range	40°C to 85°C
Storage temperature range	65°C to 150°C
Lead temperature 1.6 mm (1/16 inch) from case for 60 seconds: J package	300°C
Lead temperature 1.6 mm (1/16 inch) from case for 10 seconds: D and N package	260°C

NOTES: 1. All voltages are with respect to the network ground terminal.
2. For operation above 25°C free-air temperature, refer to Dissipation Derating Table. In the J package, SN75C198 chips are glass mounted.

DISSIPATION DERATING TABLE

PACKAGE	$T_A = 25°C$ POWER RATING	DERATING FACTOR	ABOVE T_A	$T_A = 85°C$ POWER RATING
D	950 mW	7.6 mW/°C	25°C	494 mW
J	1025 mW	8.2 mW/°C	25°C	533 mW
N	875 mW	7.0 mW/°C	25°C	455 mW

recommended operating conditions

		MIN	NOM	MAX	UNIT
Supply voltage, V_{CC+}		4.5	12	15	V
Supply voltage, V_{CC-}		−4.5	−12	−15	V
Voltage at any input terminal, V_I (see Note 3)		2+V_{CC-}		V_{CC+}	V
High-level input voltage, V_{IH}		2			V
Low-level input voltage, V_{IL}	A & B inputs			0.8	V
	$\overline{SM}$ input			0.6	V
Operating free-air temperature, T_A		−40		85	°C

NOTE 3. The algebraic convention, where the more positive (less negative) limit is designated as maximum, is used in this data sheet for logic levels only, e.g., if −10 V is a maximum, the typical value is a more negative voltage.

electrical characteristics over recommended free-air temperature range, V_{CC+} = 12 V, V_{CC-} = −12 V, V_{SM} = 2 V (unless otherwise noted)

PARAMETERS		TEST CONDITIONS		MIN	TYP*	MAX	UNIT
V_{OH}	High-level output voltage	V_{IL} = 0.8 V, R_L = 3 kΩ	V_{CC+} = 5 V, V_{CC-} = −5 V	4			V
			V_{CC+} = 12 V, V_{CC-} = −12 V	10			V
V_{OL}	Low-level output voltage (see Note 3)	V_{IH} = 2 V, R_L = 3 kΩ	V_{CC+} = 5 V, V_{CC-} = −5 V			−4	V
			V_{CC+} = 12 V, V_{CC-} = −12 V			−10	V
I_{IH}	High-level input current	V_I = 5 V				10	uA
I_{IL}	Low-level input current	V_I = 0 V				10	uA
I_{OZ}	High impedance state output current†	V_{SM} = 0.6 V	V_O = 12 V			100	uA
			V_O = −12 V			−100	uA
$I_{OS(H)}$	High-level short circuit output current†	V_I = 0.8 V, V_O = 0 V or V_O = V_{CC-}		−5.5	−10	−19.5	mA
$I_{OS(L)}$	Low-level short-circuit output current†	V_I = 2 V, V_O = 0 V or V_O = V_{CC+}		5.5	10	19.5	mA
r_o	Output resistance with power off	V_{CC+} = 0 V, V_{CC-} = 0 V, V_O = −2 V to 2 V		300			Ω

*All typical values are at T_A = 25°C.
†Not more than one output should be shorted at a time.
NOTE 3. The algebraic convention, where the more positive (less negative) limit is designated as maximum, is used in this data sheet for logic levels only, e.g., if −10 V is a maximum, the typical value is a more negative voltage.

electrical characteristics over recommended free-air temperature range

PARAMETERS		TEST CONDITIONS		MIN	TYP*	MAX	UNIT
I_{CC+}	Supply current from V_{CC+}	A and B inputs at 2 V or at 0.8 V no load V_{SM} = 2 V	V_{CC+} = 5 V, V_{CC-} = −5 V		115	160	uA
			V_{CC+} = 12 V V_{CC-} = −12 V		115	160	uA
		A and B inputs at 2 V or at 0.8 V, R_L = 3kΩ V_{SM} = 0.6 V	V_{CC+} = 5 V, V_{CC-} = −5 V		17	40	uA
			V_{CC+} = 12 V, V_{CC-} = −12 V		17	40	uA
I_{CC-}	Supply current from V_{CC-}	A and B inputs at 2 V or at 0.8 V no load V_{SM} = 2 V	V_{CC+} = 5 V, V_{CC-} = −5 V		−115	−160	uA
			V_{CC+} = 12 V V_{CC-} = −12 V		−115	−160	uA
		A and B inputs at 2 V or at 0.8 V, R_L = 3kΩ V_{SM} = 0.6 V	V_{CC+} = 5 V, V_{CC-} = −5 V		−17	−40	uA
			V_{CC+} = 12 V, V_{CC-} = −12 V		−17	−40	uA

*All typical values are at T_A = 25°C.

switching characteristics over recommended operating free-air temperature range, V_{CC+} 12 V, V_{CC-} = −12 V. See Note 1.

PARAMETER		TEST CONDITIONS	MIN	TYP*	MAX	UNIT
t_{PLH}	Propagation delay time, low to high level output†	R_L 3kΩ to 7kΩ, C_L 15pF (See Figure 1)			3	us
t_{PHL}	Propagation delay time, high to low level output†				3.5	us
t_{TLH}	Transition time, low to high level output‴		0.53	1	3.2	us
t_{THL}	Transition time, high to low level output‴		0.53	1	3.2	us

t_{TLH}	Transition time, low-to-high level output[f]	R_L 3 kΩ to 7kΩ, C_L 2500 pF (See Figure 2)		1.5		us
t_{THL}	Transition time, high-to-low level output[f]			1.5		us
t_{PZH}	Output enable time to high level	R_L 3 kΩ to 7kΩ, C_L 15 pF (See Figure 3)			50	us
t_{PHZ}	Output disable time from high level				10	us
t_{PZL}	Output enable time to low level	R_L = 3 kΩ to 7 kΩ, C_L 15 pF (See Figure 4)			15	us
t_{PLZ}	Output disable time to low level				10	us
S_R	Output Slew Rate[@]	R_L = 3 kΩ to 7 kΩ, C_L = 15 pF	6	15	30	V/us

*All typical values are at T_A = 25°C.
†t_{PHL} and t_{PLH} include the additional time due to on-chip slew rate and is measured at the 50% points.
[f]Measured between 10% and 90% points of output waveform.
[@]Measured between +3V and −3V points of output waveform.

NOTE 4: The switching characteristic limits are not 100% tested during the sampling or preproduction phase of development, but will be guaranteed and 100% tested when in full production.

PARAMETER MEASUREMENT INFORMATION

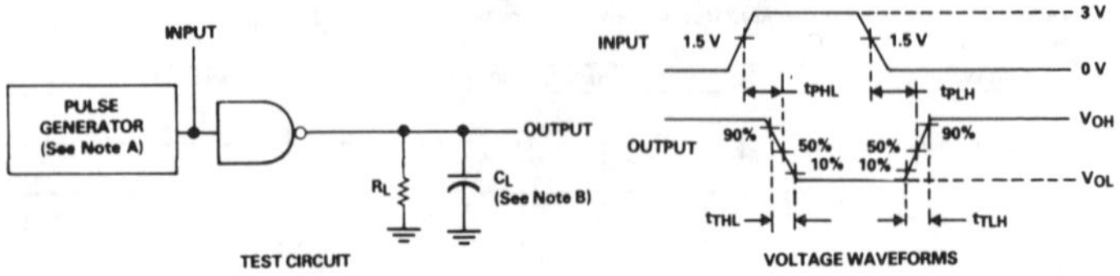

FIGURE 1. PROPAGATION AND TRANSITION TIMES

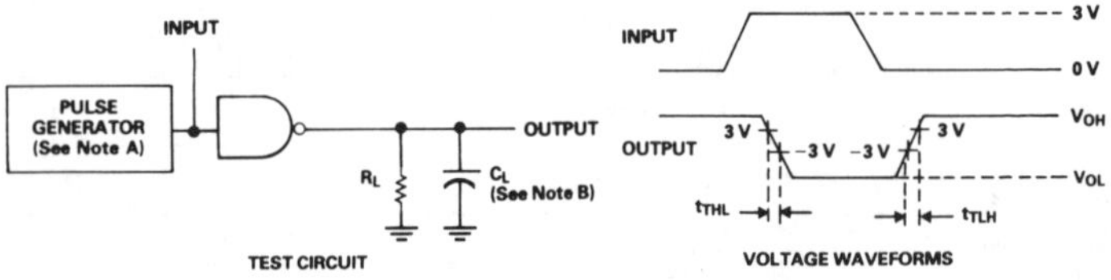

FIGURE 2. PROPAGATION AND TRANSITION TIMES

NOTE: A. The pulse generator has the following characteristics: t_w = 25μs, PRR = 20 kHz, Z_O = 50Ω, t_r = $t_f \leq$ 50ns.
B. C_L includes probe and jig capacitance.

PARAMETER MEASUREMENT INFORMATION

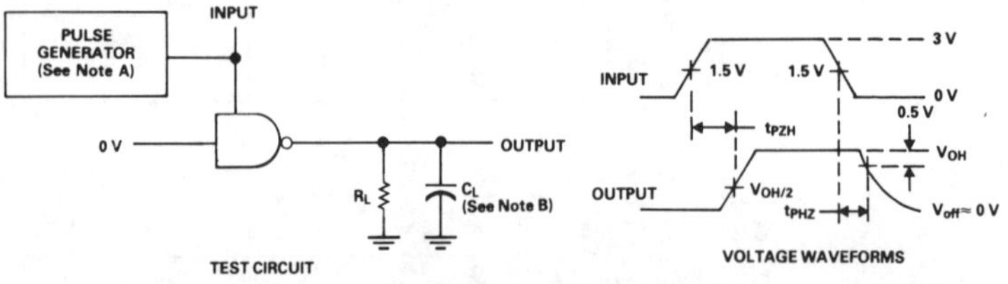

FIGURE 3. DRIVER ENABLE AND DISABLE TIMES

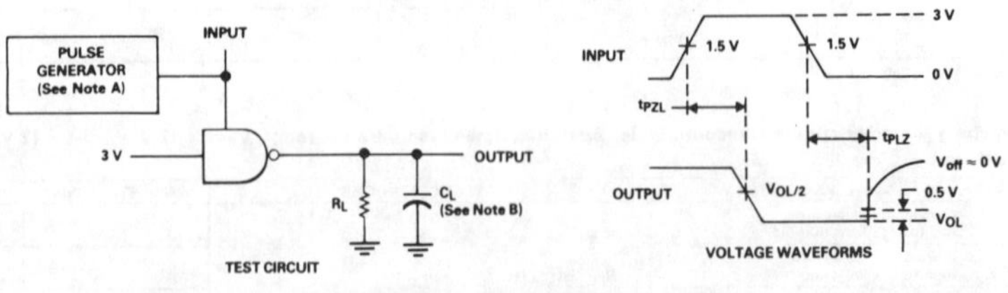

FIGURE 4. DRIVER ENABLE AND DISABLE TIMES

NOTE: A. The pulse generator has the following characteristics: t_w = 25μs, PRR = 20 kHz, Z_O = 50Ω, t_r = $t_f \leq$ 50ns.
B. C_L includes probe and jig capacitance.

schematics of inputs and outputs

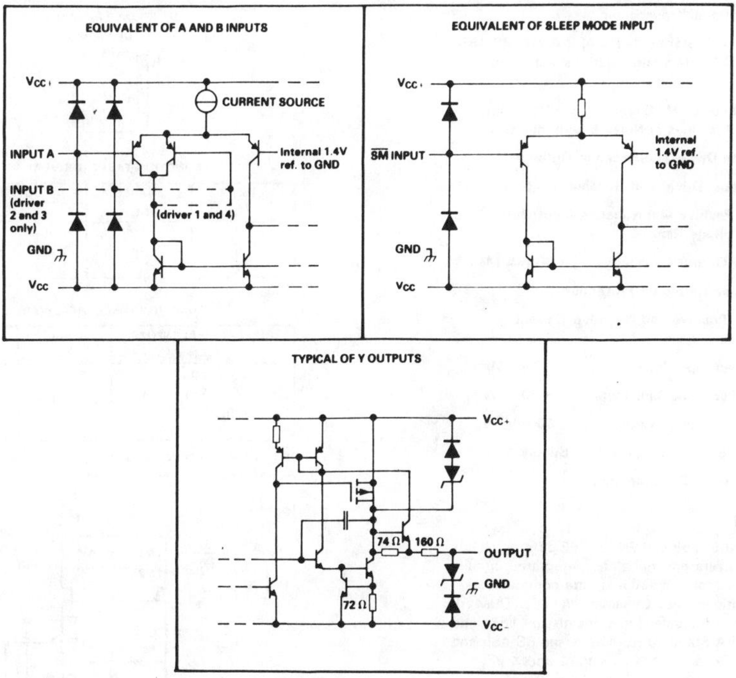

All resistor values shown are nominal.

SN75176B serial data driver/receiver

- **Bidirectional Transceiver**
- **Meets EIA Standards RS-422-A and RS-485 and CCITT Recommendations V.11 and X.27**
- **Designed for Multipoint Transmission on Long Bus Lines in Noisy Environments**
- **3-State Driver and Receiver Outputs**
- **Individual Driver and Receiver Enables**
- **Wide Positive and Negative Input/Output Bus Voltage Ranges**
- **Driver Output Capability. . . ±60 mA Max**
- **Thermal Shutdown Protection**
- **Driver Positive and Negative Current Limiting**
- **Receiver Input Impedance . . . 12 kΩ Min**
- **Receiver Input Sensitivity . . . ±200 mV**
- **Receiver Input Hysteresis . . . 50 mV Typ**
- **Operates from Single 5-Volt Supply**
- **Low Power Requirements**

D, JG, OR P PACKAGE
(TOP VIEW)

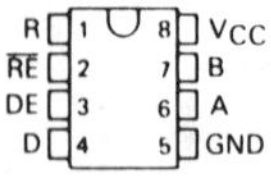

FUNCTION TABLE (DRIVER)

INPUT D	ENABLE DE	OUTPUTS A	OUTPUTS B
H	H	H	L
L	H	L	H
X	L	Z	Z

FUNCTION TABLE (RECEIVER)

DIFFERENTIAL INPUTS A – B	ENABLE $\overline{RE}$	OUTPUT R
$V_{ID} \geq 0.2$ V	L	H
-0.2 V $< V_{ID} < 0.2$ V	L	?
$V_{ID} \leq -0.2$ V	L	L
X	H	Z

H = high level, L = low level, ? = indeterminate,
X = irrelevant, Z = high impedance (off)

logic symbol†

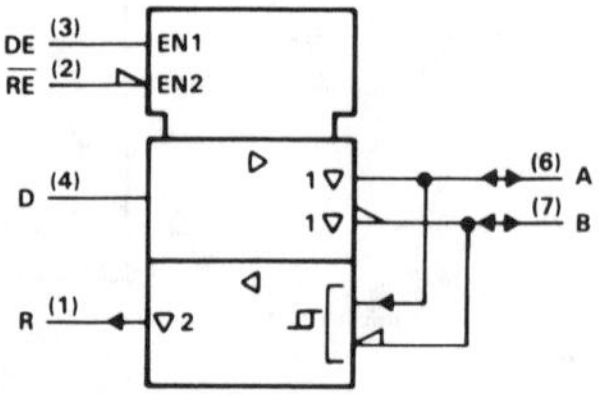

†This symbol is in accordance with ANSI/IEEE Std 91-1984 and IEC Publication 617-12.

logic diagram (positive logic)

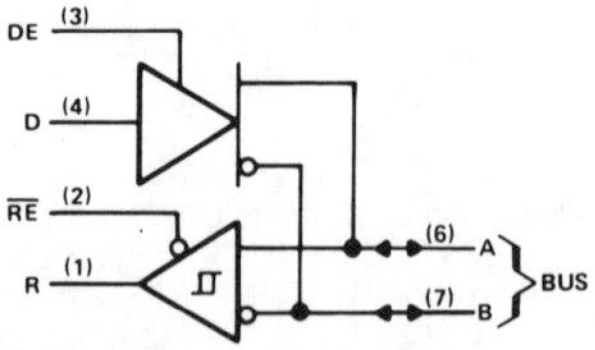

description

The SN65176B and SN75176B differential bus transceivers are monolithic integrated circuits designed for bidirectional data communication on multipoint bus transmission lines. They are designed for balanced transmission lines and meet EIA Standard RS-422-A and RS-485 and CCITT Recommendations V.11 and X.27.

The SN65176B and SN75176B combine a three-state differential line driver and a differential input line receiver both of which operate from a single 5-volt power supply. The driver and receiver have active-high and active-low enables, respectively, that can be externally connected together to function as a direction control. The driver differential outputs and the receiver differential inputs are connected internally to form differential input/output (I/O) bus ports that are designed to offer minimum loading to the bus whenever the driver is disabled or V_{CC} = 0 volts. These ports feature wide positive and negative common-mode voltage ranges making the device suitable for party-line applications.

The driver is designed to handle loads up to 60 milliamperes of sink or source current. The driver features positive- and negative-current limiting and thermal shutdown for protection from line fault conditions. Thermal shutdown is designed to occur at a junction temperature of approximately 150°C. The receiver features a minimum input impedance of 12 kΩ, an input sensitivity of ±200 millivolts, and a typical input hysteresis of 50 millivolts.

The SN65176B and SN75176B can be used in transmission line applications employing the SN75172 and SN75174 quadruple differential line drivers and SN75173 and SN75175 quadruple differential line receivers.

The SN65176B is characterized for operation from −40°C to 85°C and the SN75176B is characterized for operation from 0°C to 70°C.

schematics of inputs and outputs

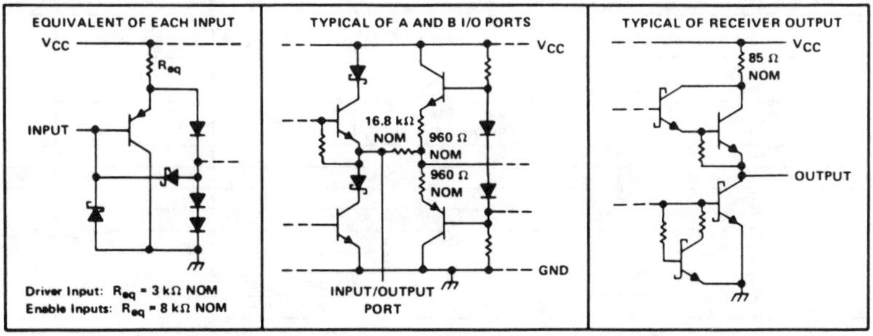

absolute maximum ratings over operating free-air temperature range (unless otherwise noted)

Supply voltage, V_{CC} (see Note 1)	7 V
Voltage at any bus terminal	− 10 V to 15 V
Enable input voltage	5.5 V
Continuous total dissipation at (or below) 25°C free-air temperature (see Note 2):	
D package	725 mW
JG package	825 mW
P package	1100 mW
Operating free-air temperature range: SN65176B	− 40°C to 85°C
SN75176B	0°C to 70°C
Storage temperature range	− 65°C to 150°C
Lead temperature 1,6 mm (1/16 inch) from the case for 60 seconds: JG package	300°C
Lead temperature 1,6 mm (1/16 inch) from case for 10 seconds: D or P package	260°C

NOTES: 1. All voltage values, except differential input/output bus voltage, are with respect to network ground terminal.
2. For operation above 25°C free air temperature, refer to Dissipation Derating Table. In the JG package, the chips are glass mounted.

DISSIPATION DERATING TABLE

PACKAGE	T_A = 25°C POWER RATING	DERATING FACTOR ABOVE T_A = 25°C	T_A = 70°C POWER RATING	T_A = 85°C POWER RATING
D	725 mW	5.8 mW/°C	464 mW	377 mW
JG	825 mW	6.6 mW/°C	528 mW	429 mW
P	1100 mW	8.8 mW/°C	702 mW	570 mW

recommended operating conditions

		MIN	TYP	MAX	UNIT
Supply voltage, V_{CC}		4.75	5	5.25	V
Voltage at any bus terminal (separately or common mode), V_I or V_{IC}				12	V
				− 7	
High-level input voltage, V_{IH}	D, DE, and $\overline{RE}$	2			V
Low-level input voltage, V_{IL}	D, DE, and $\overline{RE}$			0.8	V
Differential input voltage, V_{ID} (see Note 3)				± 12	V
High-level output current, I_{OH}	Driver			− 60	mA
	Receiver			− 400	μA
Low-level output current, I_{OL}	Driver			60	mA
	Receiver			8	
Operating free-air temperature, T_A	SN65176B	− 40		85	°C
	SN75176B	0		70	

NOTE 3: Differential-input/output bus voltage is measured at the noninverting terminal A with respect to the inverting terminal B.

DRIVER SECTION

driver electrical characteristics over recommended ranges of supply voltage and operating free-air temperature (unless otherwise noted)

PARAMETER		TEST CONDITIONS†		MIN	TYP‡	MAX	UNIT
V_{IK}	Input clamp voltage	I_I = − 18 mA				− 1.5	V
V_O	Output voltage	I_O = 0		0		6	V
V_{OD1}	Differential output voltage	I_O = 0		1.5		6	V
V_{OD2}	Differential output voltage	R_L = 100 Ω,	See Figure 1	½ V_{OD1}			
				2			V
		R_L = 54 Ω,	See Figure 1	1.5	2.5	5	V
V_{OD3}	Differential output voltage	See Note 4		1.5		5	V

ΔV_{OD}	Change in magnitude of differential output voltage§	R_L = 54 Ω or 100 Ω, See Figure 1				±0.2	V
V_{OC}	Common-mode output voltage	R_L = 54 Ω or 100 Ω, See Figure 1				+3 −1	V
ΔV_{OC}	Change in magnitude of common-mode output voltage§	R_L = 54 Ω or 100 Ω, See Figure 1				±0.2	V
I_O	Output current	Output disabled, See Note 5	V_O = 12 V			1	mA
			V_O = −7 V			−0.8	
I_{IH}	High-level input current	V_I = 2.4 V				20	μA
I_{IL}	Low-level input current	V_I = 0.4 V				−400	μA
I_{OS}	Short-circuit output current	V_O = −7 V				−250	mA
		V_O = 0				−150	
		V_O = V_{CC}				250	
		V_O = 12 V				250	
I_{CC}	Supply current (total package)	No load	Outputs enabled		42	55	mA
			Outputs disabled		26	35	

† The power-off measurement in EIA Standard RS-422-A applies to disabled outputs only and is not applied to combined inputs and outputs.

‡ All typical values are at V_{CC} = 5 V and T_A = 25°C.

§ ΔV_{OD} and ΔV_{OC} are the changes in magnitude of V_{OD} and V_{OC} respectively, that occur when the input is changed from a high level to a low level.

NOTES: 4. See EIA Standard RS-485 Figure 3.5, Test Termination Measurement 2.

5. This applies for both power on and off; refer to EIA Standard RS-485 for exact conditions. The RS-422-A limit does not apply for a combined driver and receiver terminal.

driver switching characteristics, V_{CC} = 5 V, T_A = 25°C

PARAMETER		TEST CONDITIONS		MIN	TYP	MAX	UNIT
t_{DD}	Differential-output delay time	R_L = 54 Ω,	See Figure 3		15	22	ns
t_{TD}	Differential-output transition time	R_L = 54 Ω,	See Figure 3		20	30	ns
t_{PZH}	Output enable time to high level	R_L = 110 Ω,	See Figure 4		85	120	ns
t_{PZL}	Output enable time to low level	R_L = 110 Ω,	See Figure 5		40	60	ns
t_{PHZ}	Output disable time from high level	R_L = 110 Ω,	See Figure 4		150	250	ns
t_{PLZ}	Output disable time from low level	R_L = 110 Ω,	See Figure 5		20	30	ns

SYMBOL EQUIVALENTS

DATA SHEET PARAMETER	RS-422-A	RS-485
V_O	V_{oa}, V_{ob}	V_{oa}, V_{ob}
V_{OD1}	V_o	V_o
V_{OD2}	V_t (R_L = 100 Ω)	V_t (R_L = 54 Ω)
V_{OD3}		V_t (Test Termination Measurement 2)
ΔV_{OD}	$\lvert\lvert V_t\rvert - \lvert\bar{V}_t\rvert\rvert$	$\lvert\lvert V_t\rvert - \lvert\bar{V}_t\rvert\rvert$
V_{OC}	$\lvert V_{os}\rvert$	$\lvert V_{os}\rvert$
ΔV_{OC}	$\lvert V_{os} - \bar{V}_{os}\rvert$	$\lvert V_{os} - \bar{V}_{os}\rvert$
I_{OS}	$\lvert I_{sa}\rvert$, $\lvert I_{sb}\rvert$	
I_O	$\lvert I_{xa}\rvert$, $\lvert I_{xb}\rvert$	I_{ia}, I_{ib}

RECEIVER SECTION

receiver electrical characteristics over recommended ranges of common-mode input voltage, supply voltage, and operating free-air temperature (unless otherwise noted)

PARAMETER		TEST CONDITIONS		MIN	TYP†	MAX	UNIT
V_{TH}	Differential-input high-threshold voltage	V_O = 2.7 V,	I_O = −0.4 mA			0.2	V
V_{TL}	Differential-input low-threshold voltage	V_O = 0.5 V,	I_O = 8 mA	−0.2‡			V
V_{hys}	Hysteresis§				50		mV
V_{IK}	Enable-input clamp voltage	I_I = −18 mA				−1.5	V
V_{OH}	High-level output voltage	V_{ID} = −200 mV, See Figure 2	I_{OH} = −400 μA,	2.7			V
V_{OL}	Low-level output voltage	V_{ID} = −200 mV, See Figure 2	I_{OL} = 8 mA,			0.45	V
I_{OZ}	High-impedance-state output current	V_O = 0.4 V to 2.4 V				±20	μA
I_I	Line input current	Other input = 0 V, See Note 6	V_I = 12 V			1	mA
			V_I = −7 V			−0.8	
I_{IH}	High-level enable-input current	V_{IH} = 2.7 V				20	μA
I_{IL}	Low-level enable-input current	V_{IL} = 0.4 V				−100	μA
r_I	Input resistance			12			kΩ
I_{OS}	Short-circuit output current			−15		−85	mA
I_{CC}	Supply current (total package)	No load	Outputs enabled		42	55	mA
			Outputs disabled		26	35	

[†] All typical values are at V_{CC} = 5 V, T_A = 25°C.
[‡] The algebraic convention, in which the less-positive (more-negative) limit is designated minimum, is used in this data sheet for common-mode input voltage and threshold voltage levels only.
[§] Hysteresis is the difference between the positive-going input threshold voltage, V_{T+}, and the negative-going input threshold voltage, V_{T-}. See Figure 4.
NOTE 6: This applies for both power on and power off. Refer to EIA Standard RS-485 for exact conditions.

receiver switching characteristics, V_{CC} = 5 V, T_A = 25°C

PARAMETER		TEST CONDITIONS	MIN	TYP	MAX	UNIT
t_{PLH}	Propagation delay time, low-to-high-level output	V_{ID} = 0 V to 3 V,		21	35	ns
t_{PHL}	Propagation delay time, high-to-low-level output	C_L = 15 pF, See Figure 6		23	35	ns
t_{PZH}	Output enable time to high level	C_L = 15 pF, See Figure 7		10	20	ns
t_{PZL}	Output enable time to low level			12	20	ns
t_{PHZ}	Output disable time from high level	C_L = 15 pF, See Figure 7		20	35	ns
t_{PLZ}	Output disable time from low level			17	25	ns

PARAMETER MEASUREMENT INFORMATION

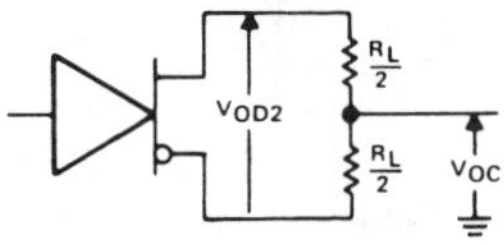

FIGURE 1. DRIVER V_{OD} AND V_{OC}

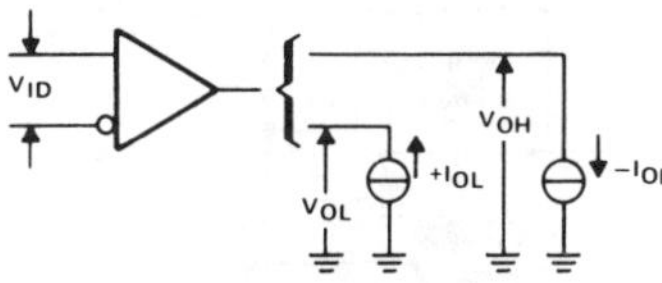

FIGURE 2. RECEIVER V_{OH} AND V_{OL}

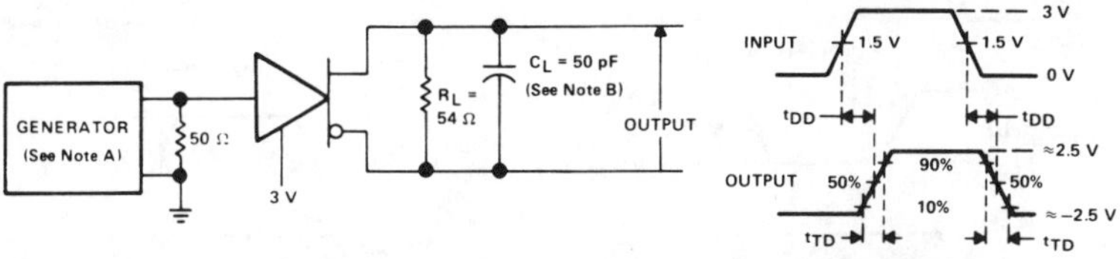

TEST CIRCUIT

VOLTAGE WAVEFORMS

FIGURE 3. DRIVER DIFFERENTIAL-OUTPUT DELAY AND TRANSITION TIMES

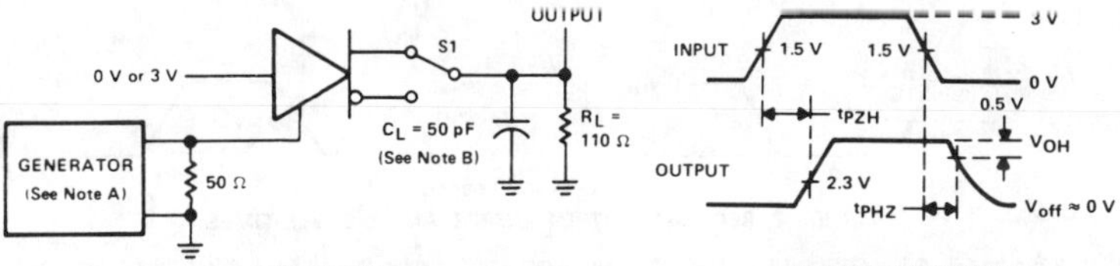

TEST CIRCUIT

VOLTAGE WAVEFORMS

FIGURE 4. DRIVER ENABLE AND DISABLE TIMES

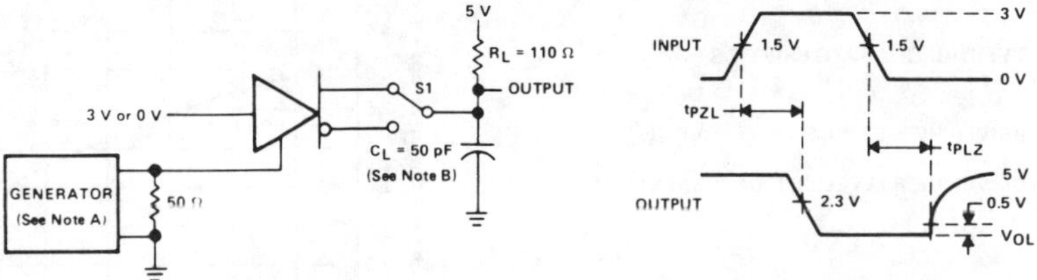

TEST CIRCUIT

VOLTAGE WAVEFORMS

FIGURE 5. DRIVER ENABLE AND DISABLE TIMES

NOTES A. The input pulse is supplied by a generator having the following characteristics: PRR ≤ 1 MHz, 50% duty cycle, t_r ≤ 6 ns, t_f ≤ 6 ns, Z_{out} = 50 Ω.
B. C_L includes probe and jig capacitance.

PARAMETER MEASUREMENT INFORMATION

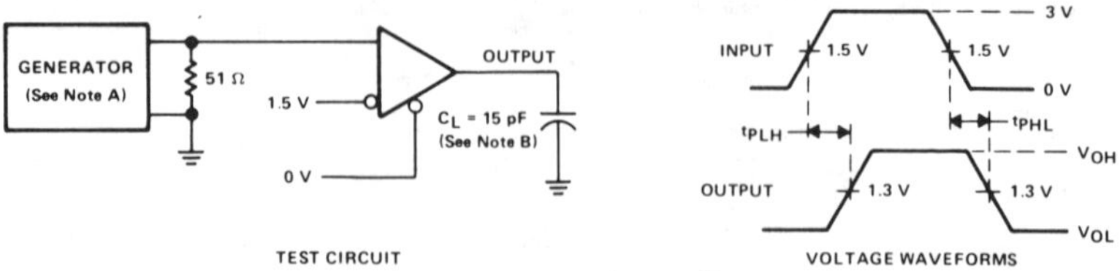

FIGURE 6. RECEIVER PROPAGATION DELAY TIMES

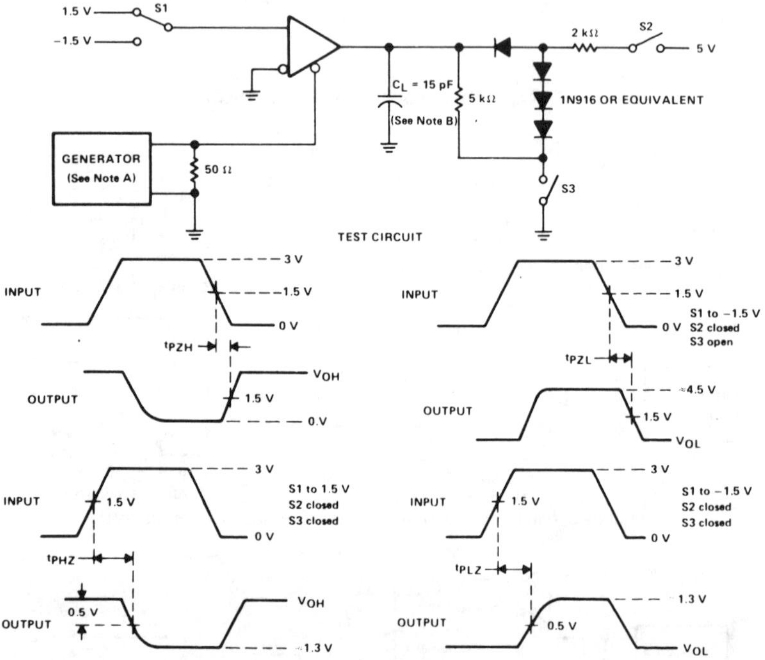

FIGURE 7. RECEIVER OUTPUT ENABLE AND DISABLE TIMES

NOTES: A. The input pulse is supplied by a generator having the following characteristics: PRR ≤ 1 MHz, 50% duty cycle, $t_r \leq 6$ ns, $t_f \leq 6$ ns, Z_{out} = 50 Ω.

B. C_L includes probe and jig capacitance.

TYPICAL CHARACTERISTICS

DRIVER HIGH-LEVEL OUTPUT VOLTAGE
vs
DRIVER HIGH-LEVEL OUTPUT CURRENT

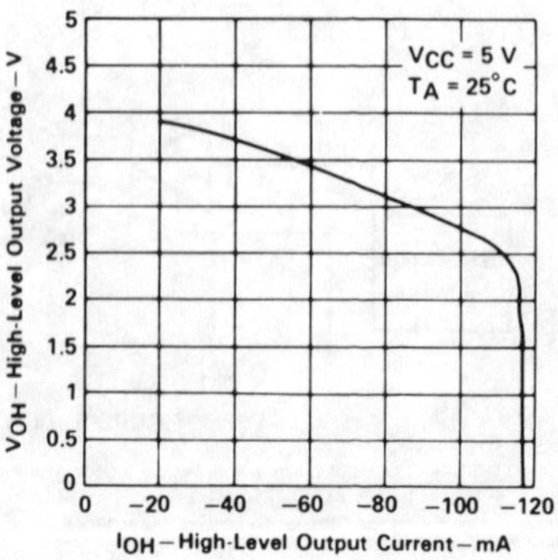

FIGURE 8

TYPICAL CHARACTERISTICS

DRIVER LOW-LEVEL OUTPUT VOLTAGE
vs
DRIVER LOW-LEVEL OUTPUT CURRENT

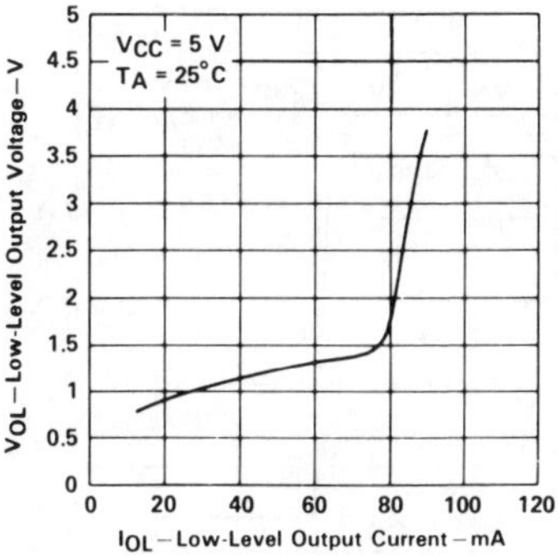

FIGURE 9

DRIVER DIFFERENTIAL OUTPUT VOLTAGE
vs
DRIVER OUTPUT CURRENT

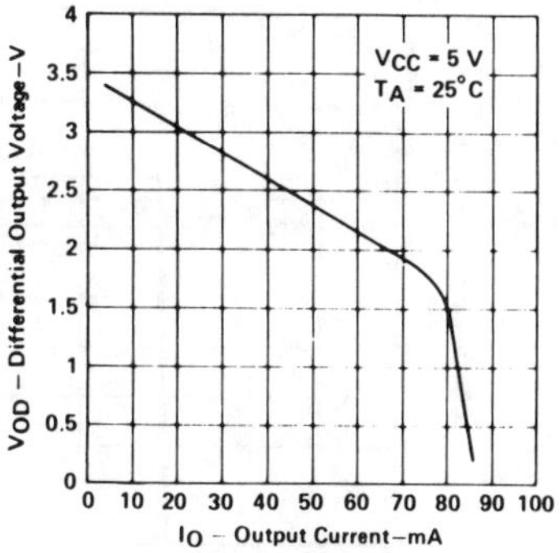

FIGURE 10

RECEIVER HIGH-LEVEL OUTPUT VOLTAGE
vs
HIGH-LEVEL OUTPUT CURRENT

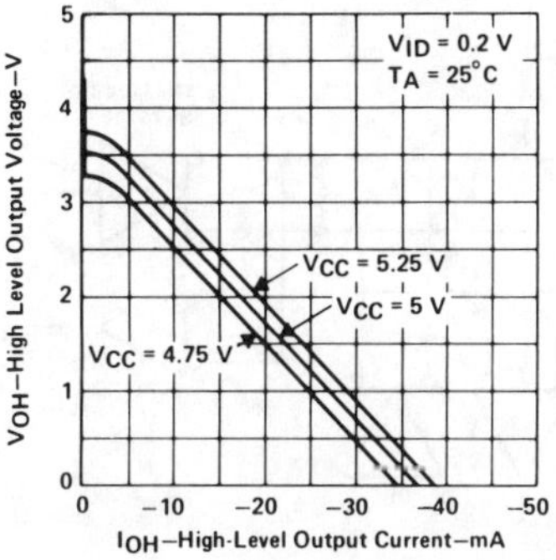

FIGURE 11

RECEIVER HIGH-LEVEL OUTPUT
vs
FREE-AIR TEMPERATURE

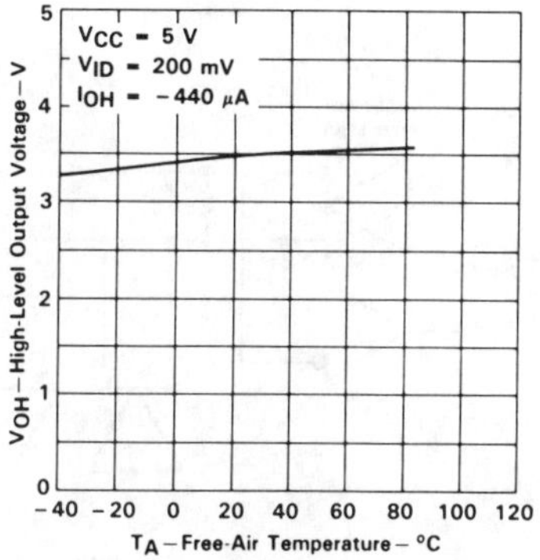

FIGURE 12

RECEIVER LOW-LEVEL OUTPUT VOLTAGE
vs
RECEIVER LOW-LEVEL OUTPUT CURRENT

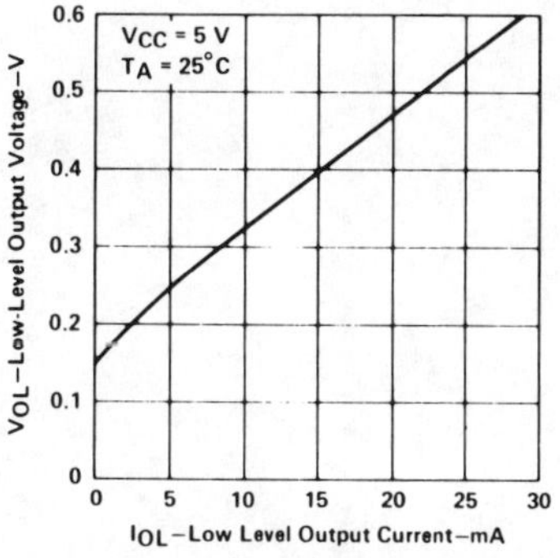

FIGURE 13

RECEIVER LOW-LEVEL OUTPUT VOLTAGE
vs
FREE-AIR TEMPERATURE

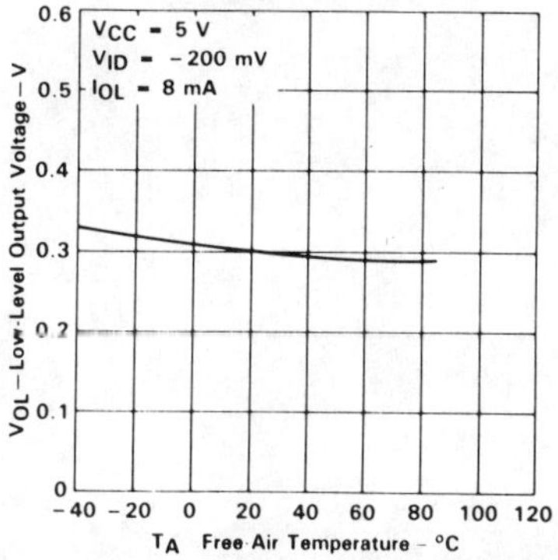

FIGURE 14

TYPICAL CHARACTERISTICS

RECEIVER OUTPUT VOLTAGE
vs
ENABLE VOLTAGE

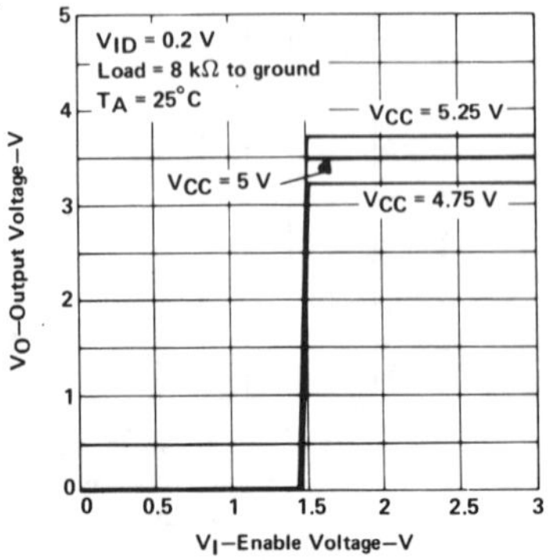

FIGURE 15

RECEIVER OUTPUT VOLTAGE
vs
ENABLE VOLTAGE

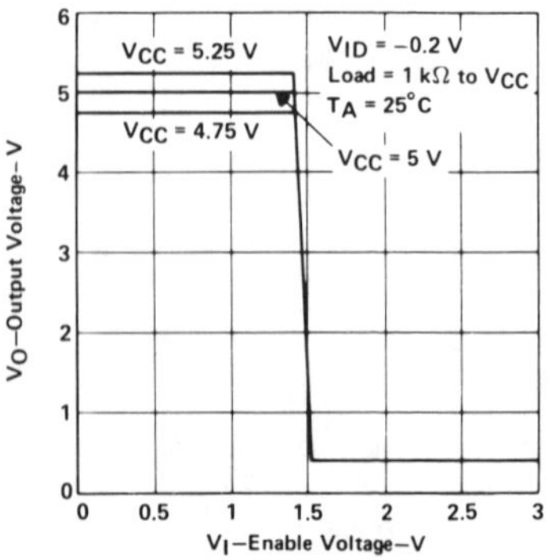

FIGURE 16

TYPICAL APPLICATION

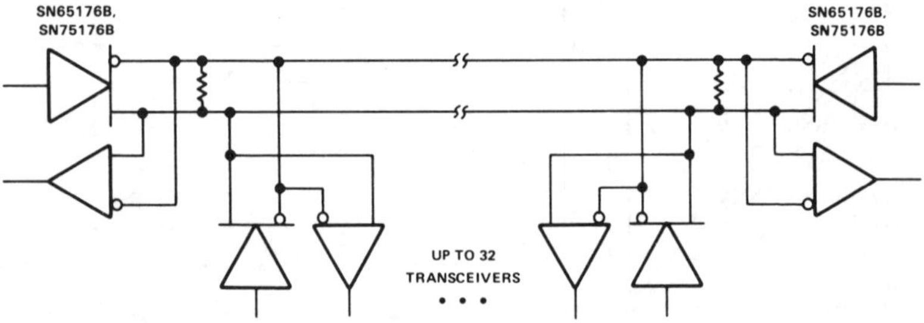

FIGURE 17. TYPICAL APPLICATION CIRCUIT

NOTE 7: The line should be terminated at both ends in its characteristic impedance. Stub lengths off the main line should be kept as short as possible.

FEATURES

- Operates from ± 5V to ± 15V Supplies
- Fully Protected Against Overload
- Outputs can be Driven ± 30V without Damage
- Three-State Outputs; Outputs Open when Off
- Bipolar Circuit—No Latch Up
- ± 30V Input Range
- Triple Driver/Receiver
- No Supply Current in Shutdown
- 30kΩ Input Impedance
- Meets All RS232 Specifications
- 16 Pin Version—Pin Compatible with MC145406
- Available in SO Package

APPLICATIONS

- RS232 Interface
- Terminals
- Modems

TYPICAL APPLICATION

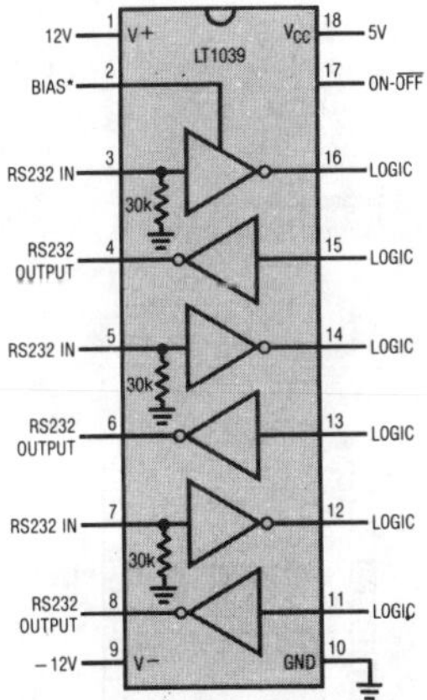

DESCRIPTION

The LT1039 is a triple RS232 driver/receiver which includes SHUTDOWN. Each receiver will accept up to ± 30V input and can drive either TTL or CMOS logic. The RS232 drivers accept TTL logic inputs and output RS232 voltage levels. The outputs are fully protected against overload and can be shorted to ground or up to ± 30V without damage to the drivers. Additionally, when the system is shut down or power is off, the outputs are in a high impedance state allowing data line sharing. Bipolar circuitry makes this driver/receiver exceptionally rugged against overloads or **ESD** damage.

A bias pin allows one receiver to be kept on while the rest of the part is shut down.

The 1039 is also available in the 16 pin version, without shutdown or bias pin functions.

For applications requiring operation from a single 5V supply, see LT1080/81 datasheet.

Driver Output Swing

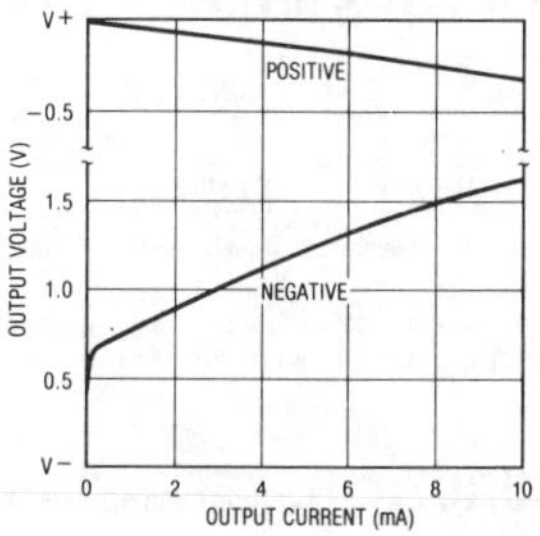

ABSOLUTE MAXIMUM RATINGS

Supply Voltage
- Driver (V +, V −) .... ± 16V
- Receiver (V_{CC}) 7V

Logic Inputs .... V − to 25V
Receiver Inputs .... ± 30V
On-$\overline{Off}$ Input .... GND to 12V
Driver Outputs .... V − + 30V to V + − 30V
Short Circuit Duration .... Indefinite
Operating Temperature Range
- LT1039M .... − 55°C to 125°C
- LT1039C .... 0°C to 70°C
- Guaranteed Functional by Design ..... − 25°C to 85°C

Lead Temperature (Soldering, 10 sec.) .... 300°C

ELECTRICAL CHARACTERISTICS

PARAMETER	CONDITIONS			MIN	TYP	MAX	UNITS
Driver $V^+ = 12V$; $V^- = -12V$; $V_{ON\text{-}\overline{OFF}} = 2.5V$							
Output Voltage Swing	Load = 3k to Ground	Positive Negative	● ●	$V^+ - 0.4$ $V^- + 1.5$	$V^+ - 0.1$ $V^- + 1$		V V
Logic Input Voltage Levels	Input Low Level (V_{OUT} = High) Input High Level (V_{OUT} = Low)		● ●	 2.0	1.4 1.4	0.8	V V
Logic Input Current	$V_{IN} \geq 2.0V$ $V_{IN} \leq 0.8V$				1 5	20 20	μA μA
Output Short Circuit Current	Sourcing Current, $V_{OUT} = 0V$ Sinking Current, $V_{OUT} = 0V$			5 −5	15 −15		mA mA
Output Leakage Current	SHUTDOWN (Notes 1 and 2); $V_{OUT} = \pm 18V$, $V_{IN} = 0$		●		10 (25°C)	200	μA
Supply Leakage Current	SHUTDOWN (Note 1)		●		1 (25°C)	100	μA
Slew Rate	$R_L = 3k\Omega$; $C_L = 51pF$			4	15	30	V/μs
Supply Current	V_{OUT} = Low				4	8	mA
Receiver $V_{CC} = 5V$; $V_{ON\text{-}\overline{OFF}} = 2.5V$							
Input Voltage Thresholds	Input Low (V_{OUT} = High) Input High (V_{OUT} = Low)		● ●	0.5	1.3 1.7	 2.8	V V
Hysteresis			●	0.1	0.4	1.0	V
Input Resistance			●		30		kΩ
Output Voltage	Output Low, $I_{OUT} = -1.6mA$ Output High, $I_{OUT} = 160\mu A$		● ●	 3.5	0.4 4.8	0.5	V V
Output Short Circuit Current	Sinking Current, $V_{OUT} = V_{CC}$ Sourcing Current, $V_{OUT} = 0V$ (Note 3)		● ●	−10 0.5	 1		mA mA
Output Leakage Current	SHUTDOWN (Note 1); $0V \leq V_{OUT} \leq V_{CC}$, $V_{IN} = 0$		●		1	10	μA
Supply Current			●		4	7	mA

ELECTRICAL CHARACTERISTICS

PARAMETER	CONDITIONS		MIN	TYP	MAX	UNITS
Supply Leakage Current	SHUTDOWN (Note 1)	●		1 (25°C)	100	μA
On-$\overline{Off}$ Pin Current	$0V \leq V_{ON\text{-}\overline{OFF}} \leq 5V$	●	−15		80	μA

The ● denotes specifications which apply over the operating temperature range.

Note 1: $V_{ON\text{-}\overline{OFF}} = 0.4V$ for $-55°C \leq T_A \leq 100°C$, and $V_{ON\text{-}\overline{OFF}} = 0.2V$ for $100°C \leq T_A \leq 125°C$. Does not apply to LT1039-16 part.

Note 2: For $T_A \geq 100°C$, leakage current is 350μA max.

Note 3: For $T_A \leq -25°C$, output source current is 0.4 mA.

PIN FUNCTIONS (Pin numbers listed are for 18 pin device).

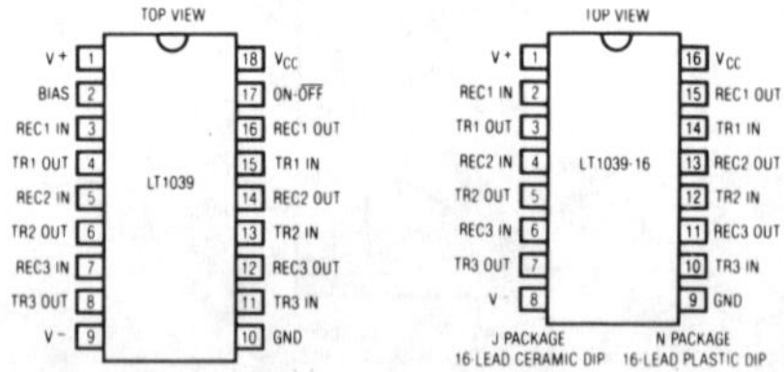

J PACKAGE 16-LEAD CERAMIC DIP N PACKAGE 16-LEAD PLASTIC DIP

V+, V− (Pins 1, 9): Driver supply pins. Supply current drops to zero in SHUTDOWN mode. Driver outputs are in a high impedance state when V+ and V− = 0V.

V_{CC} (Pin 18): 5V power for receivers.

GND (Pin 10): Ground pin.

TR IN (Pins 11, 13, 15): RS232 driver input pins. Inputs are TTL/CMOS compatible. Inputs should not be allowed to float. Tie unused inputs to V_{CC}.

TR OUT (Pins 4, 6, 8): Driver outputs with RS232 voltage levels. Outputs are in a high impedance state when in the SHUTDOWN mode or when power is off (V+ and V− = 0V) to allow data line sharing. Outputs are fully short circuit protected from V− +30V to V+ −30V with power on, off, or in the SHUTDOWN mode. Typical output breakdowns are greater than ±45V and higher applied voltages will not damage the device if moderately current limited.

REC IN (Pins 3, 5, 7): Receiver input pins. Accepts RS232 voltage levels (±30V) and has 0.4V of hysteresis to provide noise immunity. Input impedance is nominally 30kΩ.

REC OUT (Pins 12, 14, 16): Receiver outputs with TTL/CMOS voltage levels. Outputs are in a high impedance state when in the SHUTDOWN mode to allow data line sharing. Outputs are fully short circuit protected to ground or V_{CC} with power on, off, or in the SHUTDOWN mode.

ON-$\overline{\text{OFF}}$ (Pin 17): Controls the operation mode of the LT1039 and is TTL/CMOS compatible. A logic low puts the device in the SHUTDOWN mode which reduces input supply current to zero and places both driver and receiver outputs in a high impedance state.

BIAS (Pin 2): Keeps receiver 1 on while the LT1039 is in the SHUTDOWN mode. Leave BIAS pin open when not in use. See Application Hints for proper use.

TYPICAL PERFORMANCE CHARACTERISTICS

Driver Output Short Circuit Current

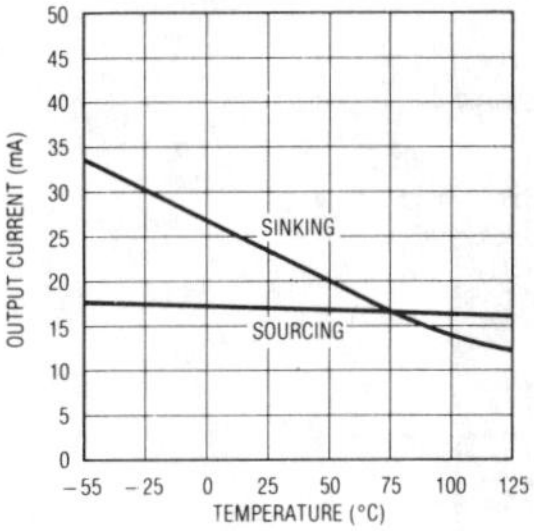

Receiver Input Thresholds

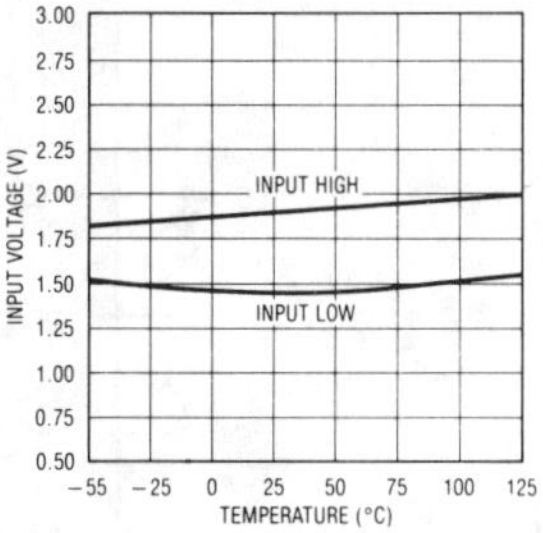

On-$\overline{\text{Off}}$ Pin Thresholds

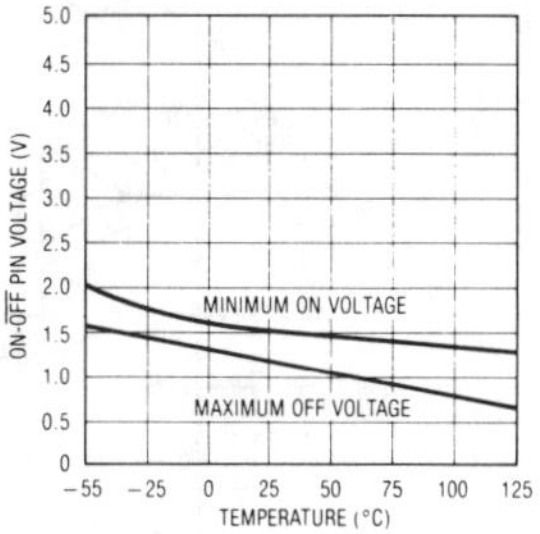

TYPICAL PERFORMANCE CHARACTERISTICS

Supply Current in SHUTDOWN

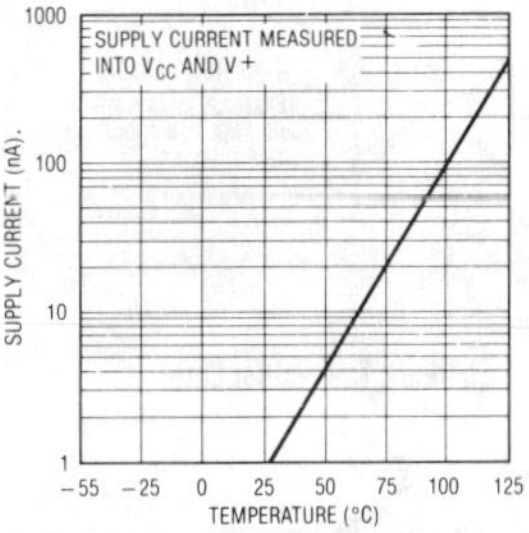

Driver Output Leakage in SHUTDOWN

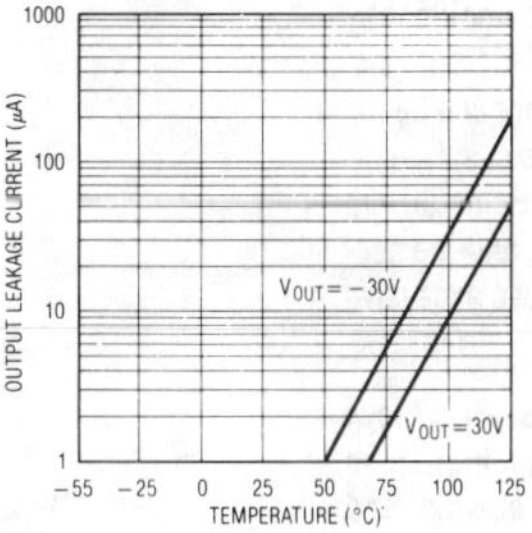

Receiver Output Short Circuit Current

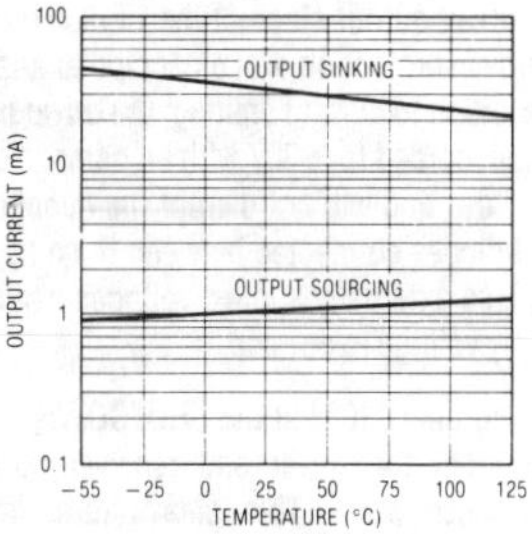

On-$\overline{\text{Off}}$ Pin Current vs Voltage

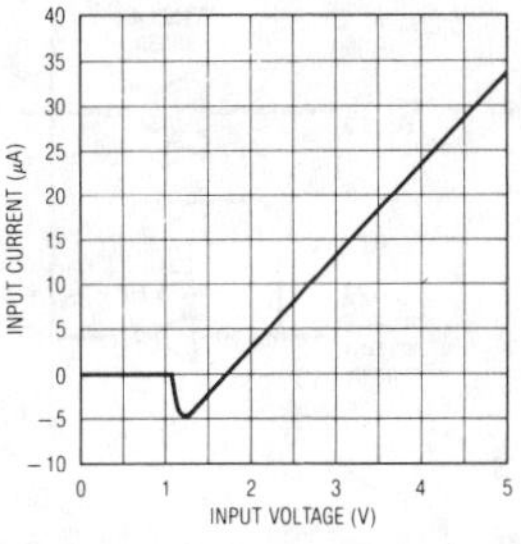

Driver Output Swing vs Current

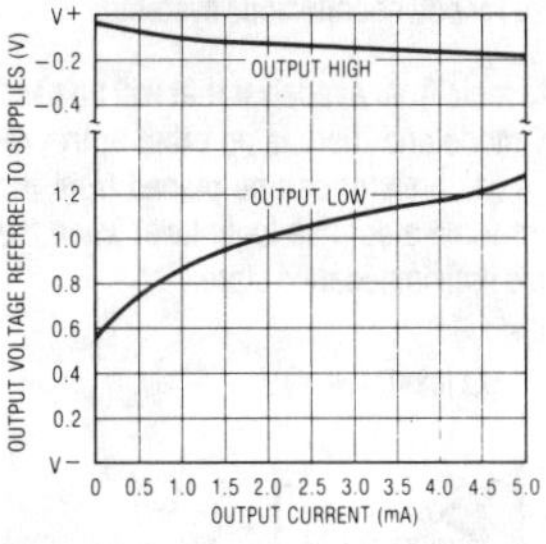

TYPICAL APPLICATION

LT1080 (Driver/Receiver with Power Supply) Driving an LT1039

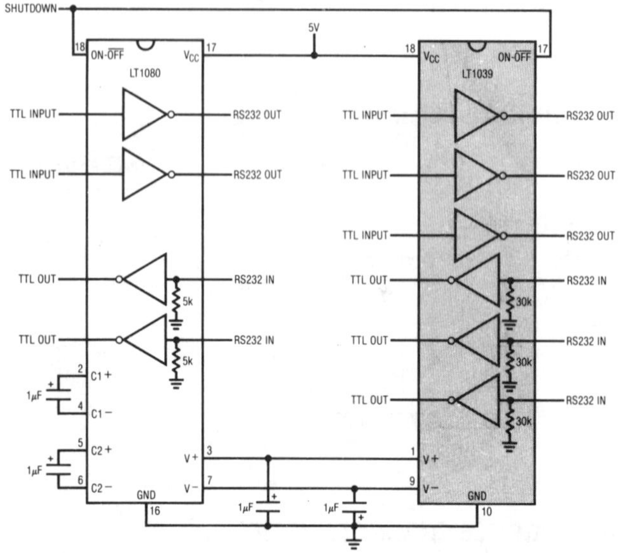

APPLICATION HINTS

The driver output stage of the LT1039 offers significantly improved protection over older bipolar and CMOS designs. In addition to current limiting, the driver output can be externally forced to ± 30V with no damage or excessive current flow, and will not disrupt the supplies. Some drivers have diodes connected between the outputs and the supplies, so externally applied voltages can cause excessive supply voltage to develop.

Placing the LT1039 in the SHUTDOWN mode (Pin 17 low) puts both the driver and receiver outputs in a high impedance state. This allows data line sharing and transceiver applications.

The SHUTDOWN mode also drops all supply currents (V_{CC}, V^+, V^-) to zero for power-conscious systems.

When driving CMOS logic from a receiver that will be used in the SHUTDOWN mode and there is no other active receiver on the line, a 51k resistor can be placed from the logic input to V_{CC} to force a definite logic level when the receiver output is in a high impedance state.

LT1039 Driver

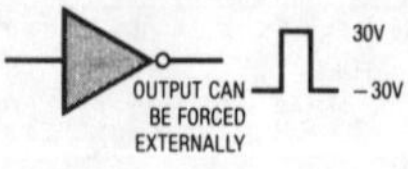

Older RS232 Drivers and Other CMOS Drivers

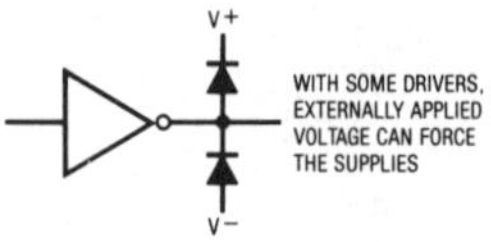

Sharing a Transmitter Line

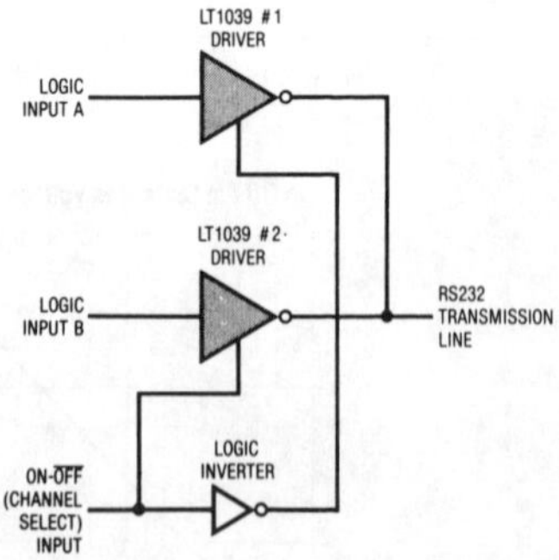

Sharing a Receiver Line

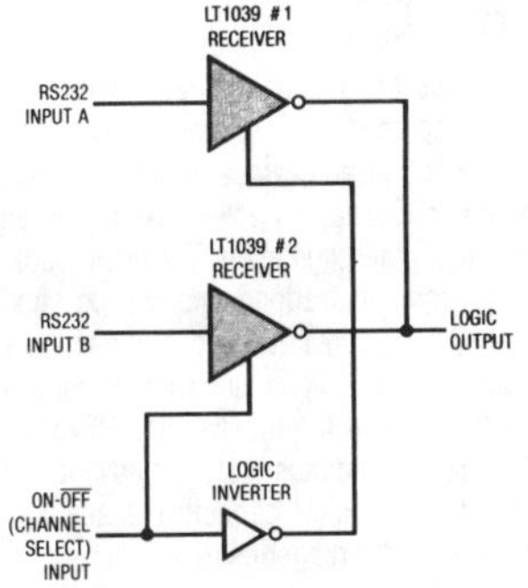

Transceiver

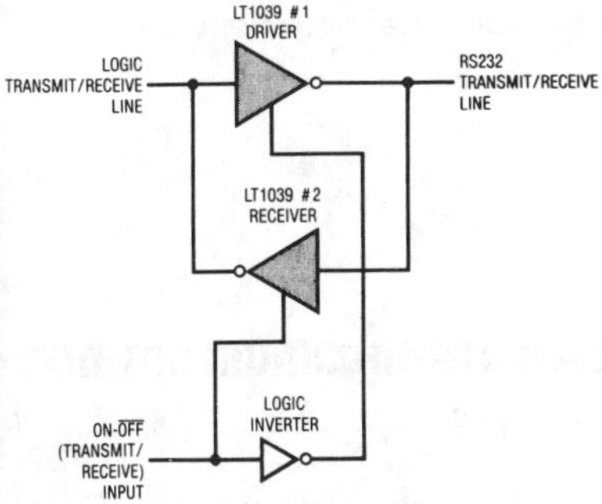

Keeping Alive One Receiver while in SHUTDOWN

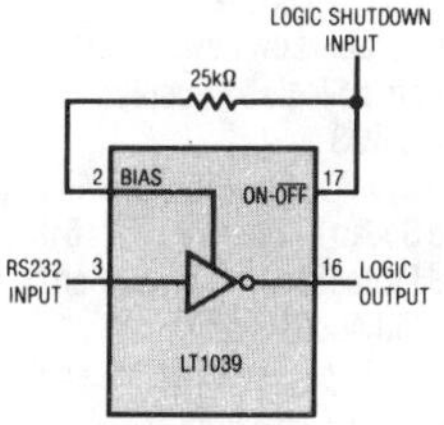

RS232 Compatible SHUTDOWN Control Line

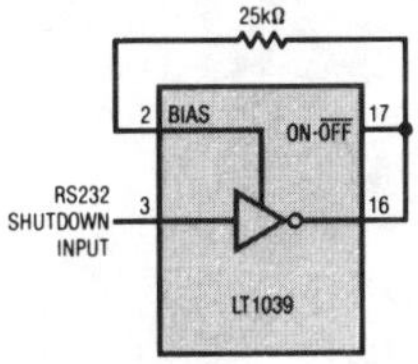

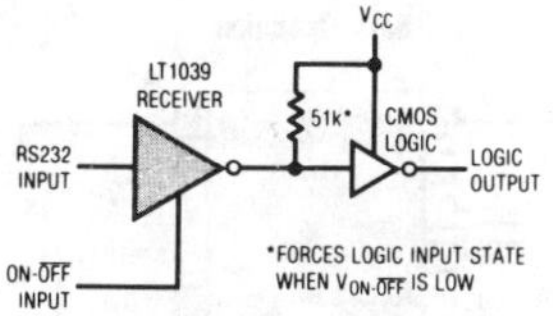

To protect against receiver input overloads in excess of ±30V, a voltage clamp can be placed on the data line and still maintain RS232 compatibility.

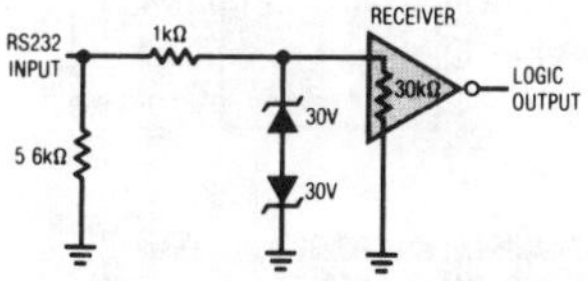

The receiver input impedance of the LT1039 is nominally 30kΩ. For applications requiring a 5kΩ input impedance, a 5.6kΩ resistor can be connected from the receiver input to ground.

Driver inputs should not be allowed to float. Any unused inputs should be tied to V_{CC}.

The bias pin is used to "keep alive" one receiver while in the SHUTDOWN mode (all other circuitry being inactive). This allows a system to be in SHUTDOWN and still have one active receiver for transferring data. It can also be used to make an RS232 compatible SHUTDOWN control line. Driving the bias pin low through a resistance of 24kΩ to 30kΩ keeps the receiver active. Do not drive the bias pin directly from a logic output without the series resistor. An unused bias pin should be left open.

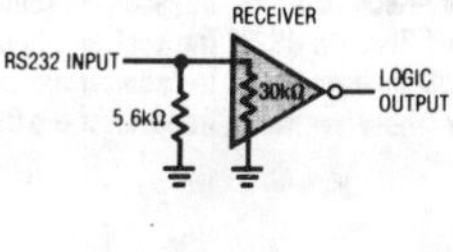

FEATURES

- Absolutely No Latchup
- CMOS Comparable Low Power — 80mW
- Operates from a **Single 5V Supply**
- **Superior to CMOS**
  - **Easy PC Layout** — Flow Through Architecture
  - Improved Speed — Operates Over 64K Baud
  - Improved Protection — Outputs Can be Forced to ±30V Without Damage
  - Three-State Outputs are High Impedance When Off
  - Only Needs 1μF Capacitors
  - Output Overvoltage Does Not Force Current Back Into Supplies
- 1μA Supply Current in Shutdown
- Available in SO Package

DESCRIPTION

The LT1130 Series are the only RS232 drivers/receivers with charge pump to guarantee absolutely no latchup. These interface optimized devices provide a realistic balance between CMOS levels of power dissipation and real world requirements for ruggedness. The driver outputs are fully protected against overload and can be shorted to ±30V. Unlike CMOS, the advanced architecture of the LT1130 does not load the signal line when "shut down" or when power is off. Both the receiver and RS232 outputs are put into a high impedance state. An advanced output stage allows driving higher capacitive loads at higher speeds with exceptional ruggedness.

For applications requiring only 2 drivers and 2 receivers with charge pump in one package see the LT1180 Series data sheet. All of Linear Technology's RS232 IC's are available in standard surface mount packages.

Basic Operation

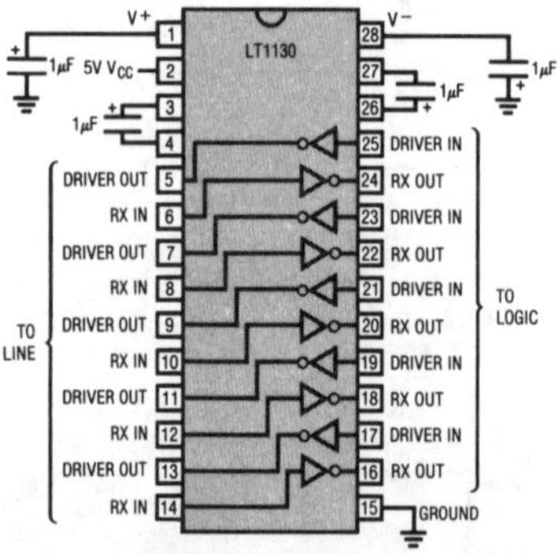

LT1130 5-Driver/5-Receiver RS232 Transceiver
LT1131 5-Driver/4-Receiver RS232 Transceiver w/Shutdown
LT1132 5-Driver/3-Receiver RS232 Transceiver
LT1133 3-Driver/5-Receiver RS232 Transceiver
LT1134 4-Driver/4-Receiver RS232 Transceiver
LT1135 5-Driver/3-Receiver RS232 Transceiver w/o Charge Pump
LT1136 4-Driver/5-Receiver RS232 Transceiver w/Shutdown
LT1137 3-Driver/5-Receiver RS232 Transceiver w/Shutdown
LT1138 5-Driver/3-Receiver RS232 Transceiver w/Shutdown
LT1139 4-Driver/4-Receiver RS232 Transceiver w/Shutdown
LT1140 5-Driver/3-Receiver RS232 Transceiver w/o Charge Pump
LT1141 3-Driver/5-Receiver RS232 Transceiver w/o Charge Pump

ABSOLUTE MAXIMUM RATINGS

Supply Voltage (V_{CC})	6V
V^+	13.2V
V^-	−13.2V
Input Voltage	
Driver	V^- to V^+
Receiver	−30V to 30V
On-Off Pin	GND to 12V
Output Voltage	
Driver	$V^- + 30V$ to $V^+ - 30V$
Receiver	−0.3V to V_{CC} + 0.3V
Short Circuit Duration	
V^+	30 Seconds
V^-	30 Seconds
Driver Output	Indefinite
Receiver Output	Indefinite
Operating Temperature Range	
Military (LT113XM/LT114XM)	−55°C to 125°C
Industrial (LT113XI/LT114XI)	−40°C to 85°C
Commercial (LT113XC/LT114XC)	0°C to 70°C

PRODUCT SELECTION TABLE

Part Number	Power Supply Voltages*	Shutdown	Drivers	Receivers	External Components
LT1130	+5	No	5	5	4 Capacitors
LT1131	+5	Yes	5	4	4 Capacitors
LT1132	+5	No	5	3	4 Capacitors
LT1133	+5	No	3	5	4 Capacitors
LT1134	+5	No	4	4	4 Capacitors
LT1135	+5, +12, −12	No	5	3	None
LT1136	+5	Yes	4	5	4 Capacitors
LT1137	+5	Yes	3	5	4 Capacitors
LT1138	+5	Yes	5	3	4 Capacitors
LT1139	+5, +12	Yes	4	4	2 Capacitors
LT1140	+5, +12, −12	Yes	5	3	None
LT1141	+5, +12, −12	Yes	3	5	None

*The LT1130, LT1131, LT1132, LT1133, LT1134, LT1136, LT1137, and LT1138 can operate with +5V and +12V supplies and two external capacitors.

5-DRIVER/5-RECEIVER

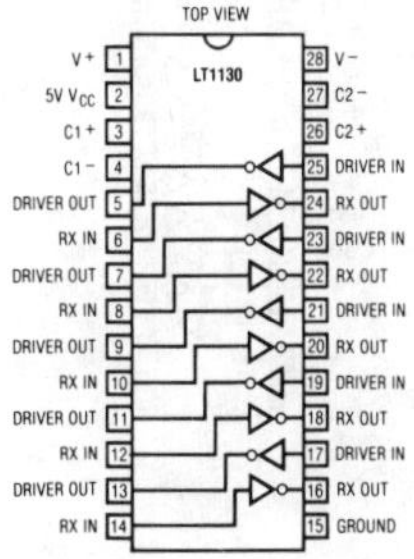

3-DRIVER/5-RECEIVER

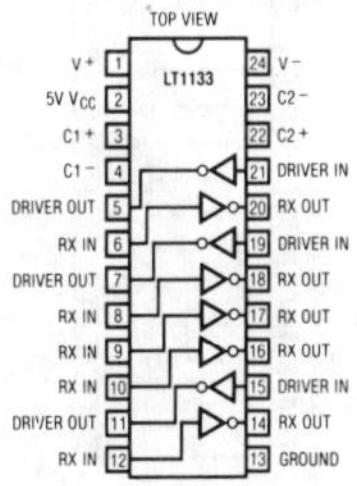

5-DRIVER/4-RECEIVER WITH SHUTDOWN

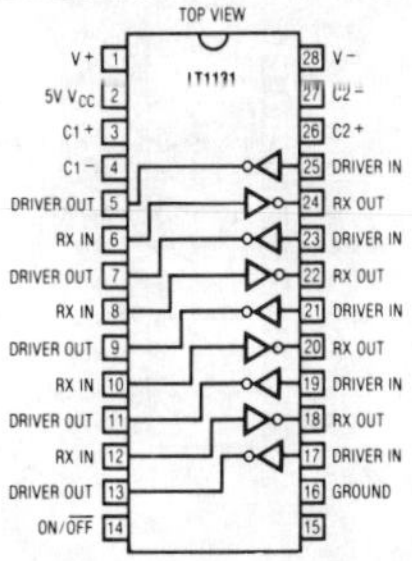

4-DRIVER/4-RECEIVER

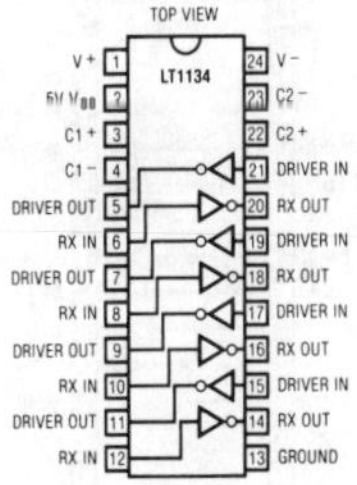

5-DRIVER/3-RECEIVER

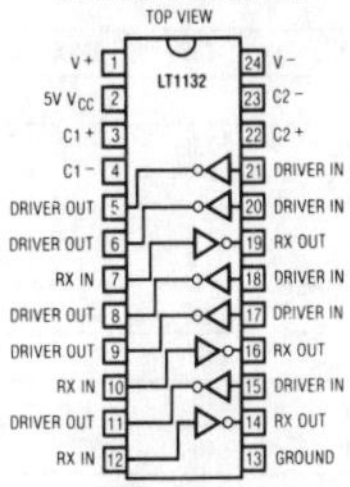

5-DRIVER/3-RECEIVER
WITHOUT CHARGE PUMP

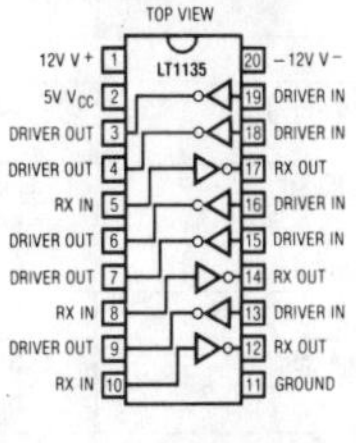

4-DRIVER/5-RECEIVER WITH SHUTDOWN

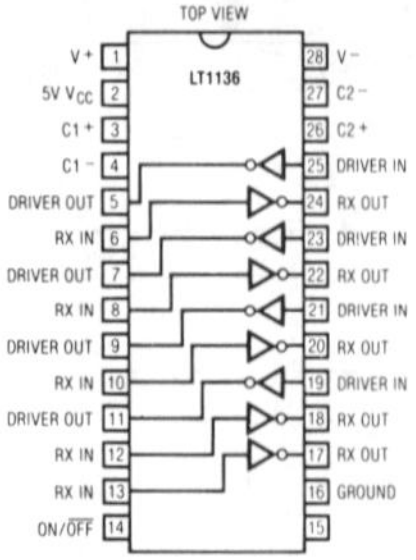

4-DRIVER/4-RECEIVER WITH SHUTDOWN WITH +12V AND +5V SUPPLIES

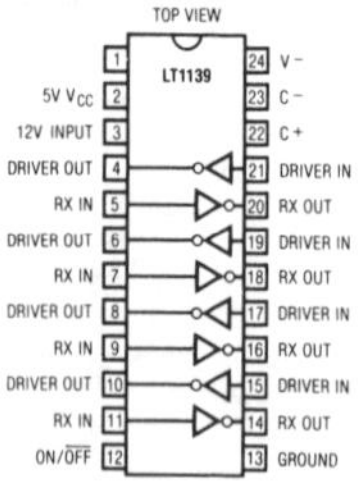

3-DRIVER/5-RECEIVER WITH SHUTDOWN

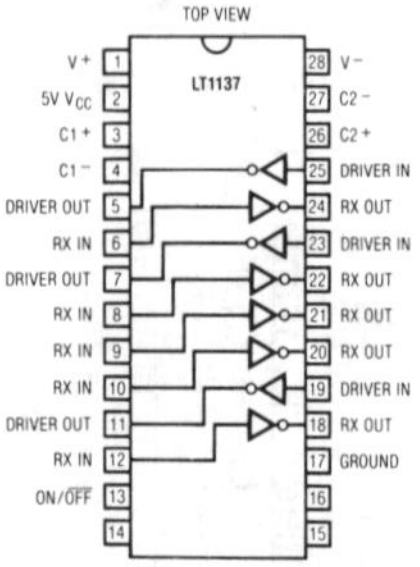

5-DRIVER/3-RECEIVER WITHOUT CHARGE PUMP

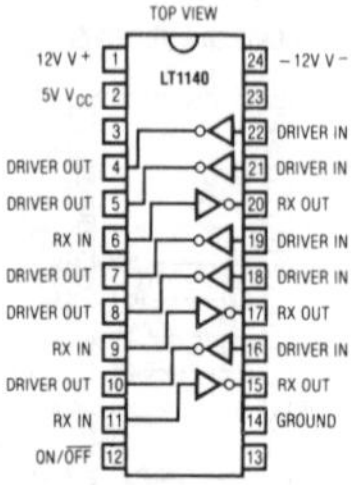

5-DRIVER/3-RECEIVER WITH SHUTDOWN

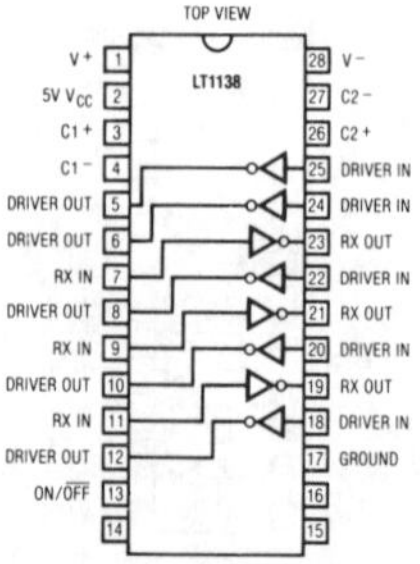

3-DRIVER/5-RECEIVER WITHOUT CHARGE PUMP

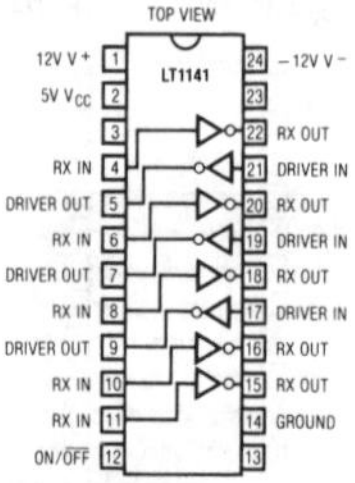

ELECTRICAL CHARACTERISTICS (Note 1)

PARAMETER	CONDITIONS			MIN	TYP	MAX	UNITS
Any Driver							
Output Voltage Swing	Load = 3k to GND	Positive	●	5.0	7.3		V
		Negative	●	−5.0	−6.5		V
Logic Input Voltage Level	Input Low Level (V_{OUT} = High)		●		1.4	0.8	V
	Input High Level (V_{OUT} = Low)		●	2.0	1.4		V
Logic Input Current	$0.8V \leq V_{IN} \leq 2.0V$		●		5	20	μA
Output Short Circuit Current	$V_{OUT} = 0V$				12		mA
Output Leakage Current	SHUTDOWN (Note 2), $V_{OUT} = \pm 30V$ (Note 3)		●		10	100	μA
Slew Rate	$R_L = 3k\Omega$, $C_L = 51pF$			4	15	30	V/μs

ELECTRICAL CHARACTERISTICS (Note 1)

PARAMETER	CONDITIONS		MIN	TYP	MAX	UNITS
Any Receiver						
Input Voltage Thresholds	Input Low Threshold, (V_{OUT} = High) Input High Threshold, (V_{OUT} = Low)		0.8	1.3 1.7	 2.4	V V
Hysteresis		●	0.1	0.4	1.0	V
Input Resistance			3	5	7	kΩ
Output Voltage	Output Low, I_{OUT} = −1.6mA Output High, I_{OUT} = 160μA (V_{CC} = 5V)	● ●	 3.5	0.2 4.8	0.4	V V
Output Short Circuit Current	Sinking Current, $V_{OUT} = V_{CC}$ Sourcing Current, V_{OUT} = 0V		−10 0.4	−20 1		mA mA
Output Leakage Current	SHUTDOWN (Note 2), $0V \le V_{OUT} \le V_{CC}$	●		1	10	μA
Power Supply Generator						
V^+ Output V^- Output				8 −7.5		V V
Supply Current				17	27	mA
Supply Leakage Current	SHUTDOWN, $-55°C \le T_A \le 125°C$ SHUTDOWN, $0°C \le T_A \le 70°C$	● ●		1 1	100 10	μA μA
Supply Rise Time	SHUTDOWN To Turn On			2		ms
On/$\overline{Off}$ Pin Current	SHUTDOWN, $0V \le V_{ON/\overline{OFF}} \le 5V$	●	−15		80	μA

The ● denotes the specifications which apply over the full operating temperature range. ($0°C \le T_A \le 70°C$ for commercial grade, $-40°C \le T_A \le 85°C$ for industrial grade, and $-55°C \le T_A \le 125°C$ for military grade).

Note 1: Testing done at V_{CC} = 5V and $V_{ON/\overline{OFF}}$ = 3V

Note 2: $V_{ON/\overline{OFF}} \le 0.1V$

Note 3: For LT1139, 40, and 41 with 12V supplies, V_{OUT} leakage is 200μA and V_{OUT} is forced to ±25V.

PIN FUNCTIONS

V_{CC}: Input supply pin. Supply current drops to zero in the SHUTDOWN mode.

GND: Ground pin.

On/$\overline{Off}$: Controls the operation mode of the device and is TTL/CMOS compatible. A logic low puts the device in the SHUTDOWN mode which reduces input supply current to zero and places both driver and receiver outputs in a high impedance state. A logic high fully enables the device.

V+: Positive supply (RS232 drivers). $V+ \approx 2V_{CC} - 1.5V$. Requires an external capacitor (≥1μF) for charge storage. Capacitor may be tied to ground or +5V input supply. V+ voltage is short circuit proof for 30 seconds. With multiple transceivers, the V+ and V− pins may be paralleled into common capacitors.

V−: Negative supply (RS232 drivers). $V- \approx -(2V_{CC} - 2.5V)$. Requires an external capacitor (≥1μF) for charge storage. Loading does reduce V− voltage. V− is short circuit proof for 30 seconds. With multiple transceivers, the V+ and V− pins may be paralleled into common capacitors.

DRIVER IN: RS232 driver input pins. Inputs are TTL/CMOS compatible. Inputs should not be allowed to float. Tie unused inputs to V_{CC}.

DRIVER OUT: Driver outputs with RS232 voltage levels. Outputs are in a high impedance state when in the SHUTDOWN mode or when power is off (V_{CC} = 0V) to allow data line sharing. Outputs are fully short circuit protected from V− +30V to V+ −30V with power on, off, or in the SHUTDOWN mode. Typical output breakdowns are greater than ±45V and higher applied voltages will not damage the device if moderately current limited. Although the outputs are protected, short circuits on one output can load the power supply generators disrupting the signal level from other outputs.

RX IN: Receiver inputs. Accepts RS232 voltage levels (±30V) and has 0.4V of hysteresis to provide noise immunity. Input impedance is nominally 5kΩ.

RX OUT: Receiver outputs with TTL/CMOS voltage levels. Outputs are in a high impedance state when in the SHUTDOWN mode to allow data line sharing. Outputs are fully short circuit protected to ground or V_{CC} with power on, off, or in the SHUTDOWN mode.

C1+; C1−; C2+; C2−: Requires an external capacitor (≥1μF) from C1+ to C1− and another from C2+ to C2−. In applications where larger positive voltages are available, such as +12V, C1 can be eliminated and the positive voltage connected directly to the C1+ terminal.

TYPICAL PERFORMANCE CHARACTERISTICS

Driver Output Voltage

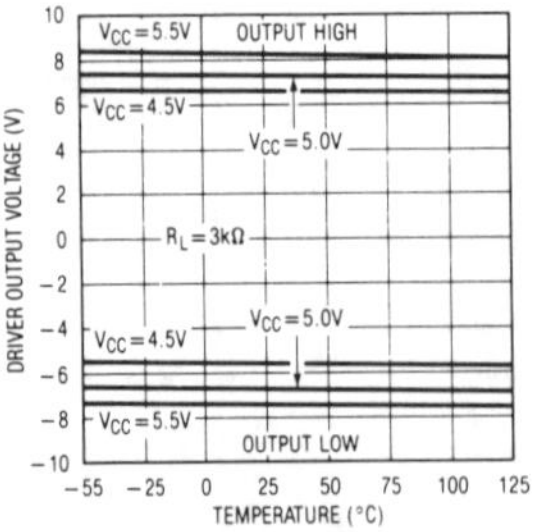

Supply Generation from V_{CC} or Shutdown

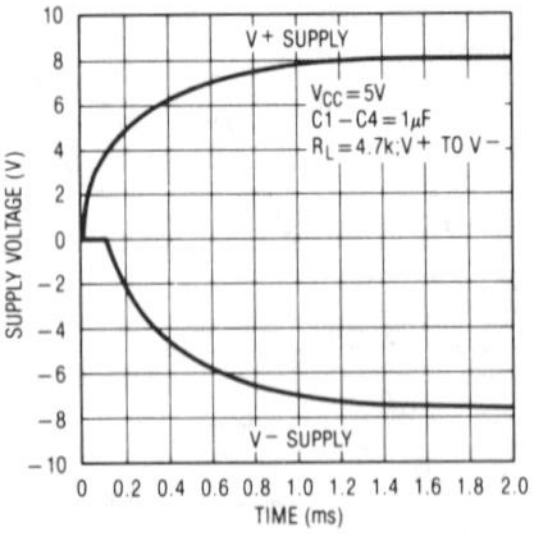

Receiver Input Thresholds

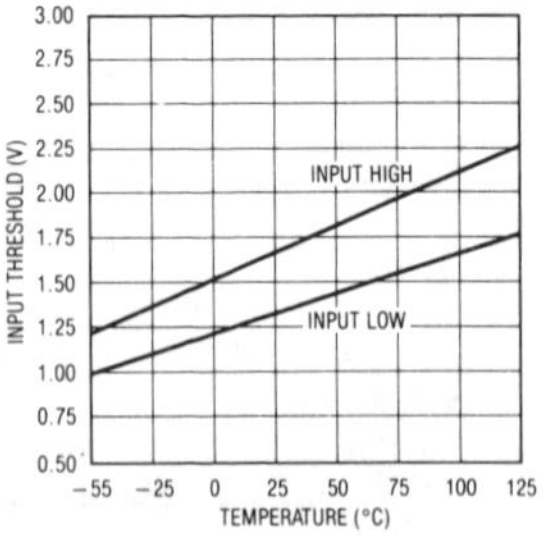

Receiver Output Short Circuit Current

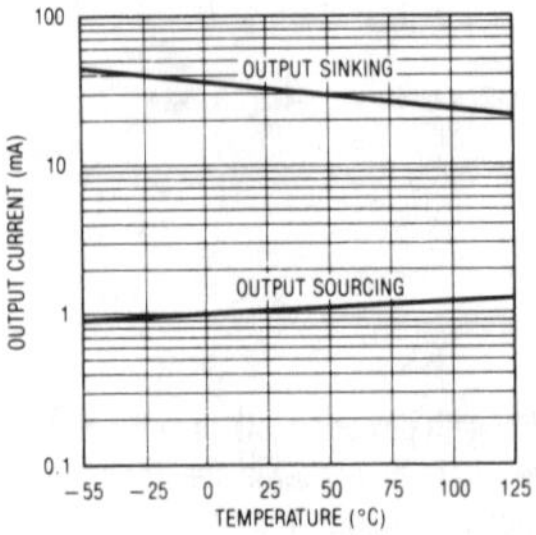

On-$\overline{\text{Off}}$ Pin Current vs Voltage

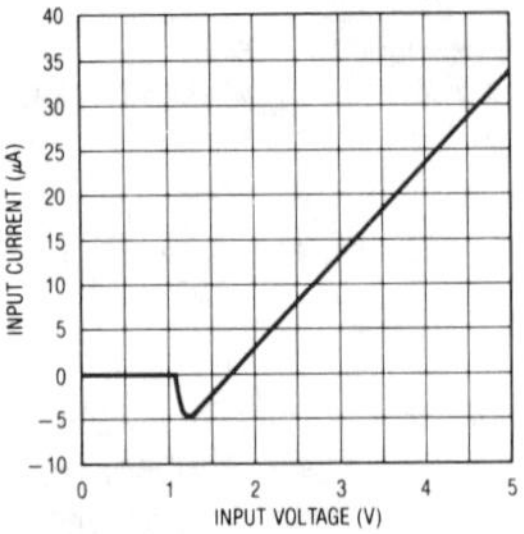

On-$\overline{\text{Off}}$ Pin Thresholds

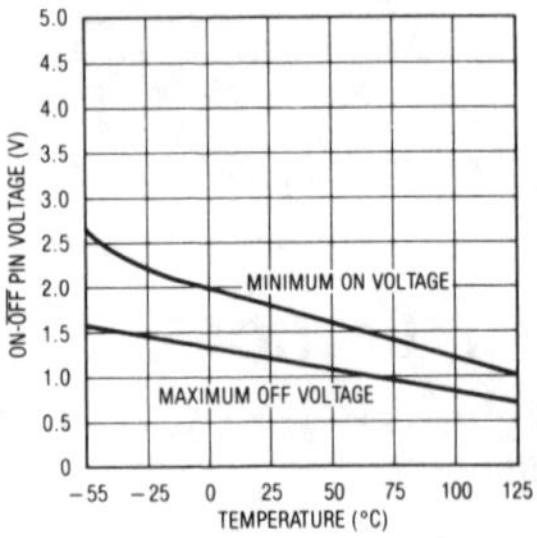

Supply Current in Shutdown

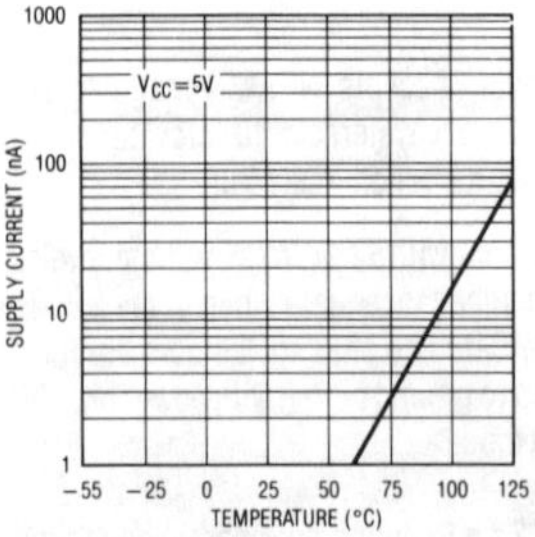

Driver Output Leakage in Shutdown

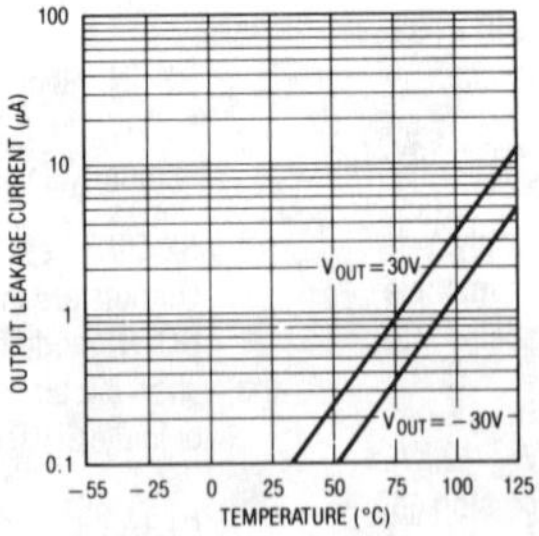

APPLICATION HINTS

The driver output stage of the LT1130 offers significantly improved protection over older bipolar and CMOS designs. In addition to current limiting, the driver output can be externally forced to ±30V with no damage or excessive current flow, and will not disrupt the supplies. Some drivers have diodes connected between the outputs and the supplies, so externally applied voltages can cause excessive supply voltage to develop.

Older RS232 Drivers and CMOS Drivers

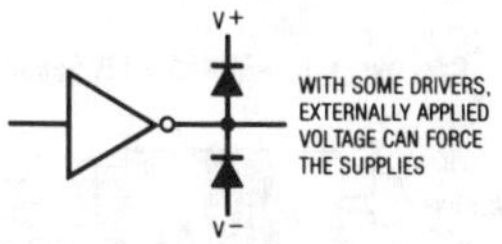

LT1130 Driver

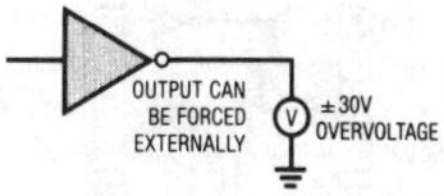

Placing the LT1130 type device in the SHUTDOWN mode puts both the driver and receiver outputs in a high impedance state. This allows data line sharing and transceiver applications.

The SHUTDOWN mode also drops input supply current to zero for power-conscious systems.

Transceiver

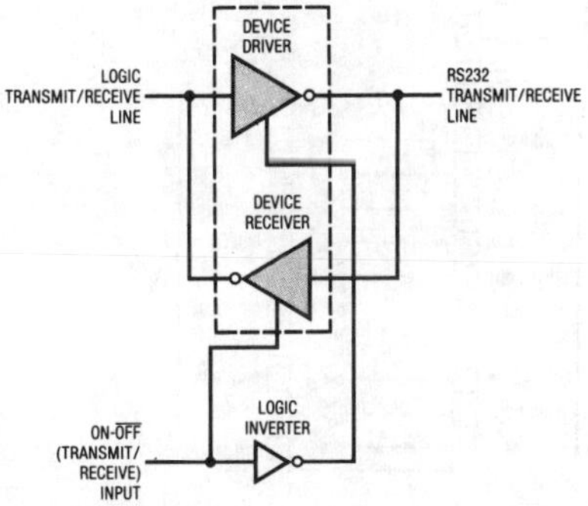

Sharing a Receiver Line

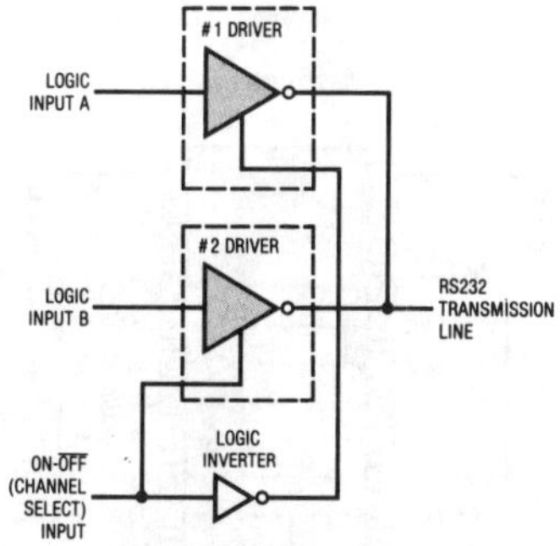

Sharing a Transmitter Line

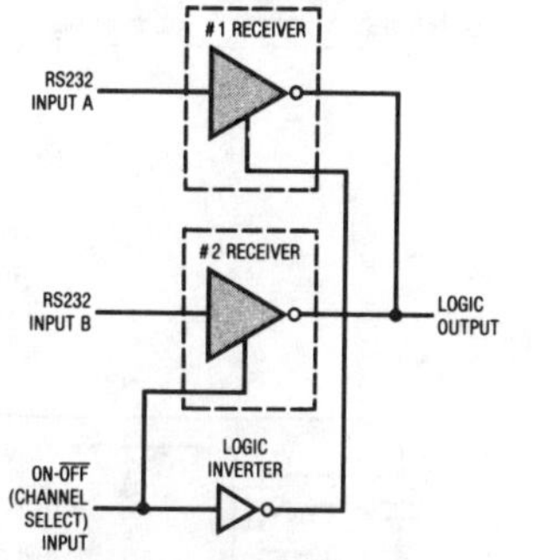

When driving CMOS logic from a receiver that will be used in the SHUTDOWN mode and there is no other active receiver on the line, a 51k resistor can be placed from the logic input to V_{CC} to force a definite logic level when the receiver output is in a high impedance state.

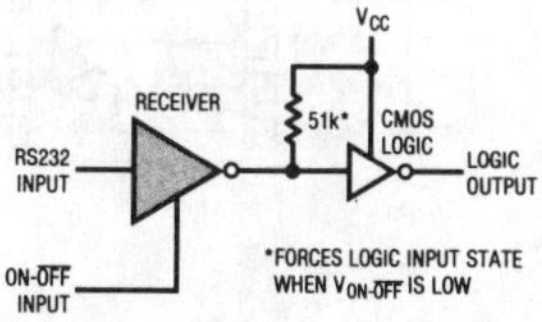

To protect against receiver input overloads in excess of ±30V, a voltage clamp can be placed on the data line and still maintain RS232 compatibility.

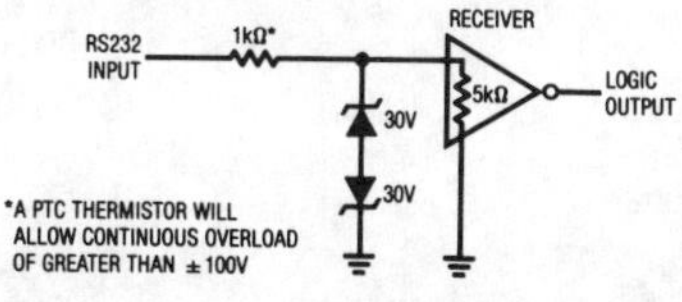

TYPICAL APPLICATIONS

Basic Operation

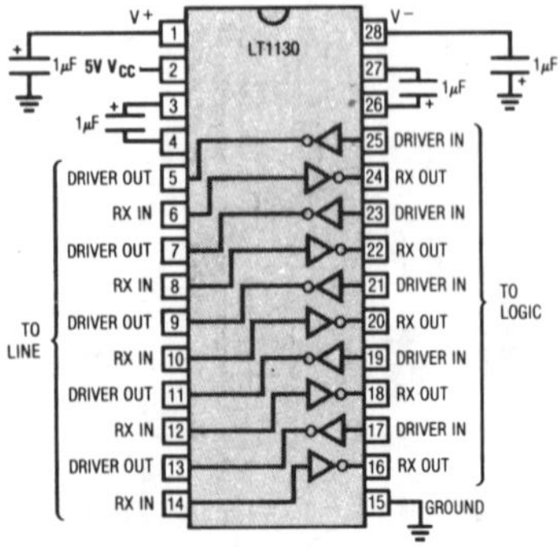

Operating with +5V and +12V Supplies

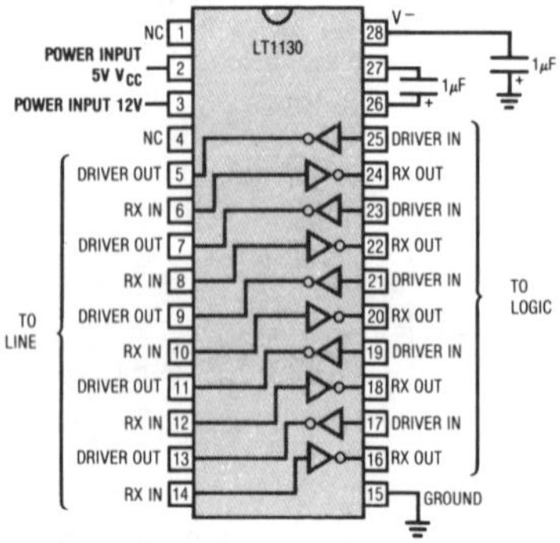

Paralleling Power Supply Generator with Common Storage Capacitors

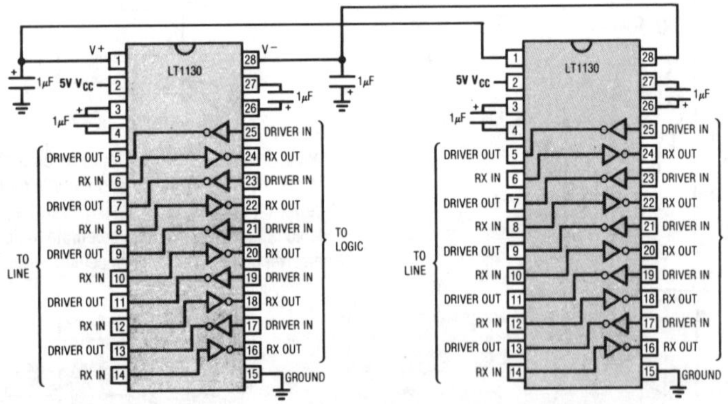

2500V Isolated 5-Driver/5-Receiver RS232 Transceiver

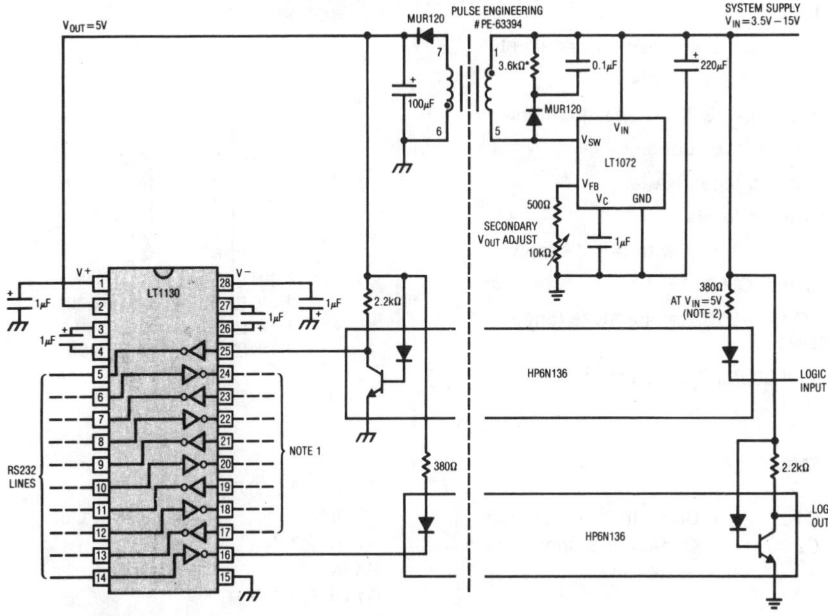

= SYSTEM GROUND

= FLOATING COMMON

NOTE 1: REPEAT THE OPTOCOUPLER CONNECTIONS FOR EACH LINE.

NOTE 2: SELECT FOR 10mA THROUGH LED.

*FOR IMPROVED EFFICIENCY, REPLACE THE 3.6kΩ RESISTOR WITH A 30V ZENER DIODE.

DS1229 serial data driver/receiver

FEATURES

- Operates from a single 5V power supply
- 3 drivers and 3 receivers
- Meets all EIA RS-232-C specifications
- On-board voltage doubler
- On-board voltage inverter
- ± 30 V input levels
- ± 9 V output levels with + 5 V supply
- Low power CMOS
- − 40 °C to + 85 °C temperature range available
- Optional 20-Pin SOIC surface mount package

PIN CONNECTIONS

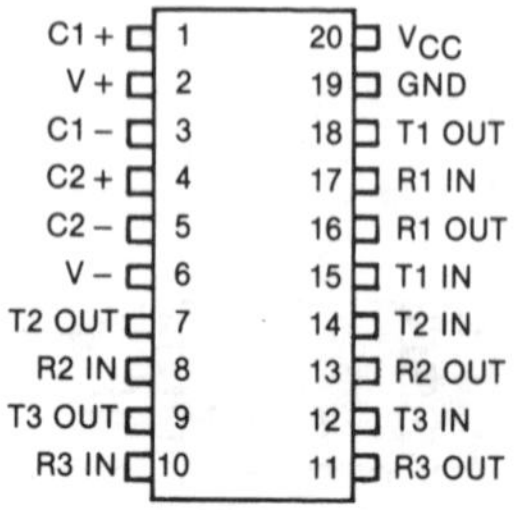

PIN NAMES

C1 + , C1	- Capacitor 1 Connections
C2 + , C2	- Capacitor 2 Connections
V + , V −	- ± 10 Volts
T1 IN, T2 IN, T3 IN	- Transmitter In

T1 OUT, T2 OUT, T3 OUT	- Transmitter Out
R1 IN, R2 IN, R3 IN	- Receiver In
R1 OUT, R2 OUT, R3 OUT	- Receiver Out
V_{CC}	- + 5 Volts
GND	- Ground

DESCRIPTION

The DS1229 is a Triple RS-232-C Receiver/Transmitter that meets all EIA specifications while operating from a single + 5 volt supply. The DS1229 has two internal charge pumps. One of the charge pumps is used to generate + 10 volts. The other is used to generate − 10 volts. The DS1229 also contains six level translators. Three of the level translators are RS-232 transmitters which convert TTL/CMOS inputs into ± 9V RS-232 outputs. The other three level translators are RS-232 receivers which convert RS-232 inputs to 5V TTL/CMOS outputs. These receivers are capable of operating with up to ± 30V inputs. The DS1229 is suitable for all RS-232-C communications and is particularly valuable where higher voltage power supplies for RS-232 drivers are not available. The power supply section of the DS1229 supplies ± 10 volts from the V_{CC} input.

OPERATION

The DS1229 has three sections: a triple transmitter, a triple receiver and a dual charge pump which generates ± 10 volts from the 5-volt supply.

CHARGE PUMP SECTION

The dual charge pumps within the DS1229 are used to generate the voltages necessary for level conversion from TTL/CMOS to RS-232. One charge pump uses external capacitor C1 to double the V_{CC} input to + 10 volts. The second charge pump uses external capacitor C2 to invert the +10 volts to −10 volts. Capacitors C3 and C4 are used to filter the + 10 volt and − 10 volt power supply. The recommended size of capacitors C1-C4 is 22 *u*F but the value is not critical. Increasing the value of C3 and C4 will lower the 16 KHz ripple on the ± 10 volt supplies and the RS-232 outputs. The value of C1 and C4 can be lowered to 1 *u*F where size is critical.

TRANSMITTER SECTION

The three transmitters are CMOS inverters powered by the internal ±10 volt supply.The input is TTL/CMOS compatible. Each input has an internal 750 K pull-up resistor so that unused transmitter inputs can be left unconnected. Unused transmitter inputs will force the outputs low. The open circuit output voltage swing is from + 10 volts to – 10 volts. Worst-case conditions for RS-232-C of ± 5 volt driving a 3 K load are met at maximum allowable ambient temperature and a V_{CC} level of 5.0 volts. Typical voltage swings of ± 9 volts occur with outputs of 5 K and V_{CC} equal to 5 volts. The slew rate at the output is limited to less than 30 volts/*u*s and the power-down output impedance will be a minimum of 300 ohms with ± 2 volts applied to the outputs and V_{CC} at zero volts. The outputs are also short-circuit-protected and can be short-circuited to ground indefinitely.

RECEIVER SECTION

The three receivers conform fully to the RS-232-C specifications. The input impedance is between 3 K ohms and 7 K ohms and can withstand up to ± 30 volts with or without V_{CC} applied. The input switching thresholds are within the ± 3 volts limit of RS-232-C specification with a V_{IL} of 0.7 volts and a V_{IH} of 2.4 volts. The receivers have 0.5 volts of hysteresis to improve noise rejection. The TTL/CMOS compatible output of the receiver will be low whenever the RS-232 input is greater than 2.4 volts. The receiver output will be high when the input is floating or driven between + 0.8 V and – 30 V.

ABSOLUTE MAXIMUM RATINGS*

V_{CC} .... + 7 volts
V+ .... + 12 volts
V– .... – 12 volts
Transmitter Inputs .... – 0.3V to (V_{CC} + 0.3V)
Receiver Inputs .... ± 30 volts
Transmitter Outputs .. (V+ + 0.3V) to (V– – 0.3V)
Receiver Outputs .... —0.3V to (V_{CC} + 0.3V)
Storage Temperature .... – 55 °C to 125 °C

RECOMMENDED D.C. OPERATING CONDITIONS (0 °C to 70 °C)

PARAMETER	SYMBOL	MIN	TYP	MAX	UNITS	NOTES
Power Supply Voltage	V_{CC}	4.5	5.0	5.5	V	1
Logic 1 Input	V_{IH}	2.2		V_{CC} + 0.3	V	1
Logic 0 Input	V_{IL}	– 0.3		+ 0.8	V	1
RS-232 Input Voltage	V_{RS}	– 30		+ 30	V	1,2,11

D.C. ELECTRICAL CHARACTERISTICS (0 °C to 70 °C, V_{CC} = + 5 volts ± 10%)

PARAMETER	SYMBOL	MIN	TYP	MAX	UNITS	NOTES
RS-232 Output Voltage	V_{ORS}	± 5	± 9	± 10	V	3,12
Power Supply Current	I_{DD}		5	10	mA	4
Transmitter Pull-up Current	I_{TP}		5	200	*u*A	5
RS-232 Input Threshold Low	V_{TL}	+ 0.7	+ 1.2		V	6

RS-232 Input Threshold High	V_{TH}		1.7	2.4	V	6
RS-232 Input Hysteresis	V_{HY}	0.2	0.5	1.0	V	
ReceiverOutput Current @2.4 V	I_{OH}	−1.0			mA	
Receiver Output Current @0.4 V	I_{OL}			+3.2	mA	
Output Resistance	R_{OUT}	300			Ω	7
RS-232 Output Short Circuit	I_{SC}			±25	mA	
Propagation Delay	t_{PD}		3		us	8
Transmitter Output Instantaneous Slew Rate	t_{SR}			30	V/us	9
Transmitter Output Transition Slew Rate	t_{tSR}		3		V/us	10
V+ Supply Voltage	V+	+5.5	9		V	
V− Supply Voltage	V−	−5.5	8.5		V	

DS1229 RS-232 TRANSMITTER/RECEIVER TEST CIRCUIT Figure 1

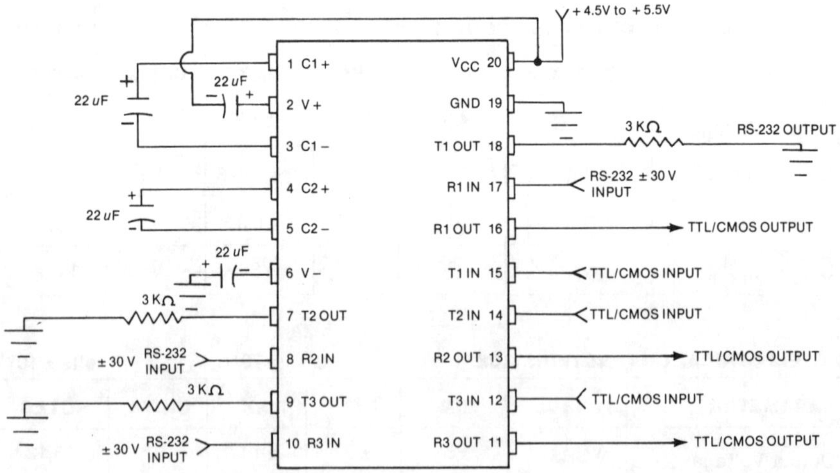

TYPICAL APPLICATIONS Figure 2

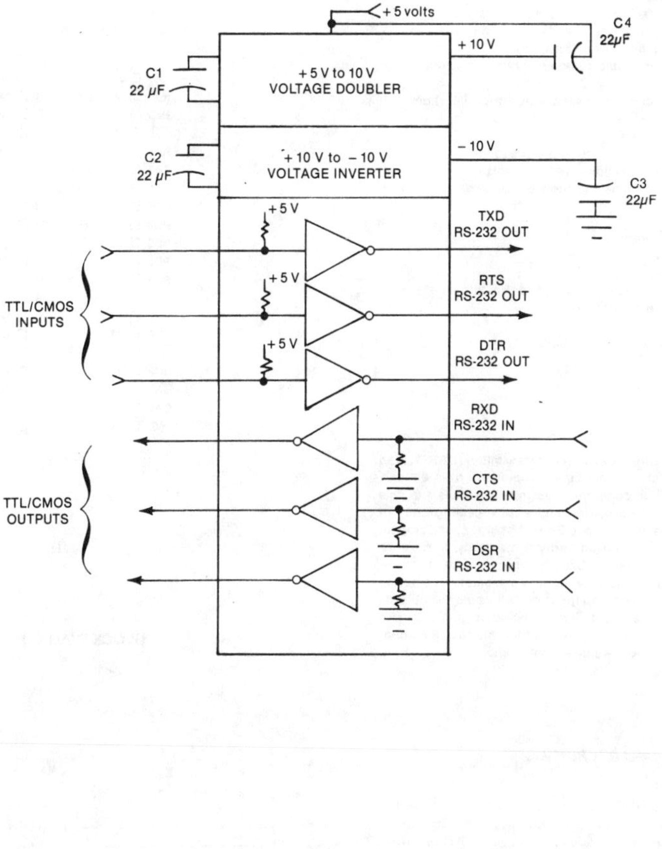

AY-3-1015D UART

FEATURES

- DTL and TTL compatible—no interfacing circuits required—drives one TTL load
- Fully Double Buffered—eliminates need for system synchronization, facilitates high-speed operation
- Full Duplex Operation—can handle multiple bauds (receiving-transmitting) simultaneously
- Start Bit Verification—decreases error rate with center sampling
- Receiver center sampling of serial input; 46% distortion immunity
- High Speed Operation
- Three-State Outputs—bus structure capability
- Low Power — minimum power requirements
- Input Protected—eliminates handling problems

AY-3-1015D

- Single Supply Operation: +4.75V to +5.25V
- 1½ stop bit mode
- External reset of all registers except control bits register
- N-channel Ion Implant Process
- 0 to 25K baud
- Pull-up resistors to V_{CC} on all inputs

PIN CONFIGURATION

40 LEAD DUAL IN LINE

Top View

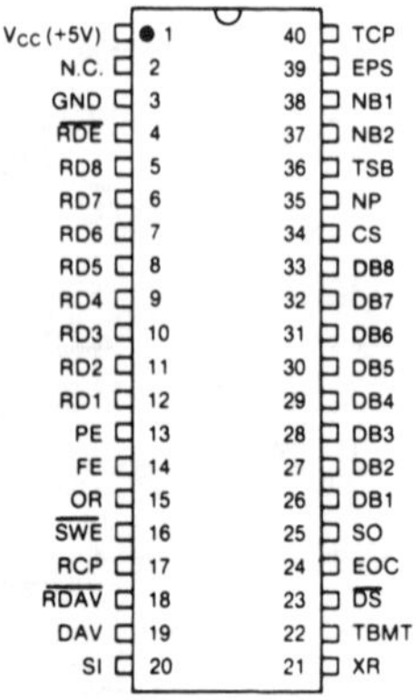

DESCRIPTION

The Universal Asynchronous Receiver/Transmitter (UAR/T) is an LSI subsystem which accepts binary characters from either a terminal device or a computer and receives/transmits this character with appended control and error detecting bits. All characters contain a start bit, 5 to 8 data bits, 1, 1½, or 2 stop bit capability, and either odd/even parity or no parity. In order to make the UAR/T universal, the baud, bits per word, parity mode, and the number of stop bits are externally selectable. The device is constructed on a single monolithic chip. All inputs and outputs are directly compatible with MTOS/MTNS logic, and also with TTL/DTL/CMOS logic without the need for interfacing components. All strobed outputs are three-state logic.

BLOCK DIAGRAM

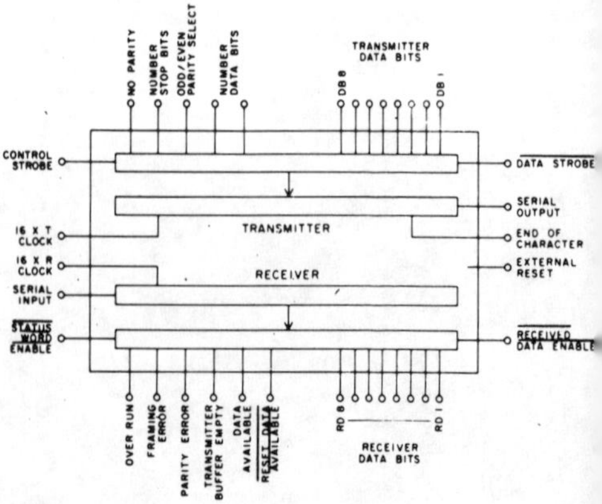

ELECTRICAL CHARACTERISTICS

Maximum Ratings*

V_{CC} (with Respect to GND) . . . . −0.3V to +16V
Storage Temperature . . . . −65°C to +150°C
Operating Temperature . . . . 0°C to +70°C
Lead Temperature (Soldering, 10 sec) . . . . +330°C

Standard Condition (unless otherwise noted):
V_{CC} = +4.75V to +5.25V
Operating Temperature (T_A) = 0°C to +70°C

*Exceeding these ratings could cause permanent damage to the device. This is a stress rating only and functional operation of this device at these conditions is not implied—operating ranges are specified in Standard Conditions. Exposure to absolute maximum rating conditions for extended periods may affect device reliability.

Data labeled "typical" is presented for design guidance only and is not guaranteed.

DC CHARACTERISTICS

Characteristic	Min	Typ**	Max	Units	Conditions
Input Logic Levels (AY-3-1015)					
Logic 0	0	—	0.8	Volts	
Logic 1	2.0	—	V_{CC}+0.3	Volts	Has internal pull-up resistors to V_{CC}.
Input Capacitance					
All inputs	—	—	20	pF	0 volts bias, f = 1MHz
Output Impedance					
Tri-State Outputs	1.0	—	—	MΩ	
Data Output Levels					
Logic 0	—	—	+0.4	Volts	I_{OL} = 1.6mA (sink)
Logic 1	2.4	—	—	Volts	I_{OH} = −40μA (source)—at V_{CC} = +5V
Output Capacitance	—	10	15	pF	
Short Ckt. Current	—	—	—	—	See Fig. 19
Power Supply Current					
I_{CC} at V_{CC} = +5V	—	10	15	mA	See Fig. 21

Standard Conditions (unless otherwise noted)

T_A = 25° C, Output load capacitance 50pF max.

AC CHARACTERISTICS

Characteristic	Min	Typ**	Max	Units	Conditions
Clock Frequency	DC	—	400	kHz	at V_{CC} = +4.75V
Baud	0	—	25	kbaud	at V_{CC} = +4.75V
Pulse Width					
Clock Pulse	1.0	—	—	μs	See Fig. 5
Control Strobe	200	—	—	ns	See Fig. 11
Data Strobe	200	—	—	ns	See Fig. 10
External Reset	500	—	—	ns	See Fig. 9
Status Word Enable	500	—	—	ns	See Fig. 17
Reset Data Available	200	—	—	ns	See Fig. 18
Received Data Enable	500	—	—	ns	See Fig. 17
Set Up & Hold Time					
Input Data Bits	20	—	—	ns	See Fig. 10
Input Control Bits	20	—	—	ns	See Fig. 11
Output Propagation Delay					
TPD0	—	—	500	ns	See Fig. 17 & 20
TPD1	—	—	500	ns	See Fig. 17 & 20

**Typical values are at +70° C and nominal voltages.

Pin No.	Name (Symbol)	Function
1	Vcc Power Supply (Vcc)	+5V Supply
2	N.C.	(Not connected)
3	Ground	Ground
4	$\overline{\text{Received Data Enable}}$ ($\overline{\text{RDE}}$)	A logic "0" on the receiver enable line places the received data onto the output lines.
5-12	Received Data Bits (RD8-RD1)	These are the 8 data output lines. Received characters are right justified: the LSB always appears on RD1. These lines have tri-state outputs; i.e., they have the normal TTL ouput characteristics when $\overline{\text{RDE}}$ is "0" and a high impedance state when $\overline{\text{RDE}}$ is "1". Thus, the data output lines can be bus structure oriented.
13	Parity Error (PE)	This line goes to a logic "1" if the received character parity does not agree with the selected parity. Tri-state.
14	Framing Error (FE)	This line goes to a logic "1" if the received character has no valid stop bit. Tri-state.
15	Over-Run (OR)	This line goes to a logic "1" if the previously received character is not read (DAV line not reset) before the present character is transferred to the receiver holding register. Tri-state.
16	$\overline{\text{Status Word Enable}}$ ($\overline{\text{SWE}}$)	A logic "0" on this line places the status word bits (PE, FE, OR, DAV, TBMT) onto the output lines. Tri-state.
17	Receiver Clock (RCP)	This line will contain a clock whose frequency is 16 times (16X) the desired receiver baud.
18	$\overline{\text{Reset Data Available}}$ ($\overline{\text{RDAV}}$)	A logic "0" will reset the DAV line. The DAV F/F is only thing that is reset.
19	Data Available (DAV)	This line goes to a logic "1" when an entire character has been received and transferred to the receiver holding register. Tri-state. Fig. 8.
20	Serial Input (SI)	This line accepts the serial bit input stream. A Marking (logic "1") to spacing (logic "0") transition is required for initiation of data reception. Fig. 7, 8.

21	External Reset (XR)	Resets all registers. Sets SO, EOC, and TBMT to a logic "1". Resets DAV, and error flags to "0". Clears input data buffer. Must be tied to logic "0" when not in use.
22	Transmitter Buffer Empty (TBMT)	The transmitter buffer empty flag goes to a logic "1" when the data bits holding register may be loaded with another character. Tri-state. See Fig. 14, 16.
23	Data Strobe ($\overline{DS}$)	A strobe on this line will enter the data bits into the data bits holding register. Initial data transmission is initiated by the rising edge of $\overline{DS}$. Data must be stable during entire strobe.
24	End of Character (EOC)	This line goes to a logic "1" each time a full character is transmitted. It remains at this level until the start of transmission of the next character. See Fig. 13, 15.
25	Serial Output (SO)	This line will serially, by bit, provide the entire transmitted character. It will remain at a logic "1" when no data is being transmitted.
26-33	Data Bit Inputs (DB1-DB8)	There are up to 8 data bit input lines available.
34	Control Strobe (CS)	A logic "1" on this lead will enter the control bits (EPS, NB1, NB2, TSB, NP) into the control bits holding register. This line can be strobed or hard wired to a logic "1" level.
35	No Parity (NP)	A logic "1" on this lead will eliminate the parity bit from the transmitted and received character (no PE indication). The stop bit(s) will immediately follow the last data bit. If not used, this lead must be tied to a logic "0".
36	Number of Stop Bits (TSB)	This lead will select the number of stop bits, 1 or 2, to be appended immediately after the parity bit. A logic "0" will insert 1 stop bit and a logic "1" will insert 2 stop bits. The combined selection of 2 stop bits and 5 bits/character will produce 1½ stop bits.
37-38	Number of Bits/Character (NB2, NB1)	These two leads will be internally decoded to select either 5, 6, 7 or 8 data bits/character.
39	Odd/Even Parity Select (EPS)	The logic level on this pin selects the type of parity which will be appended immediately after the data bits. It also determines the parity that will be checked by the receiver. A logic "0" will insert odd parity and a logic "1" will insert even parity.
40	Transmitter Clock (TCP)	This line will contain a clock whose frequency is 16 times (16X) the desired transmitter baud

NB2	NB1	Bits/Character
0	0	5
0	1	6
1	0	7
1	1	8

TIMING DIAGRAMS

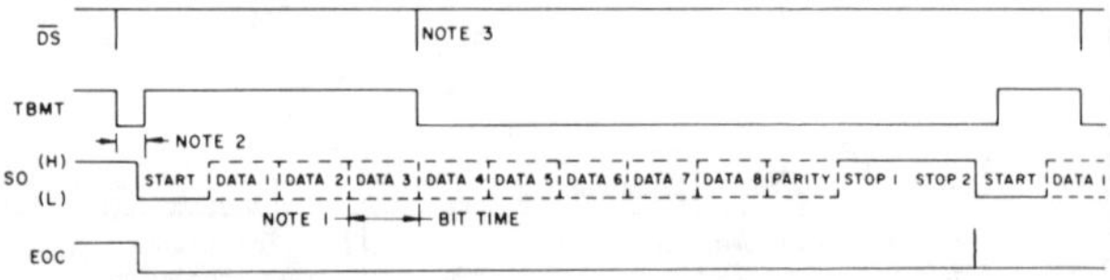

NOTE: SEE FIGURES 2, 3, 4 FOR DETAILS.

TRANSMITTER INITIALLY ASSUMED INACTIVE AT START OF DIAGRAM. SHOWN FOR 8 LEVEL CODE AND PARITY AND TWO STOPS.

1: BIT TIME = 16 CLOCK CYCLES.

2: IF TRANSMITTER IS INACTIVE THE START PULSE WILL APPEAR ON LINE 1 TO 2 CLOCK CYCLES AFTER THE DATA STROBE OCCURS. SEE DETAIL.

3: SINCE TRANSMITTER IS DOUBLE BUFFERED ANOTHER DATA STROBE CAN OCCUR ANYWHERE DURING TRANSMISSION OF CHARACTER 1 AFTER TBMT GOES HIGH.

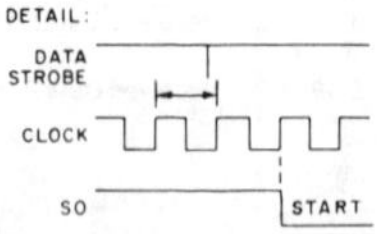

Fig. 1 UAR/T — TRANSMITTER TIMING

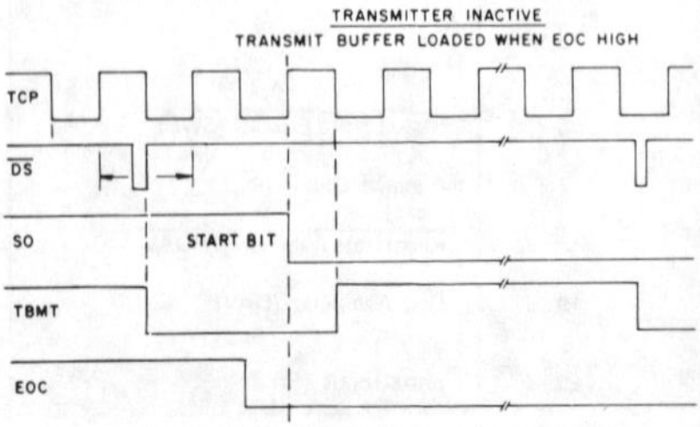

Fig. 2 TRANSMITTER AT START BIT NOT A TEST POINT

TIMING DIAGRAMS

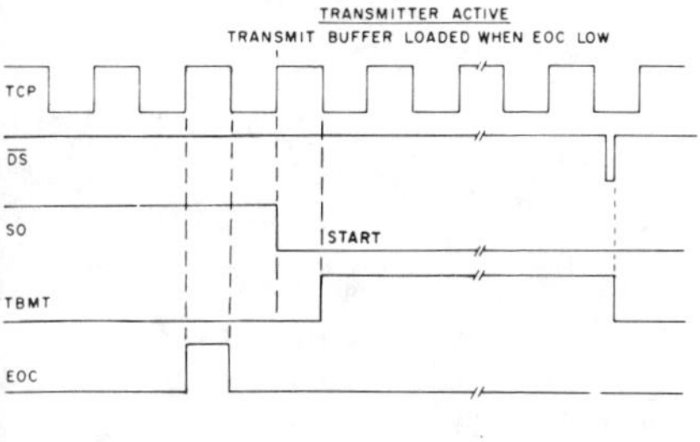

Fig. 3 TRANSMITTER AT START BIT

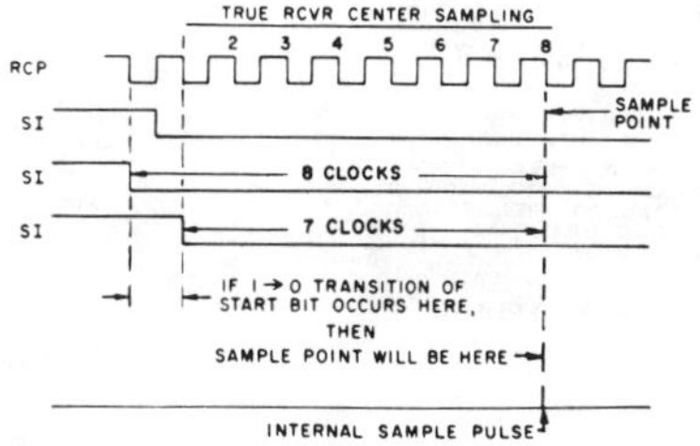

Fig. 7

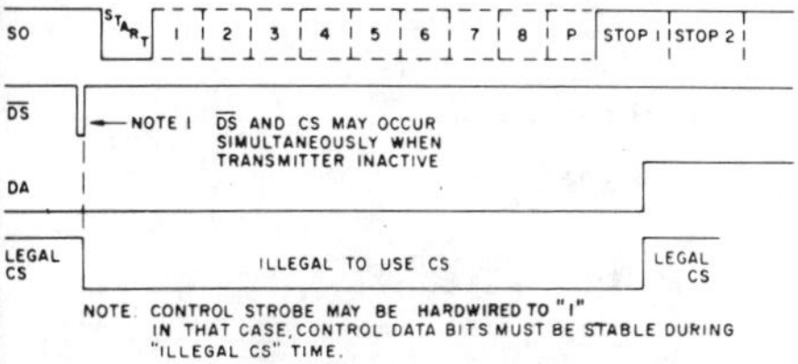

Fig. 4. ALLOWABLE POINTS TO USE CONTROL STROBE

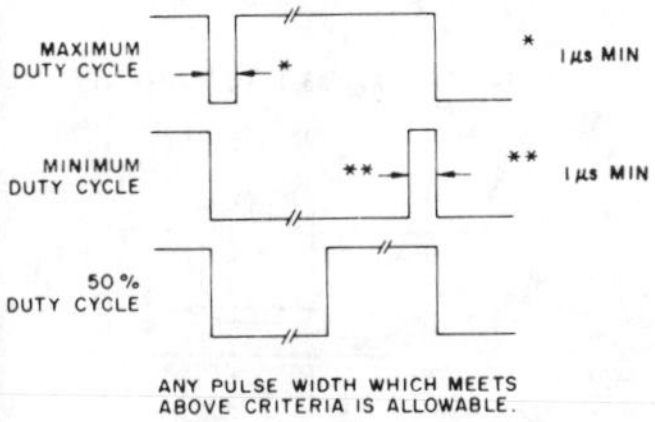

Fig. 5 ALLOWABLE TCP, RCP

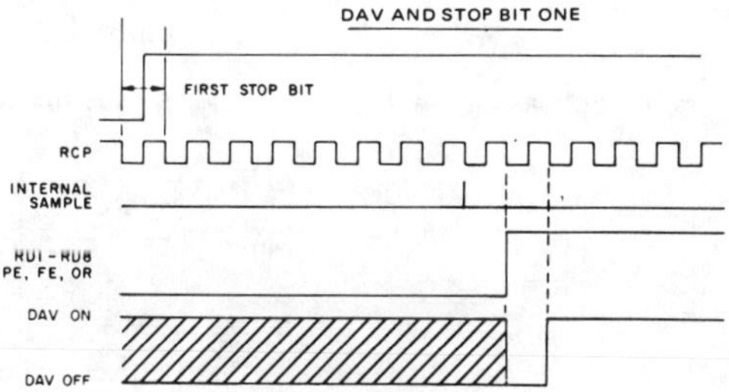

Fig. 8 RECEIVER DURING 1ST STOP BIT

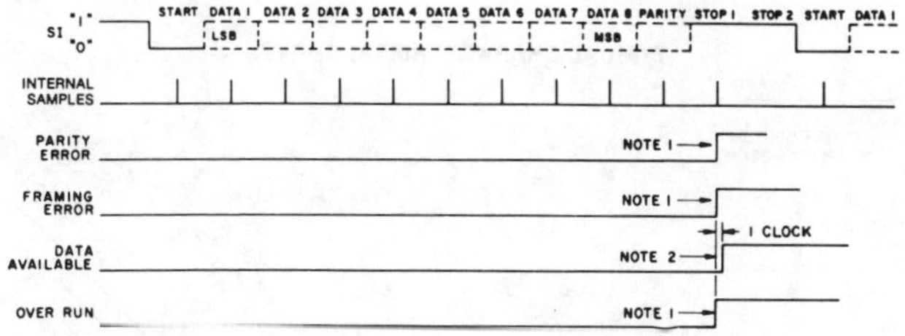

NOTES:

1. THIS IS THE TIME WHEN THE ERROR CONDITIONS ARE INDICATED, IF ERROR OCCURS.
2. DATA AVAILABLE IS SET ONLY WHEN THE RECEIVED DATA, PE, FE, OR HAS BEEN TRANSFERRED TO THE HOLDING REGISTERS. (SEE RECEIVER BLOCK DIAGRAM).
3. ALL INFORMATION IS GOOD IN HOLDING REGISTER UNTIL DATA AVAILABLE TRIES TO SET FOR NEXT CHARACTER.
4. ABOVE SHOWN FOR 8 LEVEL CODE PARITY AND TWO STOP. FOR NO PARITY, STOP BITS FOLLOW DATA.
5. FOR ALL LEVEL CODE THE DATA IN THE HOLDING REGISTER IS *RIGHT JUSTIFIED;* THAT IS, LSB ALWAYS APPEARS IN RD1 (PIN 12).

Fig. 6 UAR/T — RECEIVER TIMING

TIMING DIAGRAMS

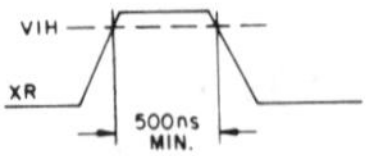

WHEN NOT IN USE, XR MUST BE HELD AT GND.

XR RESETS EVERY REGISTER EXCEPT THE CONTROL REGISTER. SO, TBMT, EOC ARE RESET TO 5V ALL OTHER OUTPUTS RESET TO OV.

Fig. 9 XR PULSE

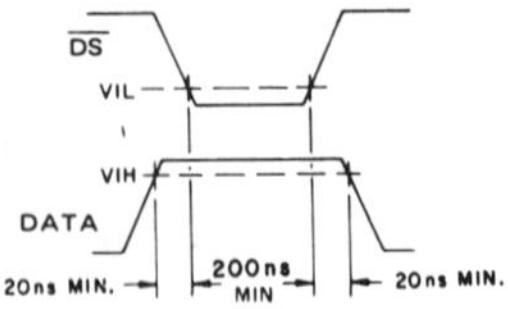

Fig. 10 $\overline{DS}$

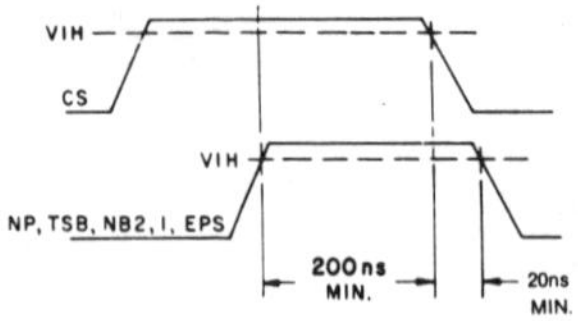

CONTROL BITS MUST BE STABLE FOR LAST 200ns OF CS.

Fig. 11a CS

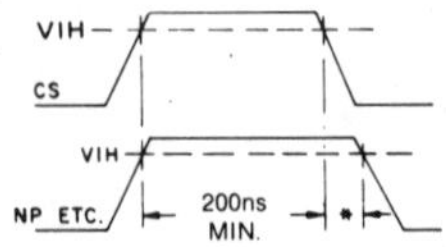

CONTROL STROBE AND CONTROL BITS MUST BE 500ns MINIMUM.

* 20ns MIN.

Fig. 11b

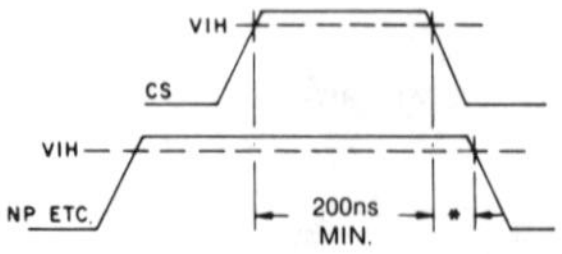

LEADING EDGE OF CONTROL DATA IS NOT CRITICAL AS LONG AS TRAILING EDGE AND PULSE WIDTH SPECS ARE OBSERVED.

Fig. 12

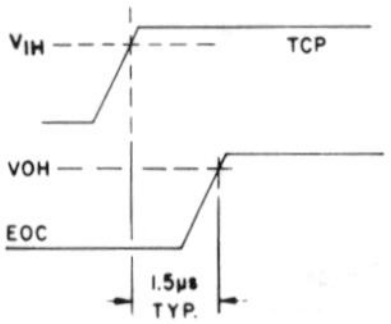

Fig. 13 EOC TURN-ON

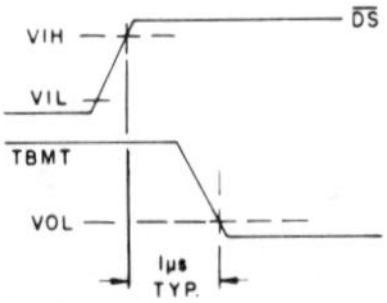

Fig. 14 TBMT TURN-OFF

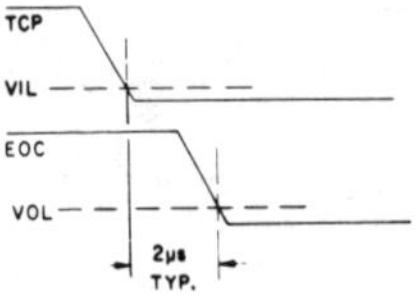

Fig. 15 EOC TURN-OFF

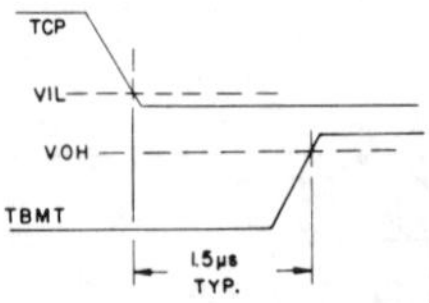

Fig. 16 TBMT TURN-ON

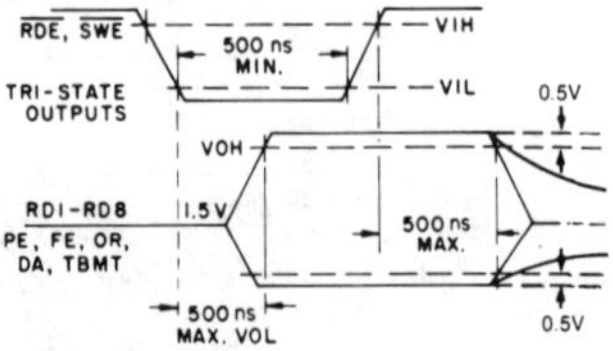

Fig. 17 RDE, SWE

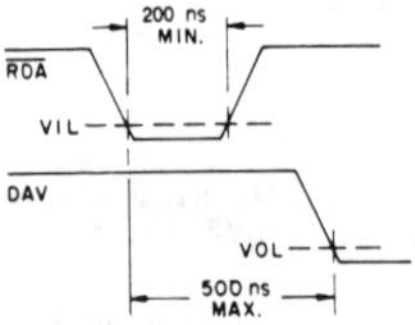

Fig. 18 RDAV

TYPICAL CHARACTERISTIC CURVES

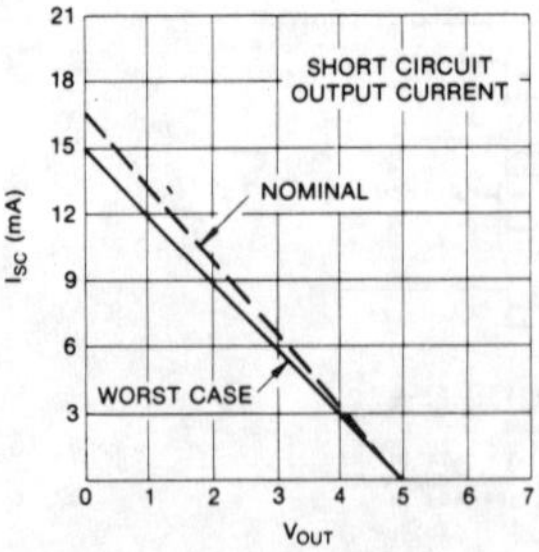

Fig. 19 SHORT CIRCUIT OUTPUT CURRENT (only 1 output may be shorted at a time)

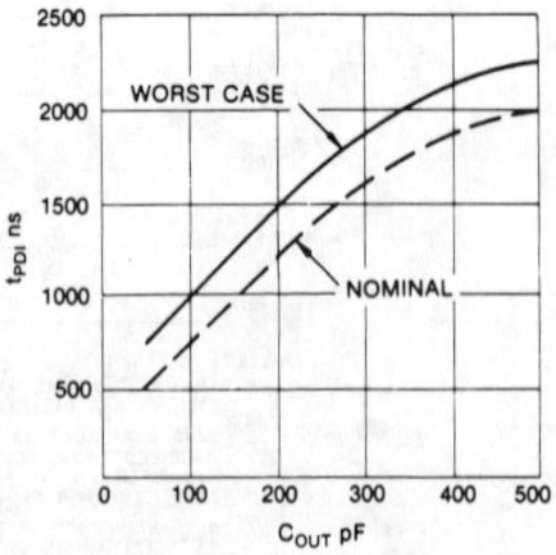

Fig. 20 RD1-RD8, PE, FE, OR, TBMT, DAV

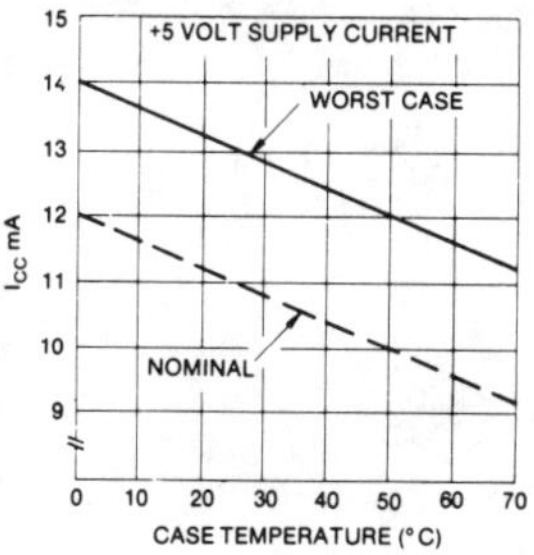

Fig. 21 +5 VOLT SUPPLY CURRENT

Initializing

Power is applied, external reset is enabled and clock pulse is applied having a frequency of 16 times the desired baud. The above conditions will set TBMT, EOC, and SO to logic "1" (line is marking).

After initializing is completed, user may set control bits and data bits with control bits selection normally occurring before data bits selection. However, one may set both $\overline{DS}$ and CS simultaneously if minimum pulse width specifications are followed. Once Data Strobe ($\overline{DS}$) is pulsed the TBMT signal will change from a logic "1" to a logic "0" indicating that the data bits holding register is filled with a previous character and is unable to receive new data bits, and transmitter shift register is transmitting previously loaded data. TBMT will return to a logic "1". When transmitter shift register is empty, data bits in the holding register are immediately loaded into the transmitter shift register for transmission. The shifting of information from the holding register to the transmitter shift register will be followed by SO and EOC going to a logic "0", and TBMT will also go to a logic "1" indicating that the shifting operation is completed and that the data bits holding register is ready to accept new data. It should be remembered that one full character time is now available for loading of the next character without loss in transmission speed due to double buffering (separate data bits holding register and transmitter shift register).

Data transmission is initiated with transmission of a start bit, data bits, parity bit (if desired) and stop bit(s). When the last stop bit has been on line for one bit time, EOC will go to a logic "1" indicating that new character is ready for transmission. This new character will be transmitted only if TBMT is a logic "0" as was previously discussed.

TRANSMITTER OPERATION

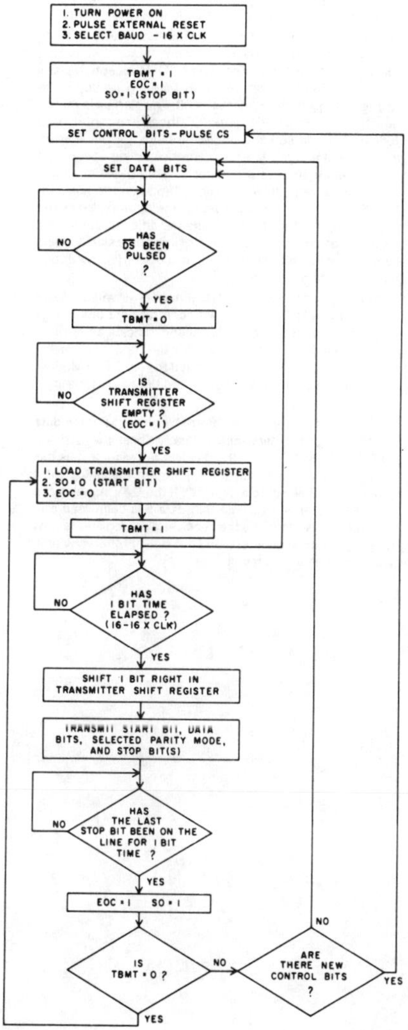

Fig. 23

Initializing

Power is applied, external reset is enabled, and clock pulse is applied having a frequency of 16 times the desired baud. The previous conditions will set data available (DAV) to a logic "1".

After initializing is completed, user should note that one set of control bits will be used for both receiver and transmitter making individual control bit setting unnecessary. Data reception starts when serial input signal changes from Marking (logic "1") to spacing (logic "0") which initiates start bit. The start bit is valid if, after transition from logic "1" to logic "0", the SI line continues to be at logic "0", when center sampled, 8 clock pulses later. If, however, line is at a logic "1" when center sampling occurs, the start bit verification process will be reset. If the Serial Input line transitions from a logic "1" to a logic "0" (marking to spacing) when the 16x clock is in a logic "1" state, the bit time, for center sampling will begin when the clock line transitions from a logic "1" to a logic "0" state. After verification of a genuine start bit, data bit reception, parity bit reception and stop bit(s), reception proceeds in an orderly manner.

While receiving parity and stop bit(s) the receiver will compare transmitted parity and stop bit(s) with control data bits (parity and number of stop bits) previously set and indicate an error by changing the parity error flip flop and/or the framing error flip flop to a logic "1". It should be noted that if the No Parity Mode is selected the PE (parity error) will be unconditionally set to a logic "0".

Once a full character is received, internal logic looks at the data available (DAV) signal to determine if data has been the read out. If the DAV signal is at a logic "1" the receiver will assume data has not been read out and the over run flip flop of the status word holding register will be set to a logic "1". If the DAV signal is at a logic "0" the receiver will assume that data has been read out. After DAV goes to a logic "1", the receiver shift register is now ready to accept the next character and has one full character time to remove the received character.

RECEIVER OPERATION

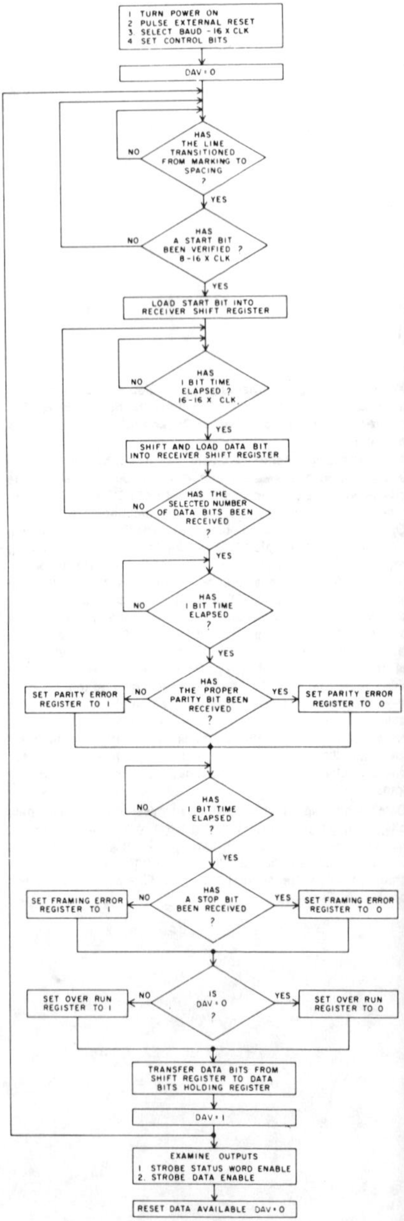

Fig. 24

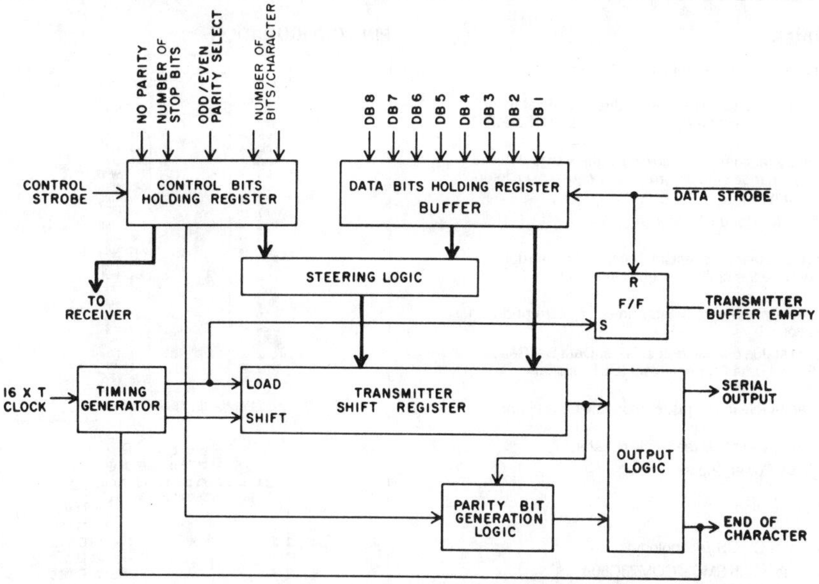

Fig. 25 TRANSMITTER BLOCK DIAGRAM

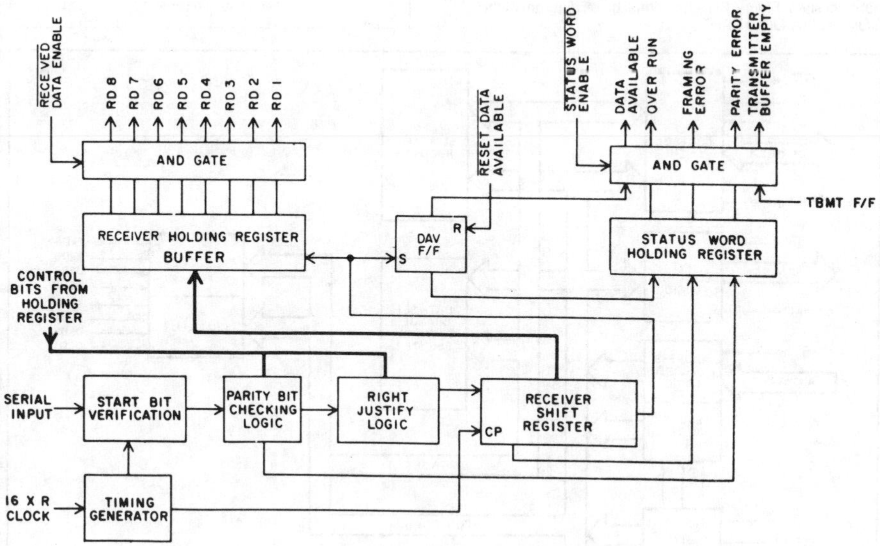

Fig. 26 RECEIVER BLOCK DIAGRAM

COM78C802 Dual UART

FEATURES

- ☐ Four independent full duplex serial data lines
- ☐ Programmable baud rates individually selectable for each line's transmitter/receiver (50 to 19,200 baud)
- ☐ Summary registers that allow a single read to detect a data set change or to determine the cause of an interrupt on any line
- ☐ Triple buffers for each receiver
- ☐ Device scanner mechanism that reports interrupt request due transmitter/receiver interrupts
- ☐ Independently programmable lines for interrupt-driven operation
- ☐ Modem status change detection for Data Set Ready (DSR) and Data Carrier Detect (DCD) signals
- ☐ Programmable interrupts for modem status changes
- ☐ Synchronizes critical read-only registers
- ☐ Single 5V Power Supply
- ☐ TTL Compatible
- ☐ Low Power CMOS Technology
- ☐ Compatible with SMC's COM78C808 and COM78C802

GENERAL DESCRIPTION

The COM78C804 Four-channel Asynchronous Receiver/Transmitter (Quad UART) is a VLSI device for new generations of asynchronous serial communication designs and for microcomputer systems. This device performs the basic operations necessary tor simultaneous reception and transmission of asynchronous messages on four independent lines. Figure 1 is a functional block diagram of the COM78C804 Quad UART.

PIN CONFIGURATION

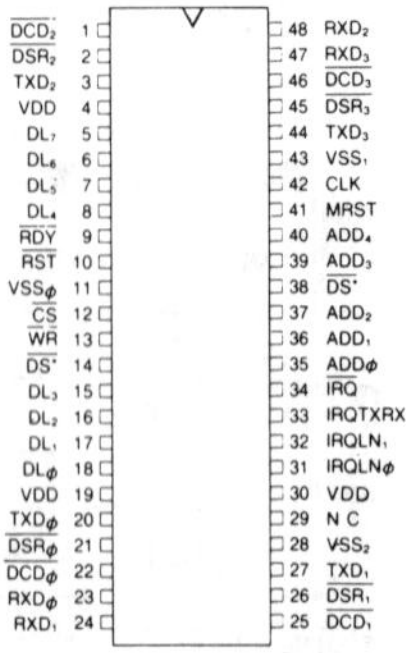

PACKAGE: 48-pin DIP

*must be connected together

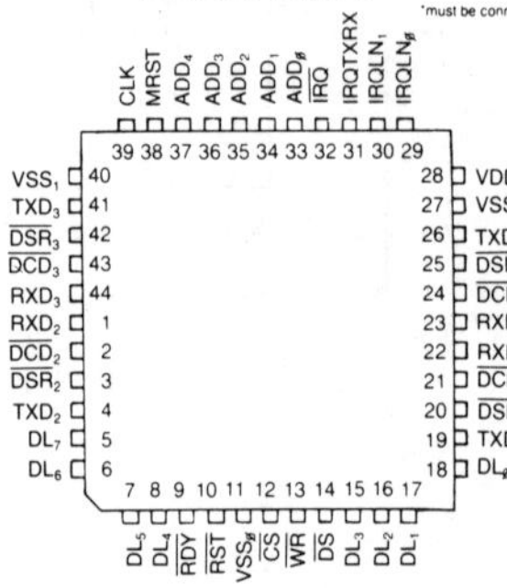

PACKAGE: 44- pin PLCC

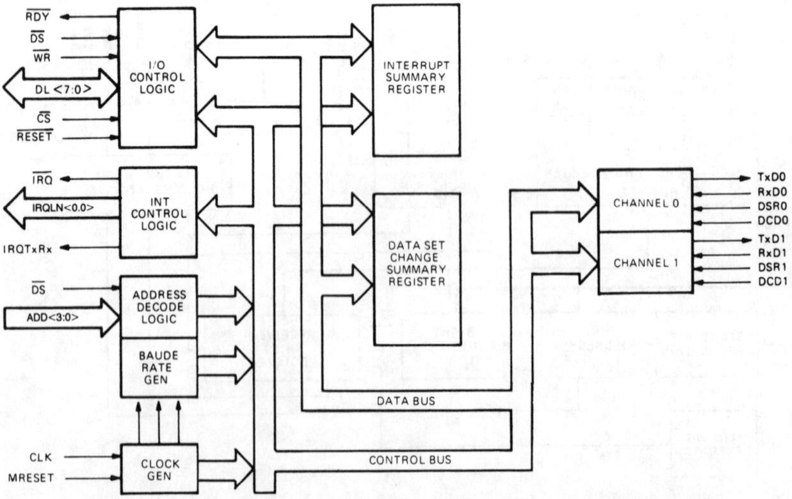

FIGURE 1: COM78C802 DUAL UART FUNCTIONAL BLOCK DIAGRAM

TABLE 1–COM78C802 PIN AND SIGNAL SUMMARY

Pin-PLCC	Pin-Dip	Signal	Input/Output	Definition/Function
5-8,15-18	4-7,14-17	DL<7:0>	input/output	Data lines <7:0>–Receives and transmits the parallel data.
33-37	30-33	ADD<3:0>	input	Address<3:0>–Selects the internal registers in the Dual UART. (Pins 36 and 37 must be connected in PLCC package.)
12	11	$\overline{CS}$	input	Chip select–Activates the Dual UART to receive and transmit data over the DL<7:0> lines.
14	13	$\overline{DS}$	input	Data strobe–Receives timing information for data transfers.
13	12	$\overline{WR}$	input	Write–Specifies direction of data transfer on the DL<7:0> lines.
9	8	$\overline{RDY}$	output	Ready–Indicates when the Dual UART is ready to participate in data transfer cycles.
10	9	RESET	input	Reset–Initializes the internal logic.
38	34	MRST	input	Manufacturing reset–For manufacturing use.
39	35	CLK	input	Clock–Clock input for timing.
20,42	20,40	$\overline{DSR<1:0>}$	inputs	Data set ready–Monitor data set ready (DSR) signals from modems.
21,43	1,21	$\overline{DCD<1:0>}$	inputs	Data set carrier detect–Monitor data set carrier detect (DCD) signals from modems.
32	29	IRQ	output	Interrupt request–Requests a processor interrupt.
29	26	IRQLN<C >	output	Interrupt request line number–Indicates the line number of originating interrupt request.
31	28	IRQTxRx	output	Interrupt request transmit/receive–Indicates whether an interrupt request is for transmitting or receiving data.
19,41	19,39	TxD<1:0>	outputs	Transmit data–Provides asynchronous bit-serial data output streams.
22,44	2,22	RxD<1:0>	input	Receive data–Accepts asynchronous bit-serial data input streams.
28	25	V_{DD}	input	Voltage–Power supply voltage +5 Vdc.
11,27,40	10,24,36	V_{SS}	input	Ground–Ground reference

COM78C804 Quad UART

FEATURES

- ☐ Two independent full duplex serial data lines
- ☐ Programmable baud rates individually selectable for each line's transmitter/receiver (50 to 19,200 baud)
- ☐ Summary registers that allow a single read to detect a data set change or to determine the cause of an interrupt on any line
- ☐ Triple buffers for each receiver
- ☐ Device scanner mechanism that reports interrupt request due transmitter/receiver interrupts
- ☐ Independently programmable lines for interrupt-driven operation
- ☐ Modem status change detection for Data Set Ready (DSR) and Data Carrier Detect (DCD) signals
- ☐ Programmable interrupts for modem status changes
- ☐ Synchronizes critical read-only registers
- ☐ Single 5V Power Supply
- ☐ TTL Compatible
- ☐ Compatible with SMC COM78C808 OCTAL UART and COM78C804 QUART

GENERAL DESCRIPTION

The COM78C802 Two-channel Asynchronous Receiver/Transmitter (Dual UART) is a VLSI device for new generations of asynchronous serial communication designs and for microcomputer systems. This device performs the basic operations necessary for simultaneous reception and transmission of asynchronous messages on two independent lines. Figure 1 is a functional block diagram of the COM78C802 Dual UART.

PIN CONFIGURATION

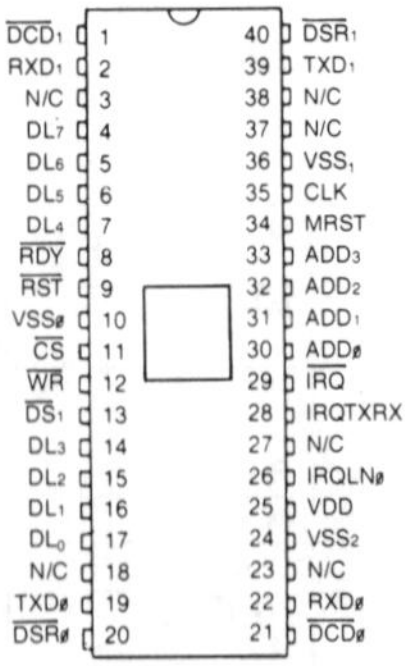

PACKAGE: 40- Pin DIP

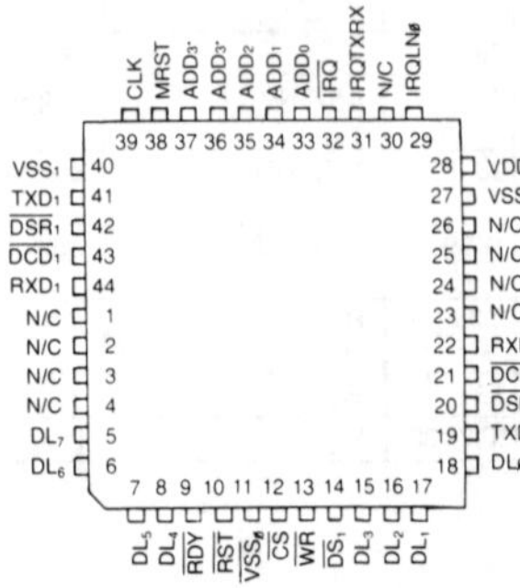

PACKAGE: 44 Pin PLCC

*Must be connected together

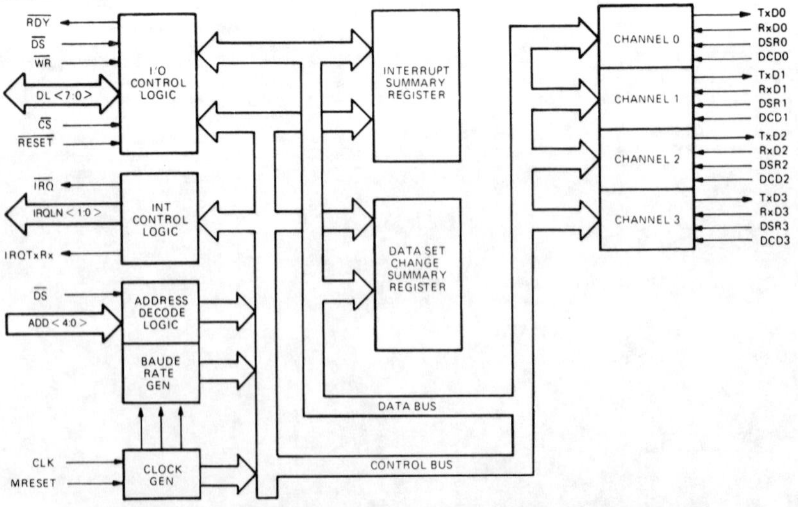

FIGURE 1: COM78C804 QUAD UART FUNCTIONAL BLOCK DIAGRAM

TABLE 1–COM78C804 PIN AND SIGNAL SUMMARY

Pin-PLCC	Pin-DIP	Signal	Input/Output	Definition/Function
5-8,15-18	5-8,15-18	DL<7:0>	input/output	Data lines <7:0>–Receives and transmits the parallel data.
33-37	35-37,39,40	ADD<0:4>	input	Address<0:4>–Selects the internal registers in the Quad UART.
12	12	$\overline{\text{CS}}$	input	Chip select–Activates the Quad UART to receive and transmit data over the DL<7:0> lines.
14	14,38	$\overline{\text{DS}}$	input	Data strobe–Receives timing information for data transfers.
13	13	$\overline{\text{WR}}$	input	Write–Specifies direction of data transfer on the DL<7:0> lines.
9	9	$\overline{\text{RDY}}$	output	Ready–Indicates when the Quad UART is ready to participate in data transfer cycles.
10	10	$\overline{\text{RESET}}$	input	Reset–Initializes the internal logic.
38	41	MRESET	input	Manufacturing reset–For manufacturing use.
39	42	CLK	input	Clock–Clock input for timing.
3,20,25,42	2,21,26,45	$\overline{\text{DSR}<3:0>}$	inputs	Data set ready–Monitor data set ready (DSR) signals from modems.
2,21,24,43	1,22,25,46	$\overline{\text{DCD}<3:0>}$	inputs	Data set carrier detect–Monitor data set carrier detect (DCD) signals from modems.
32	34	$\overline{\text{IRQ}}$	output	Interrupt request–Requests a processor interrupt.
29,30	31,32	IRQLN<0:1>	output	Interrupt request line number–Indicates the line number of originating interrupt request.
31	33	IRQTxRx	output	Interrupt request transmit/receive–Indicates whether an interrupt request is for transmitting or receiving data.
4,19,26,41	3,20,27,44	TxD<3:0>	outputs	Transmit data–Provides asynchronous bit-serial data output streams.
1,22,23,44	23,24,47,48	RxD<3:0>	input	Receive data–Accepts asynchronous bit-serial data input streams.
28	4,19,30	V_{DD}	input	Voltage–Power supply voltage +5 Vdc.
11,27,40	11,28,43	V_{SS}	input	Ground–Ground reference

Octal UART COM78C808

FEATURES

- Eight independent full duplex serial data lines
- Programmable baud rates individually selectable for each line's transmitter/receiver (50 to 19,200 baud)
- Summary registers that allow a single read to detect a data set change or to determine the cause of an interrupt on any line
- Triple buffers for each receiver
- Device scanner mechanism that reports interrupt request due transmitter/receiver interrupts
- Independently programmable lines for interrupt-driven operation
- Modem status change detection for Data Set Ready (DSR) and Data Carrier Detect (DCD) signals
- Programmable interrupts for modem status changes
- Synchronizes critical read-only registers
- Low power CMOS technology
- +5V only power supply
- Compatible with COM78C804 and COM78C802

PIN CONFIGURATION

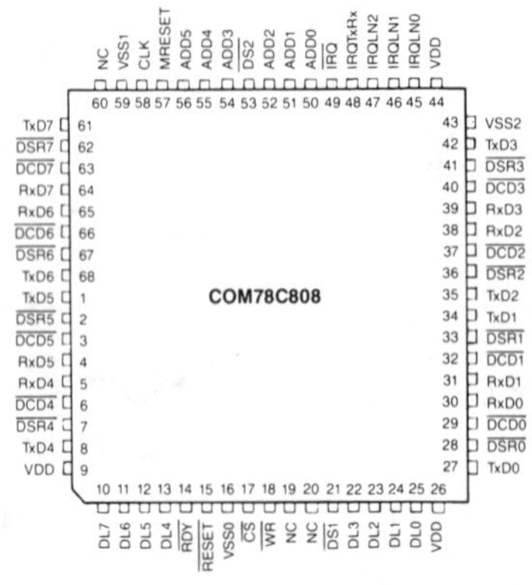

PACKAGE: 68-pin PLCC

GENERAL DESCRIPTION

The COM78C808 Eight-channel Asynchronous Receiver/Transmitter (Octal UART) is a VLSI device for new generations of asynchronous serial communication designs and for microcomputer systems. This 68-pin device performs the basic operations necessary for simultaneous reception and transmission of asynchronous messages on eight independent lines. Figure 1 is a functional block diagram of the COM78C808 Octal UART.

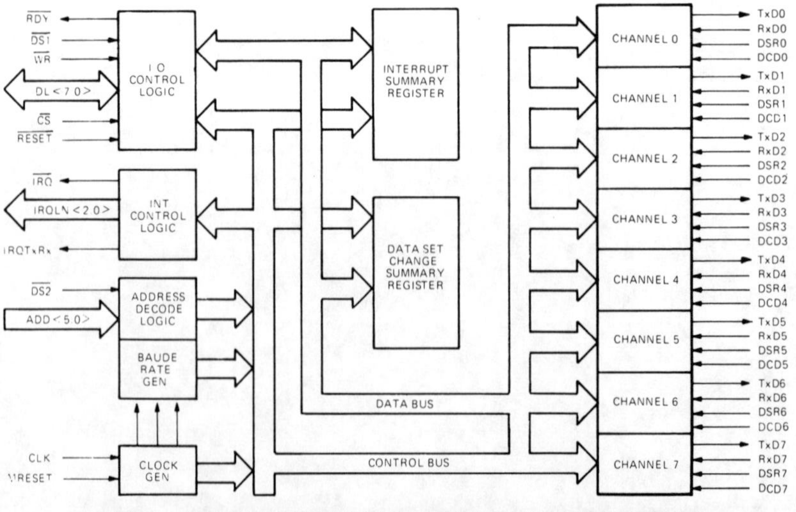

FIGURE 1 – COM78C808 OCTAL UART FUNCTIONAL BLOCK DIAGRAM

TABLE 1 – COM78C808 PIN AND SIGNAL SUMMARY

Pin	Signal	Input/Output	Definition/Function
10-13,22-25	DL<7:0>	input/output	Data lines <7:0>–Receives and transmits the parallel data.
50-52,54-56	ADD <0:5>	input	Address<0:5>–Selects the internal registers in the Octal UART.
17	$\overline{\text{CS}}$	input	Chip select–Activates the Octal UART to receive and transmit data over the DL<7:0> lines.
21,53	$\overline{\text{DS1}}$,$\overline{\text{DS2}}$	input	Data strobe 1 and 2–Receives timing information for data transfers. The $\overline{\text{DS1}}$ and $\overline{\text{DS2}}$ inputs must be connected together.
18	$\overline{\text{WR}}$	input	Write–Specifies direction of data transfer on the DL<7:0> lines.
14	$\overline{\text{RDY}}$	output	Ready–Indicates when the Octal UART is ready to participate, in data transfer cycles.
15	$\overline{\text{RESET}}$	input	Reset–Initializes the internal logic.
57	MRESET	input	Manufacturing reset–For manufacturing use.
58	CLK	input	Clock–Clock input for timing.
62,67,2,7, 41,36,33,28	$\overline{\text{DSR<7:0>}}$	inputs	Data set ready–Monitor data set ready (DSR) signals from modems.
63,66,3,6, 40,37,32,29	$\overline{\text{DCD<7:0>}}$	inputs	Data set carrier detect–Monitor data set carrier detect (DCD) signals from modems.
49	$\overline{\text{IRQ}}$	output	Interrupt request–Requests a processor interrupt.
45-47	IRQLN <0:2>	output	Interrupt request line number–Indicates the line number of originating interrupt request.
48	IRQTxRx	output	Interrupt request transmit/receive–Indicates whether an interrupt request is for transmitting or receiving data.
61,68,1,8, 42,35,34,27	TxD<7:0>	outputs	Transmit data–Provides asynchronous bit-serial data output streams.
64,65,4,5, 39,38,31,30	RxD<7:0>	inputs	Receive data–Accepts asynchronous bit-serial data input streams.
44,26,9	V_{DD}	input	Voltage–Power supply voltage +5 Vdc.
16,59,43	V_{SS}	input	Ground–Ground reference

DATA AND ADDRESS

Data lines (DL<7:0>)–These lines are used for the parallel transmission and reception of data between the CPU and the Octal UART. The receivers are active when the data strobe ($\overline{\text{DS1}}$, $\overline{\text{DS2}}$) signal is asserted. The output drivers are active only when the chip select ($\overline{\text{CS}}$) signal is asserted, the data strobe ($\overline{\text{DS1}}$, $\overline{\text{DS2}}$) signal is asserted, and the write ($\overline{\text{WR}}$) signal is deasserted. The drivers will become inactive (high-impedance) within 50 nanoseconds when one or more of the following occurs: the chip select ($\overline{\text{CS}}$) signal is deasserted, the data strobe ($\overline{\text{DS1}}$, $\overline{\text{DS2}}$) signal is deasserted, or the write ($\overline{\text{WR}}$) signal is asserted.

Address (ADD<5:0>)–These lines select which Octal UART internal register is accessible through the data I/O lines (DL<7:0>) when the data strobe ($\overline{\text{DS1}}$, $\overline{\text{DS2}}$) and chip select ($\overline{\text{CS}}$) signals are asserted. Table 2 lists the addresses corresponding to each register. The receiver buffer and transmitter holding register for each line have the same address. When the ($\overline{\text{WR}}$) signal is deasserted, the address accesses the receiver buffer register and when asserted, it accesses the transmitter holding register.

TABLE 2 – COM78C808 REGISTERS ADDRESS SELECTION

ADD Line* <5>	<4>	<3>	<2>	<1>	<0>	Read/Write	Register
0	0	0	0	0	0	Read	Line 0 Receiver Buffer
0	0	0	0	0	0	Write	Line 0 Transmitter Holding
0	0	0	0	0	1	Read	Line 0 Status
0	0	0	0	1	0	Read/Write	Line 0 Mode Registers 1,2
0	0	0	0	1	1	Read/Write	Line 0 Command
0	0	1	0	0	0	Read	Line 1 Receiver Buffer
0	0	1	0	0	0	Write	Line 1 Transmitter Holding
0	0	1	0	0	1	Read	Line 1 Status
0	0	1	0	1	0	Read/Write	Line 1 Mode Register 1,2
0	0	1	0	1	1	Read/Write	LIne 1 Command
0	1	0	0	0	0	Read	Line 2 Receiver Buffer
0	1	0	0	0	0	Write	Line 2 Transmitter Holding
0	1	0	0	0	1	Read	Line 2 Status
0	1	0	0	1	0	Read/Write	Line 2 Mode Register 1,2
0	1	0	0	1	1	Read/Write	Line 2 Command
0	1	1	0	0	0	Read	Line 3 Receiver Buffer
0	1	1	0	0	0	Write	Line 3 Transmitter Holding
0	1	1	0	0	1	Read	Line 3 Status
0	1	1	0	1	0	Read/Write	Line 3 Mode Register 1,2
0	1	1	0	1	1	Read/Write	Line 3 Command

1	0	0	0	0	0	Read	Line 4 Receiver Buffer
1	0	0	0	0	0	Write	Line 4 Transmitter Holding
1	0	0	0	0	1	Read	Line 4 Status
1	0	0	0	1	0	Read/Write	Line 4 Mode Register 1,2
1	0	0	0	1	1	Read/Write	Line 4 Command
1	0	1	0	0	0	Read	Line 5 Receiver Buffer
1	0	1	0	0	0	Write	Line 5 Transmitter Holding
1	0	1	0	0	1	Read	Line 5 Status
1	0	1	0	1	0	Read/Write	Line 5 Mode Register 1,2
1	0	1	0	1	1	Read/Write	Line 5 Command
1	1	0	0	0	0	Read	Line 6 Receiver Buffer
1	1	0	0	0	0	Write	Line 6 Transmitter Holding
1	1	0	0	0	1	Read	Line 6 Status
1	1	0	0	1	0	Read	Line 6 Mode Register 1,2
1	1	0	0	1	1	Read/Write	Line 6 Command
1	1	1	0	0	0	Read	Line 7 Receiver Buffer
1	1	1	0	0	0	Write	Line 7 Transmitter Holding
1	1	1	0	0	1	Read	Line 7 Status
1	1	1	0	1	0	Read/Write	Line 7 Mode Register 1,2
1	1	1	0	1	1	Read/Write	Line 7 Command
X	X	X	1	0	0	Read	Interrupt Summary
X	X	X	1	0	1	Read	Data Set Change Summary

*X = Either 0 or 1.

BUS TRANSACTION CONTROL

Chip select ($\overline{CS}$)–This signal is asserted to permit data transfers through the DL<7:0> lines to or from the internal registers. Data transfer is controlled by the data strobe ($\overline{DS1}$, $\overline{DS2}$) signal and write ($\overline{WR}$) signal.

Data strobe ($\overline{DS1}$, $\overline{DS2}$)– The data strobe inputs ($\overline{DS1}$ and $\overline{DS2}$) must be connected together. This input receives timing information for data transfers. During a write cycle, the CPU asserts the data strobe signal when valid output data is available and deasserts the data strobe signal before the data is removed. During a read cycle, the CPU asserts the data strobe signal and the Octal UART transfers the valid data. When the data strobe signal is deasserted, the DL<7:0> lines become a high impedance.

Write ($\overline{WR}$)–The write ($\overline{WR}$) signal specifies the direction of data transfer on the DL<7:0> pins by controlling the direction of their transceivers. If the $\overline{WR}$ signal is asserted during a data transfer (the $\overline{CS}$, $\overline{DS1}$, and $\overline{DS2}$ signals asserted), the Octal UART is receiving data from DL<7:0>. If the $\overline{WR}$ signal is deasserted during a write data transfer, the Octal UART is driving data onto the DL<7:0> lines.

INTERRUPT REQUEST

Interrupt request $\overline{IRQ}$–The $\overline{IRQ}$ pin is an open drain output. The integral interrupt scanner asserts the IRQ signal when it has detected an interrupt condition on one of the eight serial data lines.

Interrupt Request transmit/receive (IRQTxRx)—This signal indicates when the interrupt scanner in the Octal UART stops and asserts $\overline{IRQ}$ because of a transmitter interrupt condition (the IRQTxRx signal is asserted) or because of a receiver interrupt condition (the IRQTxRx signal is deasserted). The signal is valid only while $\overline{IRQ}$ is asserted. The state of IRQTxRx signal also appears as bit 0 of the interrupt summary register.

Interrupt request line number (IRQLN<2:0>)–These lines indicate the line number at which the Octal UART interrupt scanner stopped and asserted the interrupt request ($\overline{IRQ}$) signal. The number on these lines is valid only while the $\overline{IRQ}$ signal is asserted. Line IRQLN<2> is the high-order bit and the IRQLN<0> line is the low-order bit. The state of these signals also appears as bits in the interrupt summary register: IRQLN<2> as bit 3, IRQLN<1> as bit 2, and IRQLN<0> as bit 1. Table 3 shows the line numbers corresponding to settings of IRQLN<2:0>.

TABLE 3 – COM78C808 INTERRUPT REQUEST LINE ASSIGNMENTS

IRQ Line <2>	<1>	<0>	Line
0	0	0	0
0	0	1	1
0	1	0	2
0	1	1	3
1	0	0	4
1	0	1	5
1	1	0	6
1	1	1	7

SERIAL DATA

Transmit data (TxD<7:0>)–These outputs transmit the asynchronous bit-serial data streams. They remain at a high level when no data is being transmitted and a low level when the TxBRK bit in the associated line's command register is set.

Receive data (RxD<7:0>)–These lines accept asynchronous bit-serial data streams. The input signals must remain in the high state for at least one-half bit time before a high-to-low transition is recognized. (A high-to-low transition is required to signal the beginning of a "start" bit and initiate data reception).

MODEM SIGNALS

Data set ready ($\overline{DSR}$<7:0>)–These eight input pins, one for each serial data line on the COM78C808, are typically connected via intervening level converters to the data set ready outputs of modems. A TTL low at a $\overline{DSR}$ pin causes the DSR bit (bit 7) in the corresponding line's status register to be asserted. A TTL high at a $\overline{DSR}$ pin causes the DSR bit in the corresponding line's status register to be deasserted. A change of this input from high-to-low, or low-to-high, causes the assertion of the data set change (DSCHNG) bit that corresponds to this line in the data set change summary register. Changes from one state to the other and back again that occur within one microsecond may not be detected.

Carrier detect (DCD<7:0>)–These eight input pins, one for each serial data line of the Octal UART, are typically connected through intervening level converters to the received line signal detect (also called carrier detect) outputs of modems. A TTL low at a $\overline{DCD}$ pin causes the DCD bit of the corresponding line's status register to be deasserted. A change of this input from high-to-low, or low-to-high, causes the assertion of the data set change (DSCHNG) bit corresponding to this line in the data set change summary register. Changes from one state to the other and back again that occur within one microsecond may not be detected.

GENERAL CONTROL SIGNALS

Ready (RDY)–The RDY pin is an open drain output. Upon detecting a negative transition of chip select (CS), the Octal UART asserts the RDY signal to indicate readiness to take part in data transfer cycles. The RDY signal deasserts after the trailing edge of CS.

Reset (RESET)–When the RESET input is asserted, the TxD<7:0> lines are asserted and all internal status bits listed in the "Architecture Summary" discussion are cleared.

Manufacturing reset (MRESET)–This signal is for manufacturing use only and the input should be connected to ground for normal operation.

MISCELLANEOUS SIGNALS

Clock in (CLK)–All baud rates and internal clocks are derived from this input. Normal operating frequency is 4:9152 MHz ±0.1 percent and duty cycle is 50 percent ±5 percent.

POWER AND GROUND

Voltage (V_{DD})–Power supply 5 Vdc

Ground (V_{SS})–Ground reference

ARCHITECTURE SUMMARY

The Octal UART functions as a serial-to-parallel, parallel-to-serial converter/controller. It can be programmed by a microprocessor to provide different characteristics for each of its eight serial data lines (stop bits, parity, character length, split baud rates, etc.)

Each serial line functions the same as a one-line UART-type device thereby reducing the number of chips and conserving space on communication devices that require multiple communications lines.

An integral interrupt scanner checks for device interrupt conditions on the eight lines. Its scanning algorithm gives priority to receivers over transmitters. The scanner can also check for interrupts resulting from changes in modem control signals DSR and DCD.

Line-specific Registers

Each of the eight serial data lines in the Octal UART has a set of registers for buffering data into and out of the line and for external control of the line's characteristics. These registers are selected for access by setting the appropriate address on lines ADD<5:0>. Lines ADD<5:3> select one of the eight data lines. Lines ADD<2:0> select the specific register for that line. Refer to Table 2 for the register address assignments.

Receiver buffer register–Each line's receiver consists of a character assembly register and a two-entry FIFO that is the receiver buffer register. When the RxEN bit in a line's command register is set, received characters are moved automatically into the line's receiver buffer as soon as they have been deserialized from the associated communications line. When there are characters in this FIFO, the RxRDY bit is set in the status register for the line.

The assertion of the RxRDY signal for a line that already has the RxIE bit of its command register set causes the interrupt scanner logic to stop and generate an interrupt condition (the IRQ signal is asserted). When the receiver buffer is read, the interrupt condition is cleared (the IRQ signal is deasserted) and the interrupt scanner resumes operation.

If there is another entry in a line's FIFO, the RxRDY bit remains asserted. When the interrupt scanner reaches this line again, the assertion of RxRDY causes the scanner to halt and assert the IRQ again.

Asserting the RESET signal or clearing the RxEN bit initializes the receiver logic of Octal UART. The RxRDY flag is cleared and the receiver buffer register outputs become undefined. Any data in the FIFO at that time is lost.

Transmitter holding register–Each line has a writable transmitter holding register. When the TxEN bit in the line's command register is set, characters are moved automatically from the output of this register into the transmitter serialization logic whenever the serialization logic becomes idle.

When this register is empty, the TxRDY bit in the line's status register is set. If the transmitter interrupt enable (TxIE) bit in the line's command register is also set, the interrupt scanner logic halts and generates an interrupt condition. If a character is then loaded into the register, the interrupt is cleared and the scanner resumes operation.

Assertion of the RESET signal initializes the transmitter logic of the Octal UART. The TxRDY flag is cleared and the transmitter holding register's contents are lost. The transmitter enable (TxEN) bit in the line's command register is also cleared by RESET. If at the end of the reset process, the TxEN is reasserted and TxRDY bit is reasserted. Software clearing of TxEN alone produces results different from the full RESET in that the transmitter holding register's contents are not lost; they are transmitted when TxEN is set again.

Status register–Each line has a read-only status register that provides information about the current state of the given line. This register indicates a line's readiness for transmission or reception of data and flags error conditions in its bit fields. Figure 3 shows the format of the status register. Table 3 lists the flag bits in each status register.

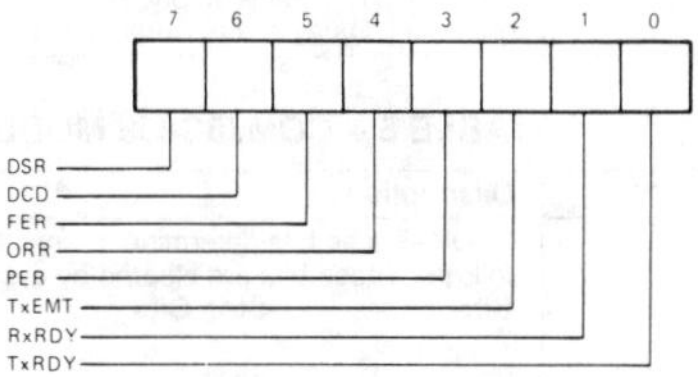

FIGURE 3 – COM78C808 STATUS REGISTERS (LINE 0-7) FORMAT

Mode registers 1 and 2—These read/write registers control the attributes (including parity, character length, and line speed) of the communications line.

Each of the eight communications lines has two of these registers, both accessed by the same address on ADD<5:0>. Successive access operations (either read or write, in any combination) alternate between the two registers at that address by use of an internal pointer. The first operation addresses mode register 1, the next address mode register 2, and another after that would recycle the pointer to mode register 1. The pointer is reset to point to mode register 1 by RESET or by a read of the command register for this line. These registers should not be accessed by bit-oriented instructions that do read/modify/write cycles such as the PDP-11 BIS, BIC, and BIT instructions.

Figure 4 shows the format of mode registers 1 and Table 5 describes the function of the register information.

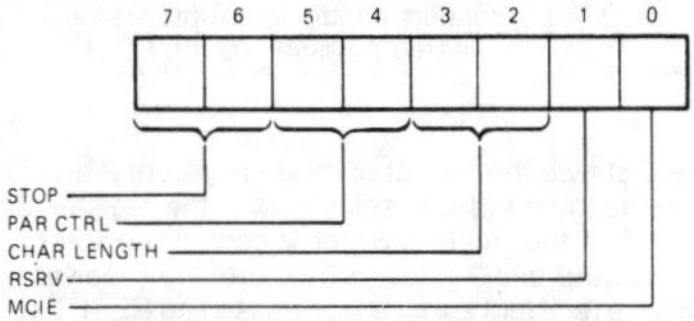

FIGURE 4 – COM78C808 MODE REGISTERS 1 (LINE 0-7) FORMAT

TABLE 4 – COM78C808 STATUS REGISTERS (LINES 0-7) DESCRIPTION

Bit	Description
7	DSR (Data set ready)–This bit is the inverted state of the DSR line.
6	DCD (Data set carrier detect)–This bit is the inverted state of the DCD line.
5	FER (Frame error)–Set when the received character currently displayed in the receiver buffer register was not framed by a stop bit. Only the first stop bit is checked to determine that a framing error exists. Subsequent reading of the receiver buffer register that indicates all zeros (including the parity bit, if any) can be interpreted as a Break condition. This bit is cleared by clearing RxEN (bit 2) of the command register, by asserting the RESET input, or by setting the reset error RERR (bit 4) of the command register.
4	ORR (Overrun error)–Set when the character in the receiver buffer register was not read before another character was received. Cleared by clearing RxEN (bit 2) of the command register, by asserting the RESET input, or by setting reset error RERR (bit 4) of the command register.
3	PER (Parity error)–If parity is enabled and this bit is set, the received character in the receiver buffer register has an incorrect parity bit. This bit is cleared by clearing RxEN (bit 2) of the command register, by asserting the RESET input, by setting reset error RERR (bit 2) of the command register, or by reading the current character in the receiver buffer register.
2	TxEMT (Transmitter empty)–Set when the transmitter serialization logic for the associated line has completed transmission of a character, and no new character has been loaded into the transmitter holding register. Cleared by loading the transmitter holding register, by clearing TxEN (0) of the command register, or by asserting the RESET input.
1	RxRDY (Receiver buffer ready)–When set, a character has been loaded into the FIFO buffer from the deserialization logic. Cleared by reading the receiver buffer register, by clearing RxEN (bit 2) in the command register, or by asserting the RESET input.
0	TxRDY (Transmitter holding register ready)—When set, this bit indicates that the transmitter holding register is empty. Cleared when the program has loaded a character into the transmitter holding register, when the transmitter for this line is disabled by clearing TxEN (bit 0) in the command register, or by asserting the RESET input. This bit is initially set when the transmitter logic is enabled by the setting of TxEN (bit 0) and the transmitter holding register is empty. This bit is not set when the automatic echo or remote loopback modes are programmed. Data can be overwritten if a consecutive write is performed while TxRDY is cleared.

TABLE 5 – COM78C808 MODE REGISTERS 1 (LINES 0-7) DESCRIPTION

Bit	Description
7,6	STOP–These bits determine the number of stop bits that are appended to the transmitted characters as follows. These bits are cleared by asserting the RESET input. **Bits** **Stop Bits** **7 6** 0 0 Invalid 0 1 1.0 1 0 1.5 1 1 2.0
5,4	PAR CTRL (Parity control)–These bits determine parity as follows and are cleared by asserting the RESET input. X = either 1 or 0. **Bits** **Parity Type** **5 4** 1 1 Even 0 1 Odd X 0 Disabled
3,2	CHAR LENGTH (Character length)–These bits determine the length (excluding start bit, parity, and stop bits) of the characters received and sent. Received characters of less than 8 bits are "right aligned" in the receiver buffer with unused high-order bits equal to zero. Parity bits are not shown in the receiver buffer. The character length bits are cleared by asserting the RESET input. The character length bits are defined as follows: **Bit** **Bit Length** **3 2** 0 0 5 0 1 6 1 0 7 1 1 8
1	RSRV (Reserved and cleared by asserting the RESET input.)
0	MCIE (Modem control interrupt enable)–When set and RxIE (bit 5) of the command register is set, the modem control interrupts are enabled. Refer to the Interrupt Scanner and Interrupt Handling information. Cleared by asserting the RESET input.

Figure 5 shows the format of mode registers 2 and Table 6 indicates the baud rate selections of the register. Bits 7 through 4 of the mode register 2 control the transmitter baud rate and bits 3 through 0 control the receiver baud rate. These registers are cleared by asserting RESET input.

Command register–These read/write registers control various functions on the selected line. Figure 6 shows the format of the command registers and Table 6 describes the function of the register information.

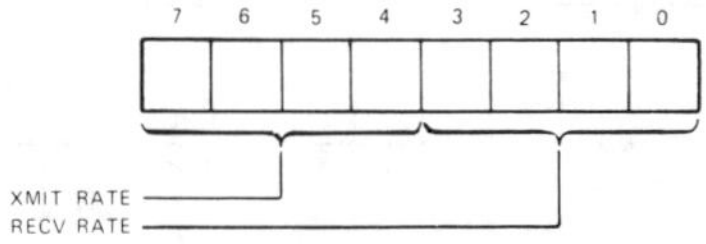

FIGURE 5 – COM78C808 MODE REGISTERS 2 (LINE 0-7) FORMAT

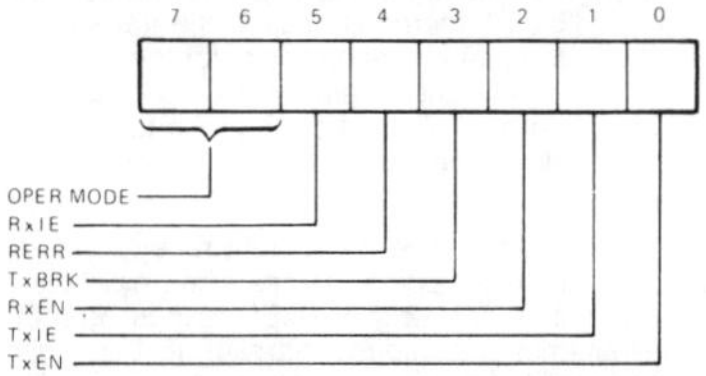

FIGURE 6 – COM78C808 COMMAND REGISTERS (LINE 0-7) FORMAT

TABLE 6 – COM78C808 MODE REGISTERS 2 (LINES 0-7) DESCRIPTION

Bit	Description
7:0	XMIT RATE/RECV RATE (Transmitter/Receiver Rate)–Selects the baud rate of the transmitter (bits 7:4) and receiver (bits 3:0) as follows:

Transmitter Bits				Receiver Bits				Nominal	Actual	Error*
7	6	5	4	3	2	1	0	Rate	Rate	(percent)
0	0	0	0	0	0	0	0	50	same	—
0	0	0	1	0	0	0	1	75	same	—
0	0	1	0	0	0	1	0	110	109.09	0.826
0	0	1	1	0	0	1	1	134.5	133.33	0.867
0	1	0	0	0	1	0	0	150	same	—
0	1	0	1	0	1	0	1	300	same	—
0	1	1	0	0	1	1	0	600	same	—
0	1	1	1	0	1	1	1	1200	same	—
1	0	0	0	1	0	0	0	1800	1745.45	3.03
1	0	0	1	1	0	0	1	2000	2021.05	1.05
1	0	1	0	1	0	1	0	2400	same	—
1	0	1	1	1	0	1	1	3600	3490.91	3.03
1	1	0	0	1	1	0	0	4800	same	—
1	1	0	1	1	1	0	1	7200	6981.81	3.03
1	1	1	0	1	1	1	0	9600	same	—
1	1	1	1	1	1	1	1	19200	same	—

*The frequency of the clock input (CLK) is 4.9152 MHz. The clock input may vary by 0.1 percent. This variance results in an error that must be added to the error listed.

TABLE 7 – COM78C808 COMMAND REGISTERS (LINES 0-7) DESCRIPTION

Bit	Description
7,6	OPER MODE (Operating mode)–These bits control the operating mode of the channel as follows. These bits are cleared by asserting the $\overline{\text{RESET}}$ input. **Bit 7 / 6 — Operating Mode** 0 0 Normal operation 0 1 Automatic echo 1 0 Local loopback 1 1 Remote loopback
5	RxIE (Receiver interrupt enable)–When set, the RxRDY flag (bit 1) of the status register for this line will generate an interrupt.
4	RERR (Reset error)–When set, this bit clears the framing error, overrun error, and parity error of the status register associated with this line. This bit is cleared by asserting the $\overline{\text{RESET}}$ input (not self-clearing).
3	TxBRK (Transmit break)–When set, this bit forces the appropriate TxD<7:0> line to the spacing state at the conclusion of the character presently being transmitted. When the program clears this bit, normal operation is restored, and any character pending in the transmitter holding register is moved into the serialization logic and transmitted. The minimum break length obtainable is twice the character length plus 1 bit time. The maximum break length depends on the amount of time between the program setting and clearing this bit, but is an integral number of bit times. This bit is cleared by asserting the $\overline{\text{RESET}}$ input.
2	RxEN (Receiver enable)–When set, this bit enables the receiver logic. When cleared, it stops the assembling of the received character, clears all receiver error bits and the RxRDY (bit 1) of the status register, clears any receiver interrupt conditions associated with this line, and initializes all receiver logic. This bit is cleared by asserting the $\overline{\text{RESET}}$ input.
1	TxIE (Transmit interrupt enable)–When set, the state of the associated TxRDY flag (bit 0) of the status register is made available to the interrupt scanner logic. When the interrupt scanner logic scans this line, it determines if the TxRDY flag is asserted and generates an interrupt by asserting the $\overline{\text{IRQ}}$ signal.
0	TxEN (Transmitter enable)–When set, this bit enables the transmitter logic. When cleared, it inhibits the serialization of the characters that follow but the serialization of the current character is completed. It also clears the TxRDY flag (bit 0) of the status register, clears any transmitter interrupt conditions associated with this line, and initializes all transmitter logic except that associated with the transmitter holding register. The character in the transmitter holding register is retained so that XON/XOFF situations can be properly processed. This bit is cleared by asserting the $\overline{\text{RESET}}$ input.

Bits 5 through 0 enable the line's receiver and transmitter, enable handling of interrupts, initiate the transmission of break characters, and reset error bits for the line. Refer to "Interrupt Scanner" and "Interrupt Handling" paragraphs for detailed interrupt information. Bits 7 and 6 control the operating mode of the line. The four modes that can be set are:

- Normal operation–The serial data received is assembled in the receiver logic and transferred in parallel to the receiver buffer register. (The RxEN bit must be set.) Data to be transmitted is loaded in parallel into the transmitter holding register, then automatically transferred into the transmitter logic and serialized for transmission. (The TxEN bit must be set.)
- Automatic echo–The serial data received is assembled into parallel in the receiver logic (the RxEN bit must be set) and transferred to the receiver buffer register. Arriving serial data is also routed to the line's TxD<n> pin for serial output. TxEN is ignored and the transmitter logic is disabled. TxRDY flags and TxEMT indications are cleared. No transmitter interrupts are generated.
- Local loopback–The serial data from the RxD<n> input is ignored and the receiver serial input receives data from the transmitter serial output. The data is assembled into parallel form in the receiver logic (the RxEN bit must be set) and transferred to the receiver buffer register where it can be read by the program. Data to be transmitted to the receiver is loaded in parallel form into the transmitter holding register from which it is automatically moved into the transmitter logic and serialized for transmission. (The TxEN bit must be set.) The transmission goes only to the receiver serial input; the TxD<n> output is held high. As in normal operation, transmission and reception baud rates are controlled by the transmitter speed and receiver speed entries in mode register 2.
- Remote loopback–The serial data received on the RxD<n> line is returned to the TxD<n> line without further action. No data is received or transmitted. The RxRDY, TxRDY, and TxEMT flags are disabled. The TxEN and RxEN bits of the command register are held cleared, causing the transmitter and receiver logic to be disabled.

SUMMARY REGISTERS

The Octal UART contains two registers that summarize the current status of all eight serial data lines, making it possible to determine that a line's status has changed with a single read operation. These registers are selected for access by setting the appropriate address on pins ADD <2:0>. Because the registers are shared by eight serial lines, the line-selection bits (ADD <5:3>) are ignored when these registers are accessed. Refer to "Interrupt Scanner and Interrupt Handling" for detailed interrupt information.

Interrupt summary register–This read-only register indicates that a transmitter or receiver interrupt condition has occured, and indicates the line number that generated the interrupt. Figure 7 shows the format of the interrupt summary register and Table 8 describes register information.

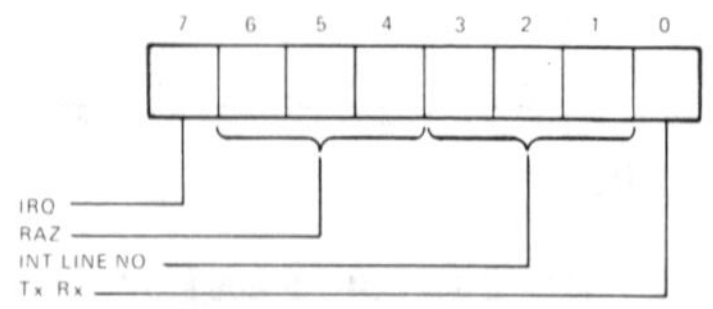

FIGURE 7 – COM78C808 INTERRUPT SUMMARY REGISTER FORMAT

Data set change summary register–When the DSR or DCD inputs that are associated with a line change state, the bit corresponding to that line in this read-only register is set. The current state of the DSR and DCD inputs can

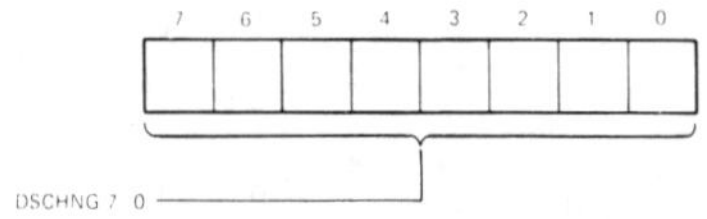

FIGURE 8 – COM78C808 DATA SET CHANGE SUMMARY REGISTER FORMAT

then be obtained from that line's status register. If the state of a line changes twice within one microsecond, the change in state may not be detected. Figure 8 shows the format of the data set change summary register.

When the MCIE bit in a line's mode register 1 is set and RxIE is also set, the modem control interrupts are enabled for that line. If DSCHNG for that line is then set, the interrupt scanner will halt and assert the IRQ signal. The data set change summary register bits are cleared by writing a 1 into the bit position. A program that uses this register should read and save a copy of its contents. The copy can then be written back to the register to clear the bits that were set. The system interrupts should be disabled and writeback should directly follow the read operation.

Assertion of the RESET signal disables and initializes the data set change logic. When the RESET signal is deasserted, future changes in DSR and DCD are reported as they occur.

INTERRUPT SCANNER AND INTERRUPT HANDLING

The interrupt scanner is a four-bit counter that sequentially checks lines 0 through 7 for a receiver interrupt (counter positions (0-7) and then checks the lines in the same order

TABLE 8 – COM78C808 INTERRUPT SUMMARY REGISTER DESCRIPTION

Bit	Description
7	IRQ (Interrupt request)–When set, this bit indicates that the interrupt scanner has found an interrupting condition among the eight serial lines of the Octal UART. These conditions also result in the Octal UART asserting the IRQ signal.
6:4	RAZ (Read as zero)–Not used
3:1*	INT LINE NO (Interrupting line number)–These bits indicate the line number upon which an interrupting condition was found. These bits correspond to the IRQLN <2:0> signals–(bit 3 = IRQLN<2>, bit 2 = IRQLN<1>, and bit 1 = IRQLN<0>. Refer to Table 3.
0*	Tx/Rx (Transmit/receive)–This bit indicates whether the interrupting condition was caused by a transmitter (Tx/Rx equals 1) or a receiver (Tx/Rx equals 0). This bit corresponds to the IRQTxRx signal of the Octal UART and is set when IRQTxRx is asserted.

*Bits 3-0 above represent the outputs of a free-running counter and are valid only when bit 7 is set.

for a transmitter interrupt (counter positions 8-15). If the scanner detects an interrupt condition, it stops and the $\overline{IRQ}$ signal is asserted. An interrupt must be serviced by software or no other interrupt request can be posted.

The scanner determines that a line has a receiver interrupt if the line's receiver buffer is ready and receiver interrupts are enabled for that line (RxRDY and RxIE = 1) or either of the line's modem status signals has changed state and both receiver and modem control interrupts are enabled for that line (DSCHNG and RxIE and MCIE = 1).

The scanner determines that a line has a transmitter interrupt if the line's transmitter holding the register is empty and transmitter interrupts are enabled for that line (TxRDY and TxIE = 1).

When the scanner detects an interrupt, it reports the line number on the IRQ<2:0> lines. The IRQTxRx signal is asserted for a transmitter interrupt and deasserted for a receiver interrupt. The appropriate bits are also updated in the interrupt summary register. The $\overline{IRQ}$ line is deasserted and the scanner is restarted for each of the following three types of interrupt conditions.

- ☐ Reading the receiver buffer or resetting the RxIE bit of the interrupting line for the first type of receiver interrupt previously described.
- ☐ Resetting the MCIE, RxIE, or DSCHNG bit of the interrupting line for the second type of receiver interrupt previously described.
- ☐ Loading the transmitter holding register or resetting the TxIE bit of the interrupting line for transmitter interrupts.

If the scanner was originally stopped by a receiver interrupt condition, the scanner resumes sequential operation from where it stopped, thus providing receivers with equal priority. If the scanner was stopped by a transmitter condition, the scanner restarts from position 0 (line 0's receiver), thus giving receivers priority over transmitters.

EDGE-TRIGGERED AND LEVEL-TRIGGERED INTERRUPT SYTSTEMS

If the interrupt system of the Octal UART is used only for generating interrupts for the RxRDY and/or TxRDY flags, the $\overline{IRQ}$ line can be connected to a processor having either edge-triggered or level-triggered interrupt capability. If the modem control interrupts are being used (MCIE in mode register 1 = 1), the $\overline{IRQ}$ line can be connected only to a processor that uses level-triggered interrupts.

MODEM HANDLING

The TxEMT (transmitter empty) bit of the status register is typically used to indicate when a program can disable the transmission medium, as when deasserting the request-to-send line of a modem. A typical program will load the last character for transmission and then monitor the TxEMT bit of the status register.

The assertion of the TxEMT bit to indicate that transmission is complete may occur a substantial time after the loading of the last character. After the last character is loaded, one character is in the transmitter holding register and one character is in the serialization logic. Therefore, it will be two character times before the transmission process is completed. Waiting for the TxRDY signal to assert before monitoring the TxEMT status shortens this by one character time because the TxRDY status bit indicates that there are no characters in the transmitter holding register. The times involved are calculated by taking the reciprocal of the baud rate being used, multiplying by the number of bits per character (a starter bit–5,6,7, or 8 data bits; plus parity bit if enabled; and 1,1.5, or 2 stop bits), and multiplying by either two characters or one, depending on when TxEMT monitoring begins.

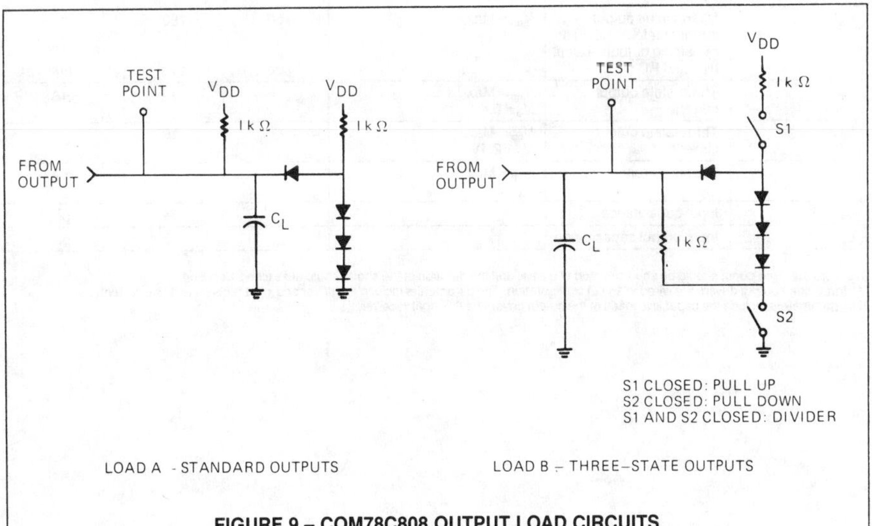

FIGURE 9 – COM78C808 OUTPUT LOAD CIRCUITS

MAXIMUM GUARANTEED RATINGS*

Operating Temperature Range .... 0°C to +70°C
Storage Temperature Range .... −55° to +125°C
Lead Temperature (soldering, 10 sec.) .... +300°C
Positive Voltage on any I/O Pin, with respect to ground .... Vcc + 0.3
Negative Voltage on any I/O Pin, with respect to ground .... −0.3V
Maximum Vcc .... +7V

*Stresses above those listed may cause permanent damage to the device. This is a stress rating only and functional operation of the device at these or at any other condition above those indicated in the operational sections of this specification is not implied.

NOTE: When powering this device from laboratory or system power supplies, it is important that the Absolute Maximum Ratings not be exceeded or device failure can result. Some power supplies exhibit voltage spikes or "glitches" on their outputs when the AC power is switched on and off. In addition, voltage transients on the AC power line may appear on the DC output. For example, the bench power supply programmed to deliver +5 volts may have large voltage transients when the AC power is switched on and off. If this possibility exists it is suggested that a clamp circuit be used.

TABLE 9 – COM78C808

DC ELECTRICAL CHARACTERISTICS T_A = 0°C to 70°C, V_{DD} = +5V ±5%

Symbol	Parameter	Test Condition	Requirements Min.	Requirements Max.	Units
V_{IH}	High-level input voltage		2.0		V
V_{IL}	Low-level input voltage			0.8	V
V_{OH}	High-level output voltage	V_{DD} = Min. I_{OH} = 3.5 mA for DL<7:0> I_{OH} = 2.0 mA for all remaining output except $\overline{IRQ}$ and $\overline{RDY}$	2.4		V
V_{OL}	Low-level output voltage	V_{DD} = Min. I_{OL} = 5.5 mA for DL<7:0> I_{OL} = 3.5 mA for all remaining outputs		0.4	V
I_{IH}	Input current at maximum input voltage	V_{DD} = Max. V_I = V_{DD}(Max.)		10	μA
I_{IL}	Input current at miminum input voltage	V_{DD} = Max. V_I = 0.0V		−10	μA
I_{OS}[1]	Short-circuit output current for DL<7:0> all remaining outputs except $\overline{IRQ}$ and $\overline{RDY}$	V_{DD} = Max.	−50 −30	−180 −110	mA mA
I_{OZL}[2]	Three-state output current	V_{DD} = Max. V_O = 0.4V		10	μA
I_{OZH}[2]	Three-state output current	V_{DD} = Max. V_O = 2.4V		10	μA
I_{DD}	Supply current	V_{DD} = Max. T_A = 0°		25	mA
C_{in}	Input capacitance			4	pF
C_{IO}[3]	Input/output capacitance			5	pF

[1] No more than one ouput should be short circuited at a time, and the duration of the short should not exceed 1 second.
[2] All three-state output drivers are wired in an I/O configuration. The parameters include the driver and input receiver leakage currents.
[3] The parameters include the capacitive loads of the output driver and the input receiver.

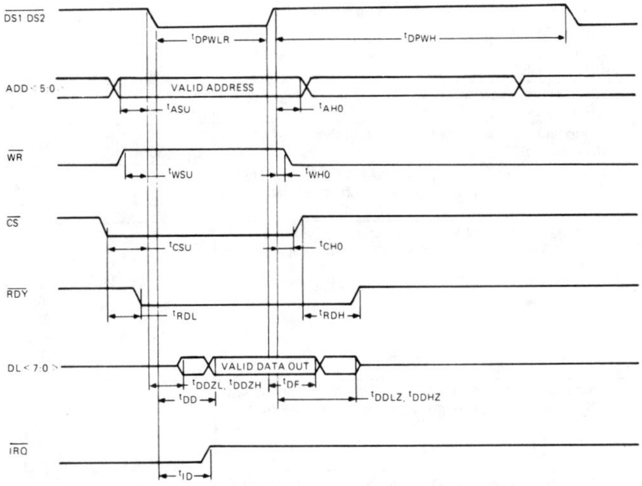

FIGURE 10 – COM78C808 BUS READ CYCLE TIMING

TIMING PARAMETERS

Figure 10 shows the signal timing for a read cycle to transfer information from the Octal UART to the processor. Figure 11 shows the signal timing for a write cycle to transfer information from the processor to the Octal UART. Table 11 lists the timing parameters for the read and write cycles.

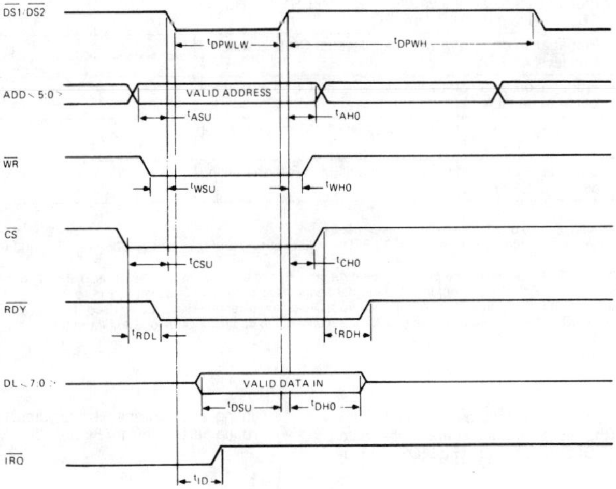

FIGURE 11 – COM78C808 BUS WRITE CYCLE TIMING

TABLE 10 – COM78C808 BUS READ AND WRITE TIMING PARAMETERS

Symbol	Definition	Requirements (ns) Min.	Requirements (ns) Max.	Load Circuit[1]
t_{AHO}	Hold time of a valid ADD <5:0> to a valid high level of $\overline{DS1}$ and $\overline{DS2}$.	10		
t_{ASU}	Setup time of a valid ADD <5:0> to the falling edge of $\overline{DS1}$ and $\overline{DS2}$.	30		
t_{CHO}	Hold time of a valid low level of $\overline{CS}$ to a valid high level of $\overline{DS1}$ and $\overline{DS2}$.	10		
t_{CSU}	Setup time of a valid low level of $\overline{CS}$ to the falling edge of $\overline{DS1}$ and $\overline{DS2}$.	30		
t_{DD}	Propagation delay of a valid low level on $\overline{DS1}$ and $\overline{DS2}$ (if $\overline{CS}$ is low and $\overline{WR}$ is high) to valid high or low data on DL <7:0>.	165		$C_L = 150$ pF
t_{DDLZ}[2] t_{DDHZ}	Propagation delay of a valid high level on $\overline{DS1}$ and $\overline{DS2}$ (if $\overline{CS}$ is low and $\overline{WR}$ is high) to DL <7:0> output drivers disabled.			
	t_{DDLZ}		50	$C_L = 50$pF
	t_{DDHZ}		50	$C_L = 50$pF
	t_{DDLZ}		60	$C_L = 100$pF
	t_{DDHZ}		60	$C_L = 100$pF
	t_{DDLZ}		65	$C_L = 150$pF
	t_{DDHZ}		65	$C_L = 150$pF
t_{DDZL}	Propagation delay of a valid low level on $\overline{DS1}$ and $\overline{DS2}$ (if $\overline{CS}$ is low and $\overline{WR}$ is high) to DL <7:0> output driver enabled.			
	t_{DDZL}	0	165	$C_L = 150$pF
	t_{DDZH}	0	165	$C_L = 150$pF
t_{DF}	Hold time provided during a read cycle by Octal UART of valid high or low data on DL <7:0> after the rising edge of $\overline{DS1}$ and $\overline{DS2}$.	0		
t_{DHO}	Hold time of a valid DL <7:0> to a valid high level of $\overline{DS1}$ or $\overline{DS2}$.	30		
t_{DPWH}	Pulse width high of $\overline{DS1}$ and $\overline{DS2}$.	450		
t_{DPWLR}	Pulse width low of $\overline{DS1}$ and $\overline{DS2}$ when $\overline{WR}$ is high (read operation). Refer to timing parameter t_{DPWLW} also.	180	10,000	
t_{DPWLW}	Pulse width low of $\overline{DS1}$ and $\overline{DS2}$ when $\overline{WR}$ is low (write operation). Refer to timing parameter t_{DPWLR} also.	130	10,000	
t_{DSU}	Setup time of a valid DL <7:0> to the rising edge of $\overline{DS1}$ and $\overline{DS2}$.	50		
t_{ID}[3]	Propagation delay of a valid low level on $\overline{DS1}$ and $\overline{DS2}$ (if $\overline{CS}$ is low) to a high level on $\overline{IRQ}$.		635	$C_L = 50$pF
t_{RDH}[4]	Propagation delay of a valid high level of $\overline{CS}$ to a valid high level on $\overline{RDY}$.		210	$C_L = 50$pF
t_{RDL}	Propagation delay of a valid low level on $\overline{CS}$ to a valid low level on $\overline{RDY}$.		90	$C_L = 50$pF
t_{WHO}	Hold time of a valid high or low level of $\overline{WR}$ to a valid high level of $\overline{DS1}$ and $\overline{DS2}$.	10		
t_{WSU}	Setup time of a valid high or low level of $\overline{WR}$ to the falling edge of $\overline{DS1}$ or $\overline{DS2}$.	30		

[1]Refer to Figure 9 for the load circuits used with these measurements.
[2]The t_{DDLZ} and t_{DDHZ} parameters are measured with $C_L = 150$ pF. The values of t_{DDLZ} and t_{DDHZ} for $C_L = 50$pF and $C_L = 100$ pF have been derived for user convenience.
[3]Total rise time depends on internal delay plus the pullup delay introduced by the external resistor being used. The t_{ID} parameter can be calculated by the following: $t_{ID} = 500 + RC_L$ where R = value of the resistor that connects to capacitor C_L in load A, Figure 9.
[4]Total rise time depends on internal delay plus the pullup delay introduced by the external resistor being used. The t_{RDH} parameter can be calculated by the following: $t_{RDH} = 75 + RC_L$ where R = value of the resistor that connects to capacitor C_L in load A, Figure 9.

Figure 12 shows the signal timing for the clock input, interrupt timing, effect of the $\overline{RESET}$ input on data strobe, data set carrier detect (DCD) and data set ready (DSR) input timing, and the transmit data output timing. Table 11 lists the timing parameters for Figure 12.

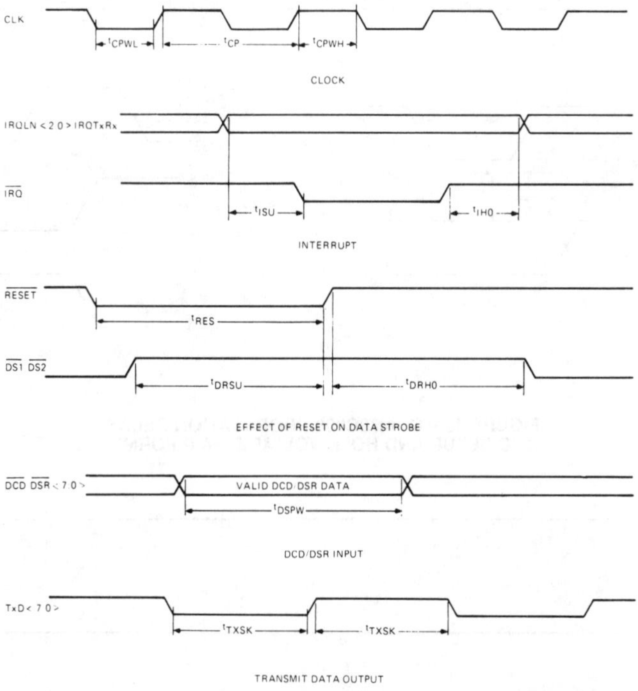

FIGURE 12–COM78C808 MISCELLANEOUS SIGNAL TIMING

TABLE 11–MISCELLANEOUS WRITE TIMING PARAMETERS

Symbol	Definition	Requirements (ns) Min.	Load Circuit*
t_{CP}	Period of CLK.	203.45 (4.9152 MHz)	
t_{CPWH}	Pulse width high of CLK.	95	
t_{CPWL}	Pulse width low of CLK.	95	
t_{DRHO}	Hold time of a valid high level of $\overline{\text{DS1}}$ and $\overline{\text{DS2}}$ to a valid high level of $\overline{\text{RESET}}$.	1,000	
t_{DRSU}	Setup time of a valid high level of $\overline{\text{DS1}}$ and $\overline{\text{DS2}}$ to the rising edge of $\overline{\text{RESET}}$.	900	
t_{DSPW}	Pulse width high or low of DCD <7:0> and DSR <7:0>.	1,000	
t_{IHO}	Hold time provided by Octal UART from a valid IRQLN <2:0> and IRQTxRx to a valid high level of IRQ.	100	$C_L = 50pF$
t_{ISU}	Setup time provided by Octal UART from a valid IRQLN <2:0> and IRQTxRx to a valid low level of $\overline{\text{IRQ}}$.	100	$C_L = 50pF$
t_{RES}	Pulse width low of $\overline{\text{RESET}}$.	1,000	
t_{TXSK}	Pulse width high or low provided by Octal UART on the TxD <7:0> lines. At each baud rate, the actual pulse widths provided vary by t_{TXSK}. This timing parameter should be used to determine cumulative reception/transmission errors.	250	$C_L = 50pF$

*Refer to Figure 9 for the load circuits used with these measurements.

Figure 13 shows the input and output voltage waveforms for the propagation delay and setup and hold measurements. Figure 14 shows the waveforms for the three-state outputs measurement.

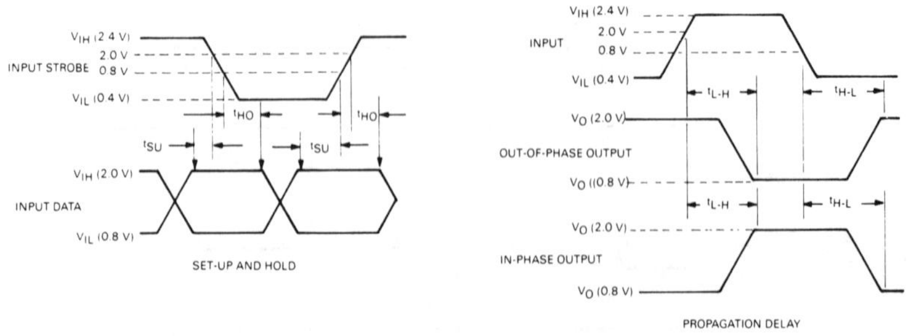

FIGURE 13 – COM78C808 PROPAGATION DELAY AND SETUP AND HOLD VOLTAGE WAVEFORMS

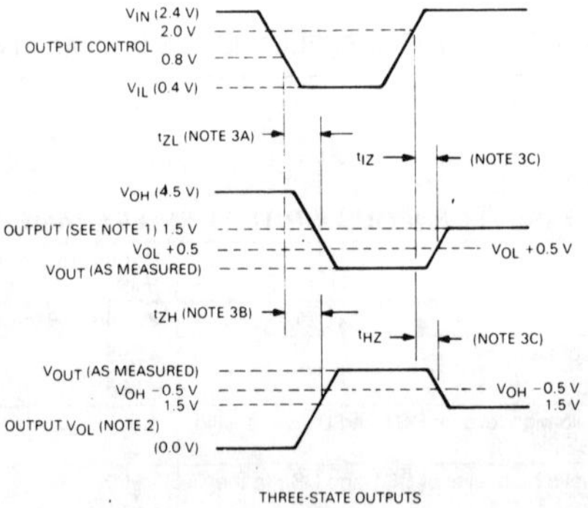

NOTES:
1. INTERNAL CONDITIONS ARE SUCH THAT THE OUTPUT IS LOW EXCEPT WHEN DISABLED BY THE OUTPUT CONTROL.
2. INTERNAL CONDITIONS ARE SUCH THAT THE OUTPUT IS HIGH EXCEPT WHEN DISABLED BY THE OUTPUT CONTROL.
3. REFER TO FIGURE 9. A = S1 CLOSED. B = S2 CLOSED. C = S1 AND S2 CLOSED.

FIGURE 14 – COM78C808 THREE-STATE OUTPUT VOLTAGE WAVEFORMS

FEATURES

- ☐ Single Chip UART With Baud Rate Generator
- ☐ Asynchronous Operation
  - –16 Selectable Baud Rate Clock Frequencies (Internal)
  - –External 16x Clock (100 KBaud)
  - –Character Length: 7 or 8 Bits
  - –1 or 2 Stop Bit Selection
- ☐ Small 20 Pin DIP (300 mil) or PLCC
- ☐ Full or Half Duplex Operation
- ☐ Double Buffering of Data
- ☐ Programmable Interrupt Generation
- ☐ Programmable Modem/Terminal Signals
- ☐ Odd or Even Parity Generate and Detect
- ☐ Parity, Overrun and Framing Error Detection
- ☐ TTL Compatible Inputs and Outputs
- ☐ High Speed Host Bus Operation (with no wait state)
- ☐ Low Power CMOS
- ☐ Single +5V Power Supply

PIN CONFIGURATION

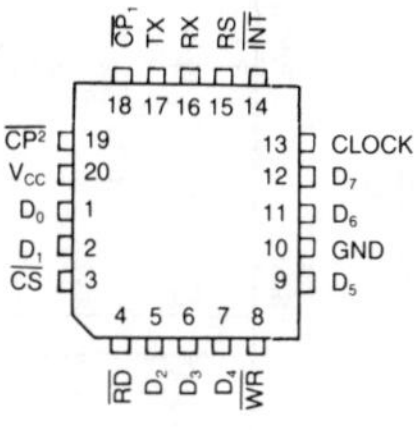

Package: 20-pin PLCC

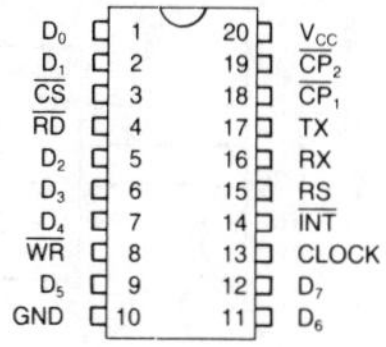

Package 20-pin DIP

GENERAL DESCRIPTION

The COM81C17 TPUART is an asynchronous only receiver / transmitter with a built in programmable baud rate generator housed in a twenty pin package. The TPUART receives serial data streams and converts them into parallel data characters for the processor. While receiving serial data, the TPUART will also accept data characters from the processor in parallel format and convert them into serial format along with start, stop and optional parity bits. The TPUART will signal the processor via interrupt when it has completely transmitted or received a character and requires service. Complete status information is available to the processor through the status register. The TPUART features two general purpose control pins that can be individually programmed to perform as terminal or modem control handshake signals.

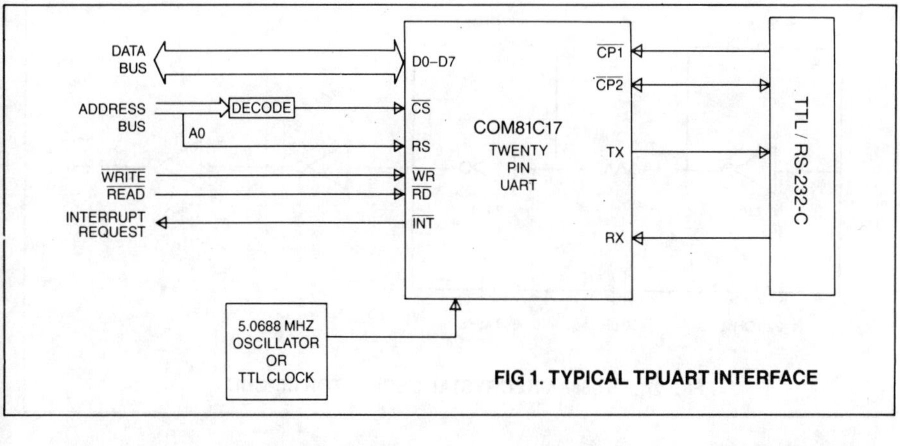

FIG 1. TYPICAL TPUART INTERFACE

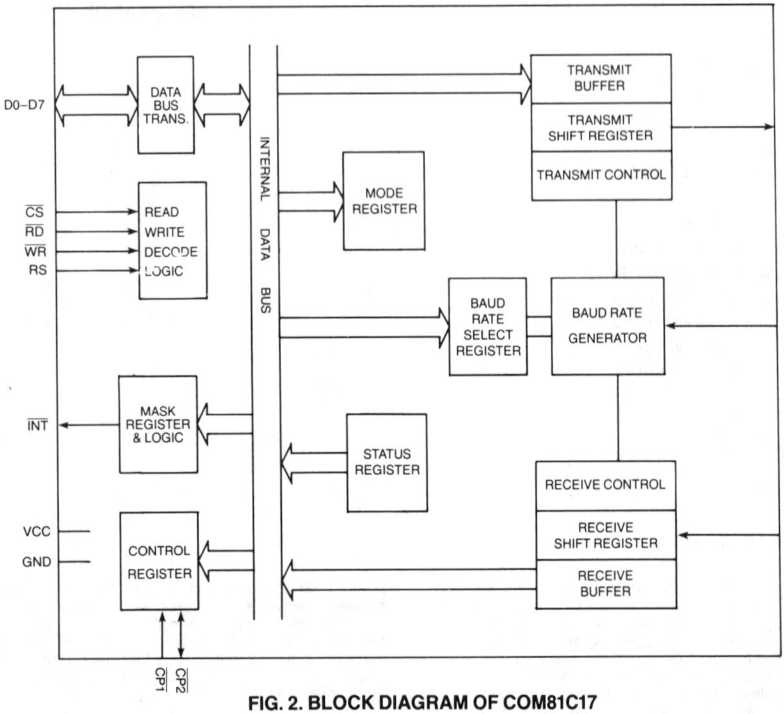

FIG. 2. BLOCK DIAGRAM OF COM81C17

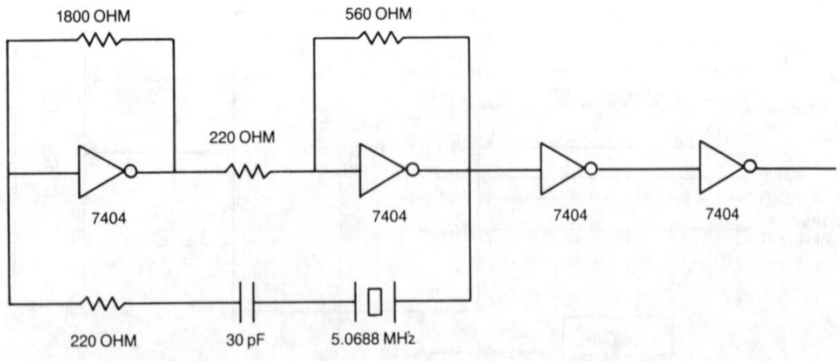

FIG. 2A. 5.0688 MHz CRYSTAL OSCILLATOR CIRCUIT

TABLE 1 – DESCRIPTION OF PIN FUNCTIONS

DIP PIN NO.	NAME	SYMBOL	DESCRIPTION
1, 2, 5–7 9, 11–12	DATA BUS	D_0–D_7	An 8 bit bi-directional DATA BUS is used to interface the TPUART to the processor Data Bus.
3	CHIP SELECT	$\overline{CS}$	A low level on this input enables the TPUART for reading and writing to the processor. When $\overline{CS}$ is high, the DATA BUS is in high impedance and the $\overline{WR}$ and $\overline{RD}$ will have no effect on the chip.
4	READ DATA STROBE	$\overline{RD}$	A low pulse on this input (when $\overline{CS}$ is low) enables the TPUART to place the data or the status information on the DATA BUS.
8	WRITE DATA STROBE	$\overline{WR}$	A low pulse on this input (when $\overline{CS}$ is low) enables the TPUART to accept the data or control word from the DATA BUS into the TPUART.
10	GROUND	GND	Power Supply Return
13	CLOCK	CLK	External TTL Clock Input (See Table 2)
14	INTERRUPT REQUEST	$\overline{INT}$	An interrupt request is asserted by the TPUART when an enabled condition has occurred in the Status Register. This is an active low, open drain output. This pin has an internal pullup register.
15	REGISTER SELECT	RS	During processor to TPUART communications, this input is used to indicate which internal register will be selected for access by the processor. When this input is low, data can be written to the TX Holding Buffer or data can be read from the RX Holding Register. When this input is high control words can be written to the Control Register or status information can be read from the Status Register.
16	RECEIVER DATA	RX	This input is the receiver serial data. A high to low transition is required to initiate data reception.
17	TRANSMITTER DATA	TX	This output is the transmitted serial data from the TPUART. When a transmission is concluded, the TX line will always return to the mark (High) state.
18	CONTROL PIN 1	$\overline{CP1}$	This control pin is an input only pin. It can be programmed to perform the functions of CTS or DSR/DCD.
19	CONTROL PIN 2	$\overline{CP2}$	This control pin can be programmed to be either an input or an output. When in input mode, this pin can perform the functions of DSR/DCD. When in output mode this pin can perform the functions of DTR or RTS.
20	POWER SUPPLY	V_{CC}	+5V Supply Voltage

FUNCTIONAL DESCRIPTION

RESETTING THE TPUART

The TPUART must be reset on power up. Since there is no external pin allocated for hardware reset, this is accomplished by writing a One (HIGH) followed by writing a Zero (LOW) to the Control Register bit 7. Following reset, the TPUART enters an idle state in which it can neither transmit nor receive data.

INITIALIZING THE TPUART

The TPUART is initialized by writing three control words from the processor. Only a single address is set aside for Mode, Baud Rate Select, Interrupt Mask and TX Buffer Registers. For this to be possible, logic internal to the chip directs information to its proper destination based on the sequence in which it is written.

Following internal reset, the first write to address zero (i.e. RS = 0) is interpreted as a Mode Control word. The second write is interpreted as Interrupt Mask word. The third write is interpreted as Baud Rate Select. The fourth and all subsequent writes are interpreted as writes to the TX Buffer Register.

There is one way in which control logic may return to anticipating a Mode, Interrupt Mask, and Baud Rate Select words. This is following an internal reset. Following initialization, the TPUART is ready to communicate.

PROGRAMMABLE CONTROL PINS

The TPUART provides two programmable control pins that can be configured to perform as modem or terminal control handshake signals. If no handshake signal is required, these pins can be used as general purpose one bit Input or Output ports.

$\overline{CP1}$ – is an input only pin that can be programmed to act as the CTS (Clear To Send) handshake signal, where it will disable data transmission by the TPUART after the contents of the Transmit Shift Register is completely flushed out. When programmed as 1, $\overline{CP1}$ will serve as a general purpose 1 bit input port. The inverted state will be reflected in Status Register bit 0 (when programmed as CTS or general purpose input bit).

$\overline{CP2}$ – is an Input/Output pin. When configured as Output, its state is directly controlled by the host processor via writes to the Control Register. This will serve the purpose of modem and terminal handshake signals as RTS (Request To Send), and DTR (Data Terminal Ready). When configured as Input, its inverted state is reflected in the Status Register bit 1 and read by the processor. This will serve the purpose of handshake signals as DCD (Data Carrier Detect) and DSR (Data Set Ready).

MODE REGISTER

BIT 1	BIT 2	
0	0	$\overline{CP2}$ is RTS output
0	1	$\overline{CP2}$ is GP output
1	X	$\overline{CP2}$ is GP input
1	X	$\overline{CP2}$ is GP input

THE ON CHIP BAUD RATE GENERATOR

The TPUART incorporates an on chip Baud Rate Generator that can be programmed to generate sixteen of the most popular baud rates. The TPUART also allows the bypassing of the Baud Rate Generator by programming Mode Register bit 3 to accept a 16X external clock. The Baud Rate Generator will not assume any given baud rate upon power up, therefore it must be programmed as desired. The following chart is based on a 5.0688 MHz CLOCK frequency.

TABLE 2 – 16X CLOCK
Clock Frequency = 5.0688 MHz

Baud Rate Select Register				Baud Rate	Theoretical Frequency 16X Clock	Actual Frequency 16X Clock	Percent Error	Duty Cycle %	Divisor
D_3	D_2	D_1	D_0						
0	0	0	0	50	0.8 KHz	0.8 KHz	—	50/50	6336
0	0	0	1	110	1.76	1.76	—	50/50	2880
0	0	1	0	134.5	2.152	2.1523	0.016	50/50	2356
0	0	1	1	150	2.4	2.4	—	50/50	2112
0	1	0	0	300	4.8	4.8	—	50/50	1056
0	1	0	1	600	9.6	9.6	—	50/50	528
0	1	1	0	1200	19.2	19.2	—	50/50	264
0	1	1	1	1800	28.8	28.8	—	50/50	176
1	0	0	0	2000	32.0	32.081	0.253	50/50	158
1	0	0	1	2400	38.4	38.4	—	50/50	132
1	0	1	0	3600	57.6	57.6	—	50/50	88
1	0	1	1	4800	76.8	76.8	—	50/50	66
1	1	0	0	7200	115.2	115.2	—	50/50	44
1	1	0	1	9600	153.6	153.6	—	48/52	33
1	1	1	0	19.200	307.2	316.8	3.125	50/50	16
1	1	1	1	38.400	614.4	633.6	3.125	50/50	8

REGISTER DESCRIPTIONS
TABLE 3 – COM81C17 MODE REGISTER DESCRIPTION (BITS 0–7)

BIT	DESCRIPTION
0	**CP1**–The Mode Register bit 0 determines whether the CP1 pin will be configured to provide the function of CTS or will serve as a general purpose 1 bit input port. In either case, its state will be reflected in Status Register bit 0. 0→$\overline{CP1}$ = CTS 1→$\overline{CP1}$ = GP INPUT
1	**CP2I/O**–The Mode Register bit 1 determines whether the CP2 pin will be configured as a general purpose 1 bit output port or will serve as a general purpose 1 bit input port. When used as an input, its state is reflected in the Status Register bit 1. When used as an output, its state is controlled by the processor via the Control Register bit 1. 0→$\overline{CP2}$ = OUTPUT 1→$\overline{CP2}$ = INPUT
2	**$\overline{CP2}$**–The mode register bit 2 determines whether the $\overline{CP2}$ pin will be configured to provide the function of RTS or will serve as a general purpose 1 bit output port. 0→$\overline{CP2}$ = RTS 1→$\overline{CP2}$ = GP OUTPUT
3	**CLOCK SELECT**–The Mode Register bit 3 determines whether the internal Baud Rate Generator will supply the TX and RX clocks or the clock on the clock pin will be used as a 16X clock. The Baud Rate Select Register contents will be bypassed when an external 16X clock is used. 0 = INTERNAL CLOCK 1 = EXTERNAL CLOCK (16X)
4	**PARITY ENABLE**–The Mode Register bit 4 determines whether parity generation and checking will be enabled. 0 = PARITY DISABLE 1 = PARITY ENABLE
5	**PARITY**–The Mode Register bit 5 determines whether odd or even parity will be generated and checked. 0 = EVEN PARITY 1 = ODD PARITY
6	**# OF DATA BITS**–The Mode Register bit 6 determines the number of data bit that will be presented in each data character (i.e. 7 or 8). 0 = 7 BITS PER CHARACTER 1 = 8 BITS PER CHARACTER
7	**STOP BITS**–The Mode Register bit 7 determines how many stop bits will trail each data unit (i.e. 1 or 2). 0 = 1 STOP BIT 1 = 2 STOP BITS A data frame will consist of a start bit, 7 or 8 data bits, an optional parity bit, and 1 or 2 stop bits.

TABLE 4 – COM81C17 STATUS REGISTERS DESCRIPTION (BITS 0–7)

BIT	DESCRIPTION
0	**CP1**–This reflects the inverted state of the control pin CP1.
1	**CP2**–This is active only when the $\overline{CP2}$ pin is programmed to be an input. It is set by its corresponding input pin and reflects the inverted state of the control pin $\overline{CP2}$. When the CP2 pin is programmed as an output, this bit is forced to a zero.
2	**TX SHIFT REGISTER EMPTY**–This signals the processor that the Transmit Shift Register is empty. A typical program will usually load the last character of a transmission and then monitor the TX SHIFT REGISTER EMPTY bit to determine when it is a safe time for disabling transmission. This bit is set when the Transmitter Shift Register has completed transmission of a character, and no new character has been loaded in the Transmit Buffer Register. This bit is also set by asserting internal reset. This bit is cleared by: a. loading the TX Buffer Register
3	**PARITY ERROR**–This signals the processor that the character stored in the Receive Character Buffer was received with an incorrect number of binary "1" bits. This bit is set when the received character in the Receiver Buffer Register has an incorrect parity bit and parity has been enabled. This bit is cleared by: a. setting Reset Errors in the Control Register b. asserting internal reset
4	**OVERRUN ERROR**–This is set whenever a byte stored in the Receive Character Buffer is overwritten with a new byte from the Receive Shift Register before being transferred to the processor. This bit is cleared by: a. setting Reset Errors in the Control Register b. asserting internal reset

5	**FRAMING ERROR**–This is set whenever a byte in the Receive Character Buffer was received with an incorrect bit format ("0" stop bits). This bit is cleared by: a. setting Reset Errors in the Control Register b. asserting internal reset
6	**TX BUFFER EMPTY**–This signals the processor that the Transmit Buffer Register is empty and that the TPUART can accept a new character for transmission. This bit is set when: a. a character has been loaded from the Transmit Buffer Register to the Transmit Shift Register b. asserting the TRANSMITTER RESET bit in the Control Register c. asserting internal reset This bit is cleared by: a. writing to the Transmit Buffer Register This bit is initially set when the transmitter logic is enabled by setting the TX Enable bit in the Control Register (also TX Buffer is empty because of reset). Data can be overwritten if a consecutive write is performed while TX Buffer Empty is zero.
7	**RX BUFFER FULL**–This signals the processor that a completed character is present in the Receive Buffer Register for transfer to the processor. This bit is set when a character has been loaded from the receive deserialization logic to the Receive Buffer Register. This bit is cleared by: a. reading the Receive Buffer Register b. asserting the RECEIVER RESET bit in the Control Register c. asserting internal reset

TABLE 5 – COM81C17 CONTROL REGISTER DESCRIPTION (BITS 0–7)

BIT	DESCRIPTION
0	Not Used (test mode bit, must be Zero)
1	**CP2**–This bit controls the $\overline{CP2}$ output pin. Data at the output is the logical complement of the register data. When the CP2 bit is set, the $\overline{CP2}$ pin is forced low. When CP2 is RTS, a 1 to 0 transition of the CP2 bit will cause the $\overline{CP2}$ pin to go high one TXc time after the last serial bit has been transmitted.
2	**RX ENABLE**–This bit when reset will disable the setting of the RX BUFFER FULL bit in the Status Register which informs the processor of the availability of a received character in the Receive Buffer Register. The error bits in the Status Register will be cleared and will remain cleared when RX is disabled.
3	**RX RESET**–This will reset the receiver block only.
4	**TX RESET**–This will reset the transmitter block only.
5	**TX ENABLE**–Data transmission cannot take place by the TPUART unless this bit is set. When this bit is reset (disable), transmission will be disabled only after the previously written data has been transmitted.
6	**RESET ERRORS**–This bit when set will reset the parity, overrun, and framing error bits in the Status Register. No latch is provided in the Control Register for saving this bit; therefore there is no need to clear it (error reset = d6.RS. $\overline{WR}$).
7	**INTERNAL RESET**–This bit enables the resetting of the internal circuitry and initializes access to address 0 to be sequential.

INTERRUPT MASK REGISTER DESCRIPTION

This is an eight bit write only register which is loaded by the processor. These bits are used to enable interrupts from the corresponding bits in the Status Register. This register is reset with internal reset.

REGISTER DECODE & TRUTH TABLE

The TPUART provides unique decode capability to three of the seven internal processor accessible register. These are the RX Buffer Register (read only), the Status Register (read only) and the Control Register (write only). The other four registers (write only) are decoded in a sequential manner following reset.

DECODE TRUTH TABLE

RS	$\overline{RD}$	$\overline{WR}$	$\overline{CS}$	
0	0	1	0	READ RX BUFFER REGISTER
0	1	0	0	WRITE TO TX BUFFER REGISTER
1	0	1	0	READ STATUS REGISTER
1	1	0	0	WRITE TO CONTROL REGISTER
X	X	X	1	DATA BUS IN TRI STATE

The first write to address zero (RS = 0) will access the Mode Register, the second will access the Interrupt Mask Register, the third will access the Baud Rate Select Register, the fourth and all subsequent writes will access the TX Buffer Register.

INTERNAL REGISTER SELECT

Following reset, the decode sequence of writes to address 0 is as follows:

RS0 – selects the Mode Control Register
RS1 – selects the Interrupt Mask Register
RS2 – selects the Baud Rate Select Register
RS3 – selects the TX Buffer Register

RS0	RS1	RS2	RS3	
0	1	1	1	AFTER RESET
1	0	1	1	AFTER FIRST WRITE
1	1	0	1	AFTER SECOND WRITE
1	1	1	0	AFTER THIRD WRITE
1	1	1	0	ALL SUBSEQUENT WRITES

MAXIMUM GUARANTEED RATINGS*

Operating Temperature Range .... 0 to 70°C
Storage Temperature Range .... −55 to 150°C
Lead Temperature (soldering, 10 seconds) .... +325°C
Positive Voltage on any pin .... V_{CC} + 0.3V
Negative Voltage on any pin, with respect to ground .... −0.3V
Maximum V_{CC} .... +7V

*Stresses above those listed may cause permanent damage to the device. This is a stress rating only and functional operation of the device at these or any other condition above those indicated in the operational sections of this specification is not implied.

NOTE: When powering this device from the laboratory or system power supplies, it is important that the Absolute Maximum Ratings not be exceeded or device failure can result. Some power supplies exhibit voltage spikes or "glitches" on their outputs when the AC power is switched on and off. In addition, voltage transients on the AC power line may appear on the DC output. If this possibility exists, it is suggested that a clamp circuit be used.

PRELIMINARY
Notice: This is not a final specification. Some parametric limits are subject to change.

TABLE 6 – ELECTRICAL CHARACTERISTICS

$T = 0°C$ to $+70°C$ $V_{CC} = 5.0\ V \pm 5\%$

PARAMETER	SYMBOL	MIN	TYP	MAX	UNITS	COMMENTS
DC CHARACTERISTICS						
LOW INPUT VOLTAGE	V_{IL}			0.8	V	
HIGH INPUT VOLTAGE	V_{IH}	2.0			V	
LOW OUTPUT VOLTAGE	V_{OL}			0.4	V	I_{OL} = 5.0ma D_0–D_7 I_{OL} = 3.5ma
HIGH OUTPUT VOLTAGE	V_{OH}	2.4			V	I_{OH} = 100 μa
INPUT LEAKAGE CURRENT	I_L			±10	μA	
INPUT CAPACITANCE	C_{IN}		10		pF	
POWER SUPPLY CURRENT	I_{CC}		15		ma	

SYMBOL	DESCRIPTION	MIN	TYP	MAX	UNITS	
AC CHARACTERISTICS						
WRITE CYCLE						
t_1	$\overline{CS}$, RS to $\overline{WR}$ ↓ setup time	50			ns	
t_2	$\overline{CS}$, RS hold time to $\overline{WR}$ ↑	0			ns	
t_3	$\overline{WR}$ pulse width	100			ns	
t_4	Data BUS in setup time to $\overline{WR}$ ↑	75			ns	
t_5	Data BUS in hold time to $\overline{WR}$ ↑	10			ns	
READ CYCLE						
t_6	$\overline{CS}$, RS to $\overline{RD}$ ↓ setup time	50			ns	
t_7	$\overline{CS}$, RS hold time to $\overline{RD}$ ↑	0			ns	
t_8	$\overline{RD}$ pulse width	100			ns	
t_9	Data access time from $\overline{RD}$ ↓	0		60	ns	@50pf max
t_{10}	Data hold time from $\overline{RD}$ ↑	0		60	ns	@50pf max
GENERAL TIMING						
t_{11}	Reset Pulse Width	1.0			μs	
t_{12}	$\overline{CP1}$ active to $\overline{INT}$			300	ns	@25pf
t_{13}	$\overline{WR}$ rising edge to $\overline{CP2}$ change			200	ns	
t_{14}	CP1, CP2 pulse width	1.0			μs	
t_{15}	Read Write Interval	100			ns	
$\overline{CP1}$, $\overline{CP2}$ data						
	Rise Time			30	ns	@25pf
	Fall Time			30	ns	@25pf
Clock Frequency						
	Rise Time			30	ns	
	Fall Time			30	ns	
	Internal Baud Rate Mode			11.0	MHz	
	External Baud Rate Mode			1.6	MHz	
	Duty Cycle			40/60	%	

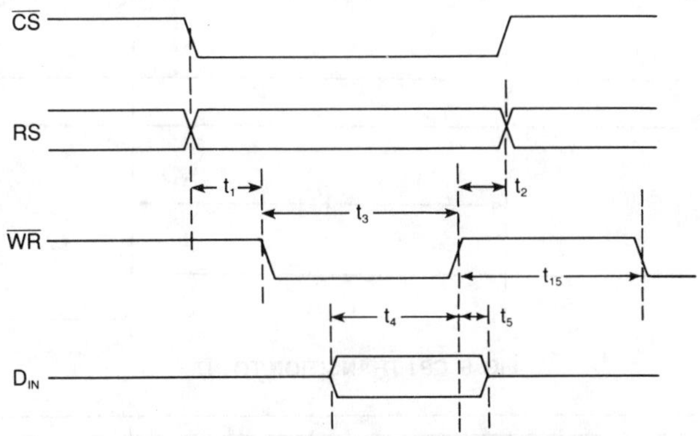

FIG. 3. PROCESSOR TO TPUART WRITE CYCLE

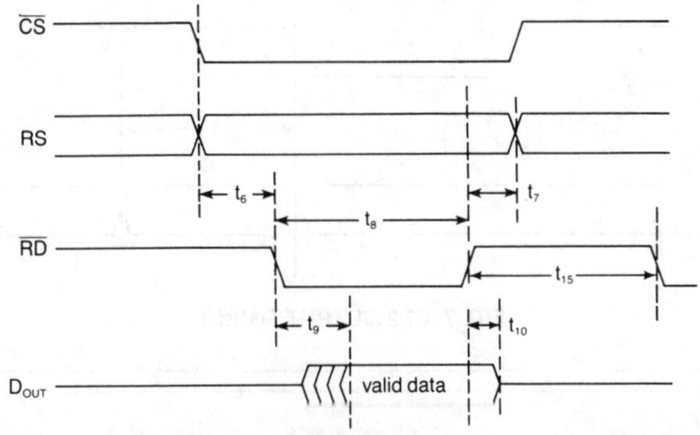

FIG. 4. PROCESSOR FROM TPUART READ CYCLE

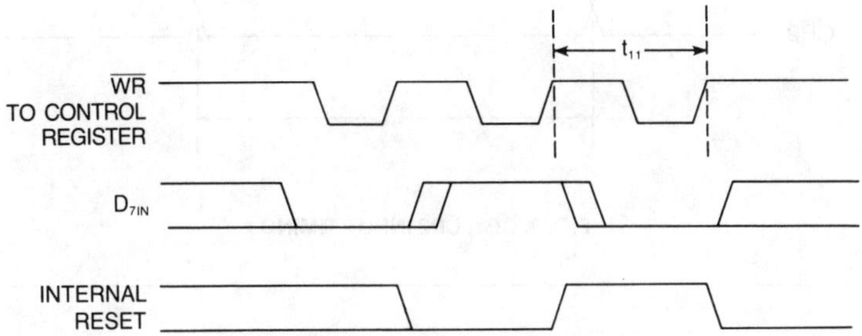

FIG. 5. INTERNAL RESET TIMING

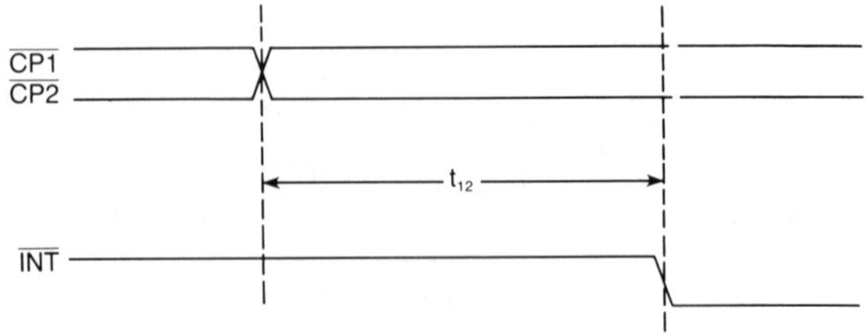

FIG. 6. $\overline{CP1}$ TRANSITION TO $\overline{INT}$

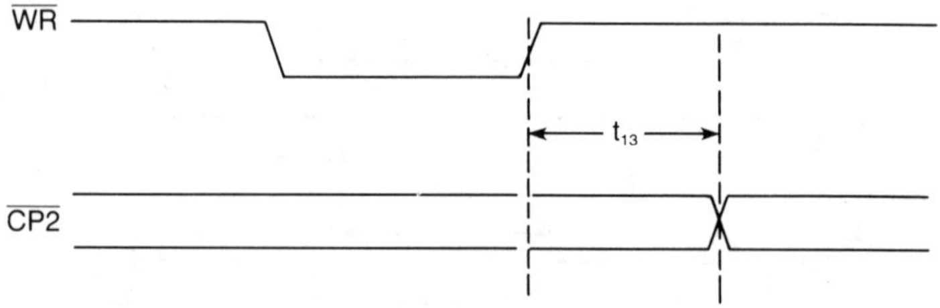

FIG. 7. $\overline{CP2}$ OUTPUT TIMING

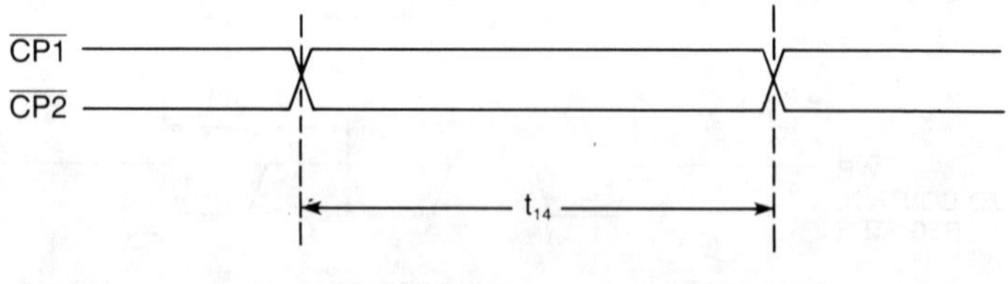

FIG. 8. $\overline{CP1}$, $\overline{CP2}$ INPUT TIMING

Bit Rate Generator MC14411

The MC14411 bit rate generator is constructed with complementary MOS enhancement mode devices. It utilizes a frequency divider network to provide a wide range of output frequencies.

A crystal controlled oscillator is the clock source for the network. A two-bit address is provided to select one of four multiple output clock rates.

Applications include a selectable frequency source for equipment in the data communications market, such as teleprinters, printers, CRT terminals, and microprocessor systems.

- Single 5.0 Vdc (±5%) Power Supply
- Internal Oscillator Crystal Controlled for Stability (1.8432 MHz)
- Sixteen Different Output Clock Rates
- 50% Output Duty Cycle
- Programmable Time Bases for One of Four Multiple Output Rates
- Buffered Outputs Compatible with Low Power TTL
- Noise Immunity = 45% of V_{DD} Typical
- Diode Protection on All Inputs
- External Clock May be Applied to Pin 21
- Internal Pullup Resistor on Reset Input

PIN ASSIGNMENT

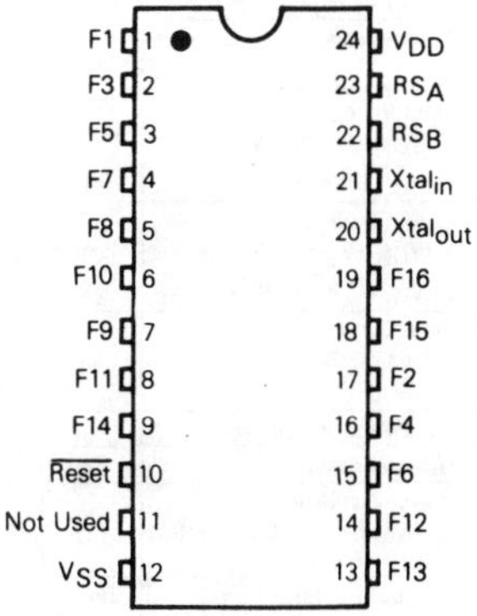

V_{DD} = Pin 24
V_{SS} = Pin 12

This device contains circuitry to protect the inputs against damage due to high static voltages or electric fields; however, it is advised that normal precautions be taken to avoid application of any voltage higher than maximum rated voltages to this high impedance circuit. For proper operation it is recommended that V_{in} and V_{out} be constrained to the range $V_{SS} \leq (V_{in}$ or $V_{out}) \leq V_{DD}$.

Unused inputs must always be tied to an appropriate logic voltage level (e.g., either V_{SS} or V_{DD}).

MAXIMUM RATINGS (Voltages referenced to V_{SS}, Pin 12.)

Rating	Symbol	Value	Unit
DC Supply Voltage Range	V_{DD}	5.25 to −0.5	V
Input Voltage, All Inputs	V_{in}	V_{DD}+0.5 to V_{SS}−0.5	V
DC Current Drain por Pin	I	10	mA
Operating Temperature Range	T_A	−40 to +85	°C
Storage Temperature Range	T_{stg}	−65 to +150	°C

BLOCK DIAGRAM

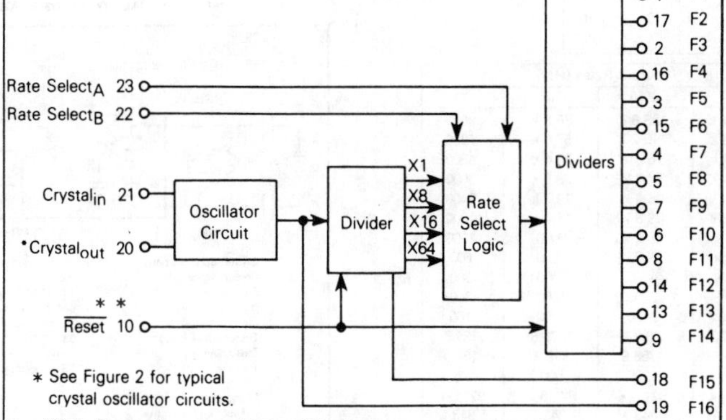

* See Figure 2 for typical crystal oscillator circuits.

** When Reset = 0, outputs F1 thru F14 = 0, outputs F15 and F16 = 1.

ELECTRICAL CHARACTERISTICS

Characteristic	Symbol	V_{DD} Vdc	−40°C Min	−40°C Max	25°C Min	25°C Typ	25°C Max	+85°C Min	+85°C Max	Unit
Supply Voltage	V_{DD}	–	4.75	5.25	4.75	5.0	5.25	4.75	5.25	V
Output Voltage "0" Level	V_{out}	5.0	–	0.05	–	0	0.05	–	0.05	V
Output Voltage "1" Level	V_{out}	5.0	4.95	–	4.95	5.0	–	4.95	–	V
Input Voltage (V_O = 4.5 or 0.5 V)	V_{IL}	5.0	–	1.5	–	2.25	1.5	–	1.5	V
(V_O = 0.5 or 4.5 Vdc)	V_{IH}	5.0	3.5	–	3.5	2.75	–	3.5	–	V
Output Drive Current (V_{OH} = 2.5 V) Source	I_{OH}	5.0	−0.23	–	−0.20	−1.7	–	−0.16	–	mA
(V_{OL} = 0.4 V) Sink	I_{OL}	5.0	0.23	–	0.20	0.78	–	0.16	–	mA
Input Current Pins 21, 22, 23	I_{in}	–	–	±0.1	–	±0.00001	±0.1	–	±1.0	μA
Pin 10	I_{in}	5.0	–	–	−1.5	–	−7.5	–	–	μA
Input Capacitance (V_{in} = 0)	C_{in}	–	–	–	–	5.0	–	–	–	pF
Quiescent Dissipation	P_Q	5.0	–	2.5	–	0.015	2.5	–	15	mW
Power Dissipation**† (Dynamic plus Quiescent) (C_L = 15 pF)	P_D	5.0				P_D = (7.5 mW/MHz) f + P_Q				mW
Output Rise Time** t_r = (3.0 ns/pF) C_L + 25 ns	t_{TLH}	5.0	–	–	–	70	200	–	–	ns
Output Fall Time** t_f = (1.5 ns/pF) C_L + 47 ns	t_{THL}	5.0	–	–	–	70	200	–	–	ns
Input Clock Frequency	f_{CL}	5.0	–	1.85	–	–	1.85	–	1.85	MHz
Clock Pulse Width	$t_{W(C)}$	–	200	–	200	–	–	200	–	ns
Reset Pulse Width	$t_{W(R)}$	–	500	–	500	–	–	500	–	ns

†For dissipation at different external capacitance (C_L) refer to corresponding formula:
$P_T(C_L) = P_D + 2.6 \times 10^{-3}(C_L - 15\ \text{pF})\ V_{DD}^2 f$
where: P_T, P_D in mW, C_L in pF, V_{DD} in Vdc, and f in MHz.
**The formula given is for the typical characteristics only.

FIGURE 1 — DYNAMIC SIGNAL WAVEFORMS

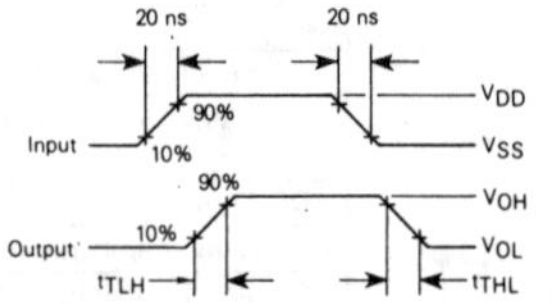

TABLE 1 — OUTPUT CLOCK RATES

Rate Select B	Rate Select A	Rate
0	0	X1
0	1	X8
1	0	X16
1	1	X64

Output Number	Output Rates (Hz) X64	X16	X8	X1
F1	614.4 k	153.6 k	76.8 k	9600
F2	460.8 k	115.2 k	57.6 k	7200
F3	307.2 k	76.8 k	38.4 k	4800
F4	230.4 k	57.6 k	28.8 k	3600
F5	153.6 k	38.4 k	19.2 k	2400
F6	115.2 k	28.8 k	14.4 k	1800
F7	76.8 k	19.2 k	9600	1200
F8	38.4 k	9600	4800	600
F9	19.2 k	4800	2400	300
F10	12.8 k	3200	1600	200
F11	9600	2400	1200	150
F12	8613.2	2153.3	1076.6	134.5
F13	7035.5	1758.8	879.4	109.9
F14	4800	1200	600	75
F15	921.6 k	921.6 k	921.6 k	921.6 k
F16*	1.843 M	1.843 M	1.843 M	1.843 M

*F16 is buffered oscillator output.

FIGURE 2 — TYPICAL CRYSTAL OSCILLATOR CIRCUIT

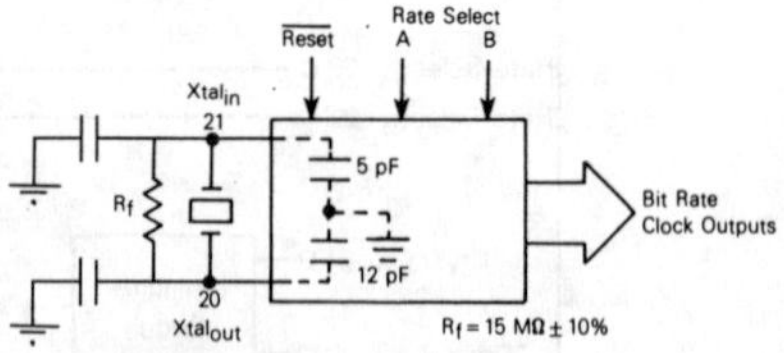

Crystal Specifications

Crystal Mode	*Parallel
Frequency	1.8432 MHz ±0.05% @ 13 pF
R_S	540 Ω max
C_0	7.0 pF max
Temperature Range	0 to 70°C
Test Level	1 mW
Test Set	TS – 330/TSM or Equivalent

*Suggested Crystal Suppliers:
Tyco, CTS Knights

Dual Baud Rate Generator
COM8116/COM8116T/COM8136/COM8136T

FEATURES

- ☐ On chip crystal oscillator or external frequency input
- ☐ Single +5v power supply
- ☐ Choice of 2 x 16 output frequencies
- ☐ 16 asynchronous/synchronous baud rates
- ☐ Direct UART/USRT/ASTRO/USYNRT compatibility
- ☐ Full duplex communication capability
- ☐ High frequency reference output*
- ☐ Re-programmable ROM via CLASP® technology allows generation of other frequencies
- ☐ TTL, MOS compatibility
- ☐ Compatible with COM 5016/COM 5036

PIN CONFIGURATION

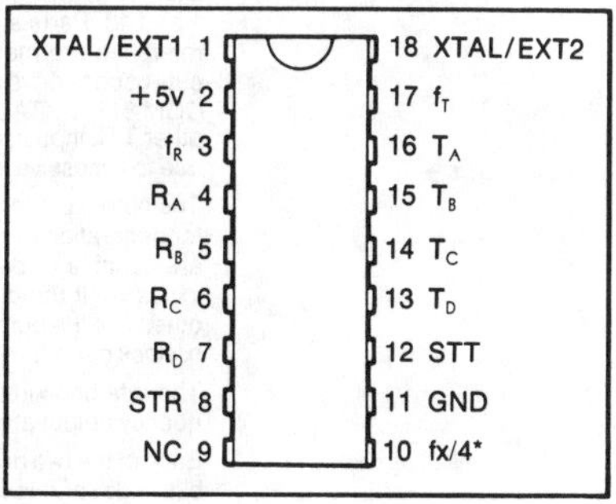

BLOCK DIAGRAM

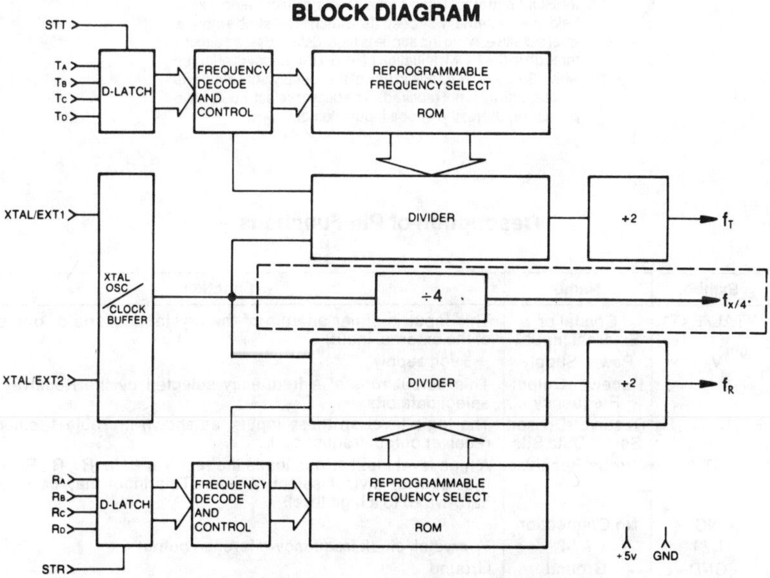

General Description

The Standard Microsystem's COM 8116/COM 8136 is an enhanced version of the COM 5016/COM 5036 Dual Baud Rate Generator. It is fabricated using SMC's patented COPLAMOS® and CLASP® technologies and employs depletion mode loads, allowing operation from a single +5v supply.

The standard COM 8116/COM 8136 is specifically dedicated to generating the full spectrum of 16 asynchronous/synchronous data communication frequencies for 16X UART/USRT devices. A large number of the frequencies available are also useful for 1X and 32X ASTRO/USYNRT devices.

The COM 8116/COM 8136 features an internal crystal oscillator which may be used to provide the master reference frequency. Alternatively, an external reference may be supplied by applying complementary TTL level signals to pins 1 and 18. Parts suitable for use only with an external TTL reference are marked COM 8116T/COM 8136T. TTL outputs used to drive the COM 8116/COM 8136 or COM 8116T/COM 8136T XTAL/EXT inputs should not be used to drive other TTL inputs, as noise immunity may be compromised due to excessive loading.

The output of the oscillator/buffer is applied to the dividers for generation of the output frequencies f_T, f_R. The dividers are capable of dividing by any integer from 6 to $2^{19} + 1$, inclusive. If the divisor is even, the output will be square; otherwise the output will be high longer than it is low by one fx clock period.

The reference frequency (fx) is used to provide a high frequency output at fx/4 on the COM 8136/T.

Each of the two divisor ROMs contains 16 divisors, each 19 bits wide, and is fabricated using SMC's unique CLASP® technology allowing up to 32 different divisors on custom parts. This process permits reduction of turn-around time for ROM patterns. Each group of four divisor select bits is held in an externally strobed data latch. The strobe input is level sensitive: while the strobe is high, data is passed directly through to the ROM. Initiation of a new frequency is effected within 3.5μs of a change in any of the four divisor select bits (strobe activity is not required). The divisor select inputs have pull-up resistors; the strobe inputs do not.

Description of Pin Functions

Pin No.	Symbol	Name	Function
1	XTAL/EXT1	Crystal or External Input 1	This input is either one pin of the crystal package or one polarity of the external input.
2	V_{CC}	Power Supply	+5 volt supply
3	f_R	Receiver Output Frequency	This output runs at a frequency selected by the Receiver divisor select data bits.
4-7	R_A, R_B, R_C, R_D	Receiver-Divisor Select Data Bits	The logic level on these inputs, as shown in Table 1, selects the receiver output frequency, f_R.
8	STR	Strobe-Receiver	A high level input strobe loads the receiver data (R_A, R_B, R_C, R_D) into the receiver divisor select register. This input may be strobed or hard-wired to a high level.
9	NC	No Connection	
10	$f_X/4$*	$f_X/4$	¼ crystal/clock frequency reference output.
11	GND	Ground	Ground
12	STT	Strobe-Transmitter	A high level input strobe loads the transmitter data (T_A, T_B, T_C, T_D) into the transmitter divisor select register. This input may be strobed or hard-wired to a high level.
13-16	T_D, T_C, T_B, T_A	Transmitter-Divider Select Data Bits	The logic level on these inputs, as shown in Table 1, selects the transmitter output frequency, f_T.
17	f_T	Transmitter Output Frequency	This output runs at a frequency selected by the Transmitter divisor select data bits.
18	XTAL/EXT2	Crystal or External Input 2	This input is either the other pin of the crystal package or the other polarity of the external input.

*COM 8136/T only

Dual Baud Rate Generator
COM8126/COM8126T/COM8146/COM8146T

FEATURES

- ☐ On chip crystal oscillator or external frequency input
- ☐ Single +5v power supply
- ☐ Choice of 16 output frequencies
- ☐ 16 asynchronous/synchronous baud rates
- ☐ Direct UART/USRT/ASTRO/USYNRT compatibility
- ☐ High frequency reference output*
- ☐ Re-programmable ROM via CLASP® technology allows generation of other frequencies
- ☐ TTL, MOS compatibility
- ☐ Compatible with COM 5026/COM 5046

PIN CONFIGURATION

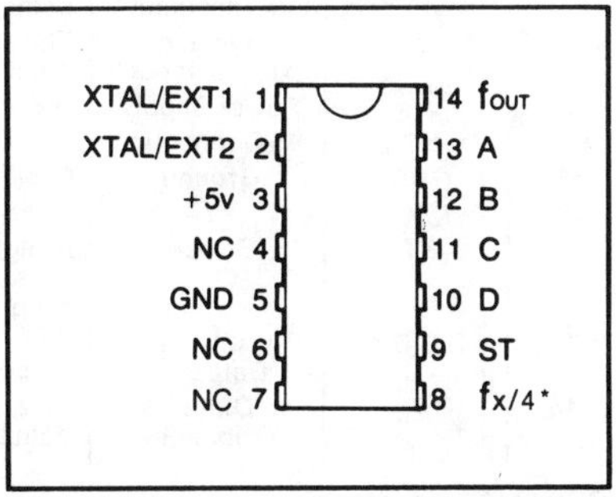

BLOCK DIAGRAM

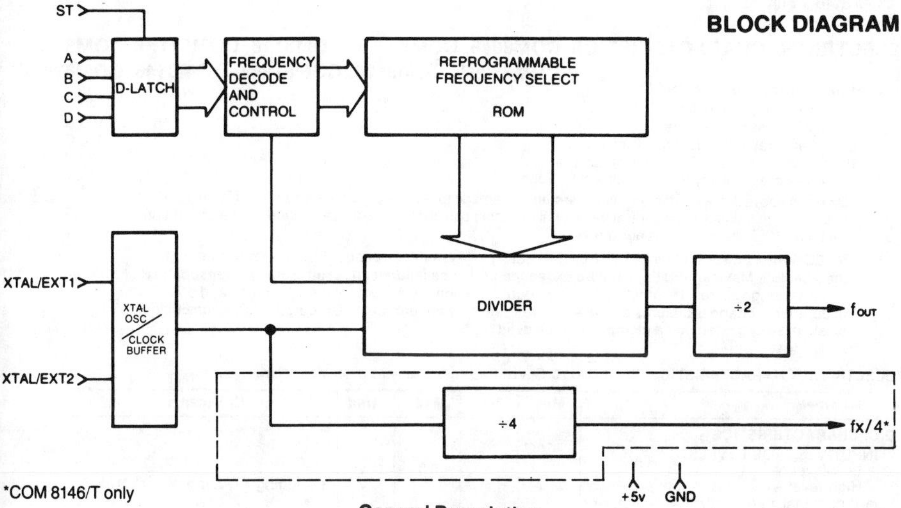

*COM 8146/T only

General Description

The Standard Microsystem's COM 8126/COM 8146 is an enhanced version of the COM 5026/COM 5046 Baud Rate Generator. It is fabricated using SMC's patended COPLAMOS® and CLASP® technologies and employs depletion mode loads, allowing operation from a single +5v supply.

The standard COM 8126/COM 8146 is specifically dedicated to generating the full spectrum of 16 asynchronous/synchronous data communication frequencies for 16X UART/USRT devices. A large number of the frequencies available are also useful for 1X and 32X ASTRO/USYNRT devices.

The COM 8126/COM 8146 features an internal crystal oscillator which may be used to provide the master reference frequency. Alternatively, an external reference may be supplied by applying complementary TTL level signals to pins 1 and 2. Parts suitable for use only with an external TTL reference are marked COM 8126T/COM 8146T. TTL outputs used to drive the COM 8126/COM 8146 or COM 8126T/COM 8146T XTAL/EXT inputs should not be used to drive other TTL inputs, as noise immunity may be compromised due to excessive loading.

The output of the oscillator/buffer is applied to the divider for generation of the output frequency. The divider is capable of dividing by any integer from 6 to $2^{19}+1$, inclusive. If the divisor is even, the output will be square; otherwise the output will be high longer than it is low by one fx clock period.

The reference frequency (fx) is used to provide a high frequency output at fx/4 on the COM 8146/T.

The divisor ROM contains 16 divisors, each 19 bits wide, and is fabricated using SMC's unique CLASP® technology. This process permits reduction of turnaround time for ROM patterns. The four divisor select bits are held in an externally strobed data latch. The strobe input is level sensitive: while the strobe is high, data is passed directly through to the ROM. Initiation of a new frequency is affected within 3.5μs of a change in any of the four divisor select bits (strobe activity is not required). This feature may be disabled through a CLASP® programming option causing new frequency initiation to be delayed until the end of the current f_{OUT} half-cycle. The divisor select inputs have pull-up resistors; the strobe input does not.

Description of Pin Functions

Pin No.	Symbol	Name	Function
1	XTAL/EXT1	Crystal or External Input 1	This input is either one pin of the crystal package or one polarity of the external input.
2	XTAL/EXT2	Crystal or External Input 2	This input is either the other pin of the crystal package or the other polarity of the external input.
3	V_{CC}	Power Supply	+5 volt supply
4,6,7	NC	No Connection	
5	GND	Ground	Ground
8	$f_X/4$ *	$f_X/4$	¼ crystal/clock frequency reference output.
9	ST	Strobe	A high level strobe loads the input data (A, B, C, D) into the input divisor select register. This input may be strobed or hard-wired to a high level.
10-13	D,C,B,A	Divisor Select Data Bits	The logic level on these inputs as shown in Table 1, selects the output frequency.
14	f_{OUT}	Output Frequency	This output runs at a frequency selected by the divisor select data bits.

*COM 8146/T only

ELECTRICAL CHARACTERISTICS COM8046, COM8046T, COM8116, COM8116T, COM8126, COM8126T, COM8136, COM8136T, COM8146, COM8146T

MAXIMUM GUARANTEED RATINGS*

Operating Temperature Range .... 0°C to + 70°C
Storage Temperature Range .... −55°C to +150°C
Lead Temperature (soldering, 10 sec.) .... +325°C
Positive Voltage on any Pin, with respect to ground .... +8.0V
Negative Voltage on any Pin, with respect to ground .... −0.3V

*Stresses above those listed may cause permanent damage to the device. This is a stress rating only and functional operation of the device at these or at any other condition above those indicated in the operational sections of this specification is not implied.

NOTE: When powering this device from laboratory or system power supplies, it is important that the Absolute Maximum Ratings not be exceeded or device failure can result. Some power supplies exhibit voltage spikes or "glitches" on their outputs when the AC power is switched on and off. In addition, voltage transients on the AC power line may appear on the DC output. If this possibility exists it is suggested that a clamp circuit be used.

ELECTRICAL CHARACTERISTICS (T_A=0°C to 70°C, V_{CC}= +5V±5%, unless otherwise noted)

Parameter	Min.	Typ.	Max.	Unit	Comments
D.C. CHARACTERISTICS					
INPUT VOLTAGE LEVELS					
Low-level, V_{IL}			0.8	V	
High-level, V_{IH}	2.0			V	excluding XTAL inputs
OUTPUT VOLTAGE LEVELS					
Low-level, V_{OL}			0.4	V	I_{OL}=1.6mA, for $f_X/4$, $f_O/16$
			0.4	V	I_{OL}=3.2mA, for f_O, f_R, f_T
			0.4	V	I_{OL}=0.8mA, for f_X
High-level, V_{OH}	3.5			V	I_{OH}=−100µA; for f_X, I_{OH}=−50µA
INPUT CURRENT					
Low-level, I_{IL}			-0.1	mA	V_{IN}=GND, excluding XTAL inputs
INPUT CAPACITANCE					
All inputs, C_{IN}		5	10	pF	V_{IN}=GND, excluding XTAL inputs
EXT INPUT LOAD		8	10		Series 7400 equivalent loads
POWER SUPPLY CURRENT					
I_{CC}			50	mA	
A.C. CHARACTERISTICS					T_A= +25°C
CLOCK FREQUENCY, f_{IN}	0.01		7.0	MHz	XTAL/EXT, 50% Duty Cycle ±5% COM 8046, COM 8126, COM 8146
	0.01		5.1	MHz	XTAL/EXT, 50% Duty Cycle ±5% COM 8116, COM 8136
STROBE PULSE WIDTH, t_{PW}	150		DC	ns	
INPUT SET-UP TIME					
t_{DS}	200			ns	
INPUT HOLD TIME					
t_{DH}	50			ns	
STROBE TO NEW FREQUENCY DELAY			3.5	µs	@ f_X=5.0 MHz

TIMING DIAGRAM

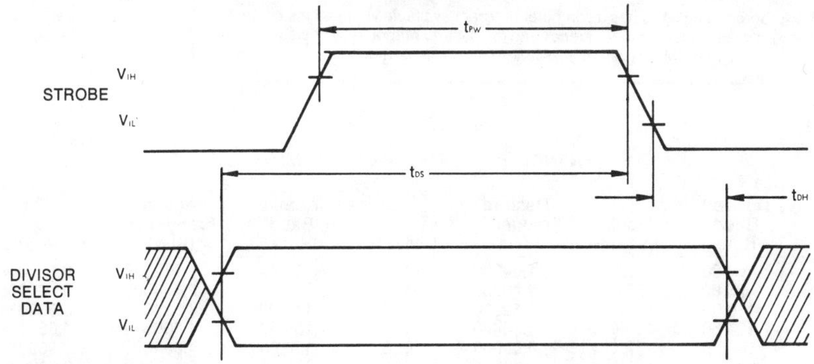

Crystal Operation
COM 8116
COM 8136

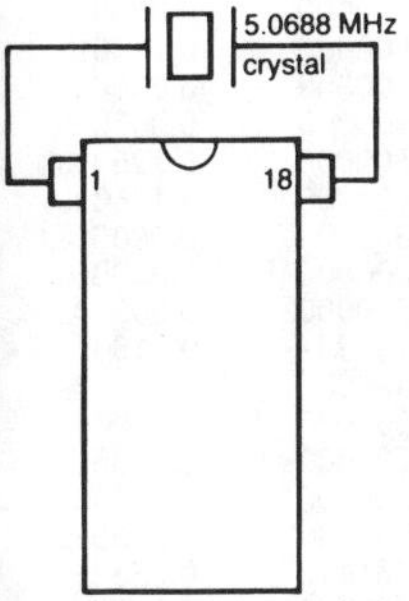

External Input Operation
COM 8116/COM 8116T
COM 8136/COM 8136T

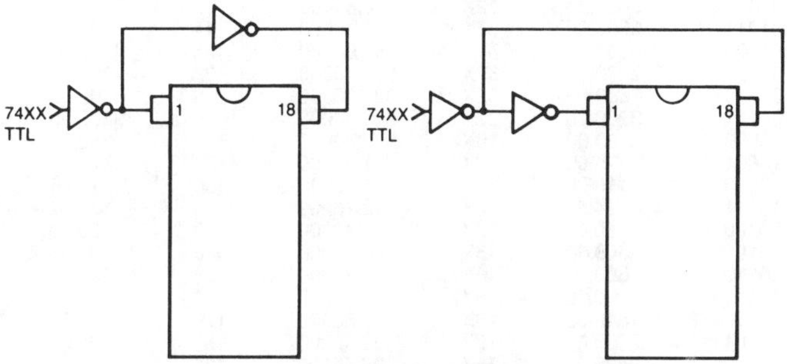

74XX—totem pole or open collector output (external pull-up resistor required)

Crystal Operation
COM 8126
COM 8146
COM 8046

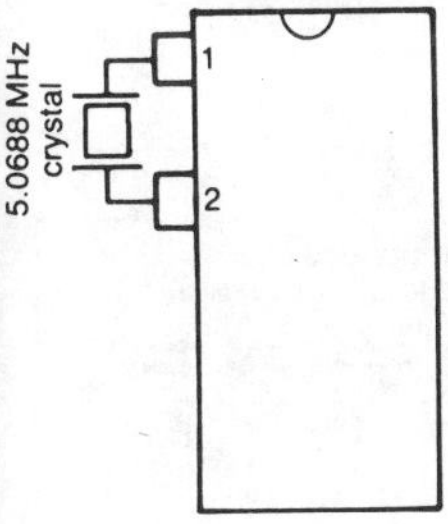

External Input Operation
COM 8126/COM 8126T
COM 8146/COM 8146T
COM 8046/COM 8046T

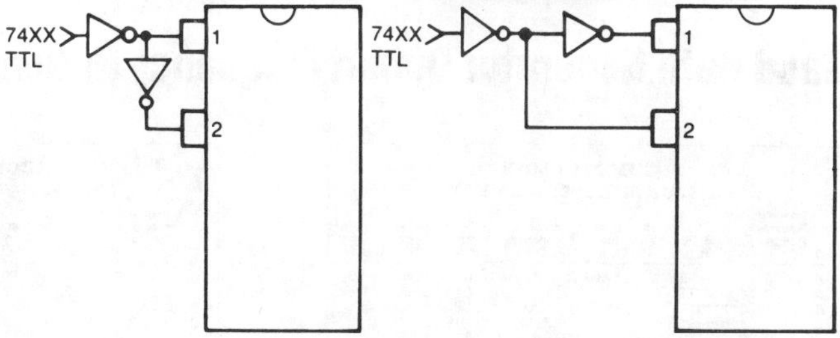

74XX—totem pole or open collector output (external pull-up resistor required)

Crystal Specifications

User must specify termination (pin, wire, other)
Prefer: HC-18/U or HC-25/U
Frequency — 5.0688 MHz, AT cut
Temperature range 0°C to 70°C

Series resistance <50 Ω
Series Resonant
Overall tolerance ± .01%
or as required

For ROM re-programming SMC has a computer program available whereby the customer need only supply the input frequency and the desired output frequencies. The ROM programming is automatically generated.

Table 2

REFERENCE FREQUENCY = 5.068800MHz

Divisor Select EDCBA	Desired Baud Rate	Clock Factor	Desired Frequency (KHz)	Divisor	Actual Baud Rate	Actual Frequency (KHz)	Deviation
00000	50.00	32X	1.60000	3168	50.00	1.600000	0.0000%
00001	75.00	32X	2.40000	2112	75.00	2.400000	0.0000%
00010	110.00	32X	3.52000	1440	110.00	3.520000	0.0000%
00011	134.50	32X	4.30400	1177	134.58	4.306542	0.0591%
00100	150.00	32X	4.80000	1056	150.00	4.800000	0.0000%
00101	200.00	32X	6.40000	792	200.00	6.400000	0.0000%
00110	300.00	32X	9.60000	528	300.00	9.600000	0.0000%
00111	600.00	32X	19.20000	264	600.00	19.200000	0.0000%
01000	1200.00	32X	38.40000	132	1200.00	38.400000	0.0000%
01001	1800.00	32X	57.60000	88	1800.00	57.600000	0.0000%
01010	2400.00	32X	76.80000	66	2400.00	76.800000	0.0000%
01011	3600.00	32X	115.20000	44	3600.00	115.200000	0.0000%
01100	4800.00	32X	153.60000	33	4800.00	153.600000	0.0000%
01101	7200.00	32X	230.40000	22	7200.00	230.400000	0.0000%
01110	9600.00	32X	307.20000	16	9900.00	316.800000	3.1250%
01111	19200.00	32X	614.40000	8	19800.00	633.600000	3.1250%
10000	50.00	16X	0.80000	6336	50.00	0.800000	0.0000%
10001	75.00	16X	1.20000	4224	75.00	1.200000	0.0000%
10010	110.00	16X	1.76000	2880	110.00	1.760000	0.0000%
10011	134.50	16X	2.15200	2355	134.52	2.152357	0.0166%
10100	150.00	16X	2.40000	2112	150.00	2.400000	0.0000%
10101	300.00	16X	4.80000	1056	300.00	4.800000	0.0000%
10110	600.00	16X	9.60000	528	600.00	9.600000	0.0000%
10111	1200.00	16X	19.20000	264	1200.00	19.200000	0.0000%
11000	1800.00	16X	28.80000	176	1800.00	28.800000	0.0000%
11001	2000.00	16X	32.00000	158	2005.06	32.081013	0.2532%
11010	2400.00	16X	38.40000	132	2400.00	38.400000	0.0000%
11011	3600.00	16X	57.60000	88	3600.00	57.600000	0.0000%
11100	4800.00	16X	76.80000	66	4800.00	76.800000	0.0000%
11101	7200.00	16X	115.20000	44	7200.00	115.200000	0.0000%
11110	9600.00	16X	153.60000	33	9600.00	153.600000	0.0000%
11111	19200.00	16X	307.20000	16	19800.00	316.800000	3.1250%

Baud Rate Generator Output Frequency Options

COM 8116T-013

CRYSTAL FREQUENCY = 2.76480 MHz

Transmit/ Receive Address D	C	B	A	Baud Rate	Theoretical Frequency 16X Clock	Actual Frequency 16X Clock	Percent Error	Duty Cycle %	Divisor
0	0	0	0	50	0.8 KHz	0.8 KHz	0	50/50	3456
0	0	0	1	75	1.2	1.2	0	50/50	2304
0	0	1	0	110	1.76	1.76	−.006	50/50	1571
0	0	1	1	134.5	2.152	2.152	−.019	50/50	1285
0	1	0	0	150	2.4	2.4	0	50/50	1152
0	1	0	1	200	3.2	3.2	0	50/50	864
0	1	1	0	300	4.8	4.8	0	50/50	576
0	1	1	1	600	9.6	9.6	0	50/50	288
1	0	0	0	1200	19.2	19.2	0	50/50	144
1	0	0	1	1800	28.8	28.8	0	50/50	96
1	0	1	0	2000	32.0	32.149	+.465	50/50	86
1	0	1	1	2400	38.4	38.4	0	50/50	72
1	1	0	0	3600	57.6	57.6	0	50/50	48
1	1	0	1	4800	76.8	76.8	0	50/50	36
1	1	1	0	9600	153.6	153.6	0	50/50	18
1	1	1	1	19,200	307.2	307.2	0	44/56	9

COM 8116T-003

CRYSTAL FREQUENCIES = 6.01835 MHz

Transmit/ Receive Address D	C	B	A	Baud Rate	Theoretical Frequency 16X Clock	Actual Frequency 16X Clock	Percent Error	Duty Cycle %	Divisor
0	0	0	0	50	0.8 KHz	799.9 Hz	0	50/50	7523
0	0	0	1	75	1.2	1200.0	0	50/50	5015
0	0	1	0	110	1.76	1759.7	0	50/50	3420
0	0	1	1	134.5	2.152	2151.7	0	50/50	2797
0	1	0	0	150	2.4	2399.6	0	50/50	2508
0	1	0	1	200	3.2	3199.5	0	50/50	1881
0	1	1	0	300	4.8	4799.3	0	50/50	1254
0	1	1	1	600	9.6	9598.6	0	50/50	627
1	0	0	0	1200	19.2	19227.9	+0.14	50/50	313
1	0	0	1	1800	28.8	28795.9	0	50/50	209
1	0	1	0	2000	32.0	32012.5	0	50/50	188
1	0	1	1	2400	38.4	38333.4	−0.17	50/50	157
1	1	0	0	3600	57.6	57868.7	+0.46	50/50	104
1	1	0	1	4800	76.8	77158.3	+0.46	50/50	78
1	1	1	0	9600	153.6	154316.6	+0.46	50/50	39
1	1	1	1	19,200	307.2	300917.5	2.04	50/50	20

COM 8116T-013A
CRYSTAL FREQUENCY—5.52960 MHz

Transmit/ Receive Address D	C	B	A	Baud Rate	Theoretical Frequency 16X Clock	Actual Frequency 16X Clock	Percent Error	Duty Cycle %	Divisor
0	0	0	0	100	1.6 KHz	1.6 KHz	0	50/50	3456
0	0	0	1	150	2.4	2.4	0	50/50	2304
0	0	1	0	220	3.52	3.5197	−.006	50/50	1571
0	0	1	1	269	4.304	4.3032	−.019	50/50	1285
0	1	0	0	300	4.8	4.8	0	50/50	1152
0	1	0	1	400	6.4	6.4	0	50/50	864
0	1	1	0	600	9.6	9.6	0	50/50	576
0	1	1	1	1200	19.2	19.2	0	50/50	288
1	0	0	0	2400	38.4	38.4	0	50/50	144
1	0	0	1	3600	57.6	57.6	0	50/50	96
1	0	1	0	4000	64.0	64.298	+.466	50/50	86
1	0	1	1	4800	76.8	76.8	0	50/50	72
1	1	0	0	7200	115.2	115.2	0	50/50	48
1	1	0	1	9600	153.6	153.6	0	50/50	36
1	1	1	0	19,200	307.2	307.2	0	50/50	18
1	1	1	1	38,400	614.8	614.8	0	44/56	9

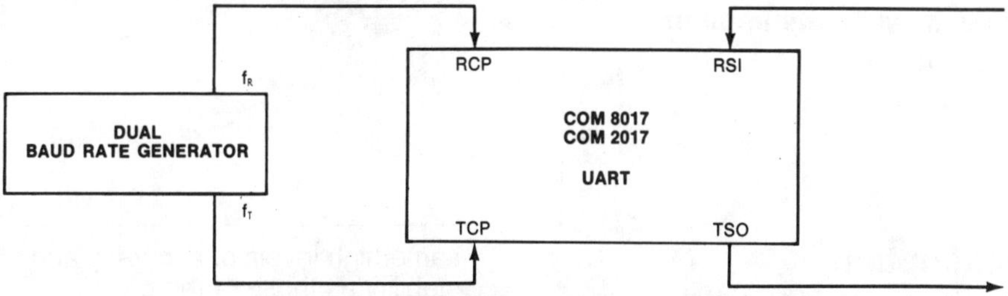

Typical UART—Dual Baud Rate Generator Configuration
Full Duplex—Split Speed

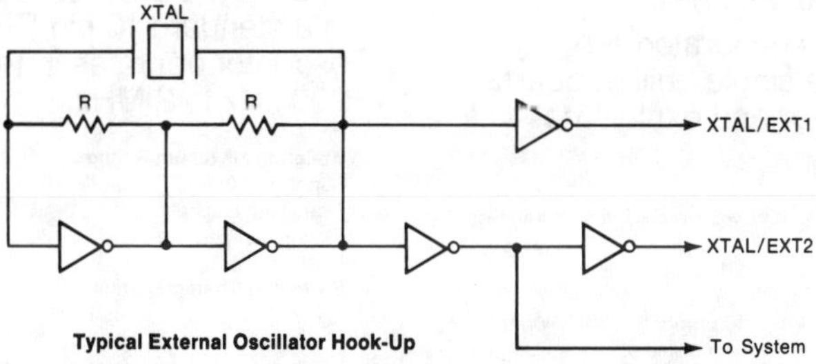

Typical External Oscillator Hook-Up

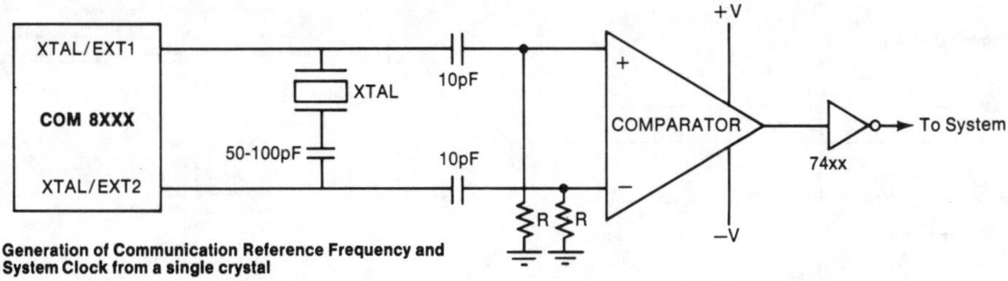

Generation of Communication Reference Frequency and System Clock from a single crystal

PXO768 Programmable Crystal Oscillator

Features

- □ Provides 57 different frequencies from a single quartz crystal.
- □ Covers broad frequency range: 0.002 Hz to 2 MHz
- □ Packaged in standard 16-pin DIP containing both IC and crystal.
- □ Laser trimmed for high accuracy.
- □ Low power consumption.
- □ Low aging.
- □ TTL compatible.

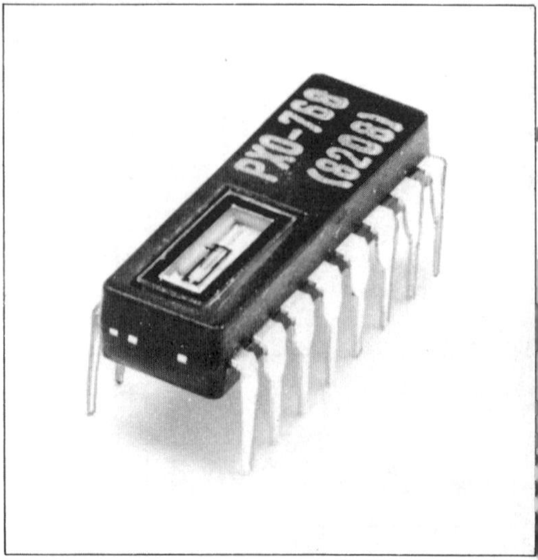

Description

The Programmable Crystal Oscillator PXO Series can be easily programmed to generate any one of 57 different frequencies in the range 0.002 Hz to 2 MHz.

All frequencies generated are derived from a single built-in quartz crystal oscillator and exhibit the same high levels of accuracy and stability as those of the base frequency supplied by the crystal.

The PXO Series is a low-power device containing a quartz crystal and a CMOS IC, both packaged in a standard 16-pin DIP. The oscillator operates in the range 200 kHz to 2 MHz.

Specifications

Specifications are typical unless otherwise noted and are subject to change without notice.

Calibration tolerance*	±100 ppm
Frequency stability**	±0.015%, −10 to +70° C
Voltage coefficient	10 ppm/V typical, 25 ppm/V maximum
Aging	10 ppm maximum first year

*Tighter tolerances available.
**Does not include calibration tolerance.

Timing Diagram

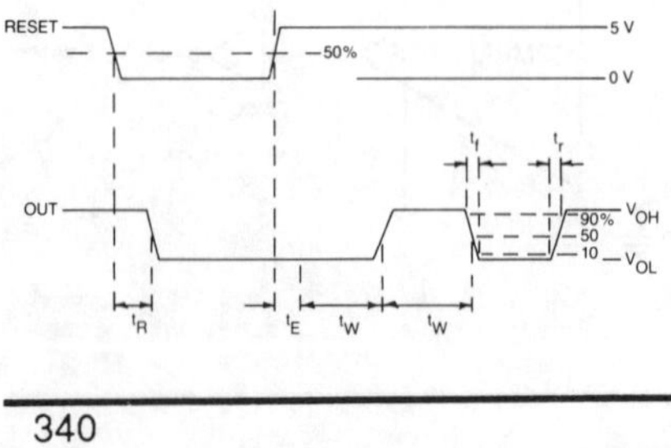

Absolute Maximum Ratings

Supply voltage	−0.3 to +10 V
Operating temperature	−10 to +70°C
Storage temperature	−30 to +85°C

Switching Characteristics

T_a=25°C V_{DD}=5V C_L=15pf

SYMBOL	PARAMETER	TYP	MAX	UNIT
t_R	Reset delay time		10	μsec
t_E	Timing error after reset released		15	μsec
t_r	Rise time	70		nsec
t_f	Fall time	30		nsec
F_{in}	External oscillator operating frequency		1.5	MHz

Pin Connections

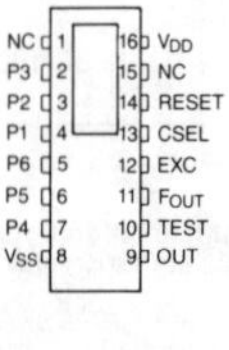

NC: Not connected

Electrical Characteristics

T_a=25°C V_{DD}=5V

SYMBOL	PARAMETER	MIN	TYP	MAX	UNIT
V_{DD}	Supply voltage	4.0	5.0	6.0	V
I_{OH}	Output current: Hi[1] (Source)			−1.0	mA
I_{OL}	Output current: Lo[2] (Sink)	1.6			mA
V_{IH}	Input voltage: logic 1	V_{DD}−1.0		V_{DD}	V
V_{IL}	Input voltage: logic 0	0.0		1.0	V
I_{IH}	Input current reset: Hi			0.5	μA
I_{IL}	Input current reset: Lo	−15			μA
I_{IH}	Input current Prog 1-6, CSEL, EXC, TEST: Hi			15	μA
I_{IL}	Input current Prog. 1-6, CSEL, EXC, TEST: Lo	−0.5			μA
I_{DD}	Supply current[3]		0.7	1.0	mA

[1]V_{OH}=4V [2]V_{OL}=0.4V [3]Crystal: 600 kHz, OUT: 60 kHz

Output Frequencies of Model PXO-32768 (0.00273 Hz - 327.68 kHz)

PROGRAM PIN SETTINGS		P4	0	0	0	0	1	1	1	1
		P5	0	0	1	1	0	0	1	1
P1	P2	P3 \ P6	0	1	0	1	0	1	0	1
0	0	0	327.680K	32.768K	3.2768K	327.68	32.768	3.2768	0.32768	0.03277
0	0	1	32.768K	3.2768K	327.68	32.768	3.2768	0.32768	0.03277	0.00328
0	1	0	163.840K	16.384K	1.6384K	163.84	16.384	1.6384	0.16384	0.01638
0	1	1	*109.226K*	*10.9226K	*1.09226K	*109.226	*10.9226	*1.09226	0.10923	0.01092
1	0	0	81.920K	8.192K	819.2	81.92	8.192	0.81920	0.08192	0.00819
1	0	1	**65.536K	6.5536K	655.36	65.536	6.5536	0.65536	0.06554	0.00655
1	1	0	*54.613K	*5.4613K	*546.13	*54.613	*5.4613	*0.54613	0.05461	0.00546
1	1	1	*27.306K	*2.7306K	*273.06	*27.306	*2.7306	*0.27306	0.02731	0.00273

*33% duty cycle **40% duty cycle

Block Diagram

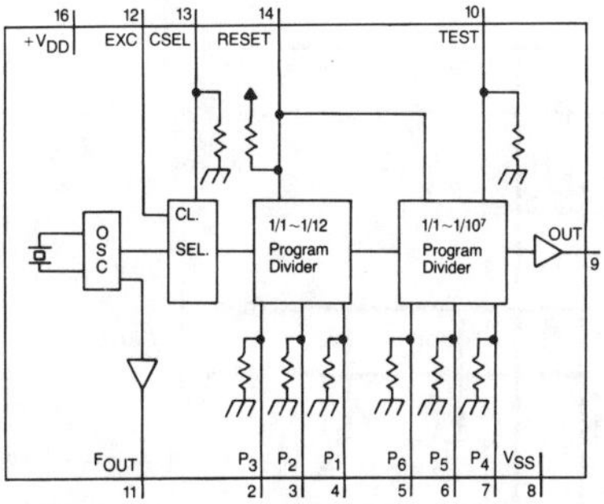

Output Frequencies of Model PXO-768 (0.0064 Hz - 768 kHz)

UNIT: Hz

PROGRAM PIN SETTINGS		P4	0	0	0	0	1	1	1	1
		P5	0	0	1	1	0	0	1	1
P1	P2	P3 \ P6	0	1	0	1	0	1	0	1
0	0	0	768K	76.8K	7.68K	768	76.8	7.68	0.768	0.0768
0	0	1	76.8K	7.68K	768	76.8	7.68	0.768	0.0768	0.00768
0	1	0	384K	38.4K	3.84K	384	38.4	3.84	0.384	0.0384
0	1	1	*256K	25.6K	2.56K	256	25.6	2.56	0.256	0.0256
1	0	0	192K	19.2K	1.92K	192	19.2	1.92	0.192	0.0192
1	0	1	**153.6K	15.36K	1.536K	153.6	15.36	1.536	0.1536	0.01536
1	1	0	128K	12.8K	1.28K	128	12.8	1.28	0.128	0.0128
1	1	1	64K	6.4K	640	64	6.4	0.64	0.064	0.0064

*33% duty cycle **40% duty cycle

Pin Functions

Prog 1 through Prog 6 control divide ratio of base frequency.

P1	P2	P3	DIVIDING RATIO	P4	P5	P6	DIVIDING RATIO
0	0	0	1/1	0	0	0	1/1
0	0	1	1/10	0	0	1	1/10
0	1	0	1/2	0	1	0	$1/10^2$
0	1	1	1/3	0	1	1	$1/10^3$
1	0	0	1/4	1	0	0	$1/10^4$
1	0	1	1/5	1	0	1	$1/10^5$
1	1	0	1/6	1	1	0	$1/10^6$
1	1	1	1/12	1	1	1	$1/10^7$

OUT: Supplies programmed output frequency with rectangular pulse shape (50% duty cycle, except as noted).

TEST: Setting this terminal Hi multiplies programmed output frequency by 1,000, except when programmed divide ratio is less than 1/1000.

F_{OUT}: Supplies base frequency of internal crystal oscillator.

EXC: External clock input.

CSEL: Clock select. Setting this terminal Hi causes the divider to count the frequency of an external clock instead of the internal clock.

RESET: Setting this terminal Lo resets all counters and sets output to Lo.

(All inputs except EXC and RESET have internal pull-down resistor. RESET has pull-up resistor.)

Baud Rate Generator

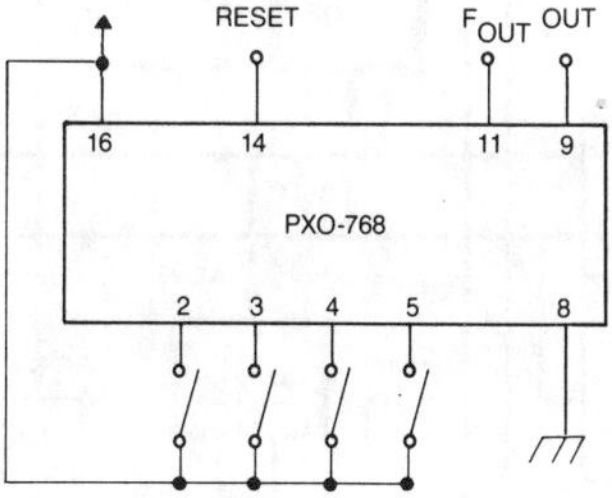

CLOCK FREQ. kHz	19.2	38.4	76.8	153.6	768
BAUD RATE bps	1200	2400	4800	9600	48000
Pin 2 (P3)	0	0	1	1	0
Pin 3 (P2)	0	1	0	0	0
Pin 4 (P1)	1	0	0	1	0
Pin 5 (P6)	1	1	0	0	0

CS8221 NEAT CHIPSet

- **100% IBM™ PC/AT Compatible New Enhanced CHIPSet™ for 12MHz to 16MHz systems**
- **Supports 16MHz 80286 operation with only 0.5–0.7 wait states for 100ns DRAMs and 12 MHz operation with 150ns DRAMs, 0 wait state 12MHz operation with 80ns DRAMs**
- **Separate CPU and AT Bus clocks**
- **Page Interleaved Memory supports single bank page mode, 2 way and 4 way page interleaved mode**
- **Integrated Lotus-Intel-Microsoft Expanded Memory Specification (LIM EMS) Memory Controller. Supports EMS 4.0.**
- **Software Configurable Command Delays, Wait states and Memory Organization**
- **Optimized for OS/2 operation**
- **Shadow RAM for BIOS and video ROM to improve system performance**
- **Complete AT/286 system board requires only 28 logic components plus memory and processor**
- **Targeted at Desktop PC/ATs, Laptops and CMOS Industrial Control Applications**
- **Available as four CMOS 84-pin PLCC or 100-pin PFP components.**

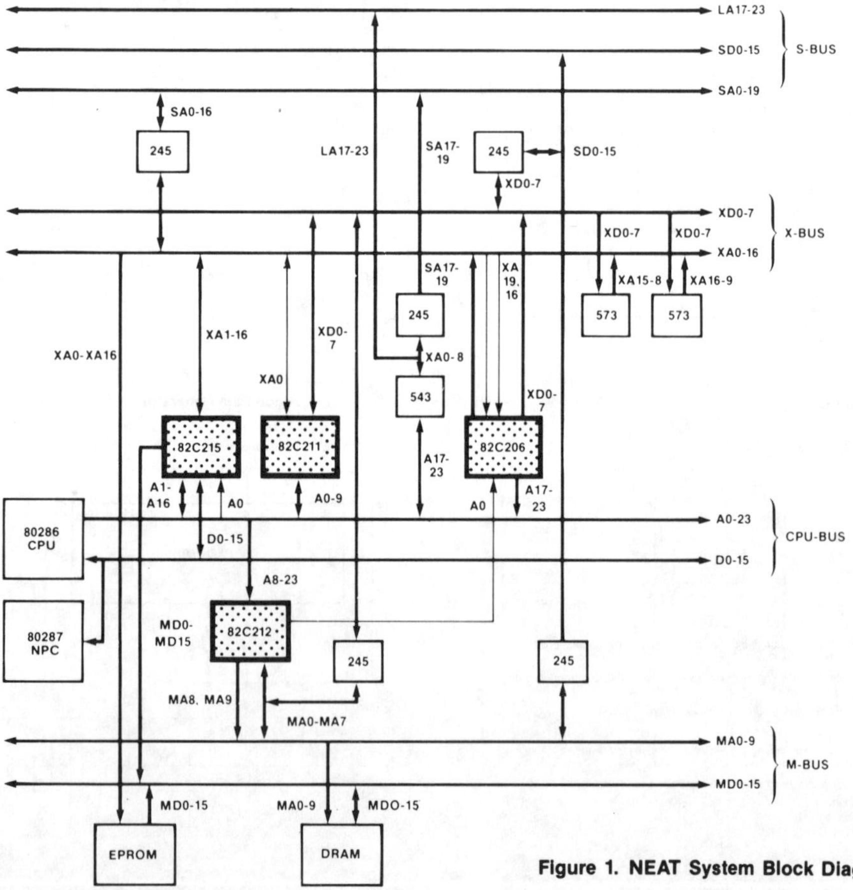

Figure 1. NEAT System Block Diagram

The CS8221 PC/AT compatible NEAT CHIPSet™ is an enhanced, high performance 4 chip VLSI implementation (including the 82C206 IPC) of the control logic used on the IBM™ Personal Computer AT. The flexible architecture of the NEAT CHIPSet™ allows it to be used in any 80286 based system.

The CS 8221 NEAT CHIPSet™ provides a complete 286 PC/AT compatible system, requiring only 24 logic components plus memory devices.

The CS8221 NEAT CHIPSet™ consists of the 82C211 CPU/Bus controller, the 82C212 Page/Interleave and EMS Memory controller, the 82C215 Data/Address buffer and the 82C206 Integrated Peripherals Controller (IPC).

The NEAT CHIPSet™ supports the local CPU bus, a 16 bit system memory bus, and the AT buses as shown in the NEAT System Block Diagram. The 82C211 provides synchronization and control signals for all buses. The 82C211 also provides an independent AT bus clock and allows for dynamic selection between the processor clock and the user selectable AT bus clock. Command delays and wait states are software configurable, providing flexibility for slow or fast peripheral boards.

The 82C212 Page/Interleave and EMS Memory controller provides an interleaved memory sub-system design with page mode operation. It supports up to 8 MB of on-board DRAM with combinations of 64Kbit, 256Kbit and 1Mbit DRAMs. The processor can operate at 16MHz with 0.5–0.7 wait state memory accesses, using 100 nsec DRAMs. This is possible through the Page Interleaved memory scheme. The Shadow RAM feature allows faster execution of code stored in EPROM, by down loading code from EPROM to RAM. The RAM then shadows the EPROM for further code execution. In a DOS environment, memory above 1Mb can be treated as LIM EMS memory.

The 82C215 Data/Address buffer provides the buffering and latching between the local CPU address bus and the Peripheral address bus. It also provides buffering between the local CPU data bus and the memory data bus. The parity bit generation and error detection logic resides in the 82C215.

The 82C206 Integrated Peripherals Controller is an integral part of the NEAT CHIPSet™. It is described in the 82C206 Integrated Peripherals Controller data book.

System Overview

The CS8221 NEAT CHIPSet™ is designed for use in 12 to 16 MHz 80286 based systems and provides complete support for the IBM PC/AT bus. There are four buses supported by the CS8221 NEAT CHIPSet™ as shown in Figure 1: CPU local bus (A and D), system memory bus (MA and MD), I/O channel bus (SA and SD), and X bus (XA and XD). The system memory bus is used to interface the CPU to the DRAMs and EPROMs controlled by the 82C212. The I/O channel bus refers to the bus supporting the AT bus adapters which could be either 8 bit or 16 bit devices. The X bus refers to the peripheral bus to which the 82C206 IPC and other peripherals are attached in an IBM PC/AT.

Notation and Glossary

The following notations are used to refer to the configuration and diagnostics registers internal to the 82C211 and 82C212:

REGnH denotes the internal register of index n in hexadecimal notation.

REGnH<x:y> denotes the bit field from bits x to y of the internal register with index n in hexadecimal notation.

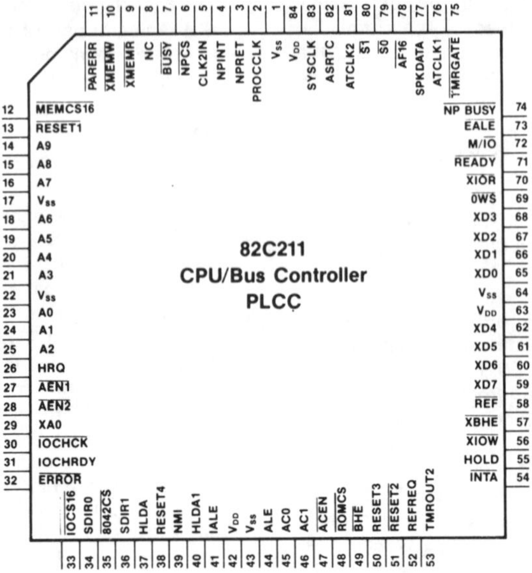

82C211 Pin Description

Pin No.	Pin Type	Symbol	Description
Clocks			
5	I	CLK2IN	CLOCK 2 input from a TTL crystal oscillator having a maximum of twice the rated frequency of the 80286 processor clock.
2	O	PROCCLK	PROCESSOR CLOCK output for the 80286 and the 82C212. It is derived from CLK2IN. It can also be programmed to be derived from ATCLK.
76	I	ATCLK1	AT Bus Clock 1 input source from crystal or oscillator. This clock input is used for the AT bus operation and is only required if the AT bus state machine clock, BCLK (internal) will not be derived from CLK2IN. This clock input should be tied low if not used. Its frequency should be lower than CLK2IN. BCLK is the AT bus state machine clock and can be programmed to be equal to ATCLK.
81	O	ATCLK2	AT Bus Clock 2 output is connected to the crystal (if a crystal is used to generate AT bus clock). A series damping resistor of 10 ohms should be used to reduce amplitude of the resonant circuit. It should be left open if a TTL oscillator is used.
83	O	SYSCLK	AT System Clock output is buffered to drive the SYSCLK line on the AT bus I/O channel. It is half the frequency of BCLK and should be between 6 and 8 MHz for maintaining correct AT I/O bus timing compatibility with the IBM™ PC/AT.

82C211 Pin Description (Continued)

Pin No.	Pin Type	Symbol	Description
Control			
13	I	$\overline{\text{RESET1}}$	RESET1 is an active low input generated by the power good signal of the power supply. When low, it activates RESET3 and RESET4. $\overline{\text{RESET1}}$ is latched internally.
51	I	$\overline{\text{RESET2}}$	RESET2 is an active low input generated from the keyboard controller (8042/8742) for a "warm reset" not requiring the system power to be shut off. It forces a CPU reset by activating RESET3.
38	O	RESET4	RESET4 is an active high output used to reset the AT bus, 82C206 IPC, 8042 keyboard controller, 82C212 memory controller. It is synchronized with the processor clock.
50	O	RESET3	RESET3 is an active high output to the 80286 when $\overline{\text{RESET1}}$ or $\overline{\text{RESET2}}$ is active. It is also activated when shut-down condition in the CPU is detected. RESET3 will stay active for at least 16 PROCLK cycles.
CPU Interface			
71	I/O	$\overline{\text{READY}}$	READY as an output, is driven low to terminate the current CPU cycle after IOCHRDY is high and $\overline{\text{0WS}}$ is high, or if "time out" condition is detected. During all other cycles, it is an input from the 82C212. It is an open collector output requiring an external pull-up resistor of 1KΩ and is connected to the 80286 $\overline{\text{READY}}$ pin.
79, 80	I	$\overline{\text{S0}}$, $\overline{\text{S1}}$	STATUS is an active low input from the CPU. The status signals are used by the 82C211 to determine the state of the CPU. Pull up resistors of 10KΩ each should be provided.
72	I	M/$\overline{\text{IO}}$	MEMORY INPUT/OUTPUT is the signal from the CPU. When high, it indicates a memory access, when low it indicates an I/O access. It is used to generate memory and I/O signals for the system. A 10KΩ pull up resistor is recommended.
55	O	HOLD	CPU HOLD REQUEST is an active high output to the CPU. It is activated during DMA, Master or refresh cycles.
37	I	HLDA	HOLD ACKNOWLEDGE is an active high input generated by the CPU to indicate to the requesting master that it has relinquished the bus. When active, it forces all commands ($\overline{\text{IOR}}$, $\overline{\text{IOW}}$, $\overline{\text{MEMR}}$, $\overline{\text{MEMW}}$, $\overline{\text{INTA}}$) to be tri-stated.
49	I/O	$\overline{\text{BHE}}$	BYTE HIGH ENABLE is an active low signal which indicates the transfer of data on the upper byte of the data bus. In conjunction with A0, it is input during CPU cycles and in conjunction with XA0, it is output during DMA, MASTER cycles. A pull up resistor of 10KΩ is required.

82C211 Pin Description (Continued)

Pin No.	Pin Type	Symbol	Description
39	O	NMI	NON MASKABLE INTERRUPT is an active high output to the NMI pin of the CPU and is generated by the 82C211 to invoke a non-maskable interrupt.
41	O	IALE	ADDRESS LATCH ENABLE (INTERNAL) is an active high output synchronized with PROCCLK and controls address latches used to hold addresses during bus cycles. It is not issued for halt bus cycles.

I/O Channel Interface

Pin No.	Pin Type	Symbol	Description
31	I	IOCHRDY	I/O CHANNEL READY is an active high input from the AT bus. When low it indicates a not ready condition and inserts wait states in AT-I/O or AT-memory cycles. When high it allows termination of the current AT-bus cycle. A series damping resistor of 53Ω at the AT bus connector is recommended to limit the negative under shoot. A 1KΩ pull up resistor is required for this open collector line.
30	I	$\overline{IOCHCK}$	I/O CHANNEL CHECK is an active low input from the AT bus causing an NMI to be generated if enabled. It is used to signal an I/O error condition from a device residing on the AT bus. A 10KΩ pull up resistor is required.
11	I	$\overline{PARERR}$	PARITY ERROR is an active low input from the 82C215 which causes an NMI if enabled. It indicates a parity error in local system memory.
44	O	ALE	ADDRESS LATCH ENABLE is an active high output to the AT bus and is synchronized with the AT state machine clock. It controls the address latches used to hold the addresses during bus cycles. This signal should be buffered to drive the AT bus.
73	O	$\overline{EALE}$	EXTERNAL ADDRESS LATCH ENABLE is an active low output used to latch the CPU A17-A23 address lines to the LA17-LA23 lines on the AT bus.

DMA Interface

Pin No.	Pin Type	Symbol	Description
40	O	HLDA1	HOLD ACKNOWLEDGE 1 is an active high output when a bus cycle is granted in response to HOLD REQUEST 1.
26	I	HRQ	HOLD REQUEST is an active high input when DMA/Master is requesting a bus cycle. For an AT compatible architecture, it should be connected to the HOLD REQUEST signal from DMA1 and DMA2.
27	I	$\overline{AEN1}$	ADDRESS ENABLE 1 is an active low input from one of the two DMA controllers enabling the address latches for 8 bit DMA transfers.
28	I	$\overline{AEN2}$	ADDRESS ENABLE 2 is an active low input from one of the two DMA controllers enabling the address latches for 16 bit DMA transfers.
48	I	$\overline{ROMCS}$	ROM CHIP-SELECT is an active low input from the 82C212. It is used to disable parity checks for local ROM cycles.

82C211 Pin Description (Continued)

Pin No.	Pin Type	Symbol	Description
Bus Inputs			
12	I	$\overline{\text{MEMCS16}}$	MEMORY CHIP SELECT 16 is an active low input from the AT bus indicating a 16 bit memory transfer. If high it implies an 8 bit memory transfer. A pull up resistor of 330Ω is required.
33	I	$\overline{\text{IOCS16}}$	I/O CHANNEL SELECT 16 is an active low input from the AT bus indicating a 16 bit I/O transfer. If high it implies an 8 bit I/O transfer. A pull up resistor of 330Ω is required.
69	I	$\overline{\text{0WS}}$	ZERO WAIT STATES is an active low input from the AT bus, causing immediate termination of the current AT bus cycle. Memories requiring zero wait states use this line to speed up memory cycles. It requires a 330Ω pull up resistor.
Device Decode			
35	O	$\overline{\text{8042CS}}$	8042 CHIP SELECT is an active low signal for the keyboard controller chip select.
82	O	ASRTC	ADDRESS STROBE to Real Time Clock is an active high signal used on the 82C206.
Refresh			
52	I	REFREQ	REFRESH REQUEST is an active high input initiating a DRAM refresh sequence. It is generated by the 8254 compatible timer controller #1 of the 82C206 IPC in a PC/AT implementation.
58	I/O	$\overline{\text{REF}}$	REFRESH is an active low signal. As an open drain output, it initiates a refresh cycle for the DRAMs. As an input, it can be used to force a refresh cycle from an I/O device. An external pull up of 620Ω is required.
X Bus Interface			
9	I/O	$\overline{\text{XMEMR}}$	X BUS MEMORY READ is an active low control strobe directing memory to place data on the data bus. It is an output if the CPU is controlling the bus and is an input if a DMA controller is in control of the bus.
10	I/O	$\overline{\text{XMEMW}}$	X BUS MEMORY WRITE is an active low control strobe directing memory to accept data from the data bus. It is an output if the CPU is controlling the bus and is an input if a DMA controller is in control of the bus.
70	I/O	$\overline{\text{XIOR}}$	X BUS I/O READ is an active low strobe directing an I/O port to place data on the data bus. It is an output if the CPU is controlling the bus and is an input if a DMA controller is in control of the bus.
56	I/O	$\overline{\text{XIOW}}$	X BUS I/O WRITE is an active low strobe directing an I/O port to accept data from the data bus. It is an output if the CPU is controlling the bus and is an input if a DMA controller is in control of the bus.

82C211 Pin Description (Continued)

Pin No.	Pin Type	Symbol	Description
57	I/O	$\overline{XBHE}$	X BYTE HIGH ENABLE is an active low signal indicating the high byte has valid data on the bus. It is an output when the CPU is in control of the bus and is an input when a DMA controller is in control of the bus. A 4.7KΩ pull-up resistor is required on this line.
59-62 65-68	I/O I/O	XD<7:4> XD<0:3>	X DATA BUS bits <7:0>
8	—	NC	No Connect
75	O	TMRGATE	TIMER GATE is an active high output that enables the timer on the 8254 compatible counter timer in the 82C206 to enable the tone signal for the speaker.
53	I	TMROUT2	TIMER OUT 2 is an active high input from the 8254 compatible counter timer in the 82C206 that can be read from port B.
77	O	SPKDATA	SPEAKER DATA is an active high output used to gate the 8254 compatible tone signal of the 82C206 to the speaker.
54	O	$\overline{INTA}$	INTERRUPT ACKNOWLEDGE is an active low output to the 82C206 interrupt controller. It is also used to direct data from the X to S bus during an interrupt acknowledge cycle.
Buffer Control			
34	O	SDIR0	SYSTEM BUS DIRECTION 0 for the low byte. A low sets the data path from the S bus to the M bus. A high sets the data path from the M bus to the S bus.
36	O	SDIR1	SYSTEM BUS DIRECTION 1 for the high byte. A low sets the data path from the S bus to the M bus. A high sets the data path from the M bus to the S bus
47	O	$\overline{ACEN}$	ACTION CODE ENABLE is an active low output that validates the action code signals AC<1, 0> that are used by the 82C215 address/data buffer.
46, 45	O	AC<1, 0>	ACTION CODE is a two bit encoded output command for bus size control and byte assembly operations performed in the 82C215.
Memory Control			
78	I	$\overline{AF16}$	AF16 is an active low input indicating that the current cycle is a local bus cycle. A high indicates an AT bus cycle. A 10KΩ pull up resistor is required.
23–25 18–21 14–18	I/O	A<0:2> A<3:6> A<7:9>	ADDRESS lines A0–A9 are input from the CPU. These lines are output during refresh. A1 is used to detect shut down condition of the CPU. A0 is used to generate the enable signal for the data bus transceivers.

82C211 Pin Description (Continued)

Pin No.	Pin Type	Symbol	Description
29	I/O	XA0	ADDRESS line XA0 from the X bus. It is an output during CPU accesses on the X bus and is an input for 8 bit DMA cycles.
CoProcessor Interface			
6	O	$\overline{\text{NPCS}}$	NUMERIC COPROCESSOR CHIP SELECT is an active low output signal used to select the internal registers of the 80287 NPX.
7	O	$\overline{\text{BUSY}}$	BUSY is an active low output to the CPU initiated by the 80287 NPX, indicatig that it is busy. A 4.7KΩ pull up resistor is required.
74	I	$\overline{\text{NPBUSY}}$	NUMERIC COPROCESSOR BUSY is an active low input from the NPX, indicating that it is currently executing a command. It is used to generate the BUSY signal to the CPU. A 4.7KΩ pull up resistor is required.
32	I	$\overline{\text{ERROR}}$	ERROR is an active low input from the NPX indicating that an unmasked error condition exists. A 4.7KΩ pull up resistor is required.
4	O	NPINT	NUMERIC COPROCESSOR INTERRUPT is an active high output . It is an interrupt request from the 80287 and is connected to the IRQ13 line of the 82C206 IPC in a PC/AT environment. A 10KΩ pull up resistor is required.
3	O	NPRESET	NUMERICAL PROCESSOR RESET is an active high reset to the 80287. It is active when RESET4 is active or when a write operation is made to Port 0F1H. In the later case, it is active for the period of the command.
Power Supplies			
42, 63, 84	—	VDD	POWER SUPPLY.
1, 17, 22 43, 64	—	VSS	GROUND.

1. 82C211 BUS CONTROLLER

1.1 Features

- Clock generation with software speed selection.
- Optional independent AT bus clock.
- CPU interface and bus control.
- Programmable command delays and wait state generation.
- Port B register.

1.2 Functional Description

The 82C211 Bus Controller consists of the following functional sub-modules as illustrated in figure 1.1:

- Reset and Shut down logic
- Clock generation and selection logic
- CPU state machine, AT bus state machine and bus arbitration logic
- Action Codes generation logic
- Port B register and NMI logic
- DMA and Refresh logic
- Numeric Coprocessor interface logic
- Configuration registers

1.2.1 Reset and Shut Down Logic

Two reset inputs RESET1 and RESET2 are provided on the 82C211 bus controller. RESET1 is the Power Good signal from the power supply. When RESET1 is active, the 82C211 asserts RESET3 and RESET4 for a system reset. RESET2 is generated from the 8042 (or 8742) keyboard controller when a "warm reset" is required. The warm reset activates RESET3 to reset the 80286 CPU.

RESET3 is also activated by the 82C211 when a shut down condition is detected in the CPU. Additionally, a low to high transition in REG60<5> causes RESET3 to be active after the current I/O command goes inactive. RESET3 is asserted for at least 16 PROCCLK cycles and then deasserted. RESET4 is used to reset the AT bus, 82C206 IPC, 8042 key-

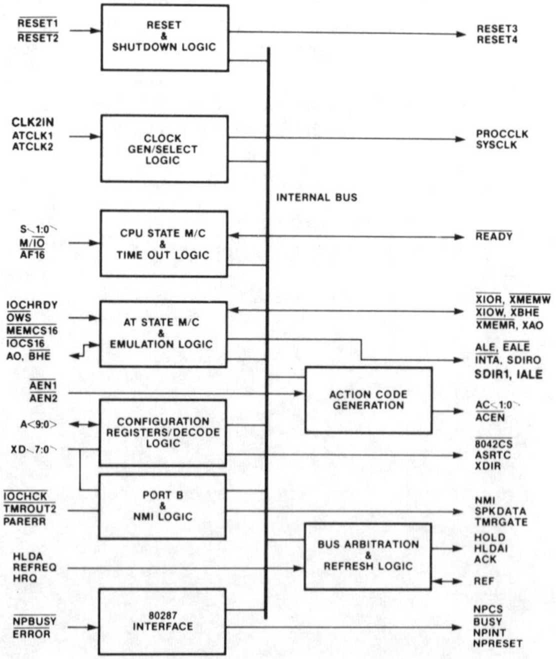

Figure 1.1 82C211 Block Diagram

board controller and the 82C212 memory controller. It is synchronized with respect to PROCCLK and is asserted as long as the Power Good signal is held low.

After a shut down condition is detected, RESET3 is asserted and held high for at least 16 PROCCLK cycles and then deasserted. RESET3 resulting from a shut down condition is synchronous with PROCCLK, ensuring proper CPU operation. Both RESET3 and RESET4 meet the setup and hold timing requirements of the 80286 CPU.

1.2.2 Clock Generation and Selection Logic

The 82C211 provides a flexible clock selection scheme as shown in Figure 1.2. It has two input clocks; CLK2IN and ATCLK. CLK2IN is driven from a TTL crystal oscillator, running at a maximum of twice the processor clock (PROCCLK) frequency. ATCLK is derived from a crystal. Typically, it should be of a lower frequency than CLK2IN. ATCLK and CLK2IN can be selected under program control.

The 82C211 generates processor clock, PROCCLK, for driving the CPU state machine and interface. SCLK (internal) is PROCCLK/2 and is in phase with the internal states of the 80286. BCLK (internal) is the AT bus state machine clock and is used for the AT bus interface. SYSCLK is the AT bus system clock and is always BCLK/2.

PROCCLK can be derived from CLK2IN or from ATCLK. In the synchronous mode, both PROCCLK and BCLK are derived from CLK2IN, so that the processor state machine and the AT bus state machine run synchronous. In the asynchronous mode, BCLK is generated from the ATCLK and PROCCLK is generated from CLK2IN or the ATCLK. In this case, the processor and AT bus state machines run asynchronous to each other. The following clock selections are possible:

Synchronous mode

1. PROCCLK = BCLK = CLK2IN
   SYSCLK = BCLK/2 = CLK2IN/2
2. PROCCLK = CLK2IN
   BCLK = CLK2IN/2
   SYSCLK = BCLK/2 = CLK2IN/4
3. PROCCLK = BCLK = CLK2IN/2
   SYSCLK = BCLK/2 = CLK2IN/4

Asynchronous mode

1. PROCCLK = CLK2IN
   BCLK = ATCLK
   SYSCLK = BCLK/2 = ATCLK/2
2. PROCCLK = ATCLK
   BCLK = ATCLK
   SYSCLK = BCLK/2 = ATCLK/2.

Under normal operation, CLK2IN should be selected as the processor clock (PROCCLK) to allow the processor to run at full speed.

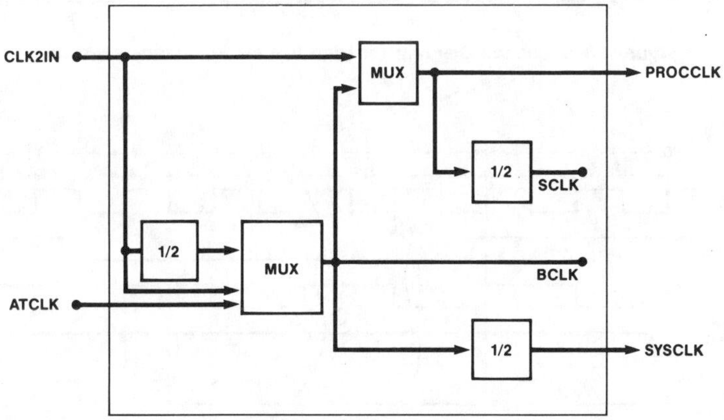

Figure 1.2 Clock Selection Block Diagram

BCLK can either be a sub-division of CLK2IN or the ATCLK. ATCLK may be selected to generate PROCCLK only when it is desired to slow down the processor for timing dependent code execution. Once the options for clock switching are set, the switching occurs with clean transition in the asynchronous or synchronous mode. During clock switching, no phases of PROCCLK are less than the minimum value or greater than the maximum value specified for the 80286 CPU. The clock source selection is made by writing to REG62H<0:1> first and then to REG60H<4>, which default to: PROCCLK = CLK2IN, SYSCLK = CLK2IN/4.

Figures 1.3 and 1.4 illustrate the sequence of events that switch PROCCLK from high to low speed and from low to high speed, upon receiving a request from the configuration register. In Figure 1.3, the falling edge (A) of PROCCLK is used to latch the command inactive condition (1). On the falling edge (B), CLK2IN is disabled on the PROCCLK line. This ensures that clock switching will occur when PROCCLK is low. Once CLK2IN has been disabled, the first rising edge (C) of BCLK latches this condition as denoted by sequence (2). BCLK then enables itself on the PROCCLK line on the falling edge (D) as denoted by sequence (3). This ensures a glitch free transition between the two clocks. It also does not violate the min and max 80286 CPU clock specifications. If BCLK is asynchronous with respect to CLK2IN, it is possible that sequence (2) could violate setup time requirements with respect to edge (C). In this case, edge (D) will register the state of PROCCLK as still being high in sequence (3). Hence, edge (E) samples PROCCLK to be low and edge (F) enables BCLK on the PROCCLK line. This case does not violate the min and max 80286 CPU clock specifications.

In Figure 1.4, the rising edge (A) of PROCCLK latches command inactive as denoted by sequence (1). Edge (B) disables BCLK on the PROCCLK line. In sequence (2), edge (C) of CLK2IN latches PROCCLK low. Edge (D) then enables CLK2IN on the PROCCLK line as denoted by sequence (3). If sequence (2)

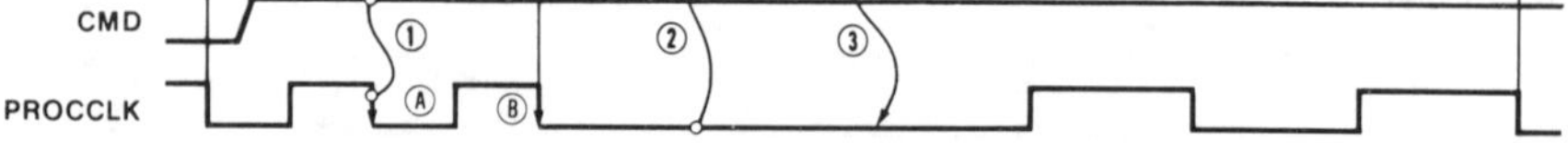

Figure 1.3 Sequence Diagram for High to Low Frequency Transition

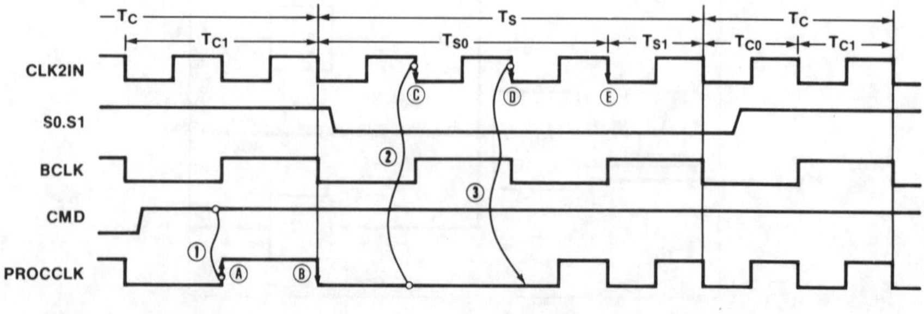

Figure 1.4 Sequence Diagram for Low to High Frequency Transition

does not meet setup time requirements of edge (C), then the state of PROCCLK is sampled as being high in sequence (2). In this case, edge (D) samples PROCCLK low and edge (E) enables CLK2IN on the PROCCLK line. In this case also, PROCCLK does not violate the min and max 80286 CPU clock specifications.

1.2.3 CPU State Machine, Bus State Machine and Bus Arbitration

In order to extract maximum performance out of the 80286 on the system board, it is desirable to run the system board at the rated maximum CPU frequency. This frequency may be too fast for the slow AT bus. In order to overcome this problem, the 82C211 has two state machines: the CPU state machine which typically runs off CLK2IN, and the AT bus state machine which runs off BCLK. The two state machines maintain an asynchronous protocol under external mode operation.

CPU State Machine

Interface to the 80286 requires interpretation of the status lines $\overline{\text{S0}}$, $\overline{\text{S1}}$, M/$\overline{\text{IO}}$ during TS0 and the synchronization and generation of $\overline{\text{READY}}$ to the CPU upon completion of the requested operation. $\overline{\text{IALE}}$ is issued in response to the beginning of a new cycle in TS1 by the 82C211. If $\overline{\text{AF16}}$ is detected as being inactive at the end of the processor TS state, control is handed over to the AT bus state machine. The CPU state machine then waits for $\overline{\text{READY}}$ to be active to terminate the current cycle. All local memory cycles are 16 bit cycles. If $\overline{\text{AF16}}$ is asserted in response to a new CPU cycle and READY is not returned to the 82C211 within 128 clocks, and REG60H<2> is enabled, then an NMI is generated to signal bus time-out, if NMI has been enabled.

AT Bus State Machine

The AT bus state machine gains control when $\overline{\text{AF16}}$ is detected inactive by the CPU state machine. It uses BCLK which is twice the frequency of AT system clock SYSCLK. When ATCLK is selected as the source for BCLK, it also performs the necessary synchronization of control and status signals between the AT bus and the processor. The 82C211 supports 8 and 16 bit transfers between the processor and 8 or 16 bit memory or I/O devices located on the AT bus. The action codes AC0, AC1 qualified by $\overline{\text{ACEN}}$ are used for bus sizing and 8, 16 bit bus conversions by the 82C215. They are discussed in section 1.2.4.

The AT bus cycle is initiated by asserting ALE in AT-TS1. On the falling edge of ALE,

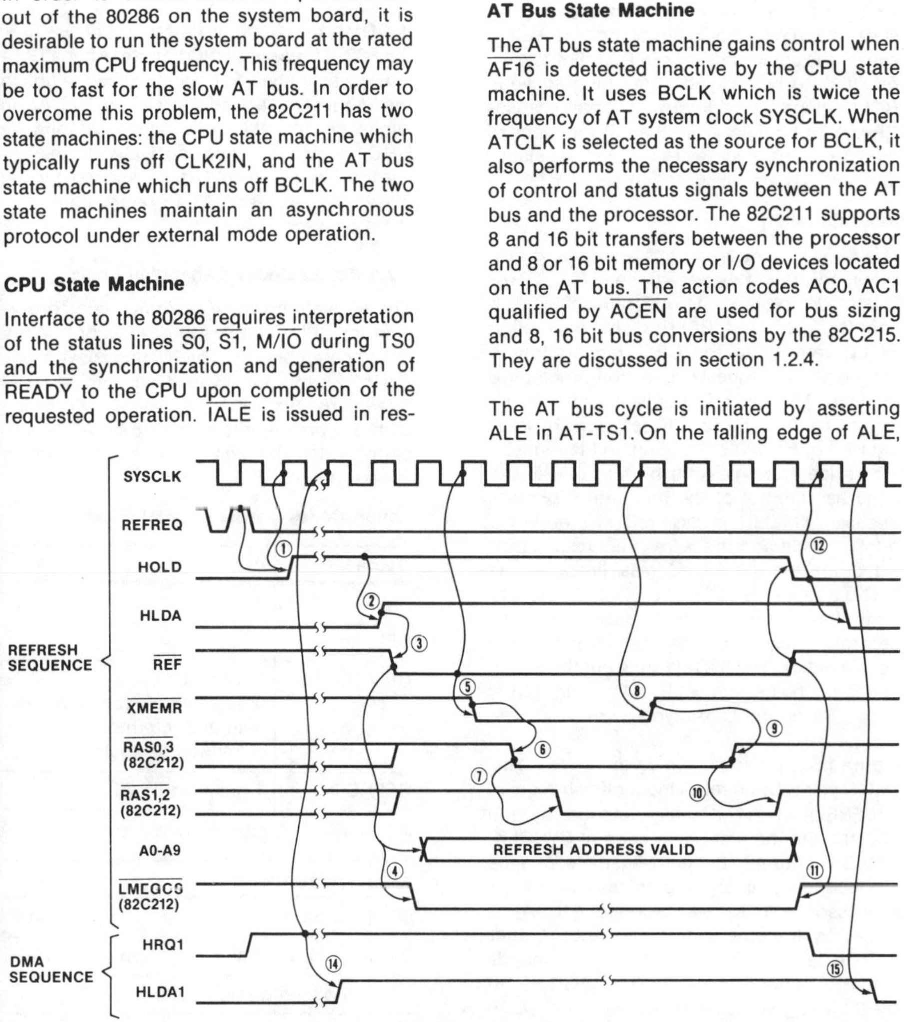

Figure 1.5 Refresh/DMA Sequence

MEMCS16 is sampled for a memory cycle to determine the bus size. It then enters the command cycle AT-TC and provides the sequencing and timing signals for the AT bus cycle. For an I/O cycle, IOCS16 is sampled in the middle of the processor TC state. These control signals emulate the lower speed AT bus signals. The command cycle is terminated when IOCHRDY is active on the AT bus and all programmed wait states have been executed.

It is possible to provide software selectable wait states and command delays to the AT state machine. Providing command delays causes the commands (XMEMR, XMEMW, XIOR or XIOW)to be delayed from going active in BCLK steps. Providing wait states causes READY to be delayed to the CPU in steps of the AT command cycles (AT-TC). The defaults and settings are discussed in section 1.4.

Bus Arbitration

The 82C211 controls all bus activity and provides arbitration between the CPU, DMA/ Master devices, and DRAM refresh logic. It handles HRQ and REFREQ by generating HOLD request to the CPU and arbitrating among these requests in a non-preemptive manner. The CPU relinquishes the bus by issuing HLDA. The 82C211 responds by issuing REF or HLDA1 depending on the requesting device. During a refresh cycle, the refresh logic has control of the bus until REF goes inactive. XMEMR is asserted low during a refresh cycle and the refresh address is provided on the A0-A9 address lines by the 82C211 to be used by the 82C212 memory controller. During a DMA cycle, the DMA controller has control of the bus until HRQ goes inactive. The 82C211 puts out the action codes for bus sizing. ALE, EALE and ACEN are active during DMA cycle.

Figure 1.5 is a sequence diagram for Refresh/ DMA cycles. Upon receiving a refresh request (REFREQ) it is internally latched by the 82C211. On the first rising edge of SYSCLK, HOLD is output to the processor in sequence 1. Depending on the current activity of the processor, a hold acknowledge (HLDA) is issued by the processor in sequence 2, after a DMA latency time. The 82C211 responds with REF active in sequence 3. LMEGCS from the 82C212 goes active in sequence 4. XMEMR is asserted low on the second rising edge of SYSCLK after REF is low in sequence 5. The 82C212 pulls all its RAS lines (RAS0-RAS3) high when REF goes low. The RAS lines go active in sequences 6 and 7 when the refresh address is active on the A0-A9 lines of the 82C211. The 82C212 uses the A0-A9 lines to generate the refresh address on the MA0-MA9 address lines. XMEMR goes inactive in sequence 8 followed by the RAS lines going inactive in sequences 9, 10. REF, LMEGCS and HOLD go inactive in sequence 11. Control is transferred to the CPU after HLDA goes inactive in sequence 12.

If a DMA device requests control of the bus, the 82C211 receives HRQ1 active. After a DMA latency time, the CPU relinquishes the bus to the requesting device by issuing HLDA1 in sequence 14. HLDA1 is active as long as HRQ1 is active. Once the DMA device deasserts HRQ1, HLDA1 is deasserted by the 82C211 in sequence 15, to return control to the processor.

1.2.4 Action Codes Generation Logic

The AT state machine performs data conversion for CPU accesses to devices not on the CPU or Memory Bus.The AT bus conversions are performed for 16 to 8 bit read or write operations. Sixteen bit transfers to/from the CPU are broken into smaller 8 bit AT bus or peripheral bus reads or writes. The action

Table 1.1

Action Codes Enable (ACEN) Generation

Operation	ACEN
DMA/MASTER	0
CPU (local)	1
CPU (AT bus)	0 for write 0 qualified by command for read and interrupt acknowledge cycles
REFRESH	1 qualified by REF

AT-Bus CPU Cycles HLDA1 = 0

AC	Operation
00	16 bit write and 8 bit write (low byte)
01	16 bit read and 8 bit read (low byte)
10	8 bit write (high byte)
11	8 bit read (high byte)

codes are generated as shown in Table 1.1 to control the buffers in the 82C215. The action codes are in response to signals MEMCS16, IOCS16.

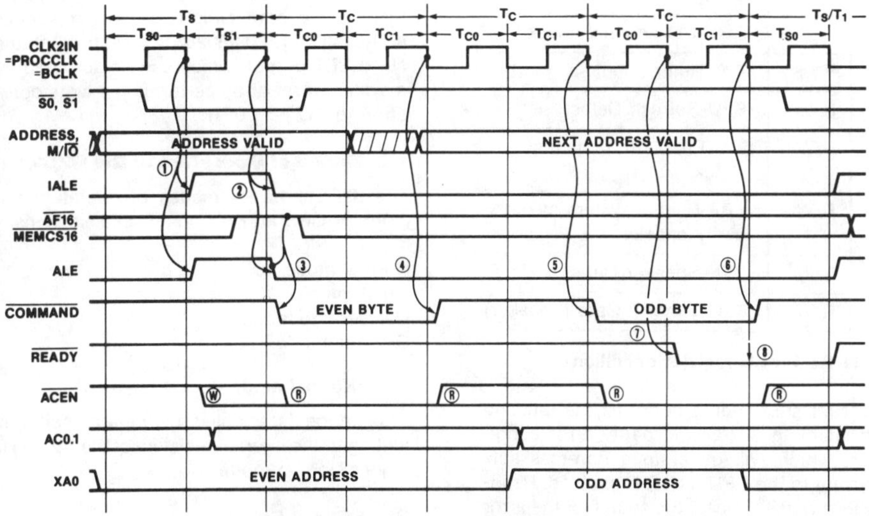

NOTE: W.S. = WAIT STATUS, C.D. = COMMAND DELAYS, R = READ CYCLE, W = WRITE CYCLE.

Figure 1.6 Quick Mode Bus Conversion Cycle (0WS, 0CD)

DMA/MASTER Cycles, HLDA1 = 1

AC	Operation
00	MD bus tri-stated from the 82C215 for 16 bit and 8 (low byte) read/write operations
01	Reserved
10	High memory write MD0-7 to MD8-15
11	High memory read MD8-15 to MD0-7

Figure 1.6 shows a sequence diagram for a data conversion cycle in Quick mode with zero wait states (0 W.S.) and zero command delays (0 C.D.). Quick mode is discussed in section 1.3.2. In Quick mode ALE is issued on the AT bus as shown in sequences 1 and 2. MEMCS16 from an external device is sampled high by the 82C211 in sequence 3, initiating a bus conversion cycle. The first command also goes active in sequence 3 for the first byte operation and is terminated in sequence 4. In order to provide sufficient back to back time between the two 8 bit cycles, the second byte command is issued two PROCCLKs later in sequence 5 and is terminated in sequence 6. No second ALE is issued for the second byte operation since only address line XA0 changes from zero to one. READY is asserted low in sequence 7 and is sampled low by the processor in sequence 8, to terminate the current cycle. ACEN and AC0, AC1 are issued by the 82C211 for bus conversion as shown.

1.2.5 Port B and NMI generation logic

The 82C211 provides access to Port B defined for the PC/AT as shown in Figure 1.7.

IO ADDR	7	6	5	4	3	2	1	0	
61H	PCK	CHK	T20	RFD	EIC	EPR	SPK	T2G	PORT B

Figure 1.7 Port B

Bits	Read/ Write	Function
7	R	PCK-System memory parity check
6	R	CHK-I/O channel check
5	R	T20-Timer 2 Out
4	R	RFD-Refresh Detect
3	R/W	EIC-Enable I/O channel check
2	R/W	ERP-Enable system memory parity check
1	R/W	SPK-Speaker Data
0	R/W	T2G-Timer 2 Gate (Speaker)

Table 1.2 Port B register definition

The NMI sub-module performs the latching and enabling of I/O and parity error conditions, which will generate a non-maskable interrupt to the CPU if NMI is enabled. Reading Port B will indicate the source of the error condition (IOCK and PCHK). Enabling and disabling of NMI is accomplished by writing to I/O address 070H. On the rising edge of XIOW, NMI will be enabled if data bit 7 (XD7) is equal to 0 and will be disabled if XD7 is equal to 1.

Numeric Coprocessor Interface

Incorporated in the 82C211 is the circuitary to interface an 80287 Numeric Coprocessor to 80286. The circuitary handles the decoding required for selecting and resetting the Numeric Coprocessor, handling NPBUSY and ERROR signals from the 80287 to the CPU, and generating interrupt signals for error handling.

The NPCS signal is active for I/O addresses 0F8H-0FFH, used to access the internal registers of the 80287. It is also active for I/O addresses 070H-NMI mask register, 0F0H-Clear Numeric Coprocessor BUSY signal, and 0F1H-Clear the Numerical Coprocessor and Numerical Coprocessor BUSY signal. While executing a task, the 80287 issues an NPBUSY signal to the 82C211. Under normal operation, it is passed out to the CPU as BUSY. If during this busy period, a numeric coprocessor error occurs, ERROR input to the 82C211 becomes active, resulting in latching of the BUSY* output and assertion of NPINT. Both signals stay active until cleared by an I/O write cycle to address 0F0H or 0F1H. A system reset clears both NPINT and BUSY latches in the 82C211. The 80287 is reset through the NPRESET output, which can be activated by a system reset or by performing a write operation to I/O port 0F1H.

1.3 Modes of Operation of the 82C211

The 82C211 has 4 modes of operation for different CPU and AT bus clock selections:

Normal mode
Quick mode
Delayed mode
External mode

1.3.1 Normal mode

This mode is enabled by default (without writing to the internal registers of the 82C211). Under Normal mode:

PROCCLK = CLK2IN
BCLK = CLK2IN/2
SYSCLK = CLK2IN/4

Since the CPU state machine clock and the AT bus state machine clock are derived from CLK2IN, this is a synchronous mode. ALE and commands (XMEMR, XMEMW, XIOR, XIOW) are issued only for AT bus cycles and not for local cycles. If activated by default, I/O cycles will have one command delay, 8 bit AT memory cycles will have 4 wait states, 16 bit AT memory cycles will have 1 wait state.

Figure 1.8 shows the sequence diagram of a Normal mode local cycle followed by an AT bus cycle with zero wait states (0 W.S.) and zero command delays (0 C.D.). In sequences 1 and 2, IALE is generated from CLK2IN. AF16 is sampled to be low in sequence 2. ALE and AT buss commands (XIOR, XIOW, XMEMR, MEMW) are not generated since it is a local cycle. For a zero wait state cycle, ready is sampled low by the 80286 CPU in sequence 3 and the cycle is terminated. For the AT bus cycle, AF16 is sampled high in sequence 4. Control is transferred to the AT bus state machine. BCLK then generates the AT bus states. ALE is generated in sequences

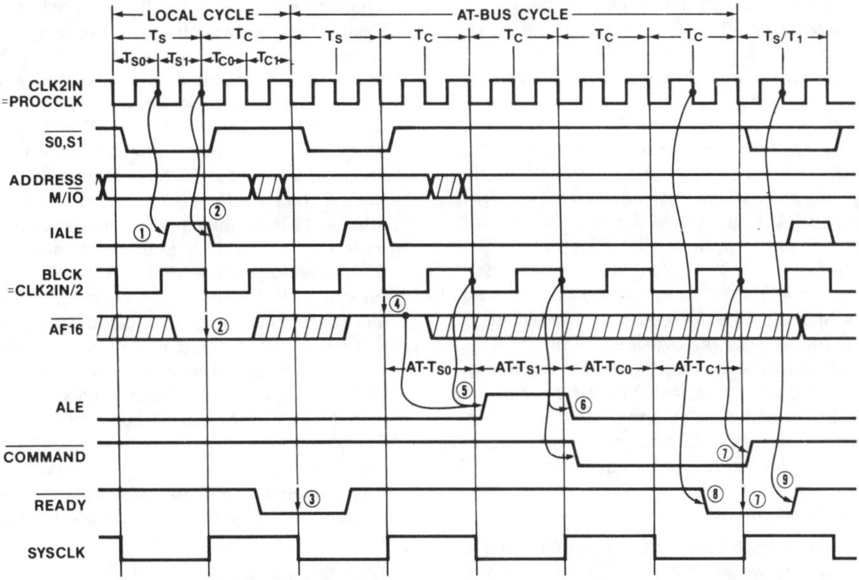

Figure 1.8 Normal Mode Local Cycle Followed by AT Bus Cycle (0WS, 0CD)

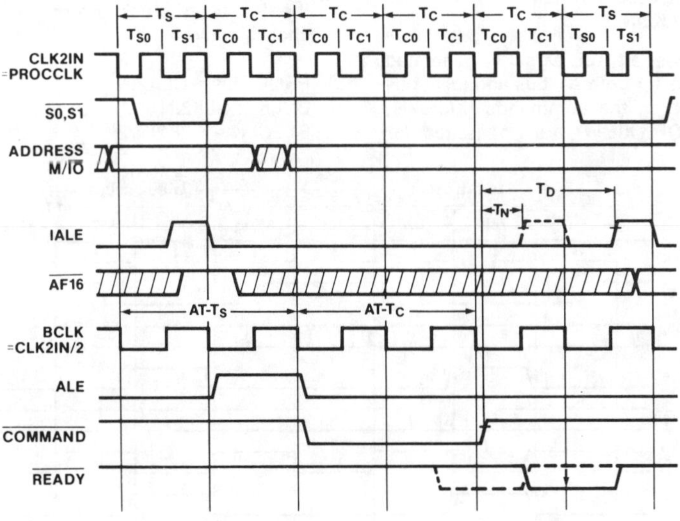

NOTE: TD = DELAYED HOLD TIME, TN = NORMAL HOLD TIME.

Figure 1.9 Normal Mode AT Bus Cycle with Additional Hold Time (0WS, 0CD)

5 and 6. The AT bus command is generated in sequences 6 and 7, for zero command delays programmed in the 82C211. For a zero wait state cycle, ready is asserted low as shown in sequences 8 and 9, to be sampled by the CPU in sequence 7. This terminates the AT bus cycle.

On the AT bus, certain slow peripherals require between 50 to 60 nanoseconds between command going inactive to the next ALE going active, to provide sufficient data recovery time. The sequence diagram in Figure 1.9 shows a Normal mode AT bus cycle with additional hold time. The dotted IALE signal would have been valid, if the additional hold time register had not been enabled in RA1<7>. Instead, IALE is delayed by one T_C state of the processor by asserting READY one T_C cycle later. The 82C212 provides an extended DLE to the 82C215 in this mode, so that data is available to the CPU during write cycles. If this mode was not invoked, then READY would have been asserted earlier as shown by the dotted line. In Delayed mode, the 82C211 provides an extended data hold time. This additional hold time can only be programmed in the Normal mode.

1.3.2 Quick mode

This mode is also a synchronous mode and is enabled by writing a zero to REG61<6> and the following clock selections have been made:

PROCCLK = BCLK = CLK2IN
SYSCLK = CLK2IN/2

In Quick mode, an ALE signal is generated on the AT bus for both AT bus and local bus cycles. However, the commands (XMEMR, XMEMW, XIOR, XIOW) are not issued for local bus cycles.

The sequence diagram for a Quick mode local cycle followed by an AT bus cycle is shown in Figure 1.10. In this mode, both IALE and ALE are generated in sequences 1 and 2 for the local cycle. Hence, an ALE is issued on the AT bus for AT or non-AT bus cycles. The local cycle is terminated when READY is sampled low by the 80286 in sequence 3. For the AT bus cycle, the command is issued after AF16 is sampled high in sequence 5. For write cycles, ACEN is activated in sequence 4. For read cycles, ACEN is activated in sequence 5. If the next cycle is not an AT bus write cycle, then ACEN is negated in sequence 6. READY is sampled low by the 80286 in sequence 6, to terminate the cycle. As seen in Figure 1.10, the AT bus states coincide with the CPU states for AT bus cycles. Hence, Quick mode is performance efficient when switching between local and AT bus cycles. This mode is useful for high speed add-on cards such as Lazer Printer interface cards.

1.3.3 Delayed mode

This mode is another synchronous mode and is enabled when Quick mode is disabled and the following clock selections have been chosen made:

PROCCLK = CLK2IN
BCLK = CLK2IN
SYSCLK = CLK2IN/2

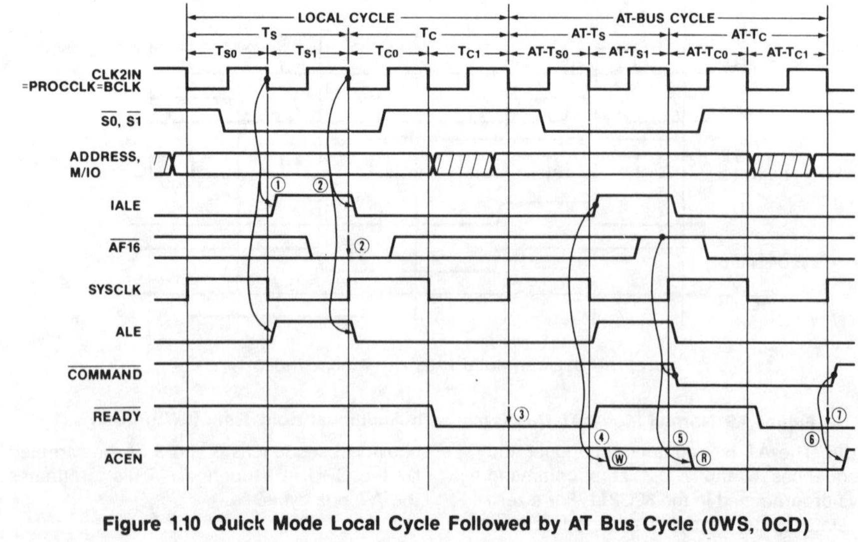

Figure 1.10 Quick Mode Local Cycle Followed by AT Bus Cycle (0WS, 0CD)

In Delayed mode, ALE and commands are issued only for AT bus cycles like in the Normal mode, except that BCLK = CLK2IN. ALE and commands are not issued for local cycles. Figure 1.11 shows a Delayed mode AT bus cycle. IALE is generated in sequences 1 and 2. ALE is asserted in sequence 3 after sampling AF16 high and it is deasserted in sequence 4. Hence the AT bus states, though synchronous, are delayed with respect to the processor states. Figure 1.11 is an example with two command delays and three wait states. The dotted lines A and B show command going active for 0 and 1 command delays. Sequence 5 shows command going active for programmed 2 command delays. Dotted lines D, E, F show command going inactive for 0, 1, 2 wait states. Sequence 6 shows command going inactive for programmed 3 wait states. READY is sampled by the 80286 in sequence 6 to terminate the current cycle. Since the AT bus states are delayed with respect to the processor states, the Local Address lines LA17-LA23 (typically un-latched) are not valid when ALE is active. In order to have the LA17-LA23 lines valid when ALE is active, they are latched by EALE as shown in sequence 7. Sequences 8, 9 show when ACEN is asserted for AT bus write (W) and read (R) cycles. ACEN is deasserted in sequence 10. This mode is useful for slow peripheral AT add-on cards.

1.3.4 External mode

This is an asynchronous mode and is enabled when ATCLK is selected as the source for BCLK. The following clock selections are required in this mode:

PROCCLK = CLK2IN
BCLK = ATCLK
SYSCLK = ATCLK/2

Since ATCLK is asynchronous to CLK2IN, the CPU state machine runs asynchronous to the AT bus state machine. ALE and commands (XMEMR, XMEMW, XIOR, XIOW) are issued only for AT bus cycles. These signals are inactive for local cycles. Figure 1.12 shows a sequence diagram for an External mode AT bus cycle. AF16 is sampled high in sequence 2 and is latched internally, using CLK2IN. The asynchronous BCLK samples this latched state on the next rising edge of BCLK. In the example shown, edge A samples the latched AF16 signal (internal) high. This causes the AT state machine to issue an ALE in sequences 3 and 4. For a zero command delay, zero wait states cycle, the command is issued on the AT bus in sequences 4 and 6, synchronized with BCLK. For write cycles, ACEN

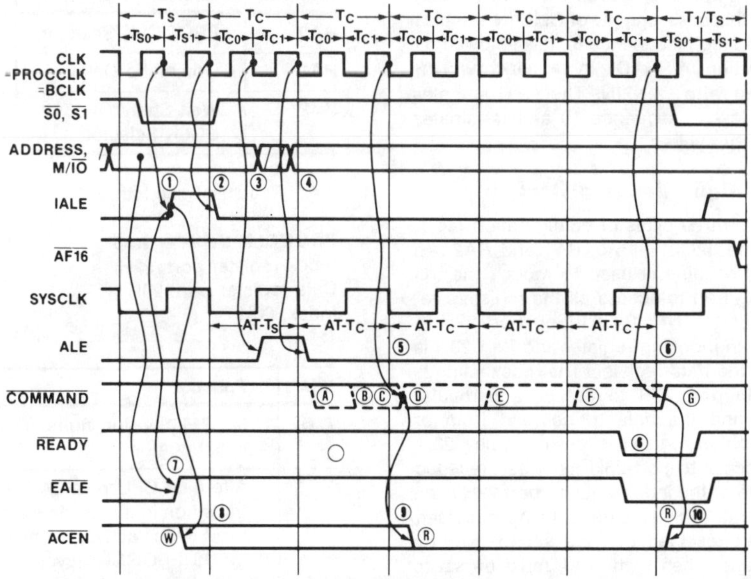

Figure 1.11 Delayed Mode AT Bus Cycle (3WS, 2CD)

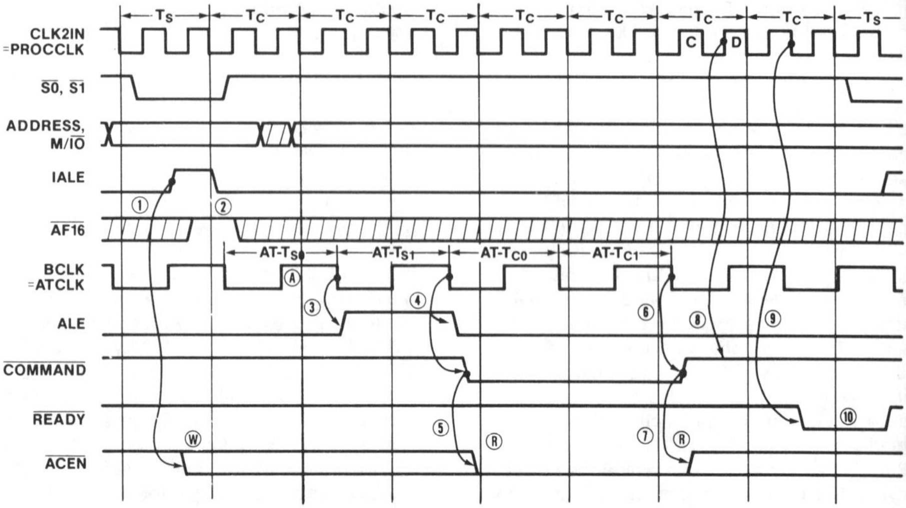

Figure 1.12 External Mode AT Bus Cycle (0WS, 0CD)

is asserted in sequence 1 and for read cycles, it is asserted in sequence 5. ACEN is de-asserted in sequence 7. The command inactive state is sampled by CLK2IN on every rising edge. In this case, edge D of CLK2IN samples command high (sequence 8). It is followed by the assertion of READY in sequence 9, synchronized with CLK2IN. The CPU samples READY low in sequence 10 and terminates the current cycle.

1.4 Configuration Registers

There are three bytes of configuration registers in the 82C211; RA0, RA1 and RA2. An indexing scheme is used to reduce the I/O ports required to access all the registers required for the NEAT CHIPSet. Port 22H is used as an indexing register and Port 23H is used as the data register. The index value is placed in port 22H to access a particular register and the data to be read from or written to that register is located in port 23H. Every access to port 23H must be preceded by a write of the index value to port 22H even if the same register data is being accessed again. All reserved bits are set to zero by default and when written to, must be set to zero. Table 1.3 lists the three registers:

Table 1.3

Register Number	Register Name	Index
RA0	PROCCLK Selector	60H
RA1	Command Delay	61H
RA2	Wait State/ BCLK Selector	62H

1.4.1 Register Description

PROCCLK Register RA0
Index register port: 22H
Data register port: 23H
Index: 60H

Bits	Function
7, 6	82C211 revision number. 00 is the initial number.
5	Alternate CPU reset. A low to high transition in this bit activates a CPU reset. Once active, it remains active for 16 PROCCLK cycles and then goes low.

4	Processor clock select is by default set to zero and selects PROCCLK = CLK2IN. If high, it selects PROCCLK = BCLK.
3	Reserved.*
2	Local bus READY timeout NMI enable. A one enables the NMI and a zero disables it. Default is 0
1	Reserved.*
0	Local bus READY timeout. A one indicates that READY timeout has occurred 128 PROCCLK cycles after $\overline{AF16}$ has been asserted. A zero indicates that READY time out has not occurred.

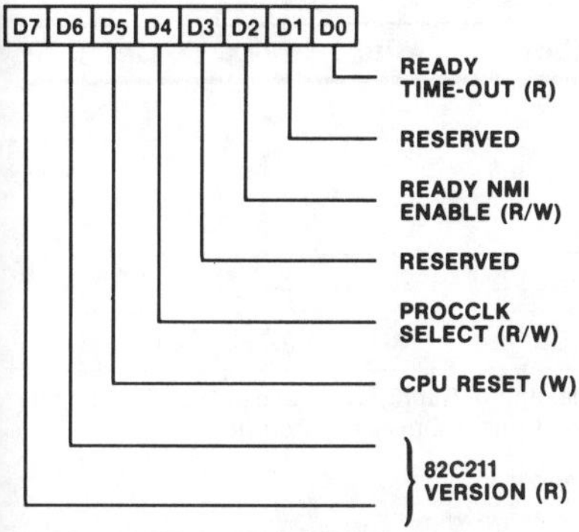

Command Delay Register RA1
Index register port: 22H
Data register port: 23H
Index: 61H

Bits	Function
1, 0	AT Bus I/O cycle command delay. Specifies between 0 to 3 BCLK cycle command delays for AT I/O cycles. Default is 1.
3, 2	AT Bus 8 bit memory command delay. Specifies between 0 to 3 BCLK cycle command delays for 8 bit AT memory cycles. Default is 1.
5, 4	AT Bus 16 bit memory command delay. Specifies between 0 and 3 BCLK cycle command delays for 16 bit AT memory cycles. Default is 0
6	Quick mode enable. A zero enables Quick mode and a one disables it. Default is 1.
7	Address hold time delay. A one enables extra address bus hold time and a zero disables it. Default is 0.

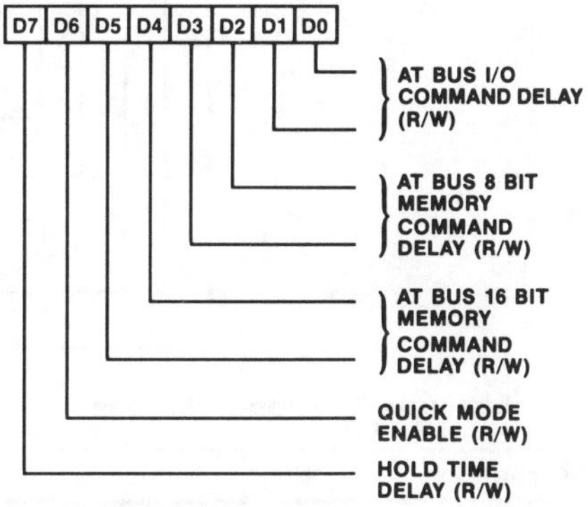

Wait States Register RA2
Index register port: 22H
Data register port: 23H
Index: 62H

Bits	Function
1, 0	Bus clock (BCLK) source select. Default is 00.
00	BCLK = CLK2IN/2
01	BCLK = CLK2IN
10	BCLK = ATCLK
11	Reserved
3, 2	8 bit AT cycle wait state generation. Default is 5.
00	2 wait states
01	3 wait states
10	4 wait states
11	5 wait states
5, 4	16 bit AT cycle wait state generation. Default is 3.
00	0 wait states
01	1 wait state
10	2 wait states
11	3 wait states
7, 6	Reserved.*

*The reserved bits are recommanded to be initialized to 1.

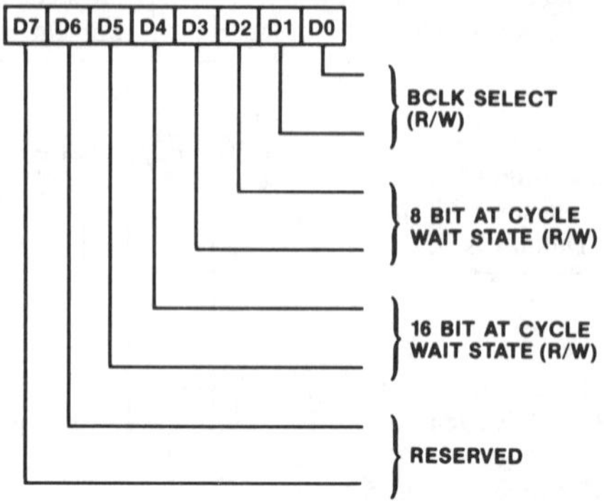

1.5 Absolute Maximum Ratings

Parameter	Symbol	Min.	Max.	Units
Supply Voltage	V_{CC}	—	7.0	V
Input Voltage	V_I	-0.5	5.5	V
Output Voltage	V_O	-0.5	5.5	V
Operating Temperature	T_{OP}	-25°	85°	C
Storage Temperature	T_{STG}	-40°	125°	C

NOTE: Permanent device damage may occur if Absolute Maximum Ratings are exceeded. Functional operation should be restricted to the conditions described under Operating Conditions.

1.6 82C211 Operating Conditions

Parameter	Symbol	Min.	Max.	Units
Supply Voltage	V_{CC}	4.75	5.25	V
Ambient Temperature	T_A	0°	70°	C

1.7 82C211 DC Characteristics

Parameter	Symbol	Min.	Max.	Units
Input Low Voltage	V_{IL}	—	0.8	V
Input High Voltage	V_{IH}	2.0	—	V
Output Low Voltage I_{OL} = 4mA	V_{OL}	—	0.45	V
Output High Voltage I_{OH} = -4mA	V_{OH}	2.4	—	V
Input Current $0<V_{IN}<V_{CC}$	I_{IL}	—	±10	μA

Power Supply Current @ 16MHz	I_{CC}	—	50	mA
Output High-Z Leakage Current $0.45<V_{OUT}<V_{CC}$	I_{OZ1}		±10	μA
PROCCLK Output Low Voltage @ I_{OL} = 5mA	V_{OLC}	—	0.45	V
PROCCLK Output High Voltage @ I_{OH} = -1mA	V_{OHC}	4.0	—	V
Standby Power Supply Current	I_{CCSB}	—	1.5	mA

1.8 82C211-12, 82C211-16 AC Characteristics

(T_A = 0°C to 70°C, V_{CC} = 5V ± 5%)

Sym	Description	Min.	Typ.	Max.	Units
t1	ALE active delay from SYSCLK↓	−1		6 (10)	ns
t2	ALE inactive delay from SYSCLK↑	−1		6 (10)	ns
t3	COMMAND active delay from SYSCLK↓	0		8	ns
t4	COMMAND inactive delay from SYSCLK↑	0		6	ns
t5	$\overline{\text{EALE}}$ active delay from SYSCLK↓	0		10	ns
t6	$\overline{\text{MEMCS16}}$ set-up time to SYSCLK↑	10			ns
t7	$\overline{\text{MEMCS16}}$ hold time to SYSCLK↑	4			ns
t8	$\overline{\text{IOCS16}}$ set-up time to SYSCLK↓	10			ns
t9	$\overline{\text{IOCS16}}$ hold time to SYSCLK↓	10			ns
t10	$\overline{\text{0WS}}$ set-up time to SYSCLK↑	9			ns
t11	$\overline{\text{0WS}}$ hold time to SYSCLK↑	4			ns
t12	IOCHRDY set-up time to SYSCLK↑	11			ns
t13	IOCHRDY hold time to SYSCLK↑	4			ns
t14	IALE active delay from PROCCLK↓	1		10	ns
t15	IALE inactive delay from PROCCLK↓	1		11 (16)	ns
t16	$\overline{\text{AF16}}$ set-up time to PROCCLK↓	15(19)			ns
t17	$\overline{\text{AF16}}$ hold time to PROCCLK↓	11(13)			ns
t18	$\overline{\text{READY}}$ input set-up time to PROCCLK↓	11			ns
t19	$\overline{\text{READY}}$ input hold time PROCCLK↓	8			ns
t20	RESET3 active delay from PROCCLK↓	2		12	ns
t21	RESET3 inactive delay from PROCCLK↓	2		16	ns
t22	RESET4 active delay from PROCCLK↓	0		8	ns
t23	RESET4 inactive delay from PROCCLK↓	1		16	ns
t24	SDIR<1:0> active delay from SYSCLK↓	3		11	ns

1.8 82C211-12, 82C211-16 AC Characteristics (Continued)
(T_A = 0°C to 70°C, V_{CC} = 5V ± 5%)

Sym	Description	Min.	Typ.	Max.	Units
t25	SDIR<1:0> inactive delay from SYSCLK↑	1		10	ns
t26	$\overline{\text{ACEN}}$ active delay from SYSCLK↓	0		7	ns
t27	$\overline{\text{ACEN}}$ inactive delay from SYSCLK↑	0		6	ns
t32	AC0 active delay from PROCCLK↓	6		17	ns
t33	AC0 inactive delay from PROCCLK↓	6		18	ns
t34	AC1 active delay from PROCCLK↓	7		18	ns
t35	AC1 active delay from PROCCLK↓	7		18	ns
t38	Hold active delay from SYSCLK↓	0		6	ns
t39	Hold inactive delay from SYSCLK↑	0		6	ns
t40	$\overline{\text{REF}}$ delay from HLDA	3		14	ns
t43	$\overline{\text{REF}}$ inactive delay from SYSCLK↑	0		6	ns
t44	XMEMR active delay from SYSCLK↑	1		9	ns
t45	XMEMR inactive delay from SYSCLK↑	0		5	ns
t46	HRQ1 set-up to SYSCLK↑	10			ns
t47	HRQ1 hold time to SYSCLK↑	4			ns
t49	HLDA1 active delay from HLDA↑	8		17	ns
t51	HLDA1 inactive delay from HLDA↓	12		20	ns
t52	$\overline{\text{NPCS}}$ active delay from PROCCLK↓	11		21	ns
t53	Overlap of $\overline{\text{NPBUSY}}$ & $\overline{\text{ERROR}}$ (both low)	8			
t54	NPINT delay from $\overline{\text{NPBUSY}}$, $\overline{\text{ERROR}}$ low	7		16	ns
t55	NPINT inactive delay from $\overline{\text{ERROR}}$↑	3		11	ns
t56	$\overline{\text{NPBUSY}}$ active pulse width	13			
t57	$\overline{\text{ERROR}}$ hold time with respect to $\overline{\text{NPBUSY}}$↑	0			
t58	$\overline{\text{ERROR}}$ set up time to $\overline{\text{NPBUSY}}$↑	3			
t59	$\overline{\text{ERROR}}$ min low pulse	8			
t60	$\overline{\text{BUSY}}$ active delay from $\overline{\text{NPBUSY}}$↓	8		18	ns
t61	$\overline{\text{BUSY}}$ inactive delay from $\overline{\text{NPBUSY}}$↑	8		15	ns
t62	$\overline{\text{BUSY}}$ delay from $\overline{\text{IOW}}$	2		12	ns
t63	NPRST active delay from $\overline{\text{IALE}}$	9		19	ns
t64	NPRST inactive delay from $\overline{\text{IALE}}$	4		15	ns

Note: Values inside ( ) are 12 MHz timing.

1.9 82C211 Timing Diagrams

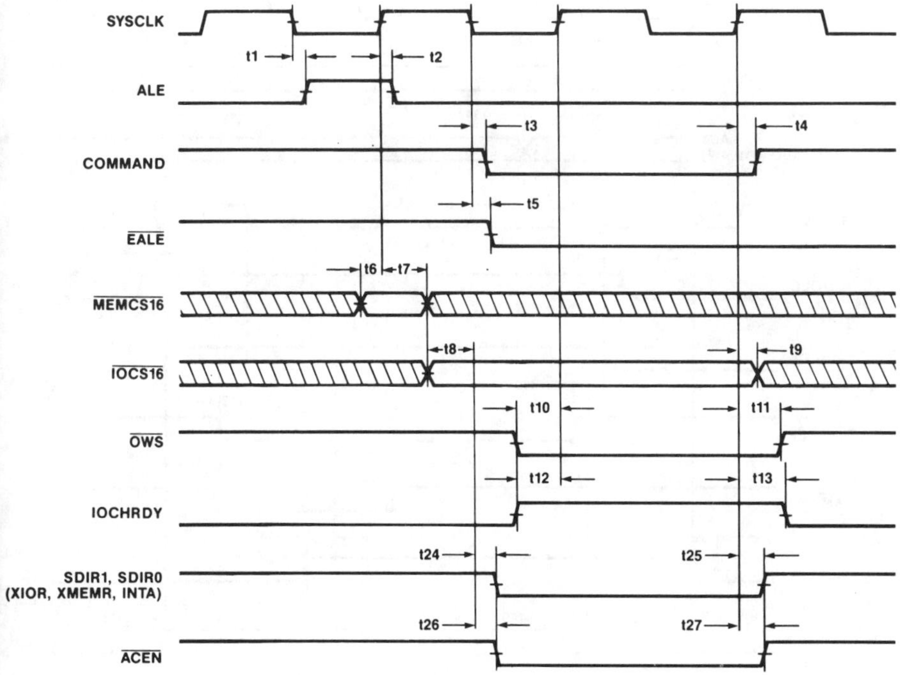

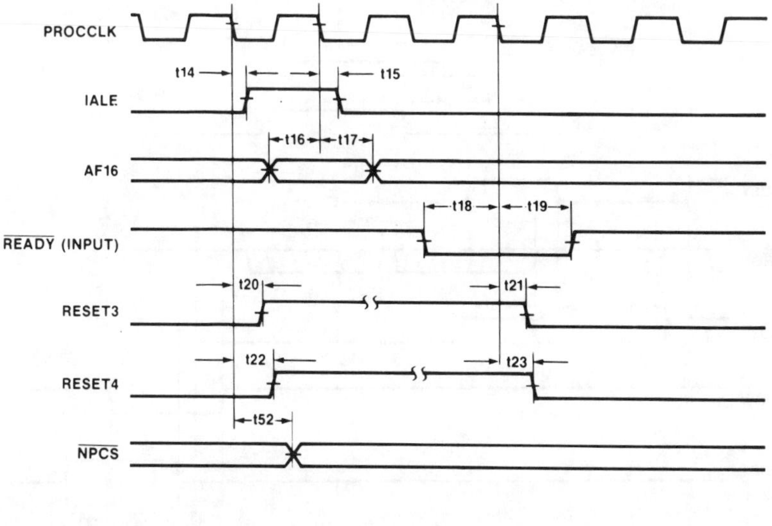

1.9 82C211 Timing Diagrams (Continued)

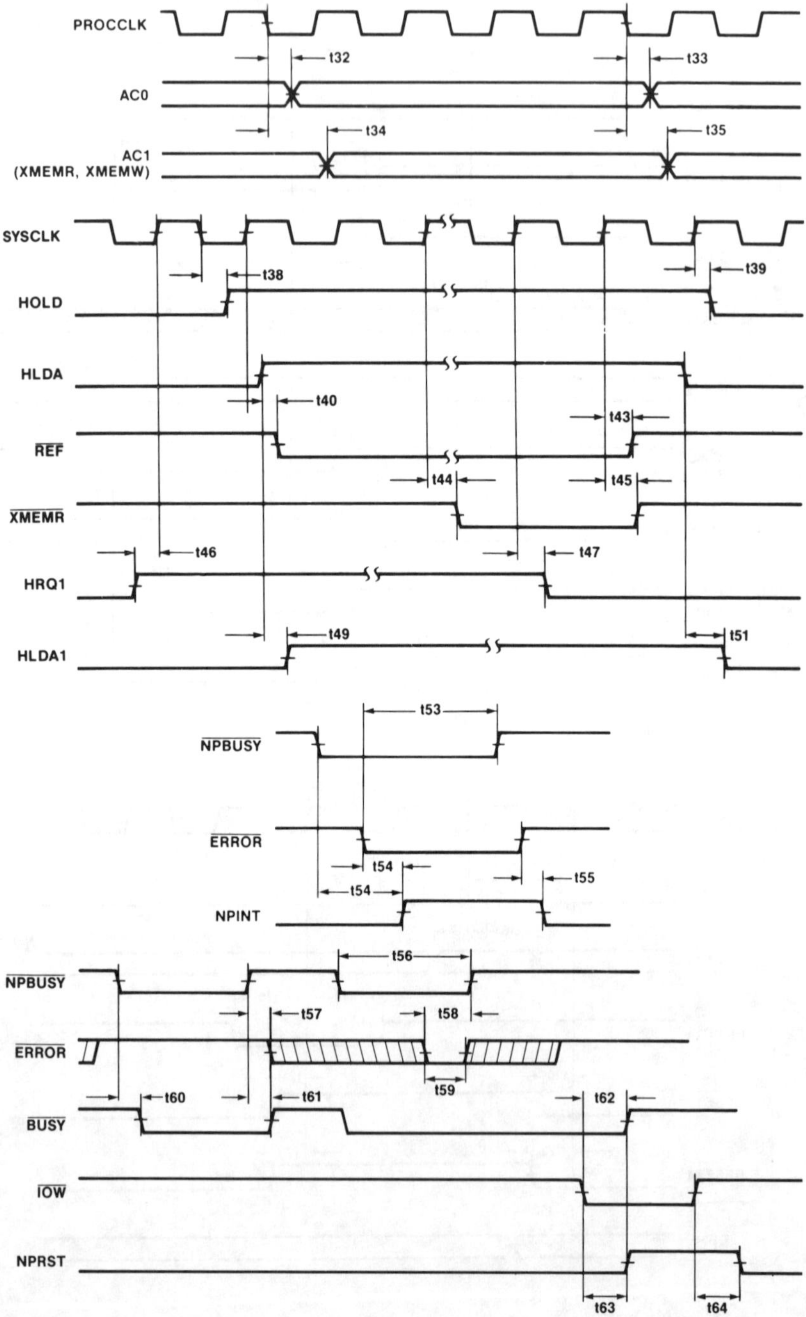

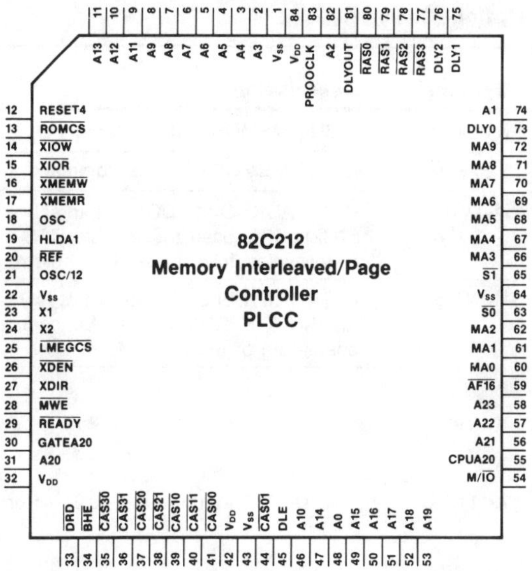

82C212 Pin Description

Pin No.	Pin Type	Symbol	Description
Clocks and Control			
83	I	PROCCLK	PROCESSOR CLOCK input from the 82C211
23	I	X1	CRYSTAL 1 input from the 14.31818 MHz crystal.
24	O	X2	CRYSTAL 2 output to the 14.31818 MHz crystal.
18	O	OSC	OSCILLATOR output for the system clock at 14.31818 MHz and has a drive capability of 24mA.
21	O	OSC/12	OSCILLATOR divided by 12 is an output with a clock frequency equal to 1/12 of the crystal frequency across the X1, X2 pins.
12	I	RESET4	RESET 4 is the active high reset input from the 82C211. It resets the configuration registers to their default values. When active, RAS<0:3> and CAS<00:31> remain high, OSC and OSC/12 remain inactive.
20	I	$\overline{REF}$	REFRESH is an active low input for DRAM refresh control from the 82C211. It initiates a refresh cycle for the DRAMs.
65, 63	I	S<1, 0>	STATUS input lines from the CPU are active low. These lines are monitored to detect the start of a cycle.
54	I	M/$\overline{IO}$	MEMORY I/O signal from the CPU. If high it indicates a memory cycle. If low, it indicates an I/O cycle.
15	I	$\overline{XIOR}$	I/O READ command, input active low.
14	I	$\overline{XIOW}$	I/O WRITE command, input active high.

82C212 Pin Description (Continued)

Pin No.	Pin Type	Symbol	Description
17	I	XMEMR	X BUS MEMORY READ command, input active low.
16	I	XMEMW	X BUS MEMORY WRITE command, input active low.
19	I	HLDA1	HOLD ACKNOWLEDGE 1 is an active high input from the 82C211. It is used to generate RAS and CAS signals for DMA cycles, in response to a hold request.
13	O	ROMCS	ROM CHIP SELECT is an active low chip select output to the BIOS EPROM. It can be connected to the output enable pin of the EPROM.
48, 74, 82		A<0:2>	
2-8		A<3:9>	
46		A10	
9-11	I	A<11:13>	ADDRESS input lines A<0:23> from the CPU local bus.
47		A14	
49-53		A<15:19>	
55-58		A<20:23>	
34	I	BHE	BYTE HIGH ENABLE is an active low input from the CPU for transfer of data on the upper byte.
29	I/O	READY	READY is the system ready signal to the CPU. It is an active low output after requested memory or I/O data transfer is completed. It is an input when the current bus cycle is an AT bus cycle and is an output for local memory and I/O cycles.
59	O	AF16	AF16 is an active low output asserted on local memory (EPROM or DRAM) cycles. It is high for all other cycles. This signal is sampled by the 82C211.
DRAM Interface			
77-80	O	RAS<3:0>	ROW ADDRESS STROBES 3 to 0 are active low outputs used as RAS signals to the DRAMs for selecting different banks. RAS3 selects the highest bank and RAS0 selects the lowest bank. These signals should be buffered and line terminated with 75Ω resistors to reduce ringing before driving the DRAM RAS lines.
41	O	CAS00	COLUMN ADDRESS STROBE 00 is an active low output used to select the low byte DRAMs of bank 0. This signal should be line terminated with a 75Ω resistor to reduce ringing before driving the DRAM CAS line.
44	O	CAS01	COLUMN ADDRESS STROBE 01 is an active low output used to select the high byte DRAMs of bank 0. This signal should be line terminated with a 75Ω resistor to reduce ringing before driving the DRAM CAS line.

82C212 Pin Description (Continued)

Pin No.	Pin Type	Symbol	Description
39	O	$\overline{\text{CAS10}}$	COLUMN ADDRESS STROBE 10 is an active low output used to select the low byte DRAMs of bank 1. This signal should be line terminated with a 75Ω resistor to reduce ringing before driving the DRAM CAS line.
40	O	$\overline{\text{CAS11}}$	COLUMN ADDRESS STROBE 11 is an active low output used to select the high byte DRAMs of bank 1. This signal should be line terminated with a 75Ω resistor to reduce ringing before driving the DRAM CAS line.
37	O	$\overline{\text{CAS20}}$	COLUMN ADDRESS STROBE 20 is an active low output used to select the low byte DRAMs of bank 2. This signal should be line terminated with a 75Ω resistor to reduce ringing before driving the DRAM CAS line.
38	O	$\overline{\text{CAS21}}$	COLUMN ADDRESS STROBE 21 is an active low output used to select the high byte DRAMs of bank 2. This signal should be line terminated with a 75Ω resistor to reduce ringing before driving the DRAM CAS line.
35	O	$\overline{\text{CAS30}}$	COLUMN ADDRESS STROBE 30 is an active low output used to select the low byte DRAMs of bank 3. This signal should be line terminated with a 75Ω resistor to reduce ringing before driving the DRAM CAS line.
36	O	$\overline{\text{CAS31}}$	COLUMN ADDRESS STROBE 31 is an active low output used to select the high byte DRAMs of bank 3. This signal should be line terminated with a 75Ω resistor to reduce ringing before driving the DRAM CAS line.
28	O	$\overline{\text{MWE}}$	MEMORY WRITE ENABLE is an active low output for DRAM write enable.
45	O	DLE	DATA LATCH ENABLE is an active high output used to enable the local memory data buffer latch in the 82C215.
33	O	$\overline{\text{DRD}}$	DATA READ is an active low output used to transfer data from the memory bus to the local CPU bus in the 82C215. If high it sets the data path from the local CPU bus to the memory bus.
81	O	DLYOUT	DELAY LINE OUT is an active high output to the delay line for generating the DRAM control signals.
73, 75, 76	I	DLY<0:2>	DELAY IN 0, 1, 2 are active high inputs from the first to third taps on the delay line used to generate DRAM control signals.
26	O	$\overline{\text{XDEN}}$	X DATA BUFFER ENABLE is an active low output asserted during I/O accesses to locations 22H and 23H. These locations contain the index and data registers for the NEAT CHIPSet™. It is used to enable the buffers between the XD and MA buses for accessing the 82C212 internal registers.

82C212 Pin Description (Continued)

Pin No.	Pin Type	Symbol	Description
27	O	$\overline{\text{XDIR}}$	X BUS DIRECTION is used to control the drivers between the X and S buses. The driver should be used such that data flow is from the S to X bus when $\overline{\text{XDIR}}$ is high and in the other direction when $\overline{\text{XDIR}}$ is low.
71-72	O	MA<8:9>	MULTIPLEXED DRAM ADDRESS lines MA8, MA9. These lines should be buffered and line terminated with 75Ω resistors before driving the DRAM address lines.
66-70 60-62	I/O I/O	MA<3:7> MA<0:2>	MULTIPLEXED DRAM ADDRESS lines MA0 to MA7. Also used as bi-directional lines to read/write to the internal registers of the 82C212. An external 74ALS245 buffer is required to isolate this path during normal DRAM operation. These lines should be buffered and line terminated with 75Ω resistors before driving the DRAM address lines.
Miscellaneous			
31	I/O	GA20	ADDRESS line 20 is the gated A20 bit which is controlled by GATEA20.
30	I	GATEA20	GATE ADDRESS 20 is an input used to force A20 low when GATEA20 is low. When high it propagates CPUA20 onto the A20 line. It is used to keep address under 1Mb during DOS operation.
25	O	$\overline{\text{LMEGCS}}$	LOW MEG CHIP SELECT is an unlatched active low output asserted when the low Meg memory address space (0 to 1024 Kbytes) is accessed or during refresh cycles. It is used to disable $\overline{\text{SMEMR}}$ and $\overline{\text{SMEMW}}$ signals on the AT bus if accesses are made beyond the 1Mbyte address space to maintain PC and PC/XT compatibility.
Power and Ground			
32, 42, 84	—	VDD	POWER SUPPLY.
1, 22, 43, 64	—	VSS	GROUND.
Controls			
14	I	$\overline{\text{ACEN}}$	ACTION CODE ENABLE is an active low input from the 82C211 that validates the action codes.
12, 13	I	AC<1:0>	ACTION CODES input from the 82C211 are used for bus sizing and byte assembly operations. They are discussed in Section 1.2.4.
76	I	DLE	DATA LATCH ENABLE is an active high input from the 82C212 used to enable the local memory data buffer latch.
74	I	$\overline{\text{DRD}}$	DATA READ is an active low input from the 82C212 used to transfer data from the M data bus to the CPU data bus. If high, it sets the data path from the CPU data bus to the M data bus.

82C215 Pin Description (Continued)

Pin No.	Pin Type	Symbol	Description
53	I	HLDA1	HOLD ACKNOWLEDGE 1 is an active high input from the 82C211 used for address and data direction control during DMA cycles.
15	I	IALE	ADDRESS LATCH ENABLE (INTERNAL) is an active high input from the 82C211 used to latch the CPU address lines on to the X address lines.
11	I	$\overline{\text{BHE}}$	BYTE HIGH ENABLE is an active low input from the CPU. It is used to enable the high byte parity checking.
10	I	A0	ADDRESS line A0 is input from the CPU. It is used to enable the low byte parity checking.
Address			
25-31 33-41	I/O I/O	A<1:7> A<8:16>	ADDRESS lines A1-A16 from the CPU. They are input during CPU and refresh cycles and output during DMA/Master cycles.
44-52 54-60	I/O I/O	XA<16:8> XA<7:1>	X ADDRESS lines XA16–XA1 (latched) are connected to the peripheral bus in the IBM™ PC/AT architecture.
Data			
2, 4, 6, 8, 16, 18, 20, 23, 3, 5, 7, 9, 17, 19, 21, 24	I/O	D<15:0>	DATA lines D15-D0 from the CPU.
82, 80, 73, 71, 69, 67, 65, 62, 81, 79, 72, 70, 68, 66, 63, 61	I/O	MD<15:0>	MEMORY DATA lines MD15-MD0 from the memory bus.
Parity			
78, 77	I/O	MP1, MP0	MEMORY PARITY bits MP1, MP0 are the parity bits for the high and low order bytes of the system DRAMs. These lines are input during memory operations for parity error detection and are output during memory write operations for parity generation.
83	O	$\overline{\text{PARERR}}$	PARITY ERROR is an active low output to the 82C211 which goes active upon detecting a parity error during a system memory read operation. It is used to generate a non-maskable interrupt to the CPU.
Power and Ground			
32, 42, 84	—	VDD	POWER
1, 22, 43 64, 75	—	VSS	GROUND

2 82C212 PAGE/INTERLEAVE AND EMS MEMORY CONTROLLER

2.1 Features

- Page mode access including single bank, 2 way and 4 way page interleaved, providing higher performance over conventional DRAM accessing schemes
- Supports 100ns DRAMs at 16MHz using page interleaved operation
- Supports up to 8Mbytes of on board memory
- Provides automatic remapping of RAM resident in 640K to 1Mbyte area to the top of the 1Mbyte address space.
- Supports Lotus Intel Microsoft-Expanded Memory System (LIM-EMS 4.0) address translation logic
- Shadow RAM feature for efficient Basic Input/Output System (BIOS) execution
- OS/2 optimization feature allows fast switching between protected and real mode
- Staggered refresh to reduce power supply noise

2.2 Overview

The 82C212 performs the memory control functions in the NEAT system, utilizing page mode access DRAMs. The various memory array configurations possible and Page/ Interleaved mode operation are discussed in this section. Figure 2.1 is a block diagram of the 82C212 chip.

2.2.1 Array Configuration

The 82C212 organizes memory as banks of 18 bit modules, consisting of 16 bits of data and 2 bits of parity information. The 16 bits of data are split into high and low order bytes, with one parity bit for each byte. This configuration can be implemented by using eighteen 1-bit wide DRAMs or by using four 4-bit wide DRAMs for data with two 1-bit wide DRAMs for parity. The minimum configuration can be a single bank operating in non-interleaved mode or can be a pair of DRAM banks operating in two way interleaved mode. If the 82C212 uses a two way interleaving scheme, the DRAMs within a pair of banks must be identical. However, each bank of DRAM pairs can be different from other pairs. For example, Banks 0, 1 may have 256K by 1 bit DRAMs and Banks 2 and 3 could have 1M by 1bit DRAMs. A typical system may be shipped

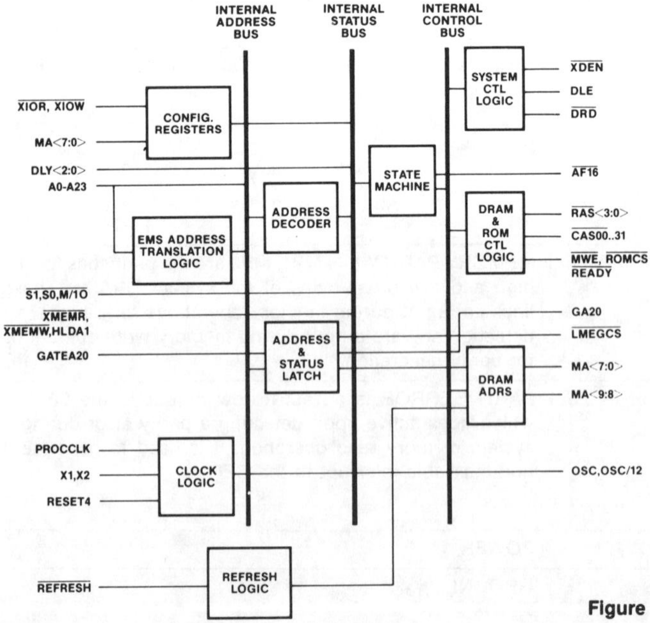

Figure 2.1 82C212 Block Diagram

with one or two banks of smaller DRAM types (eg. 256K by 1 bit DRAMs) and later upgraded with additional pairs of banks of larger DRAMs (eg. 1M by 1 bit DRAMs).

2.2.2 Page/Interleaved Operation

The 82C212 uses a page/interleaved design that is different from most interleaved memory designs. Typical two way interleaving schemes use two banks of DRAMs with even word addresses on one bank and odd word addresses on the other bank. If memory accesses are sequential, the RAS* precharge time of one bank overlaps the access time of the other bank. Typically, programs consist of instruction fetches interspersed with operand accesses. The instruction fetches tend to be sequential and the operand accesses tend to be random.

Figure 2.2 is a sequence diagram for a memory interleaved scheme using two banks 0 and 1. The RAS signals of the two banks are interleaved so that the RAS precharge time (T_{rp}) of one bank is used for the RAS active time in the other bank. This requires sequential accesses to be alternating between the two banks. For non-sequential accesses, it is possible to get wait states due to a 'miss'. Typically, this results in a 50% hit ratio (possible zero wait state accesses).

Figure 2.3 is a sequence diagram of a paged mode DRAM operation. In paged mode DRAMs, once a row access has been made, it is possible to access subsequent column addresses within that row, without the RAS precharge penalty. However, after a RAS active timeout, there is a RAS precharge period which typically occurs every 10 microseconds. Since the CAS precharge time T_{cp} is small, it is possible to make fast random accesses within a selected row. Typically, page mode access times are half the normal DRAM access times. For 256K × 1 DRAMs, each row has 512 bits. If eighteen 256K × 1 bit DRAMs are used to implement a bank, a page would have 512 × 2 bytes (excluding 2 bits for parity) = 1 Kbytes. Thus paged mode DRAMs could be interleaved at 1 Kbyte boundaries rather than 2 byte boundaries as in the regular interleaved mode operation. Any access to the currently active RAS page would occur in a short page access time and any subsequent access could be anywhere in the same 1Kbyte boundary, without incurring any penalty due to RAS precharge. If memory is configured to take advantage of this DRAM organization, significantly better performance can be achieved over normal interleaving because:

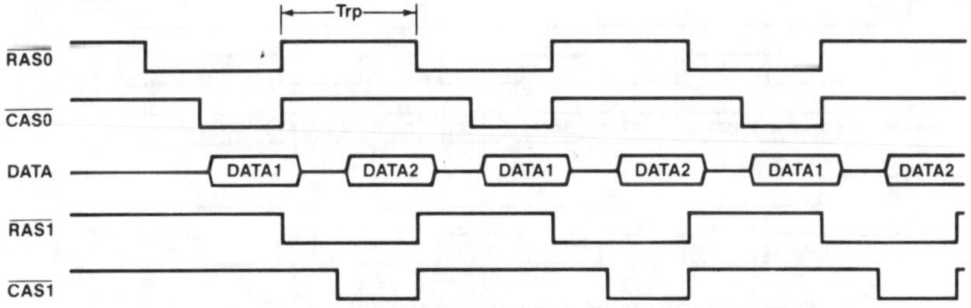

Figure 2.2 DRAM Interleaved Operation

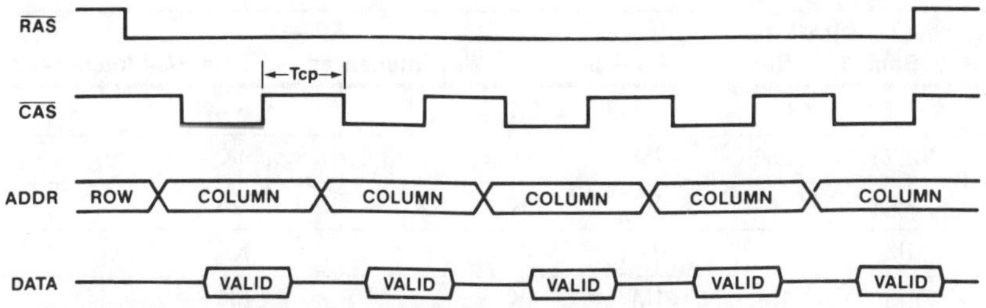

Figure 2.3 DRAM Page Mode Operation

1. Page mode access time is shorter than normal DRAM access time. This allows more time in the DRAM critical paths, to achieve penalty free accesses or 'hits'.
2. The possibility of the next access being fast is significantly higher than in a regular interleaving scheme. This is because instructions and data tend to cluster together by principle of locality of reference.

Figure 2.4 is a sequence diagram of a two way Page/Interleaved scheme using page mode DRAMs. As seen, it is possible to make zero wait state accesses between the two banks 0 and 1, by overlapping $\overline{CAS}$ precharge time of one bank with $\overline{CAS}$ active time of the other bank. The DRAM $\overline{RAS}$ lines for both banks can be held active till the $\overline{RAS}$ active time out period, at which time a $\overline{RAS}$ precharge for that bank is required. Typical hit ratios higher then 80% are possible using this scheme. With the 82C212 memory controller, using the page/interleaved scheme, 150 ns access time DRAMs can be used at 12MHz and 100 ns access time DRAMs at 16MHz.

82C212 supports both two and four way interleaved mode. If four way interleaved mode is used, the DRAMs used in the four banks must be identical. Table 2.0 shows the 0 wait state hit space for possible banks configurations.

OS/2 Optimization

The NEAT architecture features OS/2 optimization using REG6F<1> of the 82C212 in conjunction with REG60<5> of the 82C211. OS/2 makes frequent DOS calls while operating in protected mode of the 80286 CPU. In order to service these DOS calls, the 80286 CPU has to switch from protected to real mode quickly. Typical PC/AT architectures require the processor to issue two commands to the 8042 (or 8742) keyboard controller in order to reset the processor (to switch it into protected mode) and to activate GATEA20.

REG60<5> of the 82C211 is to used to invoke a software reset to the 80286 processor and REG6F<1> is used to activate GATEA20. Since this involves two I/O writes, it is possible to execute a "Fast GATEA20". In an OS/2 environment, where frequent DOS calls are made, this feature provides significant performance improvement.

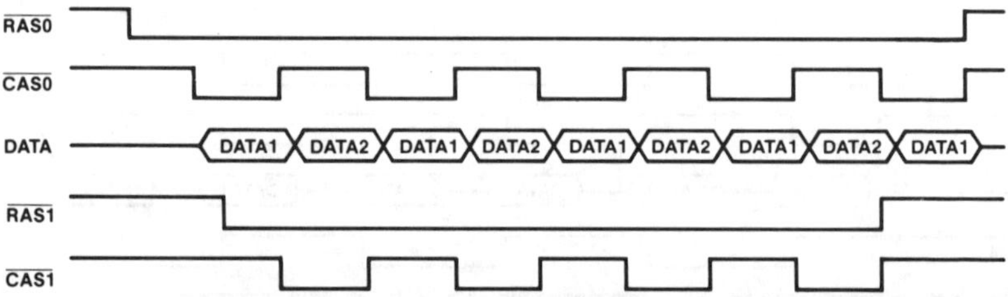

Figure 2.4 DRAM Page/Interleave Operation

Table 2.0 Average 0 Wait State Hit Space

DRAM Type					
Bank 0	**Bank 1**	**Bank 2**	**Bank 3**	**Two Way Interleaved**	**Four Way Interleaved**
256K	256K	0	0	2K	NA
256K	256K	256K	256K	2K	4K
256K	256K	1M	1M	3K	NA
1M	1M	0	0	4K	NA
1M	1M	1M	1M	4K	8K

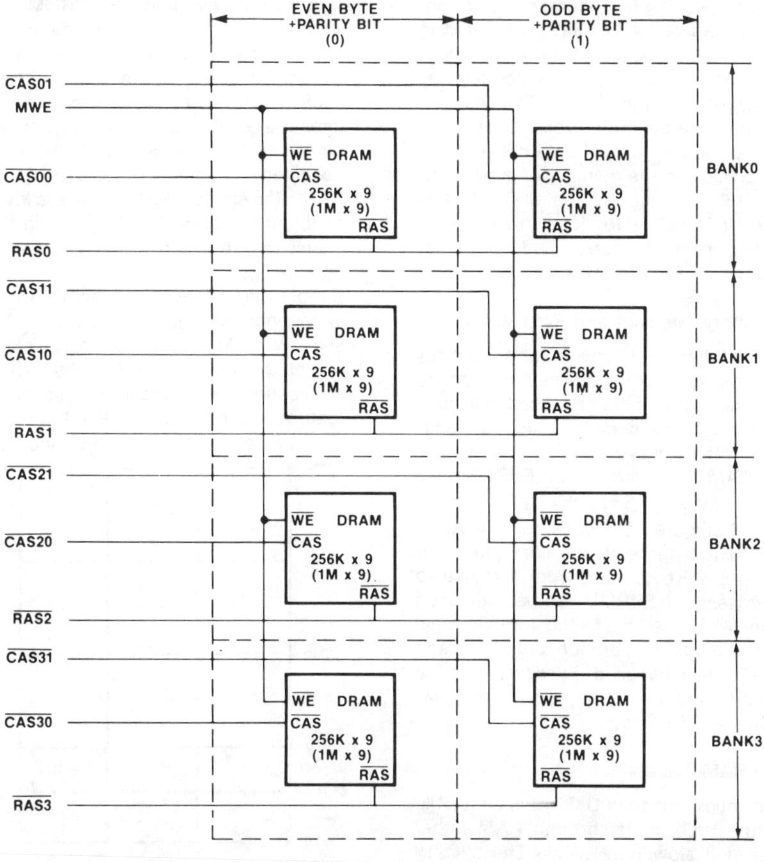

Figure 2.5 DRAM Organization

2.3 Functional Description

Figure 2.1 is a block diagram of the 82C212 memory controller. It consists of the following sub-modules:

- EPROM and DRAM control logic
- System Control logic
- Memory Mapping and Refresh logic
- Oscillator clock generation logic
- Configuration registers

2.3.1 EPROM and DRAM Control Logic

The EPROM and DRAM control logic in the 82C212 is responsible for the generation of the $\overline{\text{RAS}}$, $\overline{\text{CAS}}$ and $\overline{\text{MWE}}$ signals for DRAM accesses and the generation of $\overline{\text{ROMCS}}$ for EPROM accesses. This sub-module also generates $\overline{\text{READY}}$ to the CPU upon completion of the desired local memory operation. The appropriate number of wait states are inserted, as programmed by software (or by default) in the wait state register of the 82C212. Figure 2.5 is a block diagram of the DRAM organization for the NEAT architecture. As seen, each $\overline{\text{RAS}}$ line drives each 256K × 18 bit bank (or 1M × 18 bit bank). The $\overline{\text{CAS}}$ lines are used to drive individual bytes within each bank. $\overline{\text{MWE}}$ is connected to each DRAM bank write enable input.

2.3.2 System Control Logic

This sub-module of the 82C212 generates XDEN, DLE, $\overline{\text{DRD}}$, AF16 for system control.

XDEN is issued for I/O accesses to the internal registers of the 82C212. It is used to enable the XD0-7 lines onto the MA0-7 lines from an external buffer, for accessing the internal registers of the 82C212. The DLE and DRD signals are generated for enabling and controlling the direction of data between the CPU data bus and the memory data bus (MD bus). AF16 is issued by the 82C212 state machine. It is active for local memory accesses and meets the set up and hold times with respect to PROCCLK for the 82C211.

2.3.3 Memory Mapping and Refresh logic

The 82C212 has an extensive set of memory mapping registers for various memory organizations. The registers are discussed in section 2.3.5. Through the memory mapping logic, for up to 1 Mbyte of system RAM, it is possible to map RAM that overlaps the EPROM area (640Kbyte-1Mbyte) above the 1Mbyte area, as shown in Figure 2.6. Hence, for 1Mbyte of on board RAM, the software can address it from 0 to 640 Kbytes and from 1 Mbyte to 1.384 Mbytes. The EPROM can be addressed from the 640 Kbyte area to the 1 Mbyte area. For normal mode of operation, only one bank of DRAMs may be used. However, for the page/interleaved mode of operation, RAM bank pairs must be used.

Shadow RAM Feature

For efficient execution of BIOS, it is preferable to execute BIOS code through RAM rather than through slower EPROMs. The 82C212 provides the shadow RAM feature which if enabled allows the BIOS code to be executed from system RAM resident at the same physical address as the BIOS EPROM. The software should transfer code stored in the BIOS EPROMs to the system RAM, before enabling the shadow RAM feature. This feature significantly improves the performance in BIOS-call intensive applications. Performance improvements as high as 300 to 400% have been observed in benckmark tests on the shadow RAM. The shadow RAM feature is invoked by enabling the corresponding bits in the ROM enable register and the RAM mapping register.

If more than 1 Mbyte of system RAM exists, it is mapped as shown in Figure 2.7, if the shadow RAM feature is not invoked. This means that RAM in the 640 Kbyte to 1 Mbyte area cannot be accessed. If the shadow RAM feature is used, then the RAM is mapped as

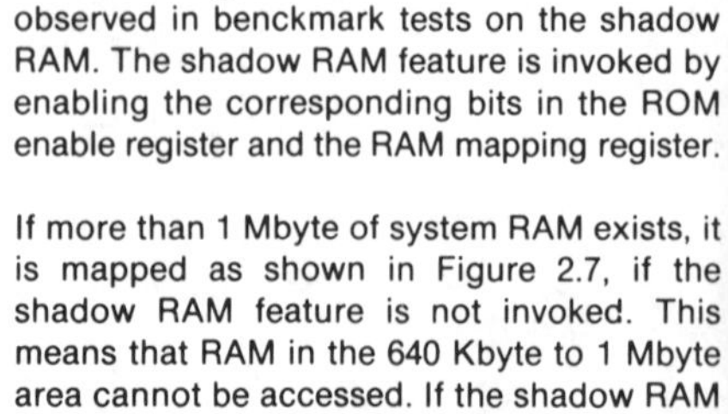

Figure 2.7 RAM/ROM Mapping Without Shadow RAM (More Than 1MB of RAM)

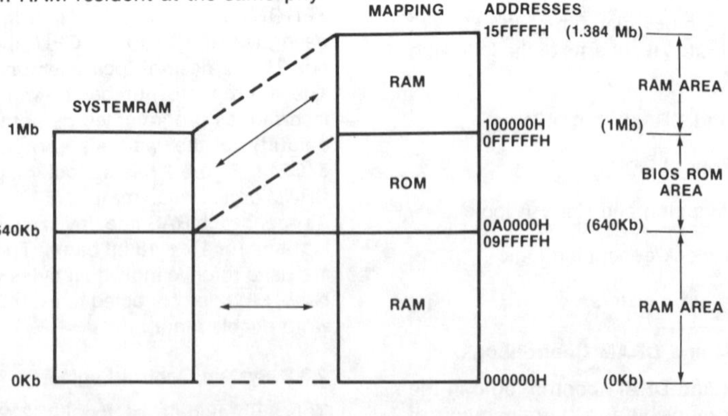

Figure 2.6 System RAM/ROM Mapping for 1MB System RAM

shown in Figure 2.8, overlapping or Shadowing the EPROM area. In both cases, for accesses beyond the 1 Mbyte address range, the processor is switched from real to protected mode from BIOS.

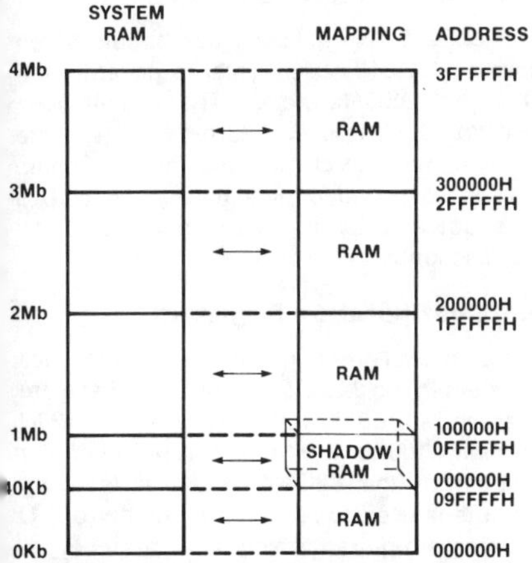

Figure 2.8 RAM Mapping with Shadow RAM (More Than 1MB of RAM)

MS Address Translation Logic

xpanded Memory System or EMS is a emory mapping scheme used to map a 64 byte block of memory in the EPROM area D0000H-DFFFFH to anywhere in the 1 Mbyte-8 Mbyte area. This 64 Kbyte memory block is segmented into four 16 Kbyte pages. Through a translation table, each 16 Kbyte segment can be mapped anywhere in the 1 Mbyte to 8 Mbyte area. Since the 82C212 uses the translation table in the EMS mode, address lines A14 to A22 are translated by the appropriate EMS mapping register. Hence, this scheme does not require switching between user and protected mode. Figure 2.9 shows the EMS organization with a possible translation scheme. It is possible for the 82C212 to map this 64 Kbyte block to anywhere in the 0 to 8 Mbyte area. However, it is desirable to map this block above the 1 Mbyte area in order to not use the RAM space in the 0 to 640 Kbyte area. Although the EMS scheme translates the 64 Kbyte block in the D0000H-DFFFFH area, it is possible to select a 64 Kbyte block from any other area.

Refresh Logic

During a refresh cycle, the 82C211 puts out the refresh address on the A0-A9 address lines and asserts the $\overline{REF}$ signal low to the 82C212. The 82C212 uses these signals to

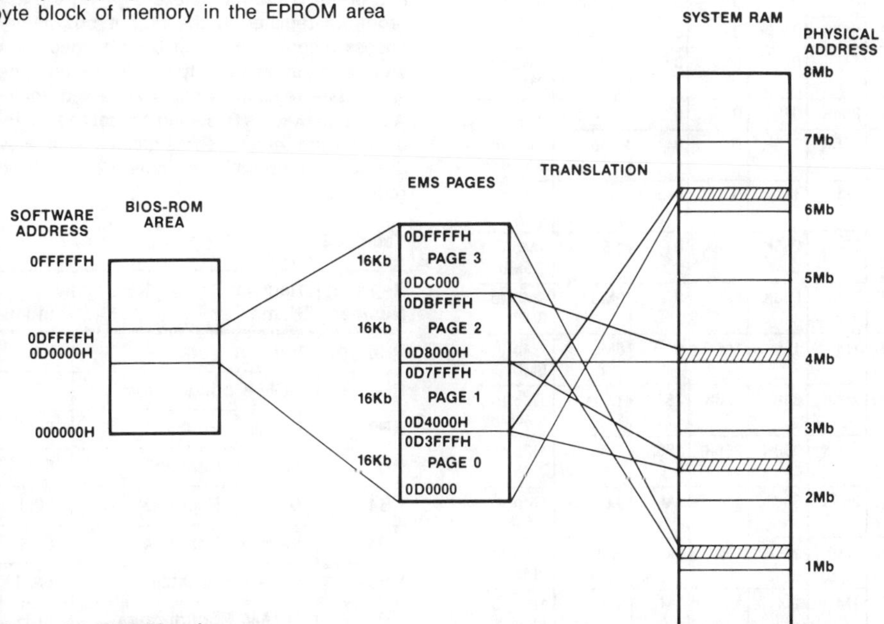

Figure 2.9 EMS Mapping

generate the refresh address on the MA0-MA9 address lines, the RAS signals and LMEGCS. Figure 1.5 is a sequence diagram for a refresh cycle. As seen, the 82C212 performs a staggered mode refresh to reduce the power supply noise generated during RAS switching. Prior to a refresh, all RAS lines are pulled high to ensure RAS precharge. Following this, RAS0 and RAS3 are asserted low. RAS1 and RAS2 are staggered by one delay unit using an external delay line, with respect to RAS0 and RAS3. The RAS0-RAS3, RAS1-RAS2 bundling is provided so that staggering is effective for a minimal 2 bank or a full 4 bank configuration.

Memory Configurations

It is possible to use 1Mbit or 256K bit (and in one case, 64K bit) DRAMs for system memory in the NEAT CHIPSet™. Each memory bank can be implemented with eighteen 1 bit wide DRAMs or four 4 bit wide DRAMs with two 1 bit wide DRAMs. Possible configurations for onboard memory are listed in Table 2.1. Each bank is 16 bits wide plus two bits for parity.

Table 2.1

	DRAM Type				Total	EMS
	Bank0	Bank1	Bank2	Bank3	Memory	Range
1	0	0	0	0	disable	0
2	256K	0	0	0	512Kb	0
3	1M	0	0	0	2Mb	1Mb to 2Mb
4	256K	64K	0	0	640Kb	0
5	256K	256K	0	0	1Mb	1Mb to 1.384Mb
6	1M	1M	0	0	4Mb	1Mb to 4Mb
7	256K	256K	256K	0	1.5Mb	1Mb to 1.5Mb
8	256K	256K	1M	0	3Mb	1Mb to 3Mb
9	1M	1M	1M	0	6Mb	1Mb to 6Mb
10	256K	64K	256K	256K	1.64Mb	1Mb to 1.64Mb
11	256K	256K	256K	256K	2Mb	1Mb to 2Mb
12	256K	64K	1M	1M	4.64Mb	1Mb to 4.64Mb
13	256K	256K	1M	1M	5Mb	1Mb to 5Mb
14	1M	1M	1M	1M	8Mb	1Mb to 8Mb

Page/interleaving is possible for only those combinations with similar pairs of DRAMs. In table 2.1, page/interleaving is possible with combinations 5, 6, 11, 13 and 14.

2.4 Clock Generation Logic

The 82C212 has an oscillator circuit which uses a 14.31818 MHz crystal to generate the OSC and OSC/12 clocks. The 1.19381 MHz OSC/12 clock is used internally to generate the RAS timeout clocks, one for each bank. RAS is deasserted for each bank when its RAS time out counter times out after about 10 microseconds.

2.5 Configuration Registers

There are twelve configuration and diagnostics registers in the 82C212, RB0-RB11. These are accessed through IO ports 22H and 23H normally found in the interrupt controller module of the 82C206 IPC. An indexing scheme is used to reduce the number of I/O addresses required to access all of the registers needed to configure and control the memory controller. Port 22H is used as an index register that points to the required data value accessed through port 23H. A write of the index value for the required data is performed to location 22H. This is then decoded and controls the multiplexers gating the appropriate register to the output bus. Every access to port 23H must be preceded by a write of the index value to port 22H even if the same data register is being accessed again. All bits marked as Reserved are set to zero by default and must be maintained that way during write operations. Table 2.2 lists these registers.

Table 2.2

Register Number	Register Name	Index
RB0	Version	64H
RB1	ROM Configuration	65H
RB2	Memory Enable-1	66H
RB3	Memory Enable-2	67H
RB4	Memory Enable-3	68H
RB5	Memory Enable-4	69H
RB6	Bank 0/1 Enable	6AH
RB7	DRAM Configuration	6BH

RB8	Bank 2/3 Enable	6CH
RB9	EMS Base Address	6DH
RB10	EMS Address Extension	6EH
RB11	Miscellaneous	6FH

2.5.1 Register Description

Version Register RB0
Index register port: 22H
Data register port: 23H
Index: 64H

Bits	Function
7	NEAT memory controller identifier. 0 = 82C212
6, 5	82C212 revision number. 00 = initial revision number
4-0	Reserved and default to 0*

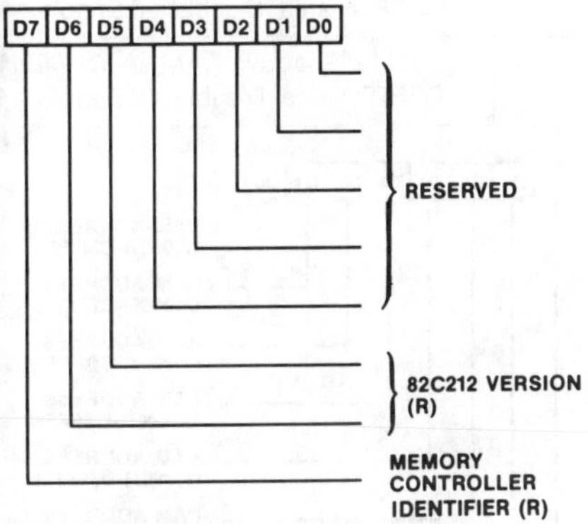

ROM Configuration Register RB1
Index register port: 22H
Data register port: 23H (R/W)
Index: 65H

Bits	Function
0	ROM at F0000H-FFFFFH (BIOS). Default = 0 = ROM enabled. ROMCS is generated.
1	ROM at E0000H-EFFFFH. Default = 1 = ROM disabled, Shadow RAM enabled. ROMCS is not generated unless bit is set to 0.
2	ROM at D0000H-DFFFFH. Default = 1 = ROM disabled, Shadow RAM enabled. ROMCS is not generated unless bit is set to 0.
3	ROM at C0000H-CFFFFH (EGA). Default = 1 = ROM disabled, Shadow RAM enabled. ROMCS is not generated unless bit is set to 0.
4	Shadow RAM at F0000H-FFFFFH in Read/Write mode. 0 = Read/Write (default), 1 = Read only (Write protected).
5	Shadow RAM at E0000H-EFFFFH in Read/Write mode. 0 = Read/Write (default), 1 = Read only (Write protected).
6	Shadow RAM at D0000H-DFFFFH in Read/Write mode. 0 = Read/Write (default), 1 = Read only (Write protected).
7	Shadow RAM at C0000H-CFFFFH in Read/Write mode. 0 = Read/Write (default), 1 = Read only (Write protected).

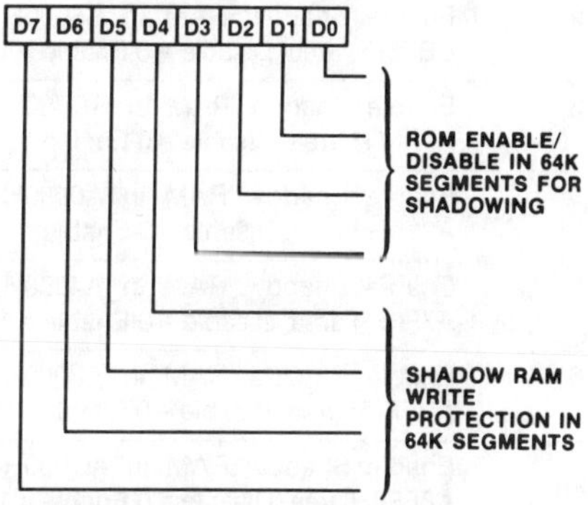

Memory Enable-1 Register RB2
Index register port: 22H
Data register port: 23H
Index: 66H

Bits	Function
0-6	Reserved and default to 0*
7	Address map RAM on system board in 80000H-9FFFFH area. 0 = Address is on the I/O channel (Default), 1 = Address is on the system board and is put out by the 82C212.

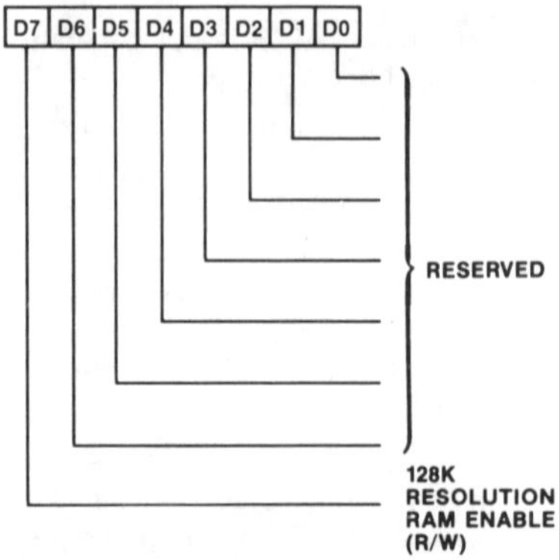

Memory Enable Register-2 RB3
Index register port: 22H
Data register port: 23H (R/W)
Index: 67H

Bits	Function
0	Enable Shadow RAM in B0000H-B3FFFH area. Disable = 0 Enable = 1.
1	Enable Shadow RAM in B4000H-B7FFFH rea. Disable = 0 Enable = 1.
2	Enable Shadow RAM in B8000H-BBFFFH area. Disable = 0 Enable = 1.
3	Enable Shadow RAM in BC000H-BFFFFH area. Disable = 0 Enable = 1.
4	Enable Shadow RAM in A0000H-A3FFFH area. Disable = 0 Enable = 1.
5	Enable Shadow RAM in A4000H-A7FFFH area. Disable = 0 Enable = 1.
6	Enable Shadow RAM in A8000H-ABFFFH area. Disable = 0 Enable = 1.
7	Enable Shadow RAM in AC000H-AFFFFH area. Disable = 0 Enable = 1.

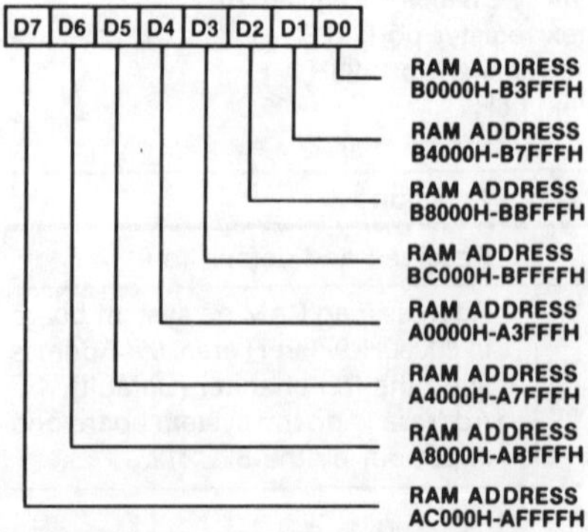

Memory Enable-3 Register RB4
Index register port: 22H
Data register port: 23H (R/W)
Index: 68H

Bits	Function
0	Enable Shadow RAM in C0000H-C3FFFH area. Disable = 0 Enable = 1.
1	Enable Shadow RAM in C4000H-C7FFFH area. Disable = 0 Enable = 1.
2	Enable Shadow RAM in C8000H-CBFFFH area. Disable = 0 Enable = 1.
3	Enable Shadow RAM in CC000H-CFFFFH area. Disable = 0 Enable = 1.
4	Enable Shadow RAM in D0000H-D3FFFH area. Disable = 0 Enable = 1.
5	Enable Shadow RAM in D4000H-D7FFFH area. Disable = 0 Enable = 1.
6	Enable Shadow RAM in D8000H-DBFFFH area. Disable = 0 Enable = 1.
7	Enable Shadow RAM in DC000H-DFFFFH area. Disable = 0 Enable = 1.

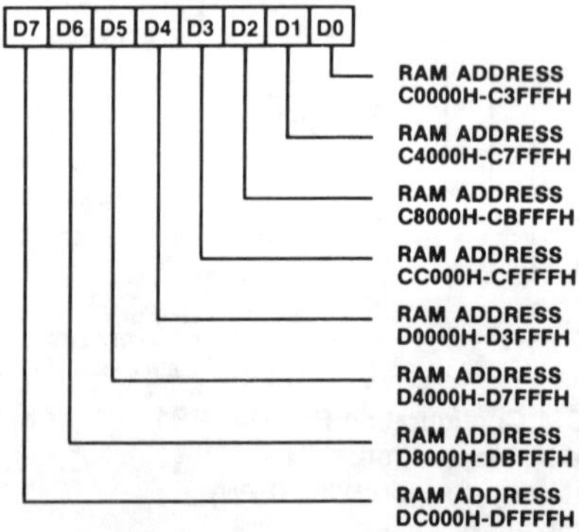

Memory Enable-4 Register (RB5)
Index register port: 22H
Data register port: 23H (R/W)
Index: 69H

Bits	Function
0	Enable Shadow RAM in E0000H-E3FFFH area. Disable = 0 Enable = 1.
1	Enable Shadow RAM in E4000H-E7FFFH area. Disable = 0 Enable = 1.

2	Enable Shadow RAM in E8000H-EBFFFH area. Disable = 0 Enable = 1.
3	Enable Shadow RAM in EC000H-EFFFFH area. Disable = 0 Enable = 1.
4	Enable Shadow RAM in F0000H-F3FFFH area. Disable = 0 Enable = 1.
5	Enable Shadow RAM in F4000H-F7FFFH area. Disable = 0 Enable = 1.
6	Enable Shadow RAM in F8000H-FBFFFH area. Disable = 0 Enable = 1.
7	Enable Shadow RAM in FC000H-FFFFFH area. Disable = 0 Enable = 1.

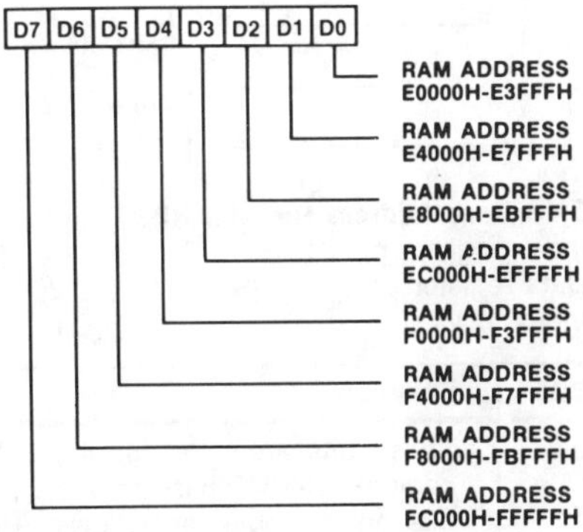

Bank 0/1 Enable Register RB6
Index register port: 22H
Data register port: 23H
Index: 6AH

Bits	Function
0-4	Reserved and default to 0*
5	Number of RAM banks used. 0 = one bank, non-interleaved mode (Default), 1 = two banks
7, 6	These bits contain the information for the DRAM types used on the system board. POST/BIOS should use the DRAM configuration data stored in the CMOS RAM of the 82C206 IPC.

7	6	DRAM Types
0	0	Disabled
0	1	256K and 64K bit DRAMs used (for 640 Kbyte combination only)
1	0	256K bit DRAMs used (Default)
1	1	1M bit DRAMs used

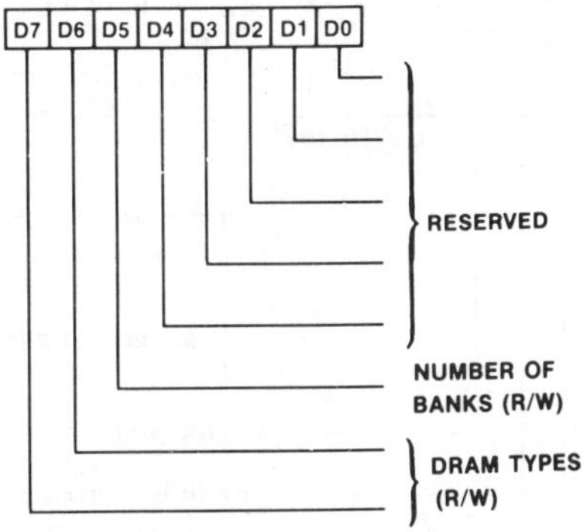

DRAM Configuration Register RB7
Index register port: 22H
Data register port: 23H (R/W)
Index: 6BH

Bits	Function
1, 0	ROM access wait states control.

1	0	Wait States
0	0	0
0	1	1
1	0	2
1	1	3 (Default)

Bits	Function
3, 2	EMS memory access wait states.

3	2	Wait States
0	0	0

Bits	Function
4	EMS enable bit.If set to 0, EMS is disabled (Default). If set to 1, EMS is enabled.
5	RAM access wait states. If set to 0, accesses have 0 wait state. If set to 1 (Default), accesses will have 1 wait state.

6	640Kbyte to 1Mbyte RAM relocation bit. A zero does not relocate local RAM. A one (Default) relocates local RAM from 0A0000-0FFFFF to 100000H-15FFFFH, provided total local RAM is 1 Mbyte only.
7	Page/Interleaved mode enable. A 0 disables the page/interleaved mode, allowing useage of normal mode for the DRAMs (Default). A 1 enables page/interleaved mode for the DRAMs.

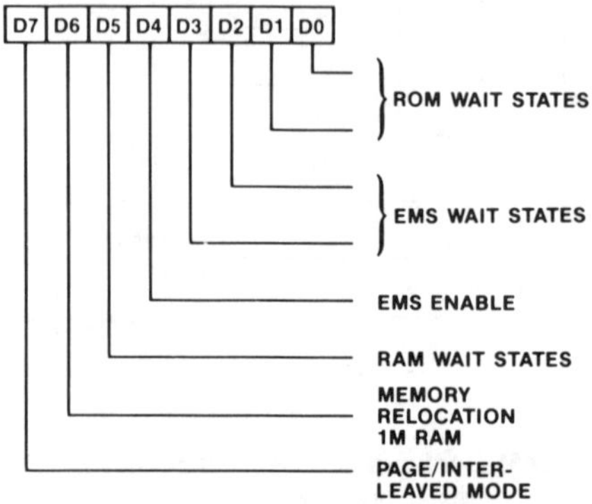

Bank 2/3 Enable Register RB8
Index register port: 22H
Data register port: 23H
Index: 6CH

Bits	Function
0-3	Reserved and default to 0*
4	A zero enable the 2-way page interleaved mode. A one (Default) enables the 4-way page interleaved mode if all 4 banks are the same DRAM devices.
5	Number of local RAM banks used. 0 = one bank used, non-interleaved mode only (Default). 1 = two banks used.
7, 6	These bits indicate the local DRAM type as listed:

7	6	DRAM Type
0	0	none (Default)
0	1	Reserved
1	0	256 Kbit
1	1	1 Mbit

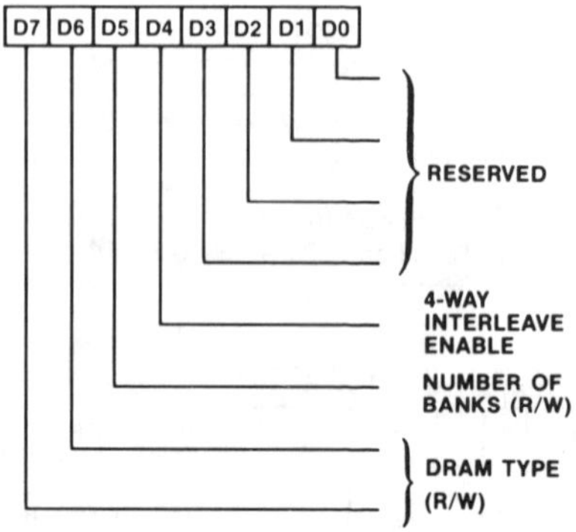

EMS Base Address Register RB9
Index register port: 22H
Data register port: 23H (R/W)
Index: 6DH

Bits	Function
0-3	These bits are used for the EMS page register I/O base address. The bits are encoded as follows, with unused combinations being reserved:

3	2	1	0	I/O Base
0	0	0	0	208H/209H
0	0	0	1	218H/219H
0	1	0	1	258H/259H
0	1	1	0	268H/269H
1	0	1	0	2A8H/2A9H
1	0	1	1	2B8H/2B9H
1	1	1	0	2E8H/2E9H

Bits	Function
7-4	These bits are used for selecting the expanded memory base addresses. They are encoded as follows, with all unused combinations being reserved:

7	6	5	4	EMS Base Addresses
0	0	0	0	C0000H, C4000H, C8000H, CC000H
0	0	0	1	C4000H, C8000H, CC000H, D0000H

0	0	1	0	C8000H, CC000H, D0000H, D4000H
0	0	1	1	CC000H, D0000H, D4000H, D8000H
0	1	0	0	D0000H, D4000H, D8000H, DC000H
0	1	0	1	D4000H, D8000H, DC000H, E0000H
0	1	1	0	D8000H, DC000H, E0000H, E4000H
0	1	1	1	DC000H, E0000H, E4000H, E8000H
1	0	0	0	E0000H, E4000H, E8000H, EC000H

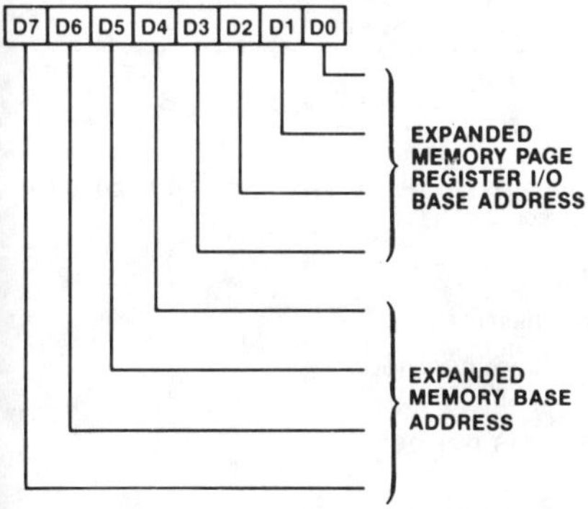

EMS Address Extention Register RB10
Index register port: 22H
Data register port: 23H (R/W)
Index: 6EH

Bits	Function
1(A22) 0(A21)	EMS Page 3 address extension bits.

1	0	Block of EMS Memory
0	0	0 Mbyte to 2 Mbyte
0	1	2 Mbyte to 4 Mbyte
1	0	4 Mbyte to 6 Mbyte
1	1	6 Mbyte to 8 Mbyte

Bits	Function
3(A22) 2(A21)	EMS Page 2 address extension bits.

3	2	Block of EMS Memory
0	0	0 Mbyte to 2 Mbyte
0	1	2 Mbyte to 4 Mbyte
1	0	4 Mbyte to 6 Mbyte
1	1	6 Mbyte to 8 Mbyte

Bits	Function
5(A22) 4(A21)	EMS Page 1 address extension bits.

5	4	Block of EMS Memory
0	0	0 Mbyte to 2 Mbyte
0	1	2 Mbyte to 4 Mbyte
1	0	4 Mbyte to 6 Mbyte
1	1	6 Mbyte to 8 Mbyte

Bits	Function
7(A22) 6(A21)	EMS Page 0 address extension bits.

7	6	Block of EMS Memory
0	0	0 Mbyte to 2 Mbyte
0	1	2 Mbyte to 4 Mbyte
1	0	4 Mbyte to 6 Mbyte
1	1	6 Mbyte to 8 Mbyte

Address lines A22 and A21 are used in EMS Address translation logic.

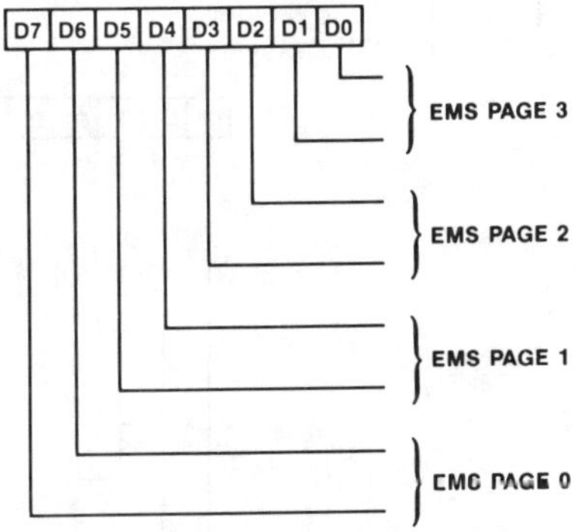

Miscellaneous Register RB12
Index register port: 22H
Data register port: 23H
Index: 6FH

Bits	Function
0	Reserved and default to 0.*
1	This bit is used for Address line A20 control and provides OS/2 optimization while switching between real and protected modes: If the bit is set to 0 it enables CPUA20 onto A20. The bit default to 1 and sets A20 = 0.

2	This bit is used to enable the RAS time-out counter for page mode operation. The counter is disabled if set to 0 (Default) and is enabled if set to 1.
3, 4	Reserved and default to 1 (bit 4), 0 (bit 3).
7-5	These bits are used to set the EMS memory space according to the following coding:

7	6	5	EMS Memory Size
0	0	0	less than 1 Mbyte
0	0	1	1 Mbyte
0	1	0	2 Mbytes
0	1	1	3 Mbytes
1	0	0	4 Mbytes
1	0	1	5 Mbytes
1	1	0	6 Mbytes
1	1	1	7 Mbytes

EMS Page Registers

Page 0	2X8/2X9H
Page 1	42X8/42X9H
Page 2	82X8/82X9H
Page 3	C2X8/C2X9H

Bits	Function
0-6	0 - A14 1 - A15 2 - A16 3 - A17 4 - A18 5 - A19 6 - A20
7	0 - page disable 1 - page enable

X can be 0, 1, 5, 6, A, B, E

*The reserved bits are recommanded to be initialized to 1.

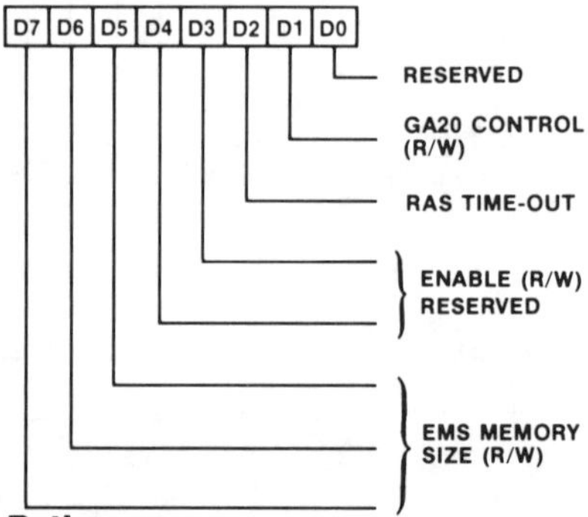

2.6 Absolute Maximum Ratings

Parameter	Symbol	Min.	Max.	Units
Supply Voltage	V_{CC}	—	7.0	V
Input Voltage	V_I	-0.5	5.5	V
Output Voltage	V_O	-0.5	5.5	V
Operating Temperature	T_{OP}	-25°	85°	C
Storage Temperature	T_{STG}	-40°	125°	C

NOTE: Permanent device damage may occur if Absolute Maximum Ratings are exceeded. Functional operation should be restricted to the conditions described under Operating Conditions.

2.7 82C212 Operating Conditions

Parameter	Symbol	Min.	Max.	Units
Supply Voltage	V_{CC}	4.75	5.25	V
Ambient Temperature	T_A	0°	70°	C

2.8 82C212 DC Characteristics

Parameter	Symbol	Min.	Max.	Units
Input Low Voltage	V_{IL}	—	0.8	V
Input High Voltage	V_{IH}	2.0	—	V
Output Low Voltage I_{OL} = 4mA	V_{OL}	—	0.45	V
Output High Voltage I_{OH} = -4mA	V_{OH}	2.4	—	V
Input Low Current $0<V_{IN}<V_{CC}$	I_{IL}	—	+10	μA
Power Supply Current @ 16MHz	I_{CC}	—	75	mA
Output High-Z Leakage Current $0.45<V_{OUT}<V_{CC}$	I_{OZ1}		+10	μA
Standby Power Supply Current	I_{CCSB}	—	1.0	mA

2.9 82C212-12, 82C212-16 AC Characteristics

(T_A = 0°C to 70°C, V_{CC} = 5V ± 5%)

Sym	Description	Min.	Typ.	Max.	Units
t1	$\overline{RAS_i}$ active delay from CLK2↓	11		16	ns
t2	$\overline{RAS_i}$ inactive delay from CLK2↓	15		25	ns
t3	DLYOUT active delay from $\overline{RAS_i}$↓	0		4	ns
t4	DLYOUT inactive delay from $\overline{RAS_i}$↑	0		6	ns
t5	Column address stable from DLY0↑	8		18	ns
t6	Column address hold from DLY0↓	6			ns
t7	$\overline{CAS_i}$ active delay from DLY1↑	7		14	ns
t8	$\overline{CAS_i}$ inactive delay from DLY1↓	11		18	ns
t9	$\overline{AF16}$ active delay from CLK2↓	7		16(19)	ns
t10	$\overline{AF16}$ inactive delay from CLK2↓	8		18(21)	ns
t11	$\overline{READY}$ active delay from CLK2↓	15		25	ns
t12	$\overline{READY}$ inactive delay from CLK2↓	11		20	ns
t13	$\overline{DRD}$ active delay from CLK2↓	10		19	ns
t14	$\overline{DRD}$ hold from DLE↓	13			ns
t15	DLE active delay from $\overline{DLY1}$↓	6		16	ns
t16	DLE inactive delay from CLK2↓	9		18	ns
t17	$\overline{LMEGCS}$ active from CLK2↓	12		21	ns
t18	$\overline{LMEGCS}$ inactive from CLK2↓	11		20	ns
t19	$\overline{GA20}$ valid delay from CPU <A20> valid	7		16 (20)	ns
t20	$\overline{GA20}$ invalid delay from CPU <A20> invalid	4		12 (16)	ns
t22	$\overline{MWE}$ active delay from CLK2↓	11		20	ns

2.9 82C212-12, 82C212-16 AC Characteristics (Continued)

(T_A = 0°C to 70°C, V_{CC} = 5V ± 5%)

Sym	Description	Min.	Typ.	Max.	Units
t23	$\overline{MWE}$ inactive delay from CLK2↑	4		12	ns
t26	$\overline{CAS_i}$ active delay from CLK2↓	10		19 (25)	ns
t27	$\overline{CAS_i}$ inactive delay from CLK2↓	11		21(26)	ns
t28	$\overline{DRD}$ inactive delay from CLK2↓	12		23	ns
t29	$\overline{CAS_i}$ inactive delay from DLE inactive	2			ns
t30	$\overline{RAS_i}$ active delay from CLK2↓	10.5		16	ns
t31	Row address set up time to $\overline{RAS_i}$↓	8			ns
t32	Row address hold time from CLK2↓	6		22	ns
t33	$\overline{RAS_i}$ inactive delay from CLK2↓	15		25	ns
t34	$\overline{RAS_i}$ precharge time (Interleaved Mode)		4 × CLK2		
t35	$\overline{ROMCS}$ active from CLK2↓	11		20	ns
t36	$\overline{ROMCS}$ inactive from CLK2↓	10		20	ns
t37	DLE hold time from $\overline{DRD}$	0		7	ns
t38	$\overline{RAS_{0\sim3}}$ inactive from $\overline{REF}$↓	13		24	ns
t39	$\overline{RAS_{0,3}}$ active from $\overline{XMEMR}$↓	9		17	ns
t40	$\overline{RAS_{0,3}}$ inactive from $\overline{XMEMR}$↑	10		19	ns
t41	$\overline{RAS_{1,2}}$ active from $\overline{RAS_{0,3}}$↓	7		15	ns
t42	$\overline{RAS_{1,2}}$ inactive from $\overline{RAS_{0,3}}$↑	11		20	ns
t43	Address setup time from $\overline{XMEMR}$↓	10			ns
t44	Address hold time from $\overline{REF}$↑	4			ns
t45	Refresh address delay	0			ns
t47	$\overline{LMEGCS}$ delay from $\overline{REF}$↓	8		16	ns
t48	$\overline{LMEGCS}$ delay from $\overline{REF}$↑	10		19	ns
t49	$\overline{RAS_{0\sim3}}$ inactive from HLDA1↑	11		20	ns
t50	$\overline{RAS_i}$ active from command active	10		18	ns
t51	$\overline{RAS_i}$ inactive from command inactive	12		21	ns
t54	Column address stable from DLY0↑	9		18	ns
t55	$\overline{CAS_i}$ active delay from DLY1↑ (while XMEMW active)	6		14	ns
t56	$\overline{CAS_i}$ inactive delay from command inactive	9		18	ns
t57	$\overline{AF16}$ active from command active	9		17	ns
t58	$\overline{AF16}$ inactive from command inactive	6		14	ns

Note: Value inside ( ) are 12 MHz timing.

2.10 82C212 Timing Diagrams

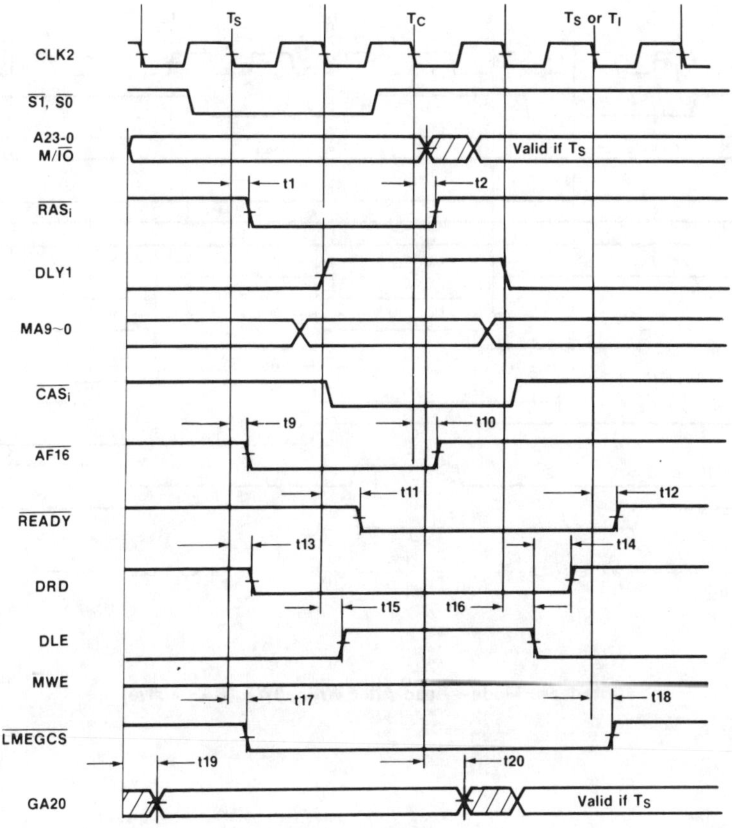

Non-Interleave Mode—Read, 0WS

2.10 82C212 Timing Diagrams (Continued)

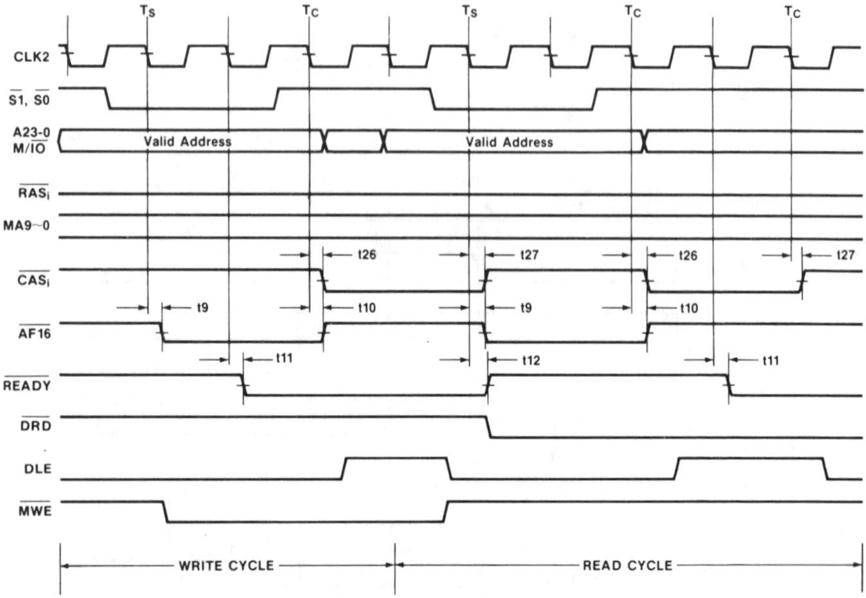

Interleave Mode—Read After Write, 0WS (RAS active)

2.10 82C212 Timing Diagrams (Continued)

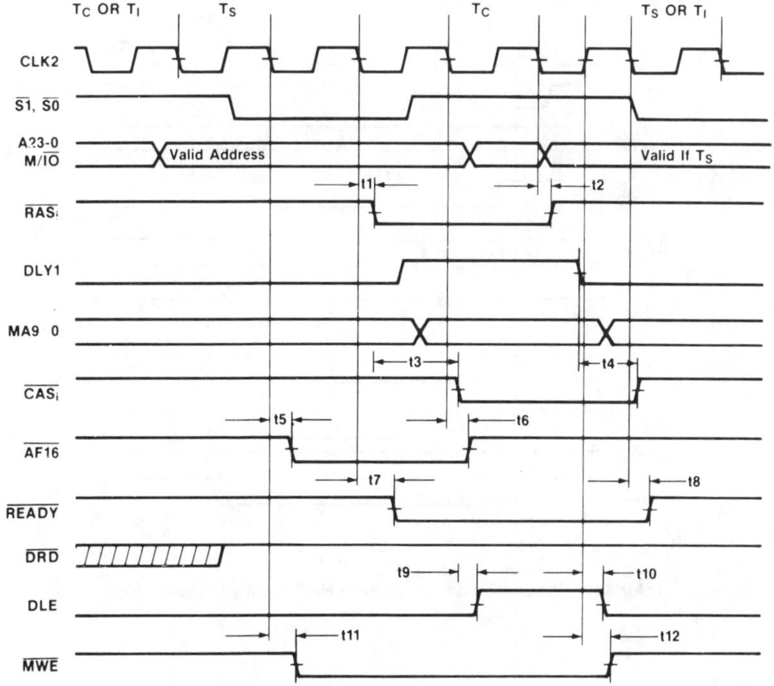

Non-Interleave Mode—0WS, Write

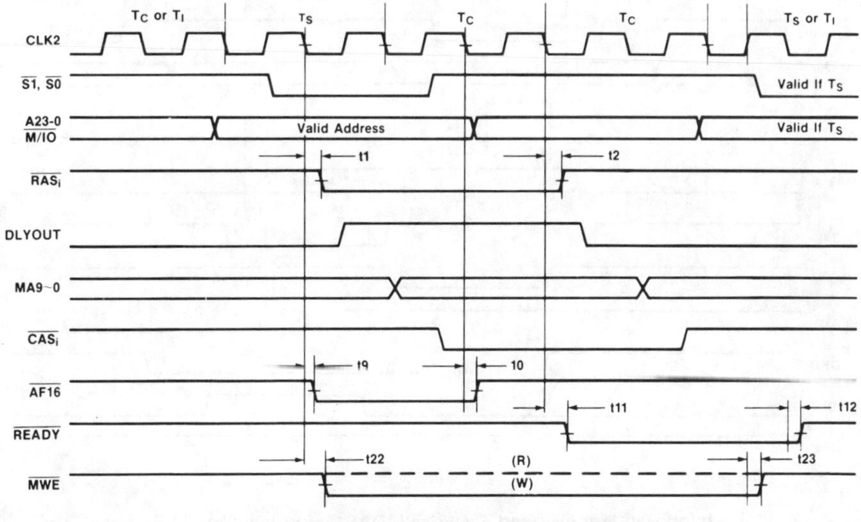

Non-Interleave Mode—1WS, Read, Write

2.10 82C212 Timing Diagrams (Continued)

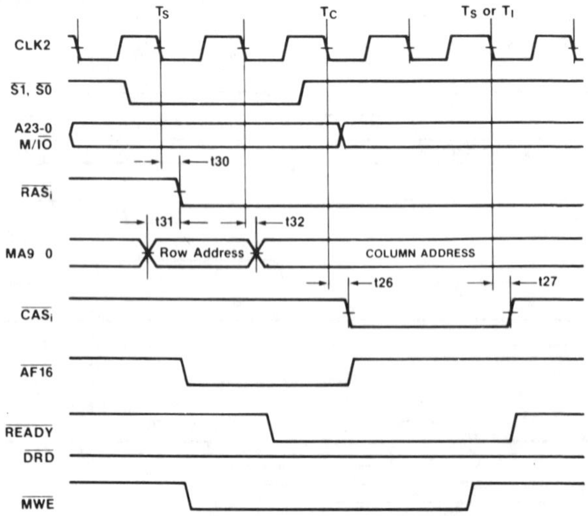

Interleave Mode—Write Cycle with RAS Being Inactive, 0WS

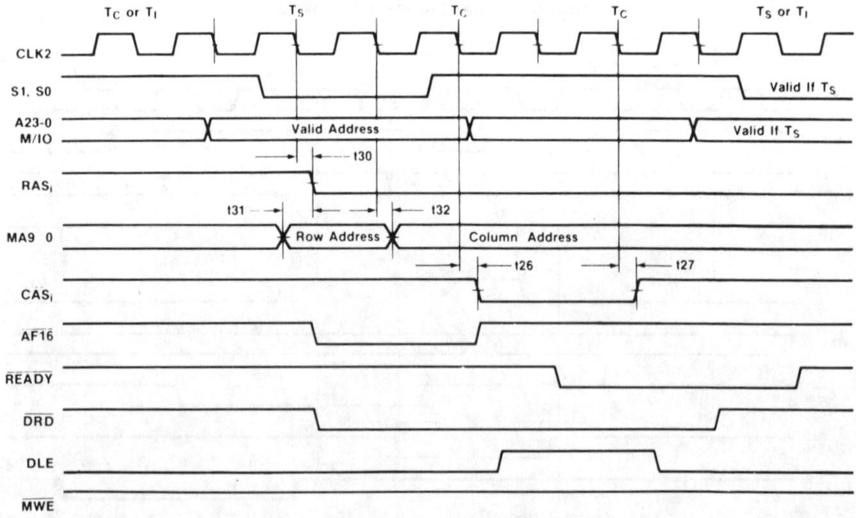

Interleave Mode—Read Cycle with RAS Being Inactive, 0WS

2.10 82C212 Timing Diagrams (Continued)

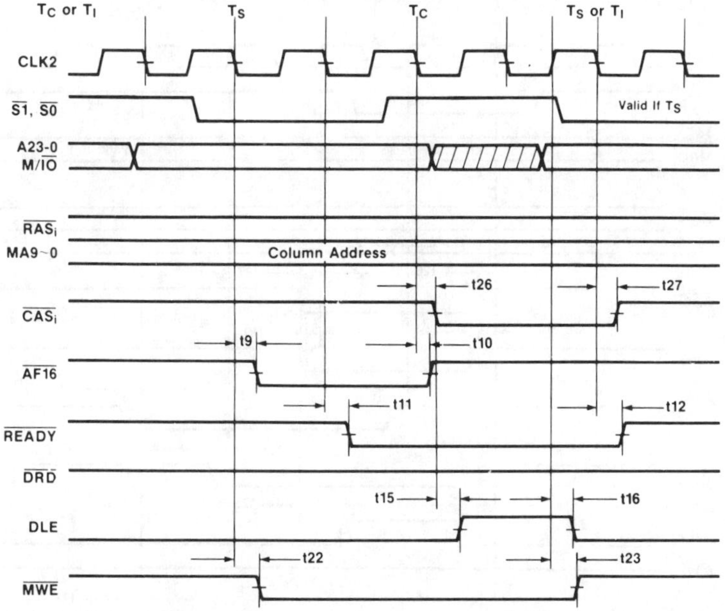

Interleave Mode—Write, 0WS (RAS active)

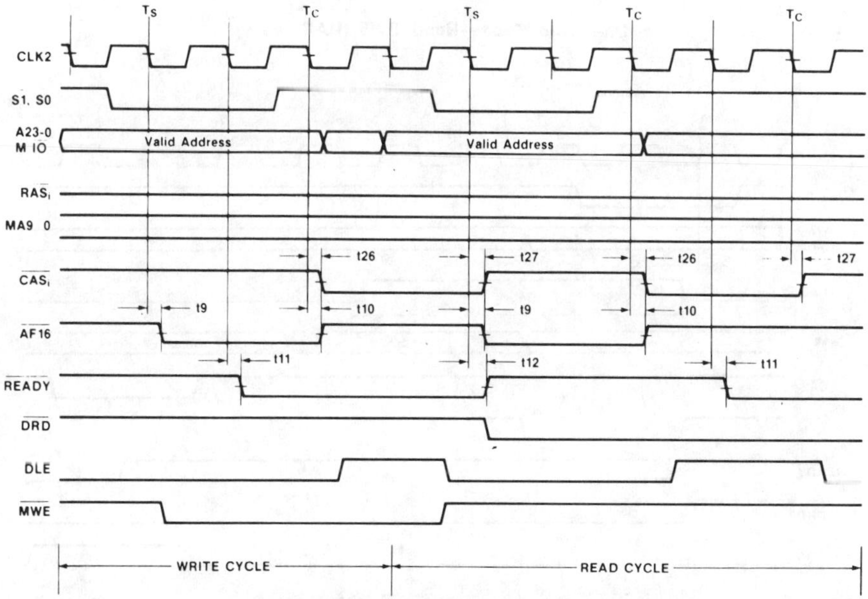

Interleave Mode—Read After Write, 0WS (RAS active)

2.10 82C212 Timing Diagrams (Continued)

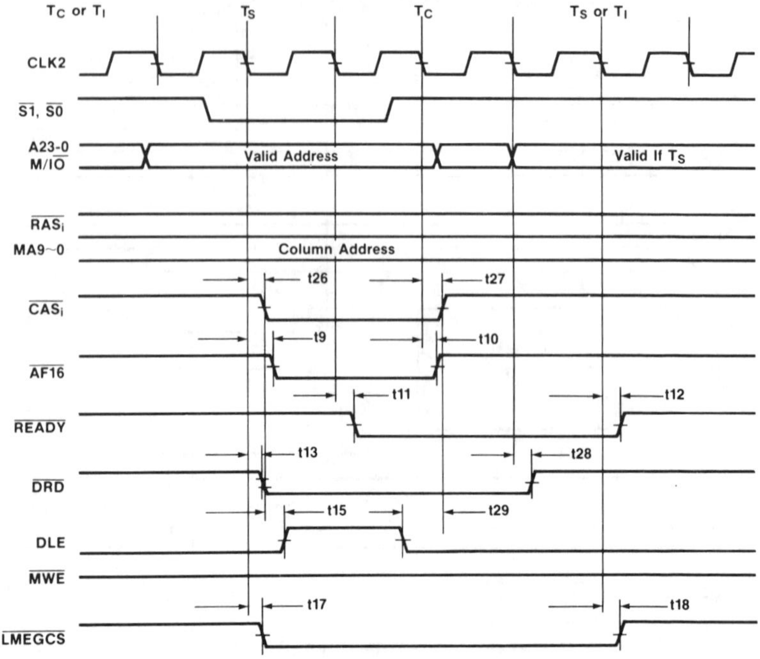

Interlevae Mode—Read, 0WS (RAS active)

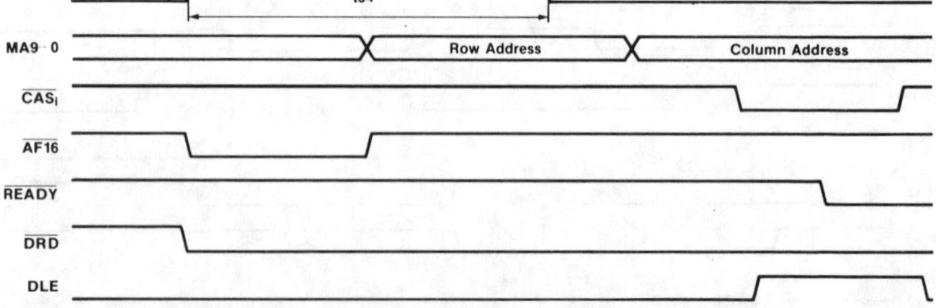

Interleave Mode—Read Miss Cycle

2.10 82C212 Timing Diagrams (Continued)

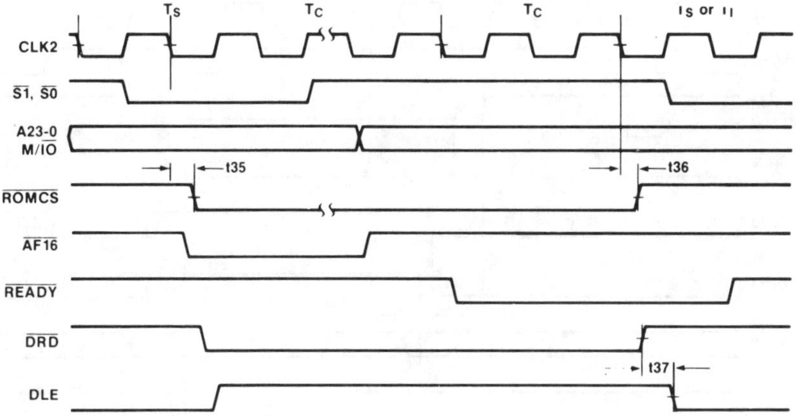

ROM Read Cycle

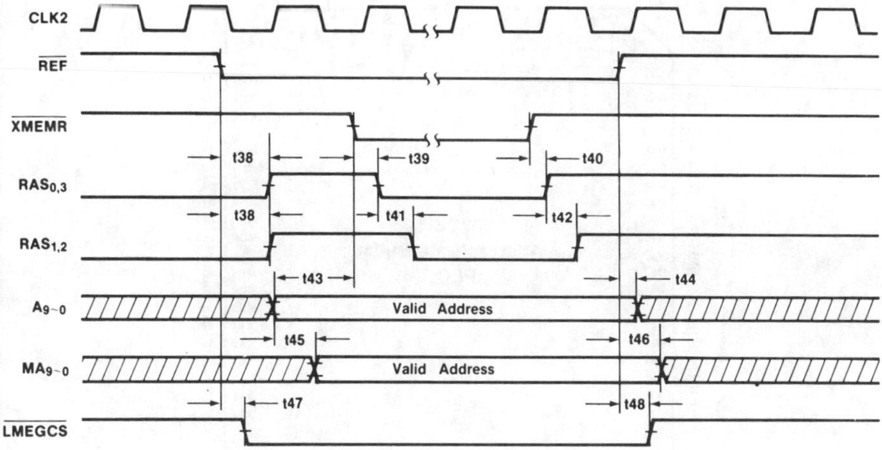

Refresh Cycle

2.10 82C212 Timing Diagrams (Continued)

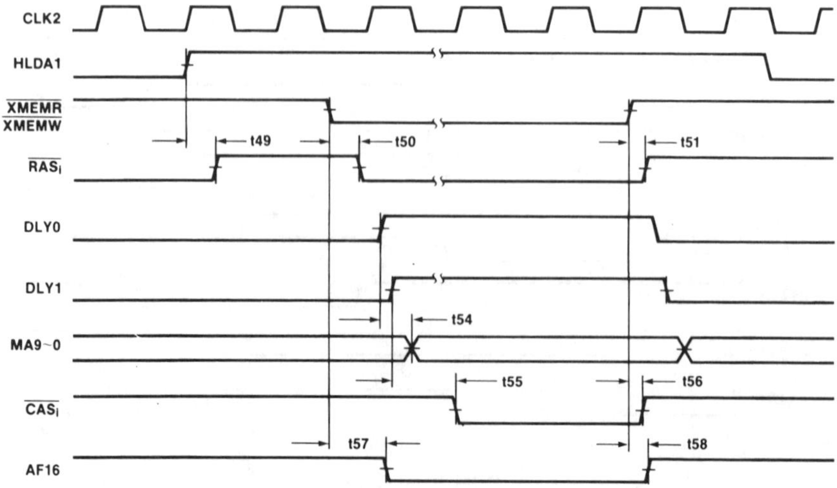

DMA Cycle

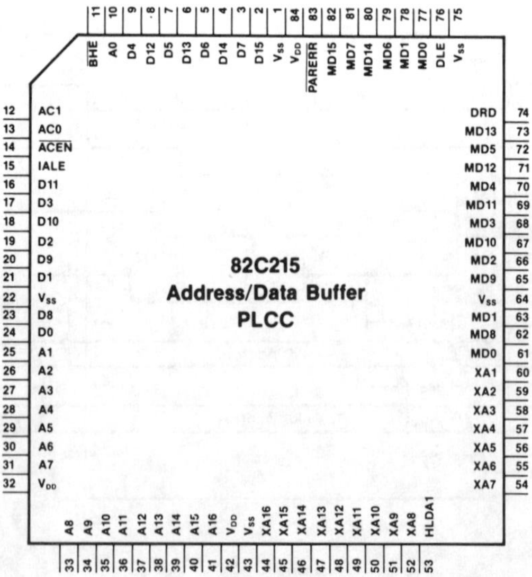

3 82C215 DATA/ADDRESS BUFFER

3.1 Features

- Bus Conversion logic for 16 bit to 8 bit transfers
- Parity generation/detection logic

3.2 Functional Description

Figure 3.1 is a block diagram of the 82C215 Data/Address buffer. It consists of four modules:

- Address buffers and latches
- Data buffers and latches
- Bus conversion logic
- Parity generation/detection logic

3.2.1 Address Buffers and Latches

The 82C215 provides the address buffering between the CPU address lines A1-A16 and the XA1-XA16 lines. These buffers drive 4 mA output low currents (I_{OL}). The CPU address lines are latched by IALE to generate the X-Address lines when HLDA is inactive.

3.2.2 Data Buffers and Latches

The 82C215 provides the buffering between the CPU data bus (D0-D15) and the memory data bus (MD0-MD15). The D0-D15 lines drive 4 mA output low currents (I_{OL}). The MD0-MD15 lines drive 8 mA I_{OL}. The enable signal for the latch between the Memory Data bus and the CPU Data bus is controlled by $\overline{DRD}$, HLDA and the action codes. This allows 16 bit reads from 8 bit peripherals controlled by the 82C211.

3.3.3 Bus Conversion Logic

The 82C215 provides data bus conversion when the 16 bit CPU reads from or writes to 8 bit devices. It also provides bus conversion for Master/DMA cycles. There are six possible cases, as seen in Table 3.1 in conjunction with Figure 3.2. These conversions are controlled by the action codes which are qualified by $\overline{ACEN}$ from the 82C211.

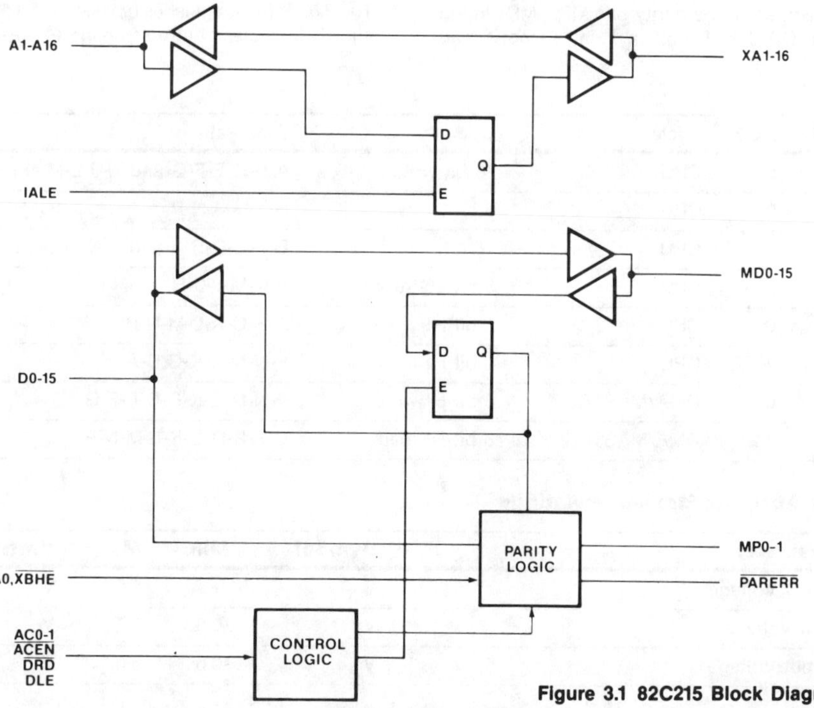

Figure 3.1 82C215 Block Diagram

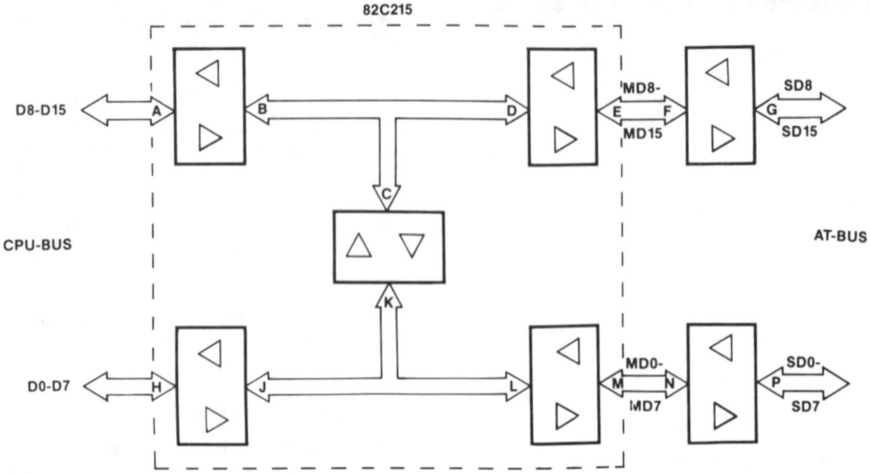

Figure 3.2 Bus Conversion Data Paths

3.3.4 Parity Generation/Detection Logic

For local RAM write cycles, the 82C215 generates even parity for each of the two bytes of the data word. These valid even parity bits are written to the parity bits MP0, MP1 in the local DRAMs. During a local memory read cycle, the 82C215 checks for even parity for each MD byte read. If the parity is detected as being odd, the 82C215 flags a parity error on the PARERR output line to the 82C211. The 82C211 distinguishes between local ROM and RAM cycles before sampling $\overline{\text{PARERR}}$.

Table 3.1

AC1	AC0	Cycle	Operation	Data Path
0	0	CPU	16 bit write	A-B-D-E-F-G and H-J-L-M-N-P
0	0	CPU	8 bit LO write	H-J-L-M-N-P
0	1	CPU	16 bit read	G-F-E-D-B-A and P-N-M-L-J-H
0	1	CPU	8 bit LO read	P-N-M-L-J-H
1	0	CPU	8 bit HI write	A-B-C-K-L-M-N-P
1	1	CPU	8 bit HI read	P-N-M-L-K-C-B-A
1	0	DMA/MASTER	8 bit HI write	P-N-M-L-K-C-D-E-F-G
1	1	DMA/MASTER	8 bit HI read	G-F-E-D-C-K-L-M-N-P

3.4 Absolute Maximum Ratings

Parameter	Symbol	Min.	Max.	Units
Supply Voltage	V_{CC}	—	7.0	V
Input Voltage	V_I	-0.5	5.5	V
Output Voltage	V_O	-0.5	5.5	V

Operating Temperature	T_{OP}	-25°	85°	C
Storage Temperature	T_{STG}	-40°	125°	C

NOTE: Permanent device damage may occur if Absolute Maximum Ratings are exceeded. Functional operation should be restricted to the conditions described under Operating Conditions.

3.5 82C215 Operating Conditions

Parameter	Symbol	Min.	Max.	Units
Supply Voltage	V_{CC}	4.75	5.25	V
Ambient Temperature	T_A	0°	70°	C

3.6 82C215 DC Characteristics

Parameter	Symbol	Min.	Max.	Units
Input Low Voltage	V_{IL}	—	0.8	V
Input High Voltage	V_{IH}	2.0	—	V
Output Low Voltage I_{OL} = 4mA	V_{OL}	—	0.45	V
Output High Voltage I_{OH} = -4mA	V_{OH}	2.4	—	V
Input Current $0<V_{IN}<V_{CC}$	I_{IL}	—	±10	μA
Power Supply Current @ 16MHz	I_{CC}	—	80	mA
Output High-Z Leakage Current $0.45<V_{OUT}<V_{CC}$	I_{OZ1}		±10	μA
Standby Power Supply Current	I_{CCSB}	—	1.0	mA

3.7 82C215-12, 82C215-16 AC Characteristics

(T_A = 0°C to 70°C, V_{CC} = 5V ± 5%)

Sym	Description	Min.	Typ.	Max.	Units
t1	MD bus 3-stated after $\overline{DRD}$ active	7.5		24	ns
t2	MD bus valid to D bus valid	8		18.5	ns
t3a	MD bus being driven after $\overline{DRD}$ inactive	7.5		28	ns
t3b	MP0, MP1 being driven after $\overline{DRD}$ inactive	6		23	ns
t4	D bus invalid after $\overline{DRD}$ inactive	4		13	ns
t5	D bus 3-stated after $\overline{DRD}$ inactive	6		15	ns
t6	D bus valid to MD bus valid	11		19	ns
t7	D bus valid to MP1, MP0 valid	11		20	ns
t8	$\overline{ACEN}$ active to D bus valid	16		27	ns

3.7 82C215-12, 82C215-16 AC Characteristics (Continued)

(T_A = 0°C to 70°C, V_{CC} = 5V ± 5%)

Sym	Description	Min.	Typ.	Max.	Units
t9	AC code valid to MD bus valid	10		19	ns
t10	AC code invalid to MD bus invalid	11		20	ns
t11	DLE inactive to $\overline{\text{PARERR}}$ enabled	17		30	ns
t12	$\overline{\text{DRD}}$ inactive to $\overline{\text{PARERR}}$ disabled	17		28	ns
t13	IALE active to XA bus valid	11		19	ns
t14	XA bus valid to A bus valid	7		16 (19)	ns
t15	MD, MP setup time to DLE trailing edge	0.0			ns
t16	MD, MP hold time from DLE trailing edge	6.0			ns
t17	$\overline{\text{DRD}}$ setup time to DLE trailing edge	12			ns
t19	MD bus hold time from $\overline{\text{ACEN}}$ trailing edge	7.5			ns
t20	MD bus valid to MP valid during DMA memory write cycle	14		24	ns
t21	MD high byte valid to MD low byte valid during DMA high memory read cycle	10		19	ns
t22	AC code valid to MD high byte valid during DMA high memory write cycle	9		18	ns
t23	AC code valid to MP valid during DMA high memory write cycle	17		28	ns

Note: Values inside ( ) are 12 MHz timing.

3.8 82C215 Timing Diagrams

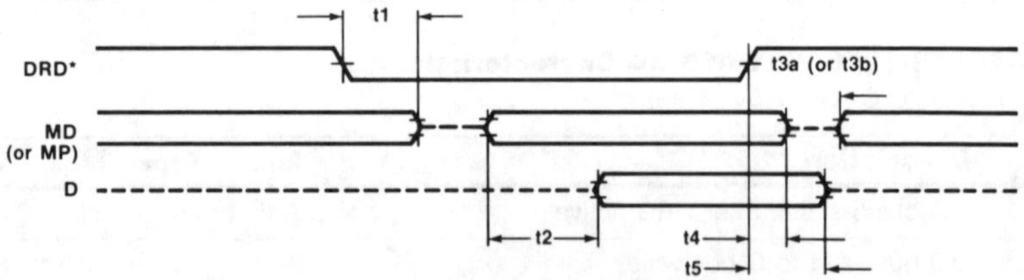

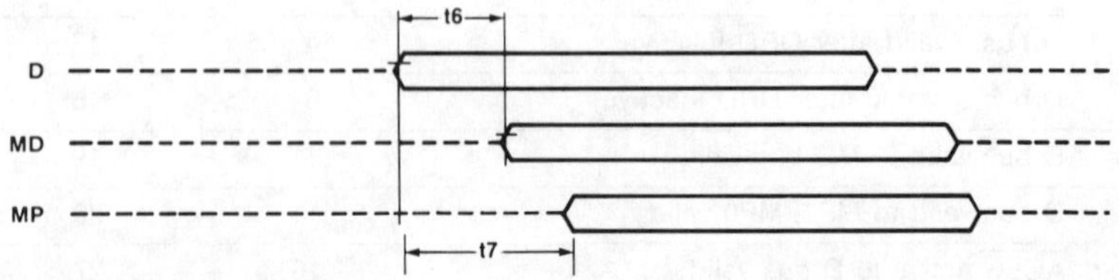

3.8 82C215 Timing Diagrams (Continued)

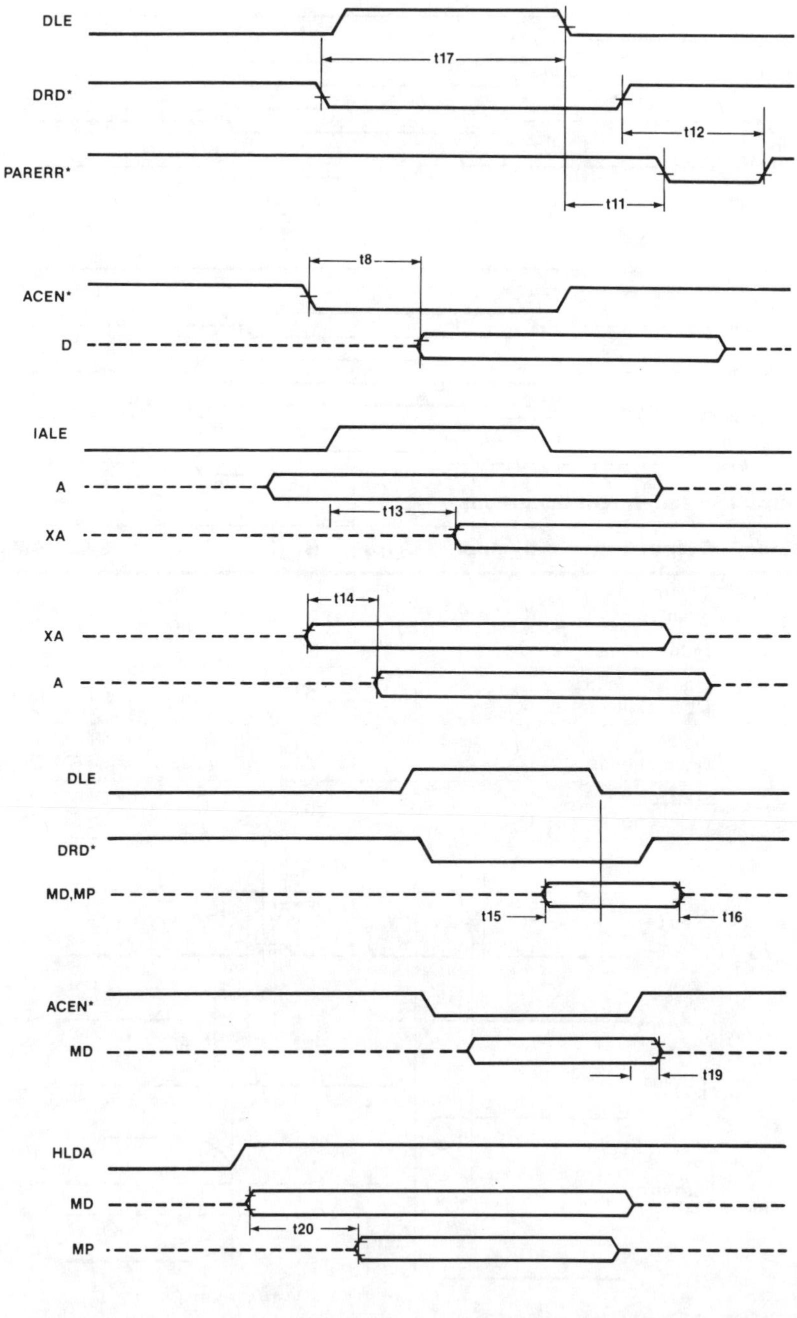

3.8 82C215 Timing Diagrams (Continued)

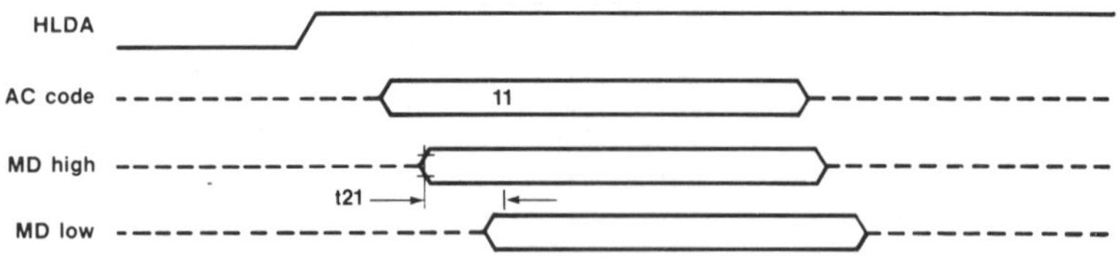

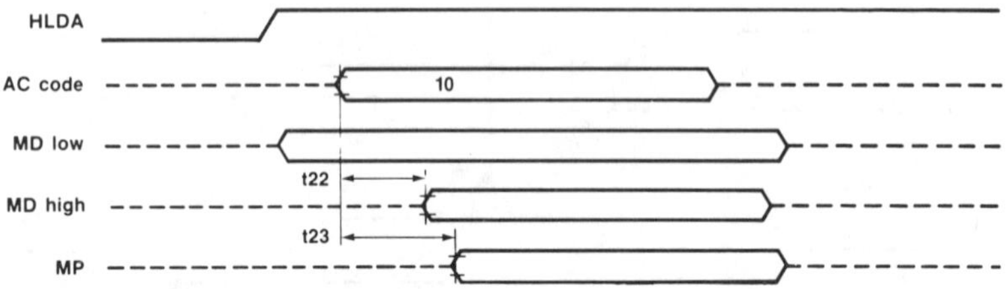

Load Circuit Measurement Conditions

Parameter	Output Type	Symbol	C_L(pF)	R_1 (Ω)	R_L (Ω)	SW_1	SW_2
Propagation Delay Time	Totem pole 3-state Bidirectional	t_{PLH} t_{PHL}	50	—	1.0K	OFF	ON
Propagation Delay Time	Open drain or Open Collector	t_{PLH} t_{PHL}	50	0.5K	—	ON	OFF
Disable Time	3-state Bidirectional	t_{PLZ} t_{PHZ}	5	0.5K	1.0K	ON OFF	ON
Enable Time	3-state Bidirectional	t_{PZL} t_{PZH}	50	0.5K	1.0K	ON OFF	ON ON

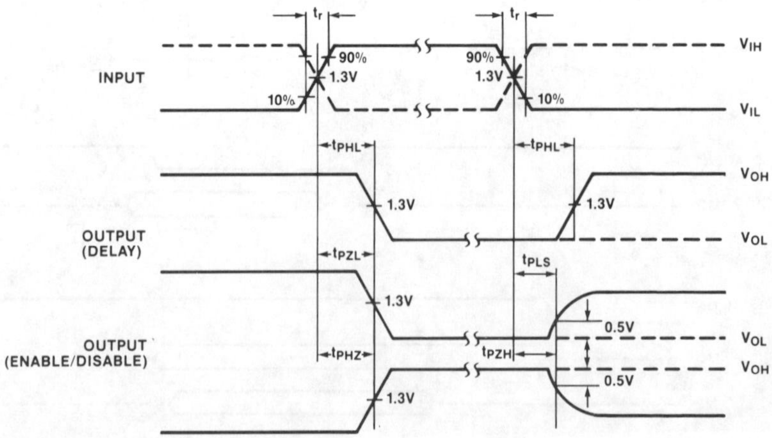

V_{IH} = 3V, V_{IL} = 0V, $t_r \leq$ 10 ns, $t_r \geq$ 5 ns

Overview of families

A highly interesting group of peripheral ICs is formed by mathematical co-processors. It can be argued that a maths co-processor is, strictly speaking, not a peripheral device because it is often more complex than the microprocessor it belongs with. Nevertheless, we have included this group in this book because co-processors are typically found in a microprocessor environment.

Co-processors were once not affordable to the average computer user, but that has changed with the arrival of a number of second source products. In principle, they are used to support the microprocessor with mathematical operations. Its special instruction set and architecture enables a co-processor to complete complex calculations much faster than a microprocessor. As a result, they can speed up certain programs considerably. Their most frequent application is, not surprisingly, with CAD/CAM programs, graphics packages and spreadsheets. To avoid disappointment about the increase in speed that can be achieved by the use of a co-processor, it is wise to first check if the program benefits at all from the increased mathematical capacity. A number of manufacturers, including AMD and Cyrix, have issued overviews of the usefulness of a co-processor with a wide range of programs. Mind you, there are also programs that can work only when a co-processor is fitted.

The best known family of co-processors is, without doubt, the one associated with the IBM PC XT/AT series of computers, and their compatibles. Only this group is dealt with in this book. Depending on the microprocessor the co-processor is used with, it belongs in one of three groups: 8087 (with the 8086 microprocessor), 80287 (with the 80286 microprocessor) or 80387 (with the 80386 microprocessor). The prime source in all cases is Intel, who pioneered the development and production of maths co-processors.

As regards compatibility between these devices, this is a matter that requires due care and attention. As shown in the table below, the 8087 family of co-processors has no second source. This means that very little can go wrong here.

8086

Intel	**speed**
D-8087	5 MHz.
D-8087-2	8 MHz.
D-8087-1	10 MHz.

The second group, formed by the 80287 devices, has a few surprises. Although all ICs are pin-compatible, not every type has direct equivalents. The main difference is found with the clock frequency at which the co-processor can operate. As shown in the table at the end of this page, large differences exist here.

A co-processor usually operates at ⅔ of the microprocessor clock frequency, it may happen that very fast co-processors can not be used at their maximum

80286

AMD	**IIT**	**Intel**	**speed**
		D80287-3	5 MHz.
		D80287-6	6 MHz.
	2C87-8	D80287-8	8 MHz.
80EC287-10	2C87-10	D80287-10	10 MHz.
80EC287-12	2C87-12	D80287-12	12 MHz.
80EC287-16			16 MHz.
	2C87-20		20 MHz.

speed, simply because the associated microprocessor is relatively slow. This problem may be solved by a small piggy-back type plug-in board that contains a separate clock oscillator. In this arrangement, the clock signal from the motherboard is not used. Some manufacturers, supply this type of separate clock board to enable users of their co-processors to use these devices at their maximum speed. The photograph below to the right shows this board.

Finally, a few words about the 80387 group of co-processors. Here, the differences between the manufacturers are much larger than with the 80287. The 80387 is supplied in a PLCC package.

Weitek's co-processor (see the table below) is not pin-compatible with Intel's 80387. However, the 3167 is supplied with a small board that can be fitted into the PLCC socket provided on the motherboard for the co-processor.

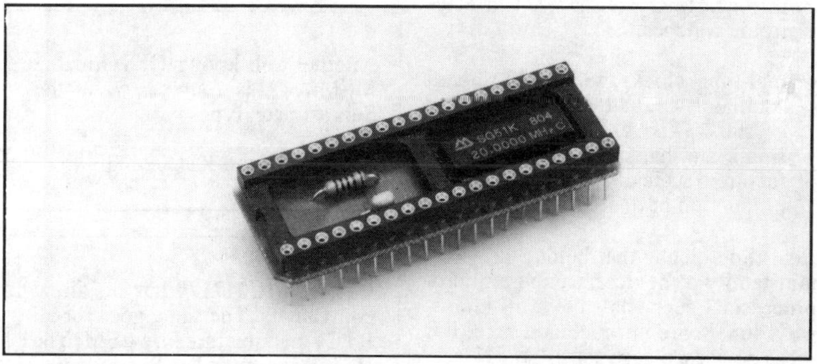

80386

Cyrix	IIT	Weitek	Intel	speed
	3C87-16	WTL3167-016-BRD	A80387-16	16 MHz.
CX83D87-20	3C87-20	WTL3167-020-BRD	A80387-20	20 MHz.
CX83D87-25	3C87-25	WTL3167-025-BRD		25 MHz.
CX83D87-33	3C87-33			33 MHz.

Timekeeping is a basic function required in almost any computer. Currently, there are few computer systems around that can work without some kind of RTC (real-time clock controller). Not surprisingly, the RTC product area is vastly differentiated both as regards available devices and manufacturers.
This second chapter in the data section of the book is aimed at providing a wide overview of RTC ICs. In principle, this type of peripheral IC may be divided into three categories:

- real-time clocks on board a component that forms part of a chip set (see that final chapter in this book). This type of RTC is of no great significance to the computer hobbyist because it forms part of another, larger, integrated circuit, whose functions it depends on and without which it can not operate.
- real-time clocks with an on-board oscillator and an external quartz crystal. This type of RTC is simple to locate on almost any PC motherboard by looking for a miniature quartz crystal as used in electronic watches.
- real-time clocks with an on-board oscillator and an on-board quartz crystal. This group is relatively small, and has devices from manufacturers typically specialized in the production of quartz crystals.

Real-time clocks that belong in a certain family of devices around a microprocessor, such as the well-known MC146818, are not included here. For these devices, please consult the Microprocessor Peripheral Databook Part 1.
Building a cross-reference on the basis of the currently available RTCs is neither easy nor particularly useful, mainly because the range of ICs with the basic time and date control functions is always being extended with ICs that provide additional features such as a built-in back-up battery. The overview below is, therefore, a list of RTCs which we can reasonably assume to be compatible as regards function and pinning. In all cases, however, the manufacturer has the final word about compatibility with other devices. Manufacturers and distributors are listed elsewhere in this book.

The following ICs contain the MSM58321 chip from OKI, and a quartz crystal:

RTC58321 .... Seiko Epson
RTC58321 .... Statek

Another well-known OKI chip, the MSM6242, is found back in the Seiko-Epson types

RTC62421 and RTC62423

Intersil's **ICM7170** has no direct equivalents. The same goes for all RTCs manufactured by µEM. The **DS1287** from Dallas Semiconductor is compatible with Motorola's MC146818.
For further information about compatibility it is recommended to make comparative checks on the basis of the databooks and datasheets supplied by the various manufacturers.

Data communication is one of the most important functions in a computer system. Both the standards and the components in the data comms field are of an astoundingly wide variety. Interestingly, there are many manufacturers and few device families. In spite of the ever increasing degree of integration (chip sets), aimed at including more and more essential functions in a single VLSI chip, there is still a wide range of discrete ICs for data communications.

There are a number of standards for communication protocols and the associated electrical specifications. The best known of these is the group of EIA protocols, which have contributed significantly to the ability of today's computers to communicate with one another (EIA = Electrical Industry Association).

The table lists only a few of the many parameters defined by the EIA standards. Among the parameters not included here are the type of connector, and the pin assignment.

Cross references of ICs for data communications show a wide variety of components which, from a functional point of view, are almost identical. The differences are usually limited to the number of (identical) line drivers or line receivers in a particular IC. The cross-references in this section of the book cover only those components included in the data section of the chapter on serial communication devices.

Many manufacturers supply ICs for which there is no direct equivalent or second source. An example is Newport Components with their series of RS232 drivers/receivers. Direct equivalents are also difficult to find for the communication ICs supplied by Maxim and Linear Technology.

EIA-requirements

Maximum cable length between transmitter and receiver (unit: foot):

RS232C	RS422	RS423	RS485
50	4000	2000	4000

Maximum transmission speed between transmitter and receiver (unit: bits per second):

RS232C	RS422	RS423	RS485
20 k	10M	300 k	10M

Maximale transmitter output voltage (unit: V):

RS232C	RS422	RS423	RS485
–25 to +25V	–6 to +6V	–7 to +1V	...

Short-circuit current at transmitter output (unit: mA):

RS232C	RS422	RS423	RS485
50	150	150	150

Receiver input resistance, R_{in} (unit: Ω):

RS232C	RS422	RS423	RS485
37 k	min. 4 k	min. 4k	12 k

Receiver input voltage (unit: V):

RS232C	RS422	RS423	RS485
–25 to +25V	–12 to +12V	–12 to +12V	–12 to +12V

The best known set of RS232C drivers/receivers is Motorola's MC1488/MC1489. As shown in the relevant cross reference, these ICs form the industry standard, and have given rise to a multitude of highly similar products from other semiconductor manufacturers.

For the sake of completeness, the cross-references list a number of IC manufacturers that are not found in the logo list and the address list elsewhere in this book. This is mainly because the relevant manufacturers are not, or no longer, active on the European market. It is also possible that they no longer manufacture the listed devices. Note that Fairchild no longer exists—the company has merged with National Semiconductor. Likewise, Signetics and Valvo are subsidiary companies within the Philips Components group.

MC1488 (RS232C Receiver)

The best known devices for RS232 communication are without doubt the MC1488 and MC1489. The prime source for these devices is Motorola. Texas Instruments' SN75188 and 75189 are pin-compatible equivalents of Motorola's MC1488 and MC1489.

XR1488	**Exar**
µA1488	**Fairchild**
MC1488	**Motorola**
µA1488/DS14(C)88/LM1488	**National Semiconductor**
RC1488	**Raytheon**
KS5788	**Samsung**
MC1488	**Samsung**
SG1488	**Silicon General**
MC1488	**Signetics**

MC1489 (RS232C Transmitter)

XR1489(A)	**Exar**
µA1489C(AC)	**Fairchild**
M75189A	**Mitsubishi**
MC1489	**Motorola**
µA1489/DS14(C)89A/LM1489A	**National Semiconductor**
MC1488	**Philips**
RC1489A	**Raytheon**
KS5789A	**Samsung**
MC1489(A)	**Samsung**
SG1489A	**Silicon General**
MC1489A	**Signetics**
MC1489(A)	**ST (SGS-Thomson)**
SN55189/SN75189	**Texas Instruments**
MC1489A	**Valvo**

A second major group of serial line drivers and receivers is the AM26LS29/30/31/32 series of devices from AMD (Advanced Micro Devices). Like the MC1488/1489, these devices have given rise to a proliferation of second sources.

AM26LS31 (RS422 Transmitter)

This RS422-zender belongs with the AM26LS32 receiver. A few remarks concerning the manufacturers mentioned below:
Fairchild has merged with National Semiconductor. Goldstar and Mitsubishi are not included in the the logo overviews and address lists simply because both manufacturers concentrate mainly on the OEM-market (Original Equipment Manufacturer) in the Far East.

AM26LS31C	**A T & T**
AM26LS31C/M	**Advanced Micro Devices**
µA26LS31C	**Fairchild**
GD26LS31C	**Goldstar**
M5A26LS31	**Mitsubishi**
AM26LS31	**Motorola**
AM26LS31C/M	**National Semiconductor**
DS26F31M/C	**National Semiconductor**
AM26LS31	**Philips**
AM26LS31	**Signetics**
AM26LS31C	**Texas Instruments**

AM26LS32 (RS422 Receiver)

AM26LS32C	**A T & T**
AM26LS32BC/M	**Advanced Micro Devices**
µA26LS32C/M	**Fairchild**
GD26LS32C	**Goldstar**
M5A26LS32A	**Mitsubishi**
AM26LS32	**Motorola**
µA26LS32C/M DS26LS32AM/C/M	**National Semiconductor**
DS26F32M/C	**National Semiconductor**

AM26LS33 (RS422/423 Receiver)

AM26LS33C	**AMD**
DS26LS33C/M	**National Semiconductor**
AM26LS33AC/AM	**Texas Instruments**

The next group of devices claiming widespread use is that manufactured by National Semiconductor. The group, referred to as DS36xx, has a few second source devices supplied by Motorola and Texas Instruments. The devices form pairs consisting of a 3486 and a 3487.

3486 (RS422/423 Receiver)

μA3486C .... **Fairchild**
MC3486 .... **Motorola**
DS3486/DS34C86 .... **National**
.... **Semiconductor**
MC3486 .... **Texas Instruments**

3487 (RS422/423 Driver)

μA3487C .... **Fairchild**
MC3487 .... **Motorola**
DS3487/DS34C87 .... **National**
.... **Semiconductor**

Finally, due space should be reserved for Texas Instruments, who supply by far the largest range of RS232 drivers and receivers. The databooks of this manufacturer have very large sections on ICs for data communications. The most popular devices are those in the SN75xxx series. The cross-references below list a number of possible equivalents for these ICs.

SN75172

μA96172 .... **Fairchild**
SN75172 .... **Motorola**
SN75176 .... **Texas Instruments**

SN75173

μA96173C .... **Fairchild**
SN75173 .... **Motorola**
SN75173 .... **Texas Instruments**

SN75174

μA96174C .... **Fairchild**
SN75174 .... **Motorola**
SN75174B .... **Texas Instruments**

SN75175

μA96175C .... **Fairchild**
SN75175 .... **Motorola**
SN75175B .... **Texas Instruments**

SN75176

μA96176C .... **Fairchild**
SN75176 .... **Motorola**
SN75176B .... **Texas Instruments**

SN75177

μA96177C .... **Fairchild**
SN75177 .... **Motorola**
SN75177B .... **Texas Instruments**

SN75178

μA96178C .... **Fairchild**
SN75178 .... **Motorola**
SN75178B .... **Texas Instruments**

Integrated circuits capable of serial-to-parallel and parallel-to-serial conversion of digital data are generally known as UARTs (universal asynchronous receiver/transmitter). When two UARTs are combined in one package, the chip is referred to as a DUART (dual UART). Similarly, quadruple and even octal versions exist under the respective names of QUART and OUART.
Since almost any computer system is based on processing of serial as well as parallel data, UARTs are in great demand and therefore supplied by many IC manufacturers. The larger number of these ICs, however, belongs to a family of devices around a specific microprocessor or microcontroller —examples are the MC685x, NS16xxx and 80xxx series. They are not included here since this book deals with universally applicable peripherals. The ICs that remain on the basis of this selection criterion form a relatively small group.

The AY-5-1015A from General Instruments (now Microchip) is probably the best known UART around. An earlier version of the AY-5-1015A, the AY-3-1013, is obsolete and no longer produced. Before listing the equivalent types in the UART group, a note about the CY232 from Cybernetic. Because of its on-board scrial-to-parallcl and parallel-to-serial converters, this IC really belongs in the group of UARTs, rather than in the group of serial drivers and receiver discussed in the previous chapter.
The following boxes bring together a number of ICs that are pin-compatible.

A third group of components used for data communications is formed by bit-rate and baud-rate generators. It should be noted that some ICs in this group are also referred to as programmable pulse generators. The main function of the ICs in this group is to provide a clock signal for a UART. Serial data communication is based on certain protocols which define, among other parameters, the speed at which the information (i.e., the databits) are transmitted. Basically, the bit/baud-rate generator (BRG) contains a quartz crystal oscillator and a programmable divider. Many BRGs these days are contained in ICs with a higher degree of integration. Broadly speaking, the range of discrete BRGs may be divided into two groups:
baud-rate generators which use an external quartz crystal;
baud-rate generators with an on-chip quartz crystal.

Here, the MC14411 is probably the best known type. Pin-compatible equivalents of this IC are not known, although a number of functional equivalents do exist.

AY-3-1015 .... Microchip
COM8602 .... SMC

AY-3-1013 .... Microchip
COM8017 .... SMC
TR1602 .... Western Digital

AY-5-8116/-36 .... Microchip
COM5015/-36 .... SMC
COM8116/-36
WD1941/-43/-45 .... Western
.... Digital

AY-5-8126 .... Microchip
MC14411 .... Motorola
COM5026/-46 .... SMC
COM8126/46

This last chapter deals with fairly recent developments in the field of peripheral ICs. The integration of certain standard ICs into so-called chip sets is a logical development given the need for compact and simple to produce computer equipment. In the case of PC motherboards, for instance, the use of chip sets allows the total printed-circuit board size, and the number of components on it, to be significantly reduced. The chip sets produced for PCs look very much alike as far as their function is concerned. Equivalent sets appear not to exist, however, because of small, yet significant, differences. It makes little sense, therefore, to compile a cross-reference of these sets. Instead, reference is made to the chapter on chip sets in the documentation overview printed on the following pages. When examining this overview, it will be noted that the type numbers used among manufacturers resemble one another quite closely. This may form an indication that certain sets are compatible at least to some extent.
Chip sets generally consist of a number of integrated circuits which are usually supplied in PLCC packages. The actual number of components in a particular set depends on the manufacturer and on the application. A further development in this area is the so-called single-chip peripheral, which combines all the functions of a chip set in a single IC. A growing number of manufacturers are already supplying these devices, which use a very high degree of integration. To illustrate the reduction in board space that can be achieved by the use of single-chip peripherals, UMC's 12-MHz PC-XT motherboard is shown in the photograph. The size of this board is a little larger than that of a double eurocard. The single-chip peripheral on this board, the UM82C088A, combines the following functions:

The photograph on this page shows that very few additional peripherals are required to put together a complete PC-XT compatible computer.
It is expected that single-chip peripherals will cause drastic price reductions in the PC XT/AT market. Apart from the reduced number of components and the total PCB area, they also offer an advantage in allowing manufacturers to simplify the PCB layout and abandon the use of (expensive) multi-layer cards.

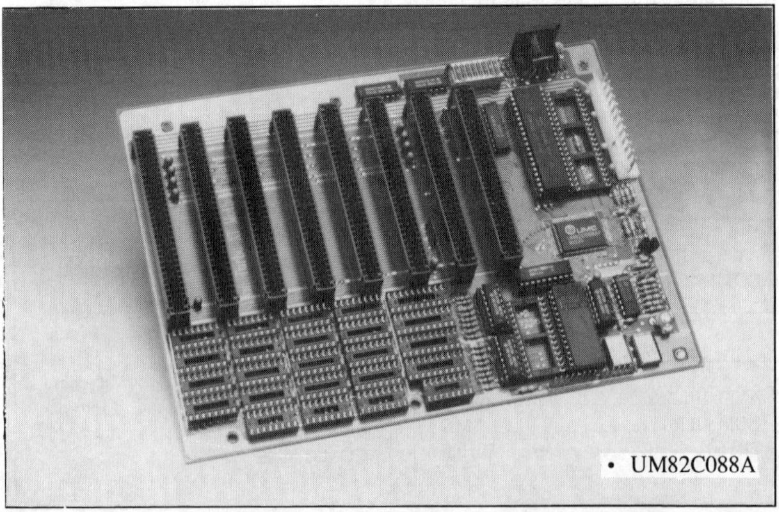

• UM82C088A

• CS 8228 chip set

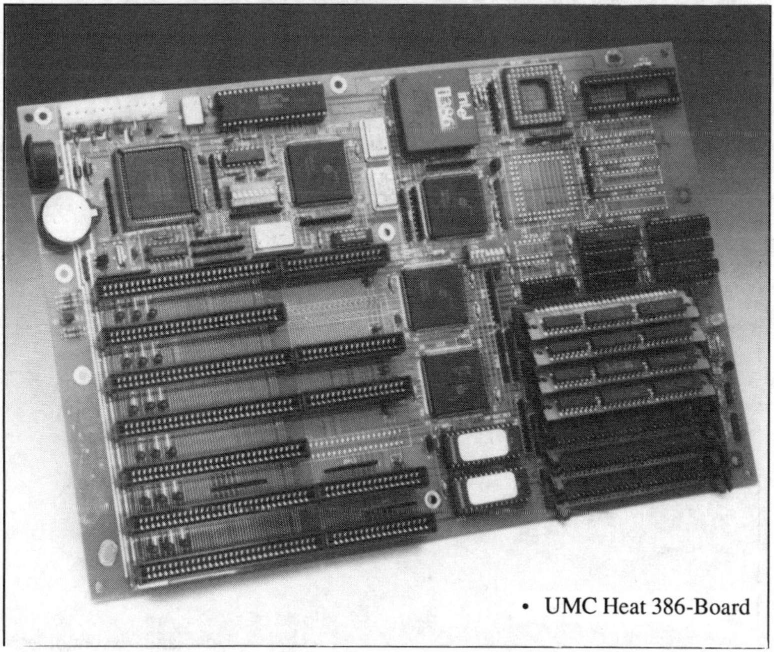

• UMC Heat 386-Board

• Headland Technology 486 chip set

Overview of databooks

The information in the chapter on co-processors was obtained from a large number of databooks and brochures on ICs typically intended for use in an PC XT or AT environment. The list that follows below is not exhaustive. Undoubtedly there are many other manufacturers and types co-processor, e.g., the ones available for the 68000 microprocessor from Motorola, and special types developed for use in, for instance, laser printers, where a lot of calculation is involved. In this chapter, however, we limit ourselves to the range of PC-compatible co-processors.

AMD

AMD has included their co-processors in the following databook:

Personal Computer Products: Processors, Coprocessors, Video, and Mass Storage (1989)

Finally, a datasheet must be mentioned that compares the performance of AMD's range of co-processors to that of Intel's:

Comparing AMD's CMOS 80C287 and 80EC287 Math Coprocessors to the Intel NMOS 80287 and CMOS 80C287A (March 1989)

Cyrix

Cyrix supplies only one type, which is an equivalent of the 80387. Cyrix support their product with two booklets:

FasMath 83D87 User's Manual (September 1989)
FasMath 83D87 Accuracy Report (August 1989)

IIT

Supplies two datasheets instead of a brochure or a databook:

IIT-2C87 80-Bit Numeric Co-Processor (April 1989)
IIT-3C87 80-Bit Numeric Co-processor (April 1989)

Intel

Data on Intel's co-processors may be found in the book:

Microprocessors 1990

The content of this book, as far as ICs are concerned, is as follows:

Weitek

This manufacturer supplies equivalents of the 80387, and a co-processor for the 80486, the 4167. Weitek have produced a number of comprehensive brochures which contain the complete data of their 'Abacus' range of maths processors. The titles are:

WTL3167 Floating Point Co-processor (September 1988)
Weitek Corporation Abacus Background Information (Juni 1988)
4167 Floating Point Co-processor (Juli 1989)
Weitek Corporation Abacus 4167 Background Information (Juli 1989)
Abacus Software Designers Guide

AMD

Cyrix

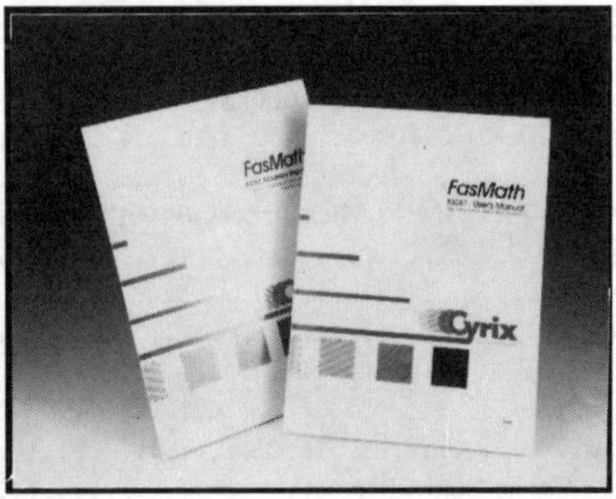

Intel

Weitek

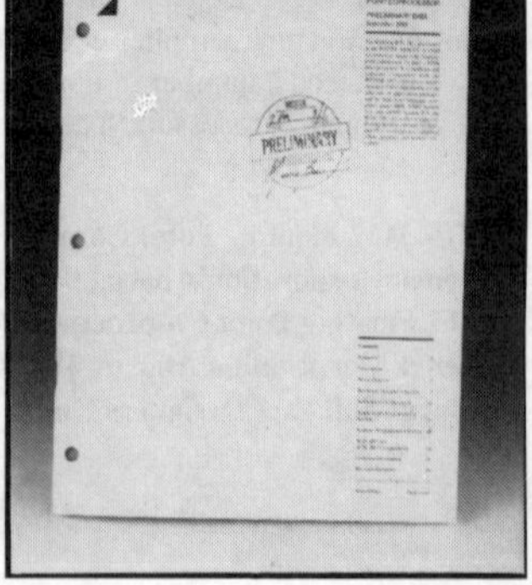

Peripheral chips also include integrated circuits for date and time control. If not contained in a chip set or more complex (VLSI) components, RTC (real-time clock) chips of the following manufacturers may be found in many types of computer equipment. The information shown here was obtained during the compiling of the chapter on real-time clocks.

Dallas Semiconductor

1989 Data Book

In a chapter called Timekeeping in their most recent databook, Dallas Semiconductors list the following real-time clocks and associated ICs:

Intersil (a Harris Semiconductor company)

Intersil manufacture only one RTC. This is contained in the still up-to-date 1987 databook:

Component Data Catalog 1987

Only the components included in Chapter 14, Timers/Clocks/Counters with Display Drivers, are listed here. Note that only the first type is an RTC.

MEM (Micro Electronic Marin)

MEM have issued four separate datasheets on their real-time clock chips:

M3001 .... Real Time Clock Circuit (March 1987)
M3002 .... Real Time Clock Circuit (August 1988)
M3003 .... Real Time Clock Circuit (January 1988)
E050-16 1-Bit .... Real Time Clock and Timer (January 1988)

National Semiconductor

This manufacturer has produced a separate databook covering its real-time clock ICs:

Advanced Peripherals: Real Time Clock Handbook (1989)

The book contains a chapter with datasheets, and a chapter with application notes. The datasheet chapter describes the following components:

OKI

Data Book Microprocessor fourth edition (March 1989)

OKI in their most recent databook lists three RTCs in the chapter on peripheral ICs:

Seiko - Epson

Seiko Epson supply their information on real-time clock modules in the form of separate leaflets. The following datasheets are available:

RTC72421/72423 .... Real Time Clock Module (December 1989)
Real Time Clock Module RTC72421 Application Manual
RTC58321 .... Real Time Clock Module (March 1988)
RTC62421/62423 .... Real Time Clock Module (September 1989)
RTC4503 .... Real Time Clock Module (December 1989)

Statek

Statek, renowned for their quartz crystals and associated products, supply a double-sided datasheet:

RTC58321 .... Real Time Clock Module (December 1987)

Dallas Semiconductor

Harris Semiconductor

National Semiconductor

OKI

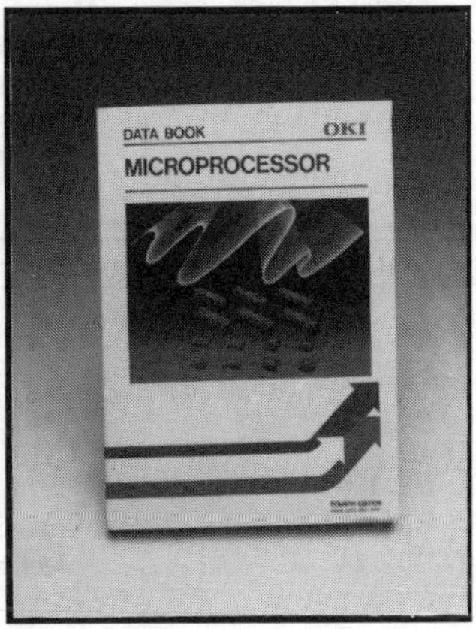

ICs developed for serial data communication form an important group of peripheral devices. Not surprisingly, a large number of manufacturers supply this type of component. The serial data transmitters and receivers that comply with the relevant EIA specifications are listed below:

AMD

Bipolar Microprocessor Logic and Interface (1985 Data Book)

AMD have included their range of serial driver and receiver ICs in the chapter 'AM 26S and AM26LS Interface family':

Dallas Semiconductor

Semiconductors 1989 Databook

The information on drivers and receivers for serial datacomms is contained in the chapter 'System Extension':

Exar

Databook USIC's, ASIC's (1987)

Section 3 of this databook lists the following data communication circuits:

Modem Basics

XR2124 .... Universal Data Buffer 3-38
XR2125 .... Bell212A Type Data Buffer 3-43
XR2130 .... Single Chip Bell212A/CCITT V.22 Modem 3-48
XR2135 .... Bell/CCIT Data Buffer 3-58
XR2400 .... V.22 bis Modem System 3-63
XR14412 .... FSK Modem System 3-66

Filters

XR2103/XR2103A .... FSK Modem Filter 3-74
XR2120 .... PSK Modem Filter 3-80
XR2126/XR2127/
XR2128/XR2129 .... Bell212A/CCITT V.22 Modem Filters 3-87

Line Interface Circuits

XR1488/XR1489 .... Quad Line Driver/Receiver 3-99

UART'S

XR88C681/XR68C681 ... CMOS Dual Channel UART (DUART) 3-104

Harris Semiconductor

Component Data Catalog 1987

Harris semiconductor manufacture only one RS-232 transmitter/receiver. This chip, which was formerly supplied under the name of Intersil, is described in 'Section 11: Data Communications':

IM26C91 .... Universal Asynchronous Receiver/Transmitter (UART) 11-1
IM4702/4712 .... Baud Rate Generator 11-19
IM6402 .... Universal Asynchronous Receiver/Transmitter (UART) 11-26
IM6403 .... Universal Asynchronous Receiver/Transmitter (UART) 11-26
ICL232 .... +5 Volt Powered Dual RS-232 Transmitter/Receiver 11-36

Linear Technology

1990 Linear Databook

Linear Technology produces so many RS-232 ICs that a separate chapter describing their specifications is included in their databook:

LT1015 .... High Speed Dual Line Receiver 13-6
LT1030 .... Quad Low Power Line Driver 10-5
LT1030CS .... Quad Low Power Line Driver 10-9
LT1032 .... Quad Low Power Line Driver 10-11
LT1039 .... RS232 Driver/Receiver with Shutdown 10-19
LTC1045 .... Programmable Micropower Hex Translator/Receiver/Driver 10-27
LT1080 .... Advanced Low Power 5V RS232 Dual Receiver 10-43
LT1081 .... Advanced Low Power 5V RS232 Dual Receiver 10-43
LT1080CS/LT1081CS ... 5V Powered RS232 Driver/Receiver with Shutdown 10-51
LT1130 .... 5-Driver/5-Receiver RS232 Transceiver 10-55

Maxim

1989 Integrated Circuits Data Book

The chapter 'Interface' contains only one datasheet, which combines the descriptions of the following types:

Motorola

Linear and Interface Integrated Circuits (1988)

Motorola have included their well-known series of EIA drivers/receivers/transceivers in the chapter on Interface Circuits. This chapter discusses Memory Interface and Control, Microprocessor Bus Interface,

Peripheral Drivers, Single-Ended Bus Transceivers, Line Transceivers, Line Drivers and Line Transceivers. Only the drivers and receivers are listed here:

Line Receivers

Line Drivers

Line Transceivers

National Semiconductor

Advanced Peripherals: Data Communications/ Local Area Networks UARTs Handbook 1988

Section 6: Transmission Line Drivers/Receivers

Newport Components

Newport Components have available a 20-page brochure, issued in 1988, which includes their full range of serial ICs:

Interface Data

Philips

Data Handbook: IC11 Linear Products (1989)

The following devices are discussed under the subhead 'Line Drivers/Receivers' in the chapter on Data Communications:

Am26LS33 .... **quad high-speed differential line receiver** **1439**
MC1488 .... **quad line driver** **1443**
MC1489 .... **quad line receiver** **1447**
MC1489A .... **quad line receiver** **1447**
NE5170 .... **octal line driver** **1450**
NE5180 .... **octal differential line receiver** **1457**
NE5181 .... **octal differential line receiver** **1457**
AN113 .... **using MC1488/MC1489 line drivers and receivers** **1463**

Samsung

Linear IC Databook (Vol.2) Telecom/Industrial (1989)

MC1488 .... **Quad Line Driver** **296**
MC1489/A .... **Quad Line Receiver** **301**

Silicon General

Product Catalog (jan. 1989)

This book contains an extensive chapter, 'Power Driver and Interface Circuits', which, however, contains only two devices for data communications:

SG1488 .... **Quad RS-232C Line Driver** **6-9**
SG1489 .... **Quad RS-232C Line Receiver** **6-13**
SG1489A .... **Quad RS-232C Line Receiver** **6-13**

ST (SGS-Thomson)

Industrial and Computer Peripheral ICs Databook 1st Edition (1988)

This book, which is not divided into chapters, lists the following RS-232 drivers/receivers:

MC1488 .... **RS232C Quad Line Driver** **679**
MC1489 .... **RS232C Quad Line Receiver** **687**
MC1489A .... **RS232C Quad Line Receiver** **687**

Teledyne Semiconductor

Precision Analog and Power Control IC Handbook (1988)

TSC232 .... **Dual RS-232 Transmitter/Receiver & Power Supply** **15-3**

Texas Instruments

Interface Circuits Data Book (1987)

Texas Instruments probably has the largest range of serial drivers/receivers/transceivers. The chapter 'Line Drivers/Receivers' contains the specifications of the following ICs:

AMD

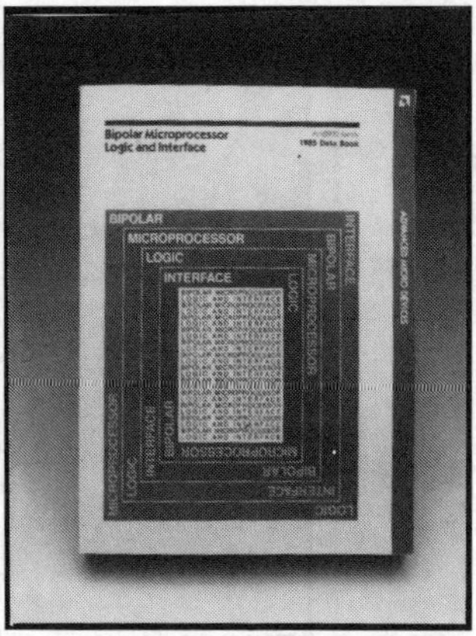

Dallas Semiconductor

Exar

Harris Semiconductor

Linear Technology

Maxim

Motorola

National Semiconductor

Philips

Samsung

Silicon General

ST (SGS-Thomson)

Teledyne Semiconductor

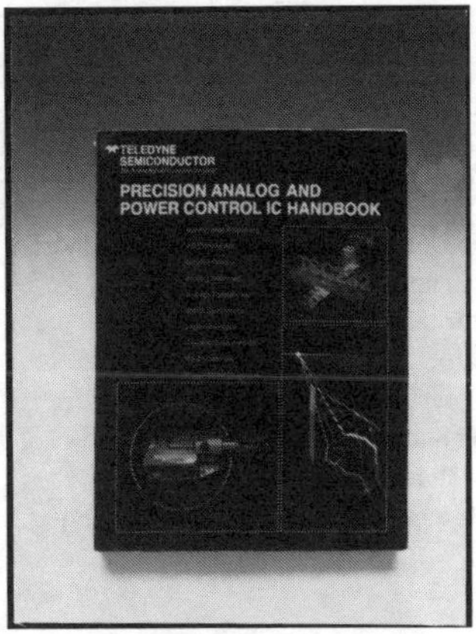

Texas Instruments

UARTs are integrated circuits use to convert serial data into parallel format, and the other way around. Although they are essential components for serial data communications in and between computers, the list of UART, DUART, QUART and OUART manufacturers is not very long. The reason for this is that we have only included 'independent' types, i.e., ICs which are not part of a family of peripheral chips around a certain microprocessor. Examples of types excluded from this list on the basis of this selection criterion are the well-known I8250 and INS16450.

Cybernetic

This manufacturer of highly specialized ICs supplies one device which is really a combination of a UART and a serial line driver/receiver. Cybernetic have published only one databook:

Cybernetic Micro Systems: Control ICs (1990)

CY232 .... Parallel/Serial Interface and Network Controller 5

Fujitsu

Fujitsu supply only one type of UART, which is described in:

8/16-Bit Microprocessors/ Microcomputers/ Peripherals 1987 Data Book

MB8868A .... UART 4-183

Harris Semiconductor

Component Data Catalog 1987

Harris Semiconductors supply two types of family-independent UART, which were formerly Intersil products. The UARTs are described in 'Section 11: Data Communications'. For the sake of completeness, all types discussed in Section 11 are listed here:

IM26C91 .... Universal Asynchronous Receiver/Transmitter(UART) 11-1
IM4702/4712 .... Baud Rate Generator 11-19
IM6402 .... Universal Asynchronous Receiver/Transmitter (UART) 11-26
IM6403 .... Universal Asynchronous Receiver/Transmitter (UART) 11-26

Microchip

The UARTs AY-3-1013 and AY-5-1015D are familiar to most, if not all, computer hardware enthusiasts. These devices, of which only the AY-5-1015D has survived, used to be supplied by General Instruments Semiconductors. In the chapter 'Logic Product Specifications', Microchip describe the following devices:

AY2661 .... Enhanced Programmable Communications Interface 5-1
AY-5-1015D .... UAR/T: Universal Asynchronous Receiver/Transmitter 5-17
AY5-8116/36 .... Dual Buad Rate Generator 5-29
AY-5-8126/46 .... Single Baud Rate Generator 5-37
AY-3-8910A/12A .... Programmable Sound Generator 5-45
AY-8930 .... Enhanced Programmable Sound Generator 5-61
AY0438-I .... 32-Segment CMOS LCD-Driver 5-81
AY500 .... 32-Command Infrared Remote Control Transmitter Chip 5-85

SMC (Standard Microsystems Corporation)

SMC is fairly strong on UARTs, witness their

1988 Components Catalog

COM1863	**UART**	**59-60**
COM78808	**Octal UART**	**135-136**
COM78C808	**CMOS 8-UART**	**137-150**
COM78C804	**QUART (4-UART)**	**121-134**
COM78C802	**DUART (2-UART)**	**107-120**
COM8017	**UART**	**153-160**
COM8018	**UART**	**59-60**
COM81C17	**UART**	**161-168**
COM8502	**UART**	**153-160**

Cybernetic

Fujitsu

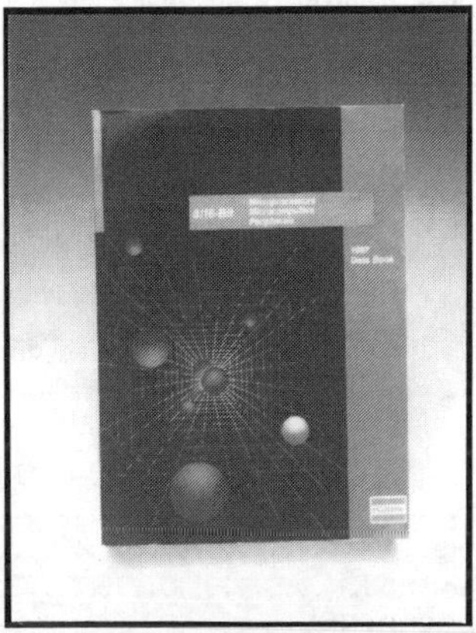

Harris Semiconductor

Microchip

SMC

The clock signal for a UART is usually supplied by a device known as a baud-rate generator (BRG). Basically, this is a combination of a crystal-controlled oscillator and a programmable divider capable of supplying a number of fixed frequencies. The ever increasing degree of integration has resulted in more and more baud-rate generators being contained, as an auxiliary function, in much more complex integrated circuits. The ones listed below however are discrete devices.

Microchip

Microchip in their latest databook list the following baud-rate generators:

AY2661 .... Enhanced Programmable Communications Interface 5-1
AY-5-1015D .... UAR/T: Universal Asynchronous Receiver/Transmitter 5-17
AY5-8116/36 .... Dual Buad Rate Generator 5-29
AY-5-8126/46 .... Single Baud Rate Generator 5-37
AY-3-8910A/12A .... Programmable Sound Generator 5-45
AY-8930 .... Enhanced Programmable Sound Generator 5-61
AY0438-I .... 32-Segment CMOS LCD-Driver 5-81
AY500 .... 32-Command Infrared Remote Control Transmitter Chip 5-85

Motorola

Motorola's baud-rate generators are included in the

Telecommunications Device Data (Q3 1989)

This book also lists a number of EIA-compatible serial drivers/receivers. The BRGs are discussed in the chapter 'Modems and Data Communications'.

Modems:

MC1488 .... Quad MDTL Line Driver 2-3
MC1489(A) .... Quad MDTL Line Receivers 2-9
MC6172 .... 2400 bps Digital Modulator (DPSK) 2-96
MC6173 .... 2400 bps Digital Demodulator (DPSK) 2-104
MC6860 .... 0-600 bps Digital Modem 2-119
MC14411 .... Bit Rate Generator 2-165
MC14412 .... Universal Low Speed Modem (0-300 bps) 2-168
MC143403 .... Quad Line Driver 2-413
MC143404 .... Quad Line Driver 2-413
MC145402 .... Serial 13-Bit Linear Codec (A/D-D/A) 2-417
MC145406 .... EIA-232-D Driver/ Receiver 2-428
MC145407 .... 5-Volt EIA-232-D Driver Receiver 2-435
MC145411 .... Bit Rate Generator 2-440
MC145414 .... Dual Tunable Low-Pass Sampled Data Filter 2-450
MC145415 .... Dual Tunable Linear Phase Low-Pass Sampled Data Filter 2-457
MC145440 .... 300 Baud Modem Filter (Bell 103) 2-556
MC145441 .... 300 Baud Modem Filter (CCIT V.21) 2-562
MC145442 .... 300 Baud Modem (CCIT V.21) 2-568
MC145443 .... 300 Baud Modem (Bell 103) 2-568
MC145445 .... 300 Baud Modem (Bell 103//CCIT V.21) 2-577
MC145450 .... 1200 Baud Modem (Bell 202/CCIT V.23) 2-582

Data Communications

MC145406 .... **EIA-32-Driver/ Receiver 2-428**
MC145407 .... **5-Volt EIA-232- Driver Receiver** **2-435**
MC145411 Bit Rate Generator **2-440**
MC145428 .... **Data Set Interface (DSI)** **2-506**
MC145488 .... **Dual Data Link Controller (DDLC) (ISDN LAPD/LAPB)** **2-590**

Seiko-Epson

Three series of BRGs are discussed in a single datasheet:

Programmable Standard Pulse Generators (November 1989)

SPG8640CN .... **1200,2400,4800,9600 and 48000 bits/sec**
SPG8650C .... **50, 100, 150, 200, 300, 600, 1200, 6000 bits/sec**
SPG8650D .... **300, 600, 1200, 2400, 4800, 9600 bits/sec**

SMC (Standard Microsystems Corporation)

1988 Components Catalog

This book contains a separate chapter devoted entirely to baud-rate generators:

COM5016(T) .... **Dual Baud Rate Generator** **271-272**
COM5026(T) .... **Single Baud Rate Generator** **273-274**
COM5036(T) .... **Dual Baud Rate Generator** **271-272**
COM5046(T) .... **Single Baud Rate Generator** **273-274**
COM8046(T) .... **Single Baud Rate Generator** **275-276**
COM8116(T) .... **Dual Baud Rate Generator** **277-278**
COM8126(T) .... **Single Baud Rate Generator** **279-286**
COM8136(T) .... **Dual Baud Rate Generator** **277-278**
COM8146(T) .... **Single Baud Rate Generator** **279-286**
COM8156(T) .... **Dual Baud Rate Generator** **287-290**
COM81C66(T) .... **Timer/Clock Generator** **291-292**
COM81C67 .... **Timer/Clock Generator** **291-292**
COM81C68 .... **Timer/Clock Generator** **291-292**

Microchip

Motorola

SMC

The term chip set in this book refers to the complex ICs used to combine several functions on PC motherboards. The documentation overview presented below provides an extensive list of the various chip sets which are currently available. It should be noted that the chip sets form a rapidly growing market. It is therefore possible that certain products or manufacturers are not listed.

Chips & Technology

This company supplies a set of datasheets, which together form a product brochure of considerable size. The reason for this is that the datasheet of a chip set is actually a set of datasheets covering the ICs in the set. The chip sets manufactured by C & T are listed below:

CS8221: PC-AT Compatible NEAT Chipset

P82C206 .... Integrated Peripherals Controller
P82C111 .... CPU/Bus Controller
P82C212 .... Page/Interleave and EMS memory Controller
P82C215 .... Data/Address Buffer

CS8223: Low Powered Enhanced AT Portable LeAPset

P82C206 .... Integrated Peripherals Controller
P82C241 .... CPU-Bus, Page/Interleave and EMS memory Controller
P82C242 .... Data/Address buffers and bus conversion logic
P82C425 .... LCD Controller
P82C609 .... Multifunction Controller (one parallel port and two UARTS)
P82C636 .... Power Control Unit

CS8230: AT/386 Chip Set

P82C301 .... Bus Controller
P82C302 .... Page/Interleave Controller
P82A303 .... Address Bus Interface
P82A304 .... Address Bus Interface
P82A305 .... Data Bus Interface
P82A306 .... Control Signal Buffer

CS8225: CHIPS/250 IBM PS/2 Model 50/60 Compatible Chip Set

P82C221 .... CPU and Micro Channel Controller
P82C222 .... Page/Interleave and EMS Memory Controller
P82C223 .... DMA Controller
P82C225 .... Data Bus Buffer
P82C226 .... System Peripherals Controller
P82C451 .... Super VGA Controller
P82C607 .... Multi-Function Controller with Analog FDC Data Separator and
.... 16550 compatible serial port

CS8283: CHIPS/280 IBM PS/2 Model 70/80 Compatible Chip Set

P82C223 .... DMA Controller
P82C226 .... System Peripherals Controller
P82C321 .... CPU and Micro Channel Controller
P82C322 .... Page/Interleave and EMS Controller

P82C325 .... Data/Buffer Controller
P82C451 .... Super VGA Controller
P82C607 .... Multi-Function Controller with Analog FDC Data Separator and 16550 compatible serial port

Headland Technology

The PC-AT (80286) chip set of this company is relatively simple to upgrade to a 80386SX chip set. Headland Technology (formerly G2) supplies a separate datasheets for every IC in the chip set. A databook is not available.

GCK101 80286 chip set

GC101 .... Peripheral Controller
GC102 .... Data Buffer
GC102 .... Address Buffer

GCK101SX 80386SX chip set

GC101SX .... Peripheral Controller
GC102 .... Data Buffer
GC113 .... Address Buffer

GCK131 80386 chip set

GC131 .... Peripheral Controller
GC132 .... CPU/Memory Controller
GC133 .... Bus Bridge

Intel

Intel has a number of chip sets in its product range. They are listed below.

I82310 Micro Channel Compatible Chip Set

I82310

This chip set for the 386-AT is described in a product brief, and contains the following components:

The set also contains a VGA Graphics controller, the I82706.

I82306 .... Local Channel Support 3
I82307 .... DMA/Micro Channel Arbitration Controller 4
I82308 .... Micro Channel Bus Controller 5
I82309 .... Address Bus Controller 6

I82311 Micro Channel Compatible Peripheral Family (March 1990)

I82311

The databook gives extensive information on the following ICs:

I82303 .... Local I/O Support Chip (LIO) 16
I82304 .... Local I/O support Chip (LIO) 26

I82350 EISA Chip Set (February 1990)

I82350

Two documents are available for this product: a beautifully styled product brief, and a databook with the above title. The chip set consists of two components for fitting on a motherboard:

The EISA chip set also contains two ICs which are not fitted on the motherboard: the I82352 and the I82355.

I82340 PC/AT Chip Set Family Product Briefs

I82340

Since a databook is not yet available, the chip sets for the -DX and the -SX processor are described in a product brief. The chip sets are supplied under the type numbers I82340 (for the -DX processor) and I82340SX (for the -SX processor).

Oak Technology

This manufacturer supplies two chip sets for laptop computers, one for 80286-based machines, and one for 80386-based machines. A databook is available that describes the five ICs in the set:

OAK Horizon Chip Set (November 1 1989)

A second book describes the following devices:

IBM PS/2 Model 30 Compatible Chip Set

Opti

A short brochure supplied by Opti describes the following chip sets:

one, a 25-MHz or 33-MHz version for the 80386:

F82C381
F82C382

and another for the 80486 (also in 25-MHz or 33-MHz versions):

F82C481
F82C482

UMC

This Taiwanese manufacturer supplies a number of chip sets ranging from simple PC-XT applications to 386-based systems. Each chip set from UMC is documented in a brochure-like datasheet which contains all the relevant information. UMC's chip sets are marketed under the following type indications:

Mortar 286 AT Chip Set (UM82C230 Series)

UM82C206 .... Integrated Peripherals Controller
UM82C231 .... System/Memory Controller
UM82C232 .... Data/Address Buffer

Neat Compatible Chip Set for 80286/80386SX Systems (UM82C210 Series)

UM82C206 .... Integrated Peripherals Controller
UM82C211 .... System Controller
UM82C212 .... Memory Controller
UM82C215 .... Data/Address Bus Buffer

UMC's 80386 chip set is described in two brochures:

High End AT Chip Set: Heat Doc A (march 21 1990); UM82C380-Set

UM82C381 .... System Controller
UM82C382 .... Address Buffer
UM82C383 .... Data Buffer
UM82C384 .... Memory Controller
UM82C388 .... Intel Cache Interface
UM82C389 .... Austek Cache Interface

The second brochure for the Heat chip set discusses its use on the demo-board shown in the photograph.

High End AT Chip Set: Heat Doc B/C/D/E/F/G/K (Jan. 20 1990)

Computer ICs 1990-1991 Data Book

The chapter 'PC mainboard' contains information on a number of chip sets. For the sake of completeness, the complete chapter content is given below:

VTI (VLSI Technology)

VL82C286 PC-AT-Compatible Chip Set

This documentation describes a chip set that consists of only two components:

VL82C320	**System Controll and Data Buffering functions**
VL82C331	**ISA Bus Controller**

VL82CPCAT 12-MHz PC-AT-Compatible Chip Set

This set consists of five ICs:

VL82C100 .... Peripheral Controller
VL82C101B .... System Controller
VL82C102A .... Memory Controller
VL82C103A .... Address Buffer
VL82C104 .... Data Buffer

VL82CPCAT 16-MHz PC-AT-Compatible Chip Set

This discusses:

VL82C100 .... Peripheral Controller
VL82C201 .... System Controller
VL82C202 .... Memory Controller
VL82C203 .... Address Buffer
VL82C204 .... Data Buffer

Zymos

Zymos produces six ICs which may be used in a chip set put together by the user. The chips are referred to as POACH (**PC On A CHip**) followed by a type number. Currently, the range consists of chip sets POACH1 to POACH6. Further information on the ICs in this series may be found in a number of separate datasheets:

Poach1/Poach2 (Poach AT)

Poach1

contains:

6818 .... Real Time Clock
8259A .... Programmable Interrupt Controller (Master)
8259A .... Programmable Interrupt Controller (Slave)
82284 .... Clock Generator & Ready Interface
82288 .... Bus Controller

Poach2

contains:

74LS612 .... Memory Mapper
8237 .... DMA Controller (2)
8254 .... Programmable Interval Timer
8284A .... Clock Generator

Poach3 (Poach ATB)

AT-Address/Data Buffer

Poach4 (Poach XT88)

8237 .... DMA Controller

8254 .... **Programmable Interval Timer**
8255 .... **Programmble Peripheral Interface**
8259A .... **Programmable Interrupt Controller**
8284A .... **Clock Generator**
8288 .... **Bus Controller**

Poach5 (XTB)

XT-Addres/Data Buffers

Poach6 (AT386)

an upgrade of the POACH AT to a 386 chip set.

Intel

Intel

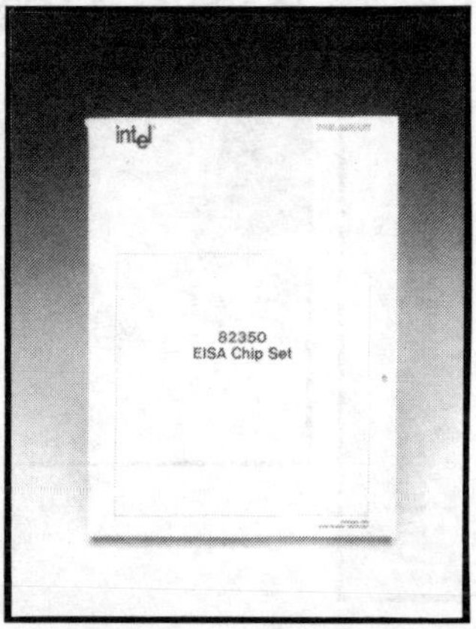

Oak

Oak

UMC

UMC

UMC

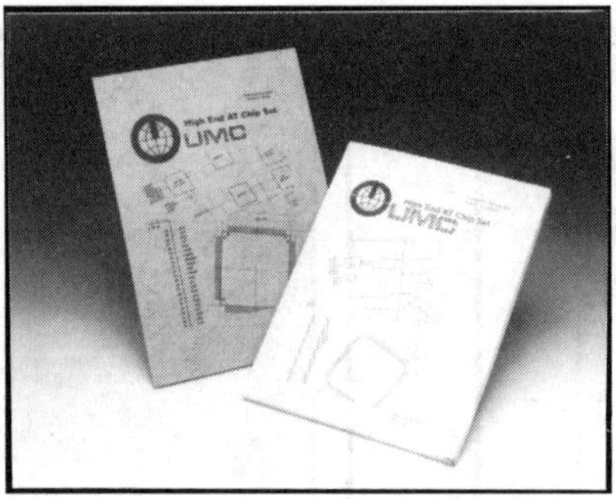

UMC

VTI (VLSI Technology)

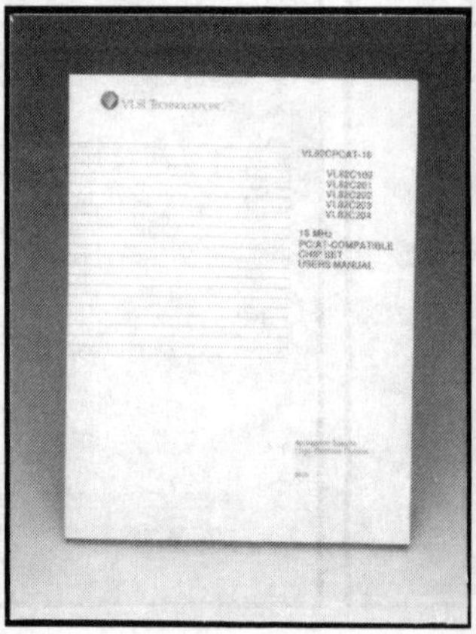

Overview of addresses

• Advanced Micro Devices

Belgium
Advanced Micro Devices S.A./N.V.
Avenue de Tervueren 419, Box 9
B-1150 Brussels
tel.: (+32) 02-7719142
fax.: (+32) 02-7623712
tlx.: 61028

Canada
Advanced Micro Devices Ltd.
300 March Road
Suite 301
Kanata, Ontario K2K 2E2
tel.: (+1) 0613-5920060
fax.: (+1) 0613-5920182

Advanced Micro Devices Ltd.
2 Sheppard Avenue East
Suite 1610
Willowdale, Ontario M2N 5Y7
tel.: (+1) 0416-2245193
fax.: (+1) 0416-2240056

France
Advanced Micro Devices S.A.
Zone Industrielle Orlytech
5, Allée du Commandant Mouchotte
F-91550 Paray-Vieille-Poste
tel.: (+33) 01-49751010
fax.: (+33) 01-49751013
tlx.: 263282

Great Britain
Advanced Micro Devices (U.K.) Ltd.
AMD House
Goldsworth Road
Woking, Surrey GU21 1JT
tel.: (+44) 0483-222121
fax.: (+44) 0483-756196
tlx.: 859103

Advanced Micro Devices (U.K.) Ltd.
The Genesis Centre
Garrett Field, Science Park South
Birchwood, Warrington WA3 7BH
tel.: (+44) 0925-828008
fax.: (+44) 0925-827693
tlx.: 628524

Hong Kong
Advanced Micro Devices Far East Ltd.
1201-2 Harcourt House
39 Gloucester Road
Wanchai
tel.: (+852) 05-8654525
fax.: (+852) 05-8654335
tlx.: 67955

Italy
Advanced Micro Devices S.p.a.
Centro Direzionale
Via Novara 570
I-20153 Milano
tel.: (+39) 02-3533241
fax.: (+39) 02-3498000
tlx.: 315286

Japan
Nihon Advanced Micro Devices
Konishi-Nissei Building
4-12-12 Minami-Senba
Chyuuou-ku
Osaka 542
tel.: (+81) 06-2433250
fax.: (+81) 06-2433253

Nihon Advanced Micro Devices
Shinjuku Kokusai Building
6-6-2 Nishi-Shinjuku
Shinjuku-ku
Tokyo 160
tel.: (+81) 03-3458241
fax.: (+81) 03-3425196
fax.: (+81) 03-3425197

Korea
Advanced Micro Devices Far East Ltd.
12th floor Dae-Han Life Insurance, 63 Building
60 Yoido-dong
Youngdeungpo-ku
Seoul 150-010
tel.: (+82) 02-7840030
fax.: (+82) 02-7848014

Norway
Advanced Micro Devices A.B.
Höviks Business Center
Sandviksveien 26
P.O.Box 156
N-1322 Hövik
tel.: (+47) 02-537810
fax.: (+47) 02-591959
tlx.: 79079

Singapore
Advanced Micro Devices Far East Ltd.
80 Marine Parade Road
17-01 Parkway Parade
Singapore 1544
tel.: (+65) 3481188
fax.: (+65) 3480161
tlx.: 55650

Sweden
Advanced Micro Devices A.B.
Box 2028, Rissneleden 140 5tr
S-17202 Sundbyberg
tel.: (+46) 08-7330350
fax.: (+46) 08 7332285
tlx.: 11602

Switzerland
Advanced Micro Devices S.A.
European Head Quarters
World Trade Center
108, Avenue Louis Casal
CH-1215 Geneva
tel.: (+41) 022-880025
tel.: (+41) 022-880251
fax.: (+41) 022-880617

Taiwan
Advanced Micro Devices Far East Ltd. Taiwan Branch
9th floor, 107 Jen-ai Road, Section 4
Taipei
tel.: (+886) 02-7213393
fax.: (+886) 02-7723422

Thailand
Advanced Micro Devices Tai Ltd.
229 Moo 4 Changwattana Road
Pakkred, Nonthaburi 11120
tel.: (+66) 02-5841591
fax.: (+66) 02-5839260
tlx.: 21391

United States of America
Advanced Micro Devices Inc.
901 Thompson Place
P.O. Box 453
Sunnyvale, Ca 94086
tel.: (+1) 0408-7232400
tlx.: 346306

West-Germany
Advanced Micro Devices GmbH
Marktplatz 3
WD-3012 Langenhagen 2/ Hannover
tel.: (+49) 0511-736085
fax.: (+49) 0511-721254
tlx.: 922850

Advanced Micro Devices GmbH
Feuerseeplatz 4/5
WD-7000 Stuttgart 1
tel.: (+49) 0711-623377
fax.: (+49) 0711-625187
tlx.: 721882

Advanced Micro Devices GmbH
Rosenheimer Strasse 143B
WD-8000 München 80
tel.: (+49) 089-41140
fax.: (+49) 089-406490
tlx.: 523883

• Chips & Technologies

Japan
Chips & Technologies Inc.
tel.: (+81) 03-07977242

Korea
Chips & Technologies Inc.
tel.: (+82) 02-5585559

Switzerland
European Head Quarters
Chips & Technology S.A.
Neuchatel
tel.: (+41) 038-552872
fax>: (+41) 038-553445

Taiwan
Chips & Technologies Inc.
Room A, 8th floor
585 Ming Sheng East Road
Taipei
tel.: (+886) 02-7175595
fax.: (+886) 02-7175646

United States of America
Chips & Technologies Inc.
18201 Von Karman Avenue
Suite 310
Irvine, Ca 92715
tel.: (+1) 0714-8528721

Chips & Technologies Inc.
2055 Gateway Place
Suite 220
San Jose, Ca 95110
tel.: (+1) 0408-4378877

Chips & Technologies Inc.
450 E. Devon Avenue
Suite 280
Itasca, Il 60413
tel.: (+1) 0312-2500075

Chips & Technologies Inc.
One Wall Street
Burlington Office Park
Burlington, Ma 01803
tel.: (+1) 0617-2733500

Chips & Technologies Inc.
18 Sentry Park West
Bluebell, Pa 194222
tel.: (+1) 0215-5402214

Chips & Technologies Inc.
15415 Katy Freeway
Suite 209
Houston, Tx 77094
tel.: (+1) 0713-5799633

Chips & Technologies Inc.
World Headquarters
3050 Zanker Road
San Jose, Ca 95134
tel.: (+1) 0408-4340600
tlx.: 272929

West Germany
Chips & Technologies GmbH
Technopark
Bretonischer Ring 16
WD-8011 Grasbrunn/ München
tel.: (+49) 089-463074
fax.: (+49) 089-4602950

• Cybernetic

United States of America
Cybernetic Microsystems Inc.
P.O.Box 3000
San Gregoria, Va 94074
tel.: (+1) 0415-7263000
fax.: (+1) 0415-7263003
tlx.: 910-3505842

• Cyrix

Cyrix Corporation
P.O. Box 850118
Richardson, Tx 75085-0118
fax.: (+1) 091-2142348397

• Dallas Semiconductor

Unites States of America
4350 Beltwood Parkway South
Dallas, Tx 75244
tel.: (+1) 0214-4500400
fax.: (+1) 0214-4580470
tlx.: 6502441669

• Exar

West Germany
Exar Corporation Central Europe
Augustenstrasse 115
WD-8000 München 40
tel.: (+49) 089-52390320
fax.: (+49) 089-23035289

United States of America
Exar Corporation
Corporate Headquarters
2222 Qume Drive
San Jose, Ca 95131
tel.: (+1) 0408-4346400
fax.: (+1) 0408-9438245

Exar Corporation West
4677 Old Ironsides, 450 # 117
Santa Clara, Ca 95050
tel.: (+1) 0408-7279788
fax.: (+1) 0408-7277088

Exar Corporation Esat
113 Terrace Hall Avenue
Burlington, Ma 01803
tel.: (+1) 0617-2733927
fax.: (+1) 0617-2297828

Exar Corporation Central
1920 Thoreau Drive, Ste 122
Schaumburg, Il 60173
tel.: (+1) 0312-3030063
fax.: (+1) 0312-3030067

Exar Corporation East/Central
23200 Chagrin Boulevard, Ste 600
Cleveland, Oh 44122
tel.: (+1) 0216-2928106
fax.: (+1) 0216-4647609

Exar Corporation East
1717-50 Veterans Memorial Highway
Central Islip, NY 11772
tel.: (+1) 0516-5824420
fax.: (+1) 0516-5824589

• Fujitsu

France
Fujitsu France
Immeuble Le Trident
3-5, Voie Felix Eboue
F-94024 Creteil Cedex
tel.: (+33) 01-42078200
fax.: (+33) 01-42077933
tlx.: 262861

Hong Kong
Fujitsu Microelectronics Pacific Asia Ltd.
805 Tsimshatsui Centre
West Wing, 66 Mody Road, Kowloon
tel.: (+852) 03-7320100
fax.: (+852) 03-7227954
tlx.: 31959

Italy
Fujitsu Microelectronics Italia S.R.L
Centro Direzionale Milanofiori
Strada 4 - Palazzo A/2
I-20094 Milano
tel.: (+39) 02-8246170/176
fax.: (+39) 02-8246189
tlx.: 318546

Japan
Fujitsu Ltd
Furukawa Sogo Building
6-1 Marunouchi 1-chome
Chiyoda-ku
Tokyo 100
tel.: (+81) 03-2163211
fax.: (+81) 03-2169771
tlx.: 7812224361

The Netherlands
Fujitsu Benelux
Europalaan 6B
NL-5623 LJ Eindhoven
tel.: (+31) 040-447440
fax.: (+31) 040-444158
tlx.: 59265

Singapore
Fujitsu Electronics PTE Ltd.
7500A Besoth Road
06-301/2 The Plaza
Singapore 0719
tel.: (+65) 2961818
fax.: (+65) 2981571
tlx.: 55573

Sweden
Fujitsu Microelectronics Ltd.
Torggatan 8
S-17154 Solna
tel.: (+46) 08-7646365
fax.: (+46) 08-280345
tlx.: 13411

Taiwan
Fujitsu Microelectronics Pacific Asia Ltd.
1906 No. 333 Keelung Road Sec. 1
Taipei
tel.: (+886) 02-7576548
fax.: (+886) 02-7576571
tlx.: 17312

United Kingdom
Fujitsu Microelectronics Ltd.
Hargrave House
Belmont Road
Maidenhead
Berkshire SL6 6NE
tel.: (+44) 0628-76100
fax.: (+44) 0628-781484
tlx.: 848955

United States of America
Fujitsu Microelectronics Inc.
3545 North First Street
San Jose, Ca 95134-1804
tel.: (+1) 0408-9229000
fax.: (+1) 0408-4329044
tlx.: 9103380190

West-Germany
Fujitsu Mikroelektronik GmbH
Lyoner Strasse 44-48
Arabella Center
9tes Obergeschoss
WD-6000 Frankfurt 71
tel.: (+49) 069-66320
fax.: (+49) 069-6632122
tlx.: 411963

Fujitsu Mikroelektronik GmbH
Am Joachimsberg 10-12
WD-7033 Herrenberg
tel.: (+49) 07032-4085
fax.: (+49) 07032-4088

Fujitsu Mikroelektronik GmbH
Arbeostrasse 5
WD-8057 Echingen
tel.: (+49) 089-3190990
fax.: (+49) 089-31909922
tlx.: 5213905

• Harris Semiconductor

Belgium
Harris Semiconductor
Mercure Center
100, Rue de la Fusée
tel.: (+32) 02-2462111
fax.: (+32) 02-2462205
fax.: (+32) 02-2462205
tlx.: 61566

France
Harris Semiconductor
2-4, Avenue de l'Europe
F-78140 Velizy
tel.: (+33) 01-34654080
fax.: (+33) 01-39464054
tlx.: 697060

Italy
Harris Semiconductor
Via Dei Missaglia 97
I-20142 Milano
tel.: (+39) 02-82291
fax.: (+39) 02-8263858
tlx.: 316381

Sweden
Harris Semiconductor
P.O. Box 1203
Kistagangen 19
S-16313 Stockholm/Spanga
tel.: (+46) 08-7939500
fax.: (+46) 08-7504944
tlx.: 10439

United Kingdom
GE-Solid State
Beech House
373-399 London Road
Camberley
Surrey GU15 3HR
tel.: (+44) 0276-685911
fax.: (+44) 0276-685255
tlx.: 858113

West-Germany
GE Solid State
Kieler Strasse 55-59
WD-2085 Quickborn
tel.: (+49) 04106-5002...04
fax.: (+49) 04106-68850
tlx.: 211582

GE Solid State
Zeppelinstrasse 35
WD-7302 Ostfildern 4
tel.: (+49) 0711-454001...04
fax.: (+49) 0711-4560256
tlx.: 723838

GE Solid State
Putzbrunnerstrasse 69
WD-8000 München 83
tel.: (+49) 089-638130
fax.: (+49) 089-6377891/ 6376201
tlx.: 529051

• Headland Technology

Belgium
Headland Technology
Keizerlaan 18
B-1900 Overijse
tel.: (+32) 02657-2403
fax.: (+32) 02657-1155

Canada
LSI Logic
401 The West Mall, Suite 110, Etobicoke
Ontario, Canada M9 C5J5
tel.: (+1) 0416-6207400
fax.: (+1) 0416-6205005

Japan
LSI Logic
Tama Plaza Daisen Bldg, 2-19-2 Utsukushi-gaoka, Midori-ku, Yokohama-shi
Kanagawa-ken
tel.: (+81) 045-9024141
fax.: (+81) 045-9024533

Great-Britain
Headland Technology Ltd
Grenville Place
The Ring, Bracknell
Berkshire RG12 1BP
tel.: (+44) 0344-426544
fax.: (+44) 0344-481039

Taiwan
Headland Technology Inc.
3rd floor, 678 Tun-Hua S. Rd.
Taipei
tel.: (+886) 02-7553433
fax.: (+886) 02-7555176

United States of America
Headland Technology Inc.
46221 Landing Parkway
Fremont, Ca 94538
tel.: (+1) 0415-6567800
fax.: (+1) 0415-6567800

West Germany
Headland Technology GmbH
Stefan-George-Ring 23
WD-8000 München 81
tel.: (+49) 089-93009811
fax.: (+49) 089-93009833

Headland Technology GmbH
Lüderitzstrasse 13
WD-6600 Saarbrücken
tel.: (+49) 0681-33469
fax.: (+49) 0681-3239163

• I.I.T.

Great Britain
DMST Ltd.
Mead House
Pinkneys Drive
Maidenhead
Berkshire SL6 6QD
tel.: (+44) 0628-777700
fax.: (+44) 0628-27237

United States of America
Corporate Headquarters
Integrated Information Technology Inc.
2540 Mission College Boulevard
Suite 105
Santa Clara, Ca 95054
tel.: (+1) 0408-7271885
fax.: (+1) 0408-9800432

• Intel

Australia
Intel Australia Pty. Ltd.
Spectrum building
200 Pacific Highway, Level 6
Crows Nest, NSW 2065
tel.: (+61) 02-9572744
fax.: (+61) 02-9232632
tlx.: AA20097

Brazil
Intel Semicondutores do Brazil Ltda
Avenida Paulista 1159 CJS 404/405
B-1311 Sao Paulo SP
tel.: (+55) 011-2875899
fax.: (+55) 011-2127631
tlx.: 1153146

Denmark
Intel
Glentevej 61, 3rd floor
DK-2400 Copenhagen NV
tel.: (+45) 01-198033
tlx.: 19567

Finland
Intel
Ruosilantie 2
I-00390 Helsinki
tel.: (+358) 0-544644
tlx.: 123332

France

Intel Corporation
1 Rue Edison
Boîte Postale 303
F-78054 St. Quentin en Yvelines Cedex
tel.: (+33) 01-30577000
tlx.: 699016

Intel Corporation
4, Quai des Etroits
F-69321 Lyon Cedex 05
tel.: (+33) 016-78424089
tlx.: 305153

Hong Kong

Intel Semiconductor Ltd.
10th floor Office 1, Citic Building
Bond Center, Queensway Central
tel.: (+852) 05-8444555
fax.: (+852) 05-8681989
tlx.: 63869

Israel

Intel
Atidim Industrial Park-Neve Sharet
P.O. Box 43202
Tel Aviv 61430
tel.: (+972) 03-498080
tlx.: 371215

Italy

Intel
Milanofiori Palazzo E
I-20090 Assago/Milano
tel.: (+39) 02-8244071
tlx.: 341286

Japan

Intel Japan K.K
5-6 Tokodai, Tsokuba-shi
Ibaraki 300-26
tel.: (+81) 029747-8511
fax.: (+81) 029747-8450
tlx.: 3656160

Intel Japan K.K.
Daiichi Mitsugi Building
1-8889 Fuchu-cho
Fuchu-Shi
Tokyo 183
tel.: (+81) 0423-607871
fax.: (+81) 0423-600315

Intel Japan K.K.
Flower-Hill Shin-machi Building
1-23-9 Shinmachi
Setagaya-ku
Tokyo 154
tel.: (+81) 03-4262231
fax.: (+81) 03-4277620

Intel Japan K.K.
Kumagaya Building
2-69 Hon-cho
Kumagaya-chi
Saitama 360
tel.: (+81) 0458-246871
fax.: (+81) 0458-247518

Intel Japan K.K.
Mitsui-Seimei Mushashi-kosugi Building
915 Shinmaruko, Nakahara-ku
Kawasaki-shi, Kanagawa 211
tel.: (+81) 044-7337011
fax.: (+81) 044-7337010

Intel Japan K.K.
Nihon Seimei Atsugi Building
1-2-1 Asahi-machi
Atsugi-shi, Kanagawa 243
tel.: (+81) 0462-293731
fax.: (+81) 0462-293781

Intel Japan K.K.
Ryokuchi-Eki Building
2-4-1 Terauchi
Toyonaka-shi
Osaka 560
tel.: (+81) 06-8631091
fax.: (+81) 06-8631084

Intel Japan K.K.
Shinmaru Building
1-5-1 Marunouchi
Chiyoda-ku
Tokyo 100
tel.: (+81) 03-2013621
fax.: (+81) 03-2016850

Intel Japan K.K.
Green Building
1-16-20 Nishiki
Naka-ku, Nagoya-shi
Aichi 450
tel.: (+81) 052-2041261
fax.: (+81) 052-2041285

Korea
Intel Technology Asia Ltd.
Business Center 16th floor
61, Yoido-Dong
Young Deung Po-Ku
Seoul 150
tel.: (+82) 02-7848186
fax.: (+82) 02-7848096
tlx.: K29312

The Netherlands
Intel Benelux
Alexander Poort Gebouw
Marten Meesweg 93
NL-3068 AV Rotterdam
tel.: (+31) 010-4071111
fax.: (+31) 010-4554688
tlx.: 22283

Singapore
Intel Singapore Technology Ltd.
101 Thomson Road 21-06
Goldhill Square
Singapore 1130
tel.: (+65) 0250-7811
fax.: (+65) 0250-9256
tlx.: 39921

Norway
Intel
Hvamveien 4
P.O. Box 92
N-2013 Skjetten
tel.: (+47) 06-842420
tlx.: 78018

Spain
Intel
Zurbaran 28
E-28010 Madrid
tel.: (+34) 01-4104004
tlx.: 46880

Sweden
Intel
Dalvagen 24
S-17136 Solna
tel.: (+46) 08-7340100
tlx.: 12261

Switzerland
Intel Switzerland
Zürichstrasse
CH-8185 Winkel-Rüti/Zürich
tel.: (+41) 01-8606262
fax.: (+41) 01-8600201
tlx.: 825977

Taiwan
Intel Technology (Far East) Ltd.
Taiwan Branch
10th floor 205 Tun Hua North Road
Taipei
tel.: (+886) 02-7169660
fax.: (+886) 02-7172455
tlx.: 13159

United Kingdom
Intel Corporation (UK) Ltd.
Pipers Way
Swindon, Wiltshire SN3 1RJ
tel.: (+44) 0793-696000
tlx.: 444447/8

West-Germany
Intel Semiconductor GmbH
Hohenzollern Strasse 5
WD-3000 Hannover 1
tel.: (+49) 051-1344081
fax.: (+49) 051-3482110
tlx.: 923625

Intel Semiconductor GmbH
Zettachring 10A
WD-7000 Stuttgart 80
tel.: (+49) 0711-7287280
fax.: (+49) 0711-7280137
tlx.: 7254826

Intel Semiconductor GmbH
Abraham Lincoln Strasse 16-18
WD-6200 Wiesbaden
tel.: (+49) 061-2176050
tlx.: 4186183

Intel Semiconductor GmbH
Dornacherstrasse 1
WD-8016 Feldkirchen/ München
tel.: (+49) 089-909920
fax.: (+49) 089-9043948
tlx.: 523173

• Linear Technology

France
Linear Technology SARL
Le Quartz
58, Chemin de la Justice
F-92290 Chatenay-Malabry
tel.: (+33) 01-46316161
fax.: (+33) 01-46314613

Great Britain
Linear Technology Ltd.
111, Windmill Road
Sunbury
Middlesex TW16 7EF
tel.: (+44) 0932-765688
fax.: (+44) 0932-781936

Japan
Linear Technology KK
4th floor, Ichidashi Building
1-8-4 Kudankita Chiyoda-Ku
Tokyo 102
tel.: (+81) 03-2377891
fax.: (+81) 03-2378010

Korea
Linear Technology Korea Branche
Namsong Building #505
Itaewon-Dong 260-199
Yongsan-Ku, Seoul
tel.: (+82) 02-7921617
fax.: (+82) 02-7921619

Singapore
Linear Technology Pte. Ltd.
101 Boon Keng Road
02-15 Kallang Industrial Estate
Singapore 1233
tel.: (+65) 2935322
fax.: (+65) 2920398

Taiwan
Linear Technology Corp.
Room 801, No. 46 Sec. 2
Chung Shan N. Road
Taipei
tel.: (+886) 02-5217575
fax.: (+886) 02-5217575

United States of America
Linear Technology Corporation
1630 McCarthy Boulevard
Milpitas, Ca 95035-7487
tel.: (+1) 0408-4321900
fax.: (+1) 0408-4340507
tlx.: 4993977

West Germany
Linear Technology GmbH
Untere Hauptstrasse 9
WD-8057 Eching
tel.: (+49) 089-3195023
fax.: (+49) 089-3194821

• Maxim

Great Britain
Maxim UK Ltd.
21C Horseshoe Park
Pangbourne
Reading RG8 7JW
tel.: (+44) 07-3575255
fax.: (+44) 07-3575257
tlx.: 94070736

Japan
Maxim Japan Co. Ltd.
Horizon 1 Building
3-30-16 Nishi-waseda
Shinjuku-Ku
Tokyo 160
tel.: (+81) 03-2326141
fax.: (+81) 03-2326149

United States of America
Maxim Integrated Products
120, San Gabriel Drive
Sunnyvale, Ca 94086
tel.: (+1) 0408-7377600
fax.: (+1) 0408-7377914
tlx.: 350 4114

West Germany
Maxim GmbH
Sandstrasse 21
WD-8000 München 2
tel.: (+49) 089-5234083
fax.: (+49) 089-5236622

• Microchip

France
Arizona Microchip Technology
Immeuble Expansion
9-11, Rue Georges Enesco
F-94008 Creteil Cedex
tel.: (+33) 043-771263
fax.: (+33) 043-991524
tlx.: 262435

Great Britain
Arizona Microchip Technology
Unit 3, Meadow Park, Furlong Road
Bourne End
Bucks. SL8 5AJ
tel.: (+44) 0628-850303
fax.: (+44) 0628-850178

Hong Kong
Arizona Microchip Technology Ltd.
Room 1103, Tower 1
South Seas Centre, 75, Mody Road
Tsimshatsui East
Kowloon
tel.: (+852) 05-3116103
fax.: (+852) 05-33115125
tlx.: 44611

Japan
Microchip Technology Inc.
4th floor Madre Matsuda Building
4-13, Kioi-Cho
Chiyoda-Ku
Tokyo 102
tel.: (+81) 03-2348774
fax.: (+81) 03-2348549

Korea
Microchip Technology Inc.
c/o Daeho Corporation
1004 Keo Yang Building
51-8 Soosong Dong
Chongro-Ku
Seoul
tel.: (+82) 02-7398543
fax.: (+82) 02-7396040
tlx.: 26880

Singapore
Microchip Technology Inc.
United House
20 Kramat Lane # 04-06
Singapore 0922
tel.: (+65) 7329433
fax.: (+65) 2355395

Taiwan
Microchip Technology Inc.
5th floor, 41 Ming Chuan Road
Hsin Tien, Taipei
tel.: (+886) 02-9146234
fax.: (+886) 02-9146234

United States of America
Microchip Technology Inc.
1411 W, 190th Street, Suite 230
Gardena, Ca 90248
tel.: (+1) 0213-3231888
fax.: (+1) 0213-3231424

Microchip Technology Inc.
2107 North First Street # 410
San Jose, Ca 95131
tel.: (+1) 0408-4367950
fax.: (+1) 0408-4367955

Microchip Technology Inc.
2860 Johnson Ferry Road N.E.
250B
Marietta, Ga 30062
tel.: (+1) 0404-6426933
fax.: (+1) 0404-5521525

Microchip Technology Inc.
800 East Diehl Road, Suite 175
Naperville, Il 60540
tel.: (+1) 0312-5050022
fax.: (+1) 0312-5050065

Microchip Technology Inc.
Five The Mountain Road, Suite 120
Framingham, Ma 01701
tel.: (+1) 0508-8203334
fax.: (+1) 0508-8720923

Microchip Technology Inc.
300 Wheeler Road, Suite 206
Hauppage, NY 11788
tel.: (+1) 0516-2321930
fax.: (+1) 0516-2321935

Microchip Technology Inc.
17480 N. Dallas Parkway, Suite 114
Dallas, Tx 75287
tel.: (+1) 0214-7330391
fax.: (+1) 0214-2504631

West Germany
Arizona Microchip Technology
Alte Landstrasse 12-14
WD-8012 Ottobrunn
tel.: (+49) 089-6096072
fax.: (+49) 089-6091997
tlx.: 524518

World Head Quarters
Microchip Technology Inc.
2355 W. Chandler Boulevard
Chandler, Az 85224-6199
tel.: (+1) 0602-963-7373

• Motorola

Headquarters European Operations
Motorola Inc. European Semiconductor Division
16, chemin de la Voie-Creuse
P.O.Box 8
CH-12111 Genève 20
Switzerland
tel.: (+41) 022 991111

Australia
Motorola Australia Pty. Ltd.
3rd floor 250 Pacific Highway
Crows Nest
Sydney, NSW 2065
tel.: (+61) 02-4381955

Motorola Australia Pty. Ltd.
666 Wellington Road
Mulgrave, Melbourne
Victoria 3170
tel.: (+61) 03-5613555

Austria
Motorola GmbH
Alserbachstrasse 30
A-1090 Wien
tel.: (+43) 0222 316545

Canada
Motorola Ltd.
490 Norfinch Drive
Downsview, Ontario M3N 1Y4
tel.: (+1) 0416-6616400

Denmark
Motorola Semiconductors A/S
Gladsaxevej 370
DK-2860 Soborg
tel.: (+45) 01-674422

France
Motorola Semiconducteurs S.A.
2,rue Auguste-Comte, B.P. 39
F-92173 Vanves Cedex
tel.: (+33) 01-7360199

Motorola Semiconducteurs S.A.
Chemin de Malacher-Zirst
F-38240 Meylan (Grenoble)
tel.: (+33) 076-902281

Motorola Semiconducteurs Commerciale S.A.
Zone Artisanale
F-35740 Pace
tel.: (+33) 099-606548

Motorola Semiconducteurs Commerciale S.A.
Avenue General-Eisenhower
F-31023 Toulouse Cedex
tel.: (+33) 061-411188

Hong Kong
Motorola Semiconductors Hong Kong Ltd.
7th floor Profit Industrial Building
Phase 2, 1-15 Kwai Fung Crescent
Kwai Chung N.T.
tel.: (+852) 05-223111

Israel
Motorola Israel Ltd.
16 Kremenetski Street
ISR- 67899 Tel Aviv
tel.: (+972) 03-388388

Italy
Motorola S.p.A. Divisione Semiconduttori
Main Sales Office
Centro Milanofiori-Strada 2-C2
I-20090 Assago (Milano)
tel.: (+39) 02-82201

Motorola S.p.A. Divisione Semiconduttori
Via Costantino Maes 68
I-00162 Roma
tel.: (+39) 06-8322186

Japan
Nippon Motorola Ltd.
5-2-32 Minami Azabu
Manato-ku
Tokyo 106
tel.: (081) 03-4403311

Korea
Motorola Korea Ltd.
445 Kwangjang Dong
Sungdong-ku, Seoul 133
tel.: (+82) 4450051

Motorola Korea Ltd.
6th floor Kwangnam Jeil Building
822-4, Yuksam-Dong
tel.: (+82) 02-5545118

Malaysia
Motorola Maylaysia Sdn. Bhd.
116 Jalan Semangat
Petaling Jaya
Selangor
tel.: (+60) 03-761166

Mexico
Motorola de Mexico S.A.
Amado Nervo 1437
Zapopan, Jalisco
tel.: (+52) 036-210921

The Netherlands
Motorola B.V. Semiconductor Group
De Waal 26
NL-5684 PH Best
tel.: (+31) 04998-61211
fax.: (+31) 04998-06290

Norway
Motorola A/S
Plogveien 1A
N-0679 Oslo 6
tel.: (+47) 02-198070

Philippines
Motorola Philippines Inc.
Bormaheco Building
km. 17, West Service Road
South Superhighway
Paranaque, Metro Manila
tel.: (+63) 02-8275911

Singapore
Motorola Singapore (Pte) Ltd.
Suite 3500, Shaw Towers
100 Beach Road
Signapore 0718
tel.: (+65) 0294-5436

Spain
Motorola Espana S.A.
Alberto Alcocer, 46 Dpdo
E-28016 Madrid
tel.: (+34) 01-4578204

Sweden
Motorola A.B.
Dalvägen 2
S-17136 Solna
tel.: (+46) 08 830200

Switzerland
Motorola (Schweiz) AG
Uitikonerstrasse 9
CH-8952 Schlieren
tel.: (+41) 022-991111
fax.: (+41) 022-17307336
tlx.: 045827716

Motorola Suisse SA
16, Chemin de la Voie Creuse
P.O. Box 8
CH-1211 Genf
tel.: (+41) 022-7991111
fax.: (+41) 022-341086
tlx.: 23905

Taiwan
Motorola Electronics Taiwan Ltd.
Sunrise Plaza Building 4/F
2 Par Deh Road, Section 3
Taipei
tel.: (+886) 02-7528944

Motorola Electronics Taiwan Ltd.
516, Chung-Hwa Road
Section 1, Chung-Li
tel.: (+886) 034-527121

United Kingdom
Motorola Ltd.
Motorola House
69 Buckingham Street
Aylesbury
Bucks HP20 2NF
tel.: (+44) 0296-35252

Motorola Ltd.
Colvilles Road
Kelvin Estate
East Kilbride
Scotland G75 0TG
tel.: (+44) 03552-39101

Motorola Ltd.
European Literature Centre
88 Tanners Drive, Blakelands
Milton Keynes MK 14 5BP
tel.: (+44) 0908-614614

United States of America
Motorla Ltd.
Highway 290 West at Willam Cannon
Austin, Texas 78762
tel.: (+1) 0512-4402000

West-Germany
Motorola GmbH Geschäftsbereich Halbleiter
Hans-Böckler-Strasse 30
WD-3012 Langenhagen
tel.: (+49) 0511-789911
fax.: (+49) 0511-744164
tlx.: 924010

Motorola GmbH Geschäftsbereich Halbleiter
Abraham-Lincoln-Strasse 22
WD-6200 Wiesbaden
tel.: (+49) 06121-761921
fax.: (+49) 06121-4186341
tlx.: 713811

Motorola GmbH Geschäftsbereich Halbleiter
Stralsunder-Strasse 1
WD-7032 Sindelfingen
tel.: (+49) 07031-83074/75
fax.: (+49) 07031-876625
tlx.: 7265680

Motorola GmbH Geschäftsbereich Halbleiter
Schatzbogen 7
WD-8000 München 82
tel.: (+49) 089-921030
fax.: (+49) 090-92103101
tlx.: 522119

Motorola GmbH Geschäftsbereich Halbleiter
Donaustrasse 26
WD-8500 Nürnberg
tel.: (+49) 0911-643044
fax.: (+49) 0911-645965
tlx.: 623922

Motorola GmbH
Gartengasse 21
A-1090 Wien
tel.: (+43) 0222-316545
fax.: (+43) 0222-1547757
tlx.: 113934

• National Semiconductor

National Semiconductor World Headquarters
2900 Semiconductor Drive
P.O.Box 58090
Santa Clara, Ca 95052-8090
United States of America
tel.: (+1) 0408-7215000
tlx.: (+1) 9103399240

Australia
National Semiconductor Australia
Building F 4th Floor
MacQuarie Tech Centre
11-17 Khartoum Road
North Ryde,N.S.W. 2113
Sydney
tel.: (+61) 02-8874455
tlx.: AA27173

Belgium
National Semiconductor Belgium
Vorstlaan 100
B-1170 Brussel
tel.: (+32) 02-6610680
fax.: (+32) 02-6602395
tlx.: 61007

Brasil
National Semiconductor Brasil
Avenida Brig. Faria Lima 830
8 Andar, 01452 Sao Paulo, S.P.
tel.: (+55) 011-2125066
tlx.: 1131931

Denmark
National Semiconductor (UK) Ltd.
Ringager 4A, 3
DK-2605, Bronby
tel.: (+45) 043-433211
fax.: (+45) 043-433111
tlx.: 15179

Finland
National Semiconductor (UK) Ltd.
Kauppakartanokatu 7 A22
SF-00930 Helsinki
tel.: (+358) 090-338033
fax.: (+385) 090-338130
tlx.: 126116

France
National Semiconductor S.A.
Centre d'Affaires "La Boursidière"
Bâtiment Champagne, Boîte Postale 90
Route Nationale 186
F-92357 Le Plessis Robinson
tel.: (+33) 01-40948888
fax.: (+33) 01-40948811
tlx.: 631065

Hong Kong
National Semiconductor Hong Kong
Austin Tower, 4th floor
22-26A Austin Avenue, Tsimshatsui, Kowloon
tel.: (+852) 03-7243645
tlx.: 52996

Ireland
National Semiconductor (UK) Ltd.
Unit 2A, Clonskeagh Square, Clonskeagh Road
Dublin 14
tel.: (+353) 01-695589

Italy
National Semiconductor S.p.A.
Strada 7
Palazzo R/3
I-20089 Rozzano - Milanofiori
tel.: (+39) 02-8242046
fax.: (+39) 02-8254758
tlx.: 352647

National Semiconductor S.p.A.
Via Del Caravaggio 107
I-00147 Roma
tel.: (+39) 06-5134880
fax.: (+39) 06-5137974

Korea
National Semiconductor Korea
Room 612
Korea Fed. of Small Bus. Building
16-2 Yoido-Dong
Youngdeungpo-Ku
Seoul
tel.: (+82) 02-7848051
tlx.: K24942

Mexico
National Semiconductor Mexico
Juventino Rosas No. 118-2
Col. Guaualupe Inn
Mexico 01020 D.F.
tel.: (+62) 0905- 5249402

The Netherlands
Postbus 90
NL-1380 AB Weesp
tel.: (+31) 02940-30448
fax.: (+31) 02940-30430
tlx.: 10956

Norway
National Semiconductor (UK) Ltd.
P.O. Box 29
N-1321 Stabekk
tel.: (+47) 02-125370
fax.: (+47) 02-125375

Singapore
200 Cantonment Road 13-01
Soutpoint
Singapore 0208
tel.: (+65) 2252226
tlx.: RS33877

Spain
National Semiconductor GmbH
Calle Agustin de Foxa 27 (9d)
E-28036 Madrid
tel.: (+34) 01-7332958
fax.: (+34) 01-7338018
tlx.: 46133

Sweden
National Semiconductor Sweden
Box 1009
Grosshandlarvägen 7
S-12702 Johanneshov
tel.: (+46) 08-7228050
fax.: (+46) 08-7229095
tlx.: 10731

Switzerland
National Semiconductor
Alte Winterthurerstrasse 53
Postfach 567
CH-8304 Wallisellen-Zürich
tel.: (+41) 01-8302727
fax.: (+41) 01-8301900
tlx.: 828444

Taiwan
National Semiconductor Taiwan
P.O.Box 68-332 Taipei
7th floor Nan Shan Life Building
302 Min. Chuan East Road
Taipei
tel.: (+886) 02-5017227
tlx.: 22837

United Kingdom
National Semiconductor (UK) Ltd.
The Maple, Kembrey Park
Swindon, Wiltshire SN2 6UT
tel.: (+44) 0793-614141
fax.: (+44) 0793-697522
tlx.: 444674

West-Germany
National Semiconductor GmbH
Misburger Strasse 81D
WD-3000 Hannover 61
tel.: (+49) 0511-575072
fax.: (+49) 0511-561740
tlx.: 923707

National Semiconductor GmbH
Flughafenstrasse 21
WD-6078 Neu-Isenburg/Zeppelinheim
tel.: (+49) 069-694512
fax.: (+49) 069-694085
tlx.: 4185397

National Semiconductor GmbH
Untere Waldplätze 37
WD-7000 Stuttgart 80
tel.: (+49) 0711-686511
fax.: (+49) 0711-6865260
tlx.: 7255993

National Semiconductor GmbH
Industriestrasse 10
WD-8080 Fürstenfeldbruck
tel.: (+49) 08141-1030
fax.: (+49) 08141-103554
tlx.: 527649

• Newport Components

Great-Britain
Newport Components Limited
Tanners Drive, Blakelands North
Milton Keynes, K14 5NA
tel.: (+44) 0908-615232
fax.: (+44) 0908-617545

• Oak Technology

Taiwan
OAK Technology Inc.
Room B, 7th floor no 370
Sec. 1, Fu Hsing S. Road
Taipei
tel.: (+886) 02-7849123
fax.: (+886) 02-7067641

United States of America
OAK Technology Inc.
Corporate Office, 139 Kifer Court
Sunnyvale, Ca 94086
tel.: (+1) 0408-7370888
fax.: (+1) 0408-7373838

• OKI

Australia
Australian Representative Office
Suite 2604, Level 26, Northpoint
100 Miller Street, North Sydney
NSW 2060
tel.: (+61) 02-9549022
fax.: (+61) 02-9593006

Bolivia
La Paz Office
Calle Prolongacion Cordero
No. 127, Casilla No. 4319
La Paz
tel.: 235-1616
fax.: 239-1022

China
Beijing Liaison Office
Minzu Hotel, Room 2723
Beijing
tel.: (+86) 01-6011632
fax.: (+86) 01-6011632
tlx.: 22859

Colombia
Bogota Office, CRA 11, no 71-40
Edificio Valparaiso, Oficina 801
Bogota D.E.
tel.: (+57) 01-2128261
fax.: (+57) 01-2128724

France
Paris Branche
148, Rue de Chevilly
F-94240 L'Hay les Roses
tel.: (+33) 01-56600328
fax.: (+33) 01-49780958

Great Britain
Ground Floor, North 3, Shortlands
Hammersmith International Centre
London W6
tel.: (+44) 01-7412324
fax.: (+44) 01-7414122
tlx.: 927029

Honduras
Tegucigalpa Office
Edificio Cruz-heath, 6a Calle
4a Avenida Colonia Alameda, Tegucigalpa D.C.
tel.: (+504) 323479
fax.: (+504) 327561
tlx.: 1119

Hong Kong
OKI Electronics (Hong Kong) Ltd.
Suite 1801-4, Tower 1, China Hong Kong City
33 Canton Road, Tsim Sha Tsui, Kowloon
tel.: (+852) 03-7362336
fax.: (+852) 03-7362395
tlx.: 45999

India
New Delhi Liaison Office
Plot no. 17, Barakhamba Road, New Delhi
tel.: (+91) 011-3319719
tlx.: 65216

Japan
OKI Electric Industry Co. Ltd.
World Head Office, 7-12 Toranomon, 1-chome
Minato-ku, Tokyo 105
tel.: (+81) 03-5013111
fax.: (+81) 03-5089465
tlx.: J02226324

Taiwan
Taipei Office
10th floor, International Building
6 Tung Hwa North Road, Taipei
tel.: (+886) 02-7512345
fax.: (+886) 02-7524391
tlx.: 8511263

United States of America
OKI Semiconductor
785 North Mary Avenue
Sunnyvale, Ca 94086
tel.: (+1) 0408-7201900
fax.: (+1) 0408-7201918
tlx.: 910-3380508

West-Germany
OKI Electric Europe GmbH
European Head Office
Hellersbergstrasse 2
WD-4040 Neuss 1
tel.: (+49) 02101-15960
fax.: (+49) 02101-103539
tlx.: 8517427

OKI Electric Europe GmbH
Rohrauerstrasse 72
WD-8000 München 71
tel.: (+49) 089-784091
fax.: (+49) 089-782913
tlx.: 897514

• Opti

United States of America
Opti Inc.
2700 Augustine Drive 165
Santa Clara, Ca 95054
tel.: (+1) 0408-9808178
fax.: (+1) 0408-9808860

• Philips

Argentina
Philips Argentina S.A.
Div. Componentes
Vedia 3892
1430 Buenos Aires
tel.: (+54) 01-5417141

Australia
Philips Components PTY Ltd.
11 Waltham Street
Artarmon, NSW 2064
tel.: (+61) 02-4393322

Austria
Österreichische Philips Industrie GmbH
Unternehmensbereich Bauelemente
Triester Strasse 64
A-1101 Vienna
tel.: (+43) 0222-60101820

Belgium
NV Philips Prof. Systems
Components Division
80, Rue Des Deux Gares
B-1070 Bruxelles
tel.: (+32) 02-5256111

Brazil
Constanta-Ibrape (Active Devices)
Avenida Brigadeiro Faria Lima 1735
Sao Paulo-SP
tel.: (+55) 011-2112600

Constanta-Ibrape (Passive Devices & Materials)
Avenida Fransisco Monteiro 702
Ribeirao-Pires-SP
tel.: (+55) 011-45982211

Canada
Philips Electronics Ltd.
Philips Components
601 Milner Avenue
Scarborough
Ontario M1B 1MB
tel.: (+1) 0416-2925161

Chile
Philips Chilena S.A.
Avenida Santa Maria 0760
Santiago
tel.: (+56) 02-773816

Colombia
Ind. Philps de Colombia S.A.
c/o Iprelenso Ltd.
Cra. 21 no. 56-17
Bogota D.E.
tel.: (+57) 01-2497624

Denmark
Philips Components S/S
Prags Boulevard 80
PB 1919
DK-2300 Copenhagen S
tel.: (+45) 01-5411433

Finland
Philips Components
Sinikalliontie 3
SF-2630 Espoo Helsinki
tel.: (+358) 0358-050261

France
RTC-Compelec
117, Quai du Président Roosevelt
F-92134 Issy-les-Moulineaux Cedex
tel.: (+33) 01-40938000

Greece
Philips Hellenique S.A.
Components Division
15 25th March Street
GR-17778 Tavros
tel.: (+30) 01-4894339

Hong Kong
Philips Hong Kong Ltd.
Components Division
15th floor Philips Ind. Building
24-28 Kung Yip Street
Kwai Chung
tel.: (+852) 0-245121

India
Peico Electronics & Electricals Ltd.
Components Department, Band Box Building
254 D. Dr. Annie Besant Road
Bombay 400025
tel.: (+91) 022-4930311

Indonesia
P.T. Philips-Ralin Electronics
Components Division
Setiabudi 2 Building, 6th floor
Jalan H.R. Rasuna Said
P.O Box 223/KBY. Kuningan
Jakarta 12910
tel.: (+62) 021-517995

Ireland
Philips Electronics (Ireland) Ltd.
Components Division
Newstead
Clonskeagh
Dublin 14
tel.: (+353) 01-693355

Italy
Philips S.p.A.
Philips Components
Piazza 4 Novembre 3
I-20124 Milano
tel.: (+39) 02-67521

Japan
Nihon Philips Corporation
Shuwa Shinagawa Building
26-33 Takanawa 3-chome
Minato-ku
Tokyo 108
tel.: (+81) 03-4485611

Signetics Japan Ltd.
8-7 Sanbanco Chiyoda-ku
Tokyo 102
tel.: (+81) 03-2301521

Republic of Korea
Philips Electronics (Korea) Ltd.
Elcoma Division, Philips House
260-199 Itaewon-dong, Yongsan-ku
Seoul
tel.: (+82) 02-7945011

Malaysia
Philips Malaysia SDN HD
Components Divion, Jalan S15/2A
Subang, 47500 Petaling Jaya
tel.: (+60) 03-7345511

Mexico
Electronica S.A. de C.V.
Carr. Mexico-Toluca km 62.5
Toluca Edo de Mexico 50140
tel.: (+52) 091-72161300

The Netherlands
Philips Nederland
marktgroep Philips Components
Postbus 90050
5600 PB Eindhoven
tel.: (+31) 040-783749

New Zealand
Philips New Zealand Ltd.
Components Division
110 Mt. Eden, C.P.O. Box 1041
Auckland
tel.: (+64) 09-605914

Norway
Norsk A/S Philips
Philips Components
Box 1
Mangierud
N-0612 Oslo
tel.: (+47) 02-680200

Pakistan
Philips Electrical Co. of Pakistan Ltd.
Philips Markaz
M.A. Jinnah Road
Karachi 3
tel.: (+92) 021-725772

Peru
Cadesa
Avenida Pardo y Aliaga 695
6th floor
San Isidro
Lima 27
tel.: (+51) 014-707080

Philippines
Philips Industrial Dev. Inc.
2246 Pasong Tamo
P.O. Box 911
Makati Comm. Centre
Makati-Rizal 3116
tel.: (+63) 02-868951

Portugal
Philips Portuguesa S.A.R.L.
Avenida Eng. Duarte Pacheco 6
1009 Lisboa Codex
tel.: (+351) 019-683121

Singapore
Philips Project Dev. (Singapore) PTE Ltd.
Components Division
Lorong 1
Toa Payoh
Singapore 1231
tel.: (+65) 3502000

Spain
Philips Components
Balmes 22
08007 Barcelona
tel.: (+34) 03-3016312

Sweden
Philips Components AB
Tegeluddsvägen 1
S-11584 Stockholm
tel.: (+46) 08-7821000

Switzerland
Philips A.G.
Components Department
Allmendstrasse 140-142
CH-8027 Zürich
tel.: (+41) 01-4882211

Taiwan
Philips Taiwan Ltd.
150 Tun Hua North Road
P.O.Box 22978
Taipei
tel.: (+886) 02-7120500

Thailand
Philips Electrical Company of Thailand Ltd.
283 Silom Road, P.O.Box 961
Bangkok
tel.: (+66) 02-23363309

Turkey
Türk Philips Ticaret A.S.
Philips Components
Talatpasa Cad no. 5
80640 Levent/Istanbul
tel.: (+90) 01-1792770

United Kingdom
Philips Components Ltd.
Mullard House
Torrington Place
London WC1E 7HD
tel.: (+44) 01-5806633

United States of America
Amperex Electronic Corporation
230 Duffy Avenue
P.O. Box 560
Hicksville
New York 11802
tel.: (+1) 516-93196200

Uruguay
Luzilectron S.A.
Avenida Uruguay 1287
P.O. Box 907
Montevideo
tel.: (+598) 02-985395

Venezuela
Ind. Venezolana Philps S.A.
c/o Magnetica S.A.
Calle 6, Ed. Last Tres Jotas
App. Post. 78117
Caracas
tel.: (+58) 02-2393931

West-Germany
Valvo Unternehmensbereich Bauelemente der Philips GmbH
Burchardstrasse 19
WD-2000 Hamburg 1
tel.: (+49) 040-3296245..248
fax.: (+49) 040-3296249
tlx.: 215401

Valvo Unternehmensbereich Bauelemente der Philips GmbH
Ikarusallee 1A
WD-3000 Hannover 1
tel.: (+49) 0511-630094
tlx.: 9230239

Valvo Unternehmensbereich Bauelemente der Philips GmbH
Lazarettstrasse 50
WD-4300 Essen 1
tel.: (+49) 0201-236001
fax.: (+49) 0201-230307
tlx.: 8571136

Valvo Unternehmensbereich Bauelemente der Philips GmbH
Theodor-Heuss-Allee 106
WD-6000 Frankfurt/Main 90
tel.: (+49) 069-7940080
fax.: (+49) 069-79400825
tlx.: 412405

Valvo Unternehmensbereich Bauelemente der Philips GmbH
Albstadtweg 12
WD-7000 Stuttgart 80
tel.: (+49) 0711-789881
fax.: (+49) 0711-7898401
tlx.: 7254755

Valvo Unternehmensbereich Bauelemente der Philips GmbH
Tullastrasse 72
WD-7800 Freiburg
tel.: (+49) 0761-508091
fax.: (+49) 0761-506998
tlx.: 7721627

Valvo Unternehmensbereich Bauelemente der Philips GmbH
Drygalski-Allee 33
WD-8000 München 71
tel.: (+49) 089-780070
fax.: (+49) 089-7800760
tlx.: 5213015

Valvo Unternehmensbereich Baulemente der Philips GmbH
Bessemerstrasse 14
WD-8500 Nürnberg 10
tel.: (+49) 0911-564091
fax.: (+49) 0911-514409
tlx.: 623829

• Samsung

Hong Kong
Samsung Semiconductor Hong Kong Branch
24th floor Tower 1; Admiralty Centre
18 Harcourt Road
tel.: (+852) 05-86269000
fax.: (+852) 05-8661343
tlx.: 80303

Japan
Samsung Japan Co.
Sudacho Verde Building 2-3
Kandasudacho Chiyoda-ku
Tokyo 101
tel.: (+81) 03-2589506
fax.: (+81) 03-2589696
tlx.: j2225206

Republic of Korea
Samsung Semiconductor
World Head Quarters
9/10th floor Samsung Main Building
250, 2-KA Taepyung-Ro
C.P.O.Box 8233, Chung-Ku
Seoul
tel.: (+82) 02-7512114
fax.: (+82) 02-7530967
tlx.: K27970

United Kingdom
Samsung (UK) Ltd.
Samsung House, 3 Riverbank Way
Great West Road
Brentford
Middlesex TW8 9RE

Southampton Row
London WC1

tel.: (+44) 01-8629311
fax.: (+44) 01-8620096
tlx.: 25823

United States of America
Samsung Semiconductor Inc.
3725 North First Street
San Jose, Ca 95134-1708
tel.: (+1) 0408-4345400
fax.: (+1) 0408-4345650
tlx.: 339544

West-Germany
Samsung Semiconductor Europe GmbH
Mergenthaler Allee 38-40
WD-6236 Eschborn
tel.: (+49) 06196-90090
fax.: (+49) 06196-900989
tlx.: 4072678

• Seiko Epson

Japan
Seiko Epson Corp. Japan
Head Office
3-5 Owa 3-Chome, Suwa-Shi
Nagano-Ken 392
tel.: (+81) 0266-524175
fax.: (+81) 0266-534844
tlx.: 3362435

The Netherlands
Epson Europe B.V.
Prof. J.H. Bavinxklaan 5
NL-1183 AT Amstelveen
tel.: (+31) 020-5475222
fax.: (+31) 020-452295

• Silicon General

Great Britain
Silicon General Ltd.
European Headquarters
17 Bridge Street
Leatherhead
Surrey KT22 8BL
tel.: (+44) 0372-377779
fax.: (+44) 0372-376843
tlx.: 851-897628

• Standard Microsystems Corporation

Great Britain
Standard Microsystems Corporation
Golden Gate, Winchester House
Garner Road
Maidenhead
Berks SL6 7RL
tel.: (+44) 0628-783631
fax.: (+44) 0628-71120
tlx.: 846263

Japan
Toyo Microsystems Corporation
Akasaka Dai-ichi Building, 12th floor
4-9-17 Akasaka
Tokyo 107
tel.: (+81) 03-4236651
fax.: (+81) 03-4236654

Taiwan
Standard Microsystems Corporation (Asia)
9th floor, 169 Sec 4 Chung
Hsaid E. Road
Taipei
tel.: (+886) 02-7112840
fax.: (+886) 02-71 12845
tlx.: 21664

United States of America
Standard Microsystems Corporation
4010 Moorpark, Ste 105
San Jose, Ca 95117
tel.: (+1) 0408-2495000
fax.: (+1) 0408-2475122

Standard Microsystems Corporation
P.O.Box 292497
3411 Office Park Drive, Ste. 106
Kettering, Oh 45429
tel.: (+1) 0513-2935393
fax.: (+1) 0513-2937557
tlx.: 62882274

West Germany
Standard Microsystems GmbH
Arabella Strasse 5 , Büro 131
WD-8000 München 81
tel.: (+49) 089-9195964
fax.: (+49) 089-918173
tlx.: 5214433

• Statek

Great-Britain
Euroquartz Ltd.
5/7 Church Street
Crewkerne
Somerset TA18 7HR
tel.: (+44) 0460-74321

United States of America
512 N. Main
Orange, Ca 92668
tel.: (+1) 0714-6397810
tlx.: 678394

• ST SGS - Thomson

Australia
SGS-Thomson Microelectronics
Suite 211, Edgecliff centre
203-233 New South Head Road
NSW 2027 Edgecliff
tel.: (+61) 02-3273922
fax.: (+61) 02-3276176
tlx.: 071-126911

Brazil
SGS-Thomson Microelectronics
R. Henrique Schaumann 286-CJ33
B-05413 Sao Paulo
tel.: (+55) 011-8835455
fax.: (+55) 011-12822367
tlx.: 3911137988

Canada
SGS-Thomson Microelectronics
341 Main Street North
Brampton, Ontario
tel.: (+1) 0416-4550505
fax.: (+1) 0416-4552606

Denmark
SGS-Thomson Microelectronics
Herlev Torv. 4
DK-2730 Herlev
tel.: (+45) 042-948533
fax.: (+45) 042-948694
tlx.: 35411

Finland
SGS-Thomson Microelectronics
Karjalankatu 2
Lohja SF-08150
tel.: (+358) 012-15511
fax.: (+358) 012-15566

France
SGS-Thomson Microelectronics
7 Avenue Gallieni, BP 93
F-94253 Gentilly Cedex
tel.: (+33) 01-47407575
fax.: (+33) 01-40407910
tlx.: 632570

SGS-Thomson Microelectronics
20, Place des Halles
F-67000 Strasbourg
tel.: (+33) 088-755066
fax.: (+33) 088-222932
tlx.: 870001

Great-Britain
SGS-Thomson Microelectronics
Planar House, Parkway
Globe Park
Marlow, Bucks
tel.: (+44) 0628-890800
fax.: (+44) 0628-890391

Hong Kong
SGS-Thomson Microelectronics
22nd floor - Hopewell Centre
183 Queens Road East, Wanchai
tel.: (+852) 05-8615788
fax.: (+852) 05-8656589
tlx.: 222722

India
SGS-Thomson Microelectronics
Liason Office, 62, Upper Ground Floor
World Trade Centre, Barakhamba Lane
tel.: (+91) 3715191
fax.: (+91) 3715192
tlx.: 031-66816

Italy
SGS-Thomson Microelectronics
V.le Milanofiori- Strada 4 - Palazzo A/4/a
I-20090 Assago (Mi)
tel.: (+39) 02-892131
fax.: (+39) 02-8250449
tlx.: 330131

SGS-Thomson Microelectronics
Via R. Fucini 12
I-40033 Casalecchio di Reno (Bo)
tel.: (+39) 051-591914
fax.: (+39) 051-591305
tlx.: 512442

SGS-Thomson Microelectronics
Via A. Torlonia 15
I-00161 Roma
tel.: (+39) 06-8443341
fax.: (+39) 06-8444474
tlx.: 620653

Japan
SGS-Thomson Microelectronics
Nisseki Takanawa Building 4th floor
2-18-10 Takanawa, Minato-ku
Tokyo 108
tel.: (+81) 02-2804121
fax.: (+81) 02-2804131

Korea
SGS-Thomson Microelectronics
8th floor Shinwon Building
823-14 Yuksam-Dong, Kang-Nam-Gu
tel.: (+82) 0553-0399
fax.: (+82) 0552-1051
tlx.: K29998

Netherlands
SGS-Thomson Microelectronics
Meerenakkerweg 1
NL-5652 AR Eindhoven
tel.: (+31) 040-550015
fax.: (+31) 040-528835
tlx.: 51186

Singapore
SGS-Thomson Microelectronics
28 Ang Mo Kio - Industrial ark 2
Singapore 2056
tel.: (+65) 4821411
fax.: (+65) 4820240
tlx.: RS55201

Spain
SGS-Thomson Microelectronics
Calle Platon 6, 4th floor, 5th door
E-08021 Barcelona
tel.: (+34) 03-4143300
tel.: (+34) 03-4143361
fax.: (+34) 03-2021461

SGS-Thomson Microelectronics
Calle Albacete 5
E-28027 Madrid
tel.: (+39) 01-4051615
fax.: (+39) 01-4031134

Sweden
SGS-Thomson Microelectronics
Borgarfjordsgatan 13, Box 1094
S-16421 Kista
tel.: (+46) 08-7939220
fax.: (+46) 08-7504950
tlx.: 12078

Switzerland
SGS-Thomson Microelectronics
Chemin François-Lehmann 18A
CH-1218 Grand-Saconnex/Geneva
tel.: (+41) 022-7986462
fax.: (+41) 022-7984869
tlx.: 415493

Taiwan
SGS-Thomson Microelectronics
12th floor, 571, Tun Hua South Road, Taipei
tel.: (+886) 02-7554111
fax.: (+886) 02-7554008
10310

United States of America
SGS-Thomson Microelectronics
303 Williams Avenue; Suite 1031
Huntsville, Al 35801-5104
tel.: (+1) 0205-5335995
fax.: (+1) 0205-5339320

SGS-Thomson Microelectronics
1000 East Bell Road
Phoenix, Az 85022-2699
tel.: (+1) 0602-8676340
fax.: (+1) 0602-8676102

SGS-Thomson Microelectronics
601 South Bowen Street
Longmont, Co 80501-6301
tel.: (+1) 0303-4499000
fax.: (+1) 0303-6517976

SGS-Thomson Microelectronics
18004 Skypark Circle; Suite 104
Irvine, Ca 92714-6427
tel.: (+1) 0714-2500455
fax.: (+1) 0714-2611505

SGS-Thomson Microelectronics
600 Mission Avenue Boulevard; Suite 104
Santa Clara, Ca 95054-1216
tel.: (+1) 0408-9708585
fax.: (+1) 0408-9708738

SGS-Thomson Microelectronics
600 North Meacham; Suite 304
Schaumburg, Il 60173-4941
tel.: (+1) 0312-4901890
fax.: (+1) 0312-4901899

SGS-Thomson Microelectronics
240 Bear Hill Road
Waltham, Ma 02154-1004
tel.: (+1) 0617-8906688
fax.: (+1) 0617-8906263
tlx.: RCA 200297

SGS-Thomson Microelectronics
21411 Civic Center Drive # 309
Southfield, Mi 48076-3910
tel.: (+1) 0313-3584250
fax.: (+1) 0313-3584307
tlx.: 810-224-4684

SGS-Thomson Microelectronics
The Pavilions of Greentree
Route # 73; Suite 101
Marlton, NJ 08053
tel.: (+1) 0609-5969200
fax.: (+1) 0609-4247437

SGS-Thomson Microelectronics
330 Motor Parkway; Suite 100
Hauppage, NY 11788-5104
tel.: (+1) 0516-4351050
fax.: (+1) 0516-4351064

SGS-Thomson Microelectronics
387 Hooker Avenue; office no. 2
Poughkeepsie, NY 12603-3633
tel.: (+1) 0914-4548813
fax.: (+1) 0914-4541320

SGS-Thomson Microelectronics
1310 Electronics Drive; MS 1137
Carrollton, Tx 75006-5039
tel.: (+1) 0214-4668844
fax.: (+1) 0214-4666358

West-Germany
SGS-Thomson Microelectronics
Eckenerstrasse 5
WD-3000 Hannover 1
tel.: (+49) 0511-634191
fax.: (+49) 0511-633552
tlx.: 175118418

SGS-Thomson Microelectronics
Frankfurterstrasse 22a
WD-5200 Siegburg
tel.: (+49) 02241-6608486
fax.: (+49) 02241-67584
tlx.: 889510

SGS-Thomson Microelectronics
Gutleutstrasse 322
WD-6000 Frankfurt 71
tel.: (+49) 069-237492
fax.: (+49) 069-231957
tlx.: 176997689

SGS-Thomson Microelectronics
Oberer Kirchhaldenweg 135
WD-7000 Stuttgart 1
tel.: (+49) 0711-692041
fax.: (+49) 0711-691408
tlx.: 721718

SGS-Thomson Microelectronics
Bretonischer Ring 4
Neukeferloh Technopark
Postfach 1122
WD-8011 Grasnrunn/ München
tel.: (+49) 089-460060
fax.: (+49) 089-4605454
tlx.: 528211

SǴS-Thomson Microelectronics
Erlenstegenstrasse 72
WD-8500 Nürnberg 20
tel.: (+49) 0911-597032
fax.: (+49) 0911-5980701
tlx.: 626243

• Teledyne Components

France
Teledyne Components France
85, rue Anatole France
F-92300 Levallois-Perret
tel.: (+33) 01-47571970
fax.: (+33) 01-47599269
tlx.: 611752

Great-Britain
Teledyne Components
The Harlequin Centre
Southall Lane, Southall
Middlesex UB2 6-5NH

United States of America
Teledyne Components
1300 Terra Bella Avenue
P.O. Box 7267
Mountain View, Ca 94039-7267
tel.: (+1) 0415-9689241
Fax: (+1) 0415-9671590

Teledyne Components
Eastern Sales Office
11 E. Chase St., Suite 5B
Baltimore, Md 21202
tel.: (+1) 0301-6599880
fax: (+1) 0301-6599882

Teledyne Components
New England Sales Office
52 Guild St., Suite 16
Norwood, Ma 02062
tel.: (+1) 0617-7699420
fax: (+1) 0617-7690469

West Germany
Teledyne Components
Abraham Lincoln Strasse 38-42
WD-6200 Wiesbaden
tel.: (+49) 06121-7680
fax : (+49) 06121-768155
tlx.: 4186134

• Texas Instruments

Argentina
Texas Instruments Argentina
Viamonte 1119
ARG-1053 Capital Federal Buenos Aires
Argentina
tel.: (+54) 0748-3699

Australia & New Zealand
Texas Instruments Australia Ltd.
6-10 Talavera Road, North Ryda (Sydney)
New South Wales
Australia 2113
tel.: (+61) 02-8871122

Austria
Texas Instruments GmbH
Hietzinger Kai 101-105
A-1130 Wien
tel.: (+43) 0222-91000
tlx.: 136796

Belgium
S.A. Texas Instruments Belgium N.V.
11, Avenue Jules Bordet, Jules Bordetlaan 11
B-1140 Bruxelles
tel.: (+32) 02-2423080
tlx.: 61161

Denmark
Texas Instruments A/S
Marielundvej
DK-2730 Herlev
tel.: (+45) 02-917400
fax.: (+45) 02-918400
tlx.: 35123

Finland
Texas Instruments Oy
Ahertajantie 3
P.O.Box 81
SF-0201 Espoo
tel.: (+358) 090-0461422
tlx.: 121457

France
Texas Instruments France
8-10, Avenue Morane Saulnier
B.P. 67
F-78141 Vélizy Villacoublay Cedex
tel.: (+33) 01-30701003
tlx.: 698707

Texas Instruments France
B.P. 5
F-06270 Villeneuve-Loubet
tel.: (+33) 093-222001
fax.: (+33) 093-222095
tlx.: 470127

Great-Britain
Texas Instruments Ltd.
Manton Lane
Bedford MK41 7PA
tel.: (+44) 0234-270111
tlx.: 82178

Hong Kong
Texas Instruments Hong Kong Ltd.
8th Floor World Shipping Centre
7 Canton Road
Kowloon
tel.: (+852) 03-7351223

Ireland
Texas Instruments Ireland Ltd.
7/8 Harcourt Street
Dublin 2
tel.: (+353) 01-781677
tlx.: 32626

Italy
Texas Instruments Italia
Divisione Semiconduttori
Viale Europa 40
I-20093 Cologno Monzese (Milano)
tel.: (+39) 02-253001
tlx.: 332633

Texas Instruments Italia
Divisione Semiconduttori
Via Castello della Magliana 38
I-00148 Roma
tel.: (+39) 06-5222651
fax.: (+39) 06-5220447
tlx.: 610587

Texas Instruments Italia
Divisione Semiconduttori
Via Amendola 17
I-40100 Bologna
tel.: (+39) 051-554004

Japan
Tokyo Marketing (sales headquarters)
Texas Instruments Japan Ltd.
MS Shibeura Building, 9th floor
4-13-23 Shibeura
Minatu-ku
Tokyo 108
tel.: (+81) 03-7695700

Korea
Texas Instruments Korea Ltd.
28th floor Trade Towe # 169
Samsung-Dong, Kangnam-ku
Seoul
tel.: (+82) 02-5512810

Mexico
Texas Instruments de Mexico S.A.
Alfonso Reyes 115
Col. Hypodromo Condesa
Mexico D.F.
Mexico 06120
tel.: (+52) 0525-3860

The Netherlands
Texas Instruments Holland B.V.
Hogehilweg 19
Postbus 12995
NL-1100 AZ Amsterdam-Zuidoost
tel.: (+31) 020-5602911
tlx.: 12196

Norway
Texas Instruments Norge A/S
P.O.Box 106
Refstad (Sinsenveien 53)
N-0585 Oslo 5
tel.: (+47) 02-155090

Portugal
Texas Instruments Equipamento Electronico (Portugal) LDA.
Rua Eng. Frederico Ulrich 2650
Moreira Da Maia, P-4480 Maia
tel.: (+351) 02-9481003
tlx.: 22485

Spain
Texas Instruments Espana S.A.
Calle José Galdiano # 6
E-28036 Madrid
tel.: (+34) 01-4581458
fax.: (+34) 01-4579404
tlx.: 23634

Texas Instruments Espana S.A.
Calle Diputacion, 279-3-5
E-08007 Barcelona
tel.: (+34) 03-3179180
fax.: (+34) 03-3018461
tlx.: 50436

Sweden
Texas Instruments International Trade Corporation
Sverigefilialen, Box 30
S-16493 Stockholm
tel.: (+46) 08-7525800
fax.: (+46) 08-7519715
tlx.: 10377

Switzerland
Texas Instruments Switzerland AG
Riedstrasse 6
CH-8953 Dietikon
tel.: (+41) 01-7402220
tlx.: 825260

West Germany
Texas Instruments Deutschland GmbH
Kurfürstendamm 195-196
WD-1000 Berlin 15
tel.: (+49) 030-8827365
tlx.: 526529

Texas Instruments Deutschland GmbH
Kirchhorster Strasse 2
WD-3000 Hannover 51
tel.: (+49) 0511-64680
tlx.: 526529

Texas Instruments Deutschland GmbH
3 Hagen 43/Kibbelstrasse 19
WD-4300 Essen 1
tel.: (+49) 0201-24250
tlx.: 526529

Texas Instruments Deutschland GmbH
Düsseldorferstrasse 40
WD-6236 Eschborn 1
tel.: (+49) 06196-8070
tlx.: 526529

Texas Instruments Deutschland GmbH
Maybachstrasse 2
WD-7302 Ostfildern
tel.: (+49) 0711-34030
tlx.: 526529

Texas Instruments Deutschland GmbH
Haggertystrasse 1
WD-8050 Freising
tel.: (+49) 08161-800
tlx.: 526529

• U M C

Hong Kong
United Microelectronics Company Ltd.
Room 1003, Tower B
Hunghom Comm. Center
37-39 Ma Tau Wai Road
Hunghom
Kowloon
tel.: (+852) 766-7122
fax.: (+852) 765-7483

Japan
UMC K.K.
3rd floor 20-29, 2-Chome Takanawa
Minato-Ku
Tokyo
tel.: (+81) 03-280-3661
fax.: (+81) 03-280-3663

The Netherlands
United Microelectronics (Europe) B.V.
Hoekenrode 2
NL-1102 BR Amsterdam Zuidoost
tel.: (+31) 020-970766
fax.: (+31) 020-877826
tlx.: 11677

Taiwan
No3. Industrial East Third Road
Science-Based Industrial Park
Hsinchu City
Taiwan
tel.: (+886) 02-7152455
fax.: (+886) 02-7166291
tlx.: 28560

United States of America
NMC Corporation
3350 Scott Boulevard Building 57
Santa Clara, Ca 95054
tel.: (+1) 0408-7279239
fax.: (+1) 0408-9700548
tlx.: 172730

• VLSI

France
VLSI Technology France s.a.r.l.
2, Allée des Garays
F-91124 Palaiseau Cedex
tel.: (+33) 01-64470479
fax.: (+33) 01-64470480
tlx.: 600759

Great Britain
VLSI Technology GmbH
486-488 Midsummer Boulevard
Saxon Gate West, Central
Milton Keynes, MK9 2EQ
tel.: (+44) 0908-667595
fax.: (+44) 0908-670027
tlx.: 825135

Hong Kong
VLSI Technology Inc.
Shui On Centre 28/12
8 Harbor Road
tel.: (+852) 05-8653755
fax.: (+852) 05-8653159

Italy
VLSI Technology GmbH
Filiale Italia
Centro Direzionale Colleoni
Palazzo Cassiopea 3
I-20041 Agrate Brianza (Milano)
tel.: (+39) 039-6056791
fax.: (+39) 039-6056808

Japan
VLSI Technology Inc.
Shuwa-Kioichi TBR Building, Room 101
5-7 Kojimachi, Chiyoda-ku
Tokyo 102
tel.: (+81) 03-2395211
fax.: (+81) 03-2395215

United States of America
VLSI Technology Inc.
1109 McKay Drive
San Jose, Ca 95131
tel.: (+1) 0408-4343100

West-Germany
VLSI Technology GmbH
Rosenkavalierplatz 10
WD-8000 München 81
tel.: (+49) 089-9269050
fax.: (+49) 089-92690545
tlx.: 5214279

• Weitek

Great-Britain
Weitek Corporation
European Representative
Churcham House
1 Bridgeman Road
Teddington
Middlesex
tel.: (+44) 081-9777727
fax.: (+44) 081-9773404

Japan
Weitek Corporation
Japanese Representative
4-8-1 Tsuchihashi
Miyamae-Ku
Kawasaki, Kanagawa-Pre
213 Japan
tel.: (+81) 044-8521135
fax.: (+81) 044-8883158

United States of America
Weitek Corporation
Corporate Headquarters
1060 E. Arques Avenue
Sunnyvale, Ca 94086
tel.: (+1) 0408-7388400
fax.: (+1) 0408-7381185

Weitek Corporation
Corporate Place 4
111 South Bedford Street
Suite 200
Burlington, Ma 01803
tel.: (617)-229-8080
fax.: (617)-229-4902

• Zymos

Hong Kong
ZyMOS Hong Kong
1901 Henan Building
90-92 Jaffe Road
Wanchal
tel.: (+852) 05-8611231
fax.: (+825) 05-202186

Korea
ZyMOS Korea
27th floor
Korea World Trade Centre
159 Samsung-Dong
Kangnamku
Seoul
Korea 135-729
tel.: (+82) 02-5512787
fax.: (+82) 02-5512710

Taiwan
ZyMOS Taiwan
8th floor Shin Kong World Commercial Building
287 Sec 3 Nanking East Road
Taipei
tel.: (+886) 02-07129368
fax.: (+886) 02-07130812

United States of America
ZyMOS North West
Western Area Sales
3350 Scott Boulevard # 12
Santa Clara, Ca
tel.: (+1) 0408-9861780

ZyMOS International
477 North Mathilda Avenue
Sunnyvale, Ca 94086
tel.: (+1) 0408-7305400
fax.: (+1) 0408-7305473

ZyMOS South West
19600 Fairchild
Suite 150
Irvine, Ca 92715
tel.: (+1) 0714-7520426

ZyMOS North East
1740 Massachusetts Avenue
Boxborough, Ma 01719
tel.: (+1) 0508-2637873

ZyMOS Central
555 Republic Dr. Suite 200
Plano, Tx 75074
tel.: (+1) 0214-4225587